A. KENT MORTON

ADVANCED CALCULUS

INTERNATIONAL SERIES IN
PURE AND APPLIED MATHEMATICS

William Ted Martin and E. H. Spanier
CONSULTING EDITORS

AHLFORS · Complex Analysis
BELLMAN · Stability Theory of Differential Equations
BUCK · Advanced Calculus
CODDINGTON AND LEVINSON · Theory of Ordinary Differential Equations
DETTMAN · Mathematical Methods in Physics and Engineering
EPSTEIN · Partial Differential Equations
GOLOMB AND SHANKS · Elements of Ordinary Differential Equations
GRAVES · The Theory of Functions of Real Variables
GREENSPAN · Introduction to Partial Differential Equations
GRIFFIN · Elementary Theory of Numbers
HAMMING · Numerical Methods for Scientists and Engineers
HILDEBRAND · Introduction to Numerical Analysis
HOUSEHOLDER · Principles of Numerical Analysis
LASS · Elements of Pure and Applied Mathematics
LASS · Vector and Tensor Analysis
LEIGHTON · An Introduction to the Theory of Differential Equations
LEPAGE · Complex Variables and the Laplace Transform for Engineers
NEHARI · Conformal Mapping
NEWELL · Vector Analysis
ROSSER · Logic for Mathematicians
RUDIN · Principles of Mathematical Analysis
SIMMONS · Introduction to Topology and Modern Analysis
SNEDDON · Elements of Partial Differential Equations
SNEDDON · Fourier Transforms
STOLL · Linear Algebra and Matrix Theory
STRUBLE · Nonlinear Differential Equations
WEINSTOCK · Calculus of Variations
WEISS · Algebraic Number Theory

ADVANCED CALCULUS

R. CREIGHTON BUCK

Professor of Mathematics
University of Wisconsin

McGRAW-HILL BOOK COMPANY, INC.

New York Toronto London

1956

ADVANCED CALCULUS

Library of Congress Catalog Card Number 56-6949

IX

08725

THE MAPLE PRESS COMPANY, YORK, PA.

PREFACE

In writing this book, we have had in mind four main objectives: to review elementary calculus with rigor, but without losing the student's interest by retracing too-familiar ground; to give a systematic and modern approach to the differential and integral calculus of functions and transformations; to develop analytical techniques for attacking some of the typical problems which arise in applications of mathematics; to give an introduction to modern points of view in mathematics, especially valuable for those few who will continue with graduate work in mathematics or physics, without becoming so abstract that the rest gain nothing.

There is a growing tendency in American colleges to present the elementary calculus from a more theoretical point of view. When this is done, it is almost invariably found that certain topics are slighted; these lie chiefly in the theory of functions of several variables. For this reason, we have directed the treatment toward a development of the fundamentals of analysis, simultaneously for functions of one variable and of several variables, unified by regarding both as functions of a point. It is not intended to be an all-inclusive treatise; for example, we have chosen to include only a brief sketch, rather than a detailed treatment, of the foundations of the real-number system. Again, although we have striven for clarity, we have not attempted to write a book which eliminates the need for an instructor; much of the value of a course at this level lies in the observation of the instructor by the students, as he presents in his own way the motivations and reasonings which yield the proof of a theorem, or the solution of an exercise.

The reader will notice a number of innovations in subject and treatment. For example, he will find that the double integral appears before the fundamental theorem of calculus is discussed; this was done in order to emphasize the essential distinction between integration and antidifferentiation, and to lend added understanding to the study of methods for approximate integration. Again, the theory of (exterior) differential forms appears in Chapter 7, specialized to 3-space; it has been included partly because the easily learned technique simplifies many calculations involving transformation of coordinates and because it permits a unified treatment of Stokes' and Green's theorems.

In carrying out the third of our objectives, we have tried to maintain a balance between theory and application. We share the view that applied mathematics may not exist—only applied mathematicians. The basic tools of the latter should not be restricted to the material in the traditional engineering advanced calculus course. In its preliminary mimeographed forms, the book has been used for a two-semester course given to a mixture of mathematics, physics, and engineering majors, at the level of the junior, senior, or first-graduate year.

A word of explanation about the use of "we" in the remarks above: in all the work on this book, I have had the active collaboration of my wife, Ellen F. Buck, who has revised large portions of the early drafts, suggested many clarifications of the treatment, and (I hope) discovered all the hiatuses in the proofs. It is only at her insistence that her name does not also appear on the title page.

Thanks go also to my colleagues who gave me a free hand in the development of the course, and to the students whose enthusiastic response to the notes prompted the book itself.

R. Creighton Buck

CONTENTS

CHAPTER 1

ELEMENTARY TOPOLOGY

1.1. Geometry

All the theorems about calculus rest ultimately upon properties of the real numbers. A complete discussion of these is usually left for a later course; we have therefore summarized in the Appendix the properties that will be assumed and used. A brief glance will show the reader that most of these are quite familiar, and in fact often go under the name of "rules of algebra." The less familiar ones may be mentioned from time to time as need for their use arises. From these properties of numbers, there derive certain simple geometrical or topological notions which are common to the plane, to space, and to general Euclidean n-dimensional space.

We first adopt several conventions. A point will usually be denoted by a single letter, for example, the **point** p. If we are specifically dealing with a point in the **plane,** we may also represent it in coordinate form, $p = (x, y)$ or $p = (a, b)$. If p is a point in **space,** we may write $p = (x, y, z)$ or $p = (u, v, w)$. We are not bound to the use of prescribed letters for the coordinates, but may choose them to suit our convenience; a point in the plane might also be represented by (y, x). For this reason, we sometimes say that the letter "a" in (a, b) denotes the *first* coordinate of the point, rather than the X coordinate. A point in **n-space** can be represented in coordinate form by $(x_1, x_2, \ldots, x_n)$. We shall sometimes use E^n to refer to n-space; following this notation, E^2 is the plane, E^3 ordinary space, and E^1 is the line or 1-space.

Certain algebraic operations can be defined for points. If

$$p = (x_1, x_2, \ldots, x_n) \qquad q = (y_1, y_2, \ldots, y_n)$$

then the **sum** of these points is the point

$$p + q = (x_1 + y_1, x_2 + y_2, \ldots, x_n + y_n)$$

and the **inner product** of these points is the number

$$p \cdot q = x_1y_1 + x_2y_2 + \cdots + x_ny_n.$$

We can also multiply points by real numbers. If λ is a number, then

$$\lambda p = (\lambda x_1, \lambda x_2, \ldots, \lambda x_n).$$

To illustrate these definitions, let $p = (2, 1, -3)$ and $q = (3, 0, 4)$. Then, $p + q = (5, 1, 1)$, $p \cdot q = -6$, $2p = (4, 2, -6)$,

$$-3q = (-9, 0, -12),$$

and $p - q = p + (-1)q = (-1, 1, -7)$.

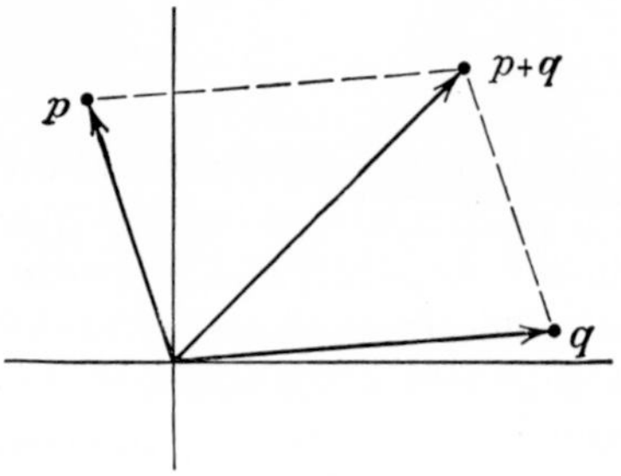

FIG. 1-1

If a point in the plane is represented by the directed line segment which starts at the origin and ends at the point, then addition of points corresponds to the familiar addition of line segments, regarded as vectors, while the inner product of two points is the scalar or "dot" product of the corresponding vectors (Fig. 1-1).

These operations obey familiar algebraic laws, with the origin

$$\mathbf{0} = (0, 0, \ldots, 0)$$

playing the role of zero. For any three points p, q, r in E^n and any real λ,

$$\begin{aligned} p + q &= q + p \\ p + (q + r) &= (p + q) + r \\ \lambda(p + q) &= \lambda p + \lambda q \\ (\lambda_1 + \lambda_2)p &= \lambda_1 p + \lambda_2 p \\ p \cdot q &= q \cdot p \\ p \cdot (q + r) &= p \cdot q + p \cdot r \\ p + \mathbf{0} &= p \\ 0p &= \mathbf{0} \end{aligned} \tag{1-1}$$

The routine checking of these is left as an exercise.

We also associate with each point a number called its norm. If $p = (x_1, x_2, \ldots, x_n)$, then the **norm** of p is

$$|p| = \sqrt{p \cdot p} = \sqrt{x_1^2 + x_2^2 + \cdots + x_n^2}.$$

In the plane, if $p = (x, y)$, then $|p| = \sqrt{x^2 + y^2}$, which is recognized to be distance from p to the origin and is the length of the vector associated with p. We use the norm to define distance in n-space, and say that the **distance** between two points is given by dist $[p, q] = |p - q|$. If $p = (x, y, z)$ and $q = (a, b, c)$, then

$$|p - q| = \sqrt{(x - a)^2 + (y - b)^2 + (z - c)^2},$$

which is of course the familiar formula.

If we specialize the previous discussion to 1-space, it takes on a slightly different appearance. Since the line or 1-space is just the space of real numbers, we may write simply $p = x$. Addition of points and the inner product of points reduce to the customary addition and multiplication of real numbers. The formula for norm yields $|x| = \sqrt{x^2}$. We recall that when A is a positive number, the symbol $\sqrt{A}$ always means the *positive* number whose square is A; thus $\sqrt{x^2}$ is not always x. We therefore find

$$|x| = \sqrt{x^2} = \begin{cases} x & \text{if } x \geq 0 \\ -x & \text{if } x \leq 0, \end{cases}$$

so that the norm of a real number is its **absolute value.** The distance between x and y, $|x - y|$, is the absolute value of their difference.

Additional properties of norm and distance are included in the Exercises, in particular the very important **triangle inequality,** which is the analytical equivalent of the statement that no side of a triangle can be longer than the sum of the lengths of the other two sides (Exercises 4 and 5).

Analysis has been called the theory of inequalities. Certainly, a facility in this direction is almost indispensable. A good illustration is the following, chosen because of the mode of proof and because it is one of the more useful tools in the analyst's kit.

Theorem 1 (Schwarz Inequality). *For any two points p and q, $p \cdot q \leq |p|\,|q|$.*

Taking the points in coordinate form, this asserts that for any values of the real numbers $a_1, \ldots, a_n, b_1, \ldots, b_n$, $(a_1b_1 + a_2b_2 + \cdots + a_nb_n)^2 \leq (a_1^2 + \cdots + a_n^2)(b_1^2 + \cdots + b_n^2)$. In E^2 or E^3 a geometric proof can be given. A familiar formula for inner product is $p \cdot q = |p|\,|q| \cos \theta$, where θ is the angle subtended at the origin by the points p and q. Since $\cos \theta \leq 1$, the inequality follows. To prove it for E^n, we use a different method which depends upon the fact that the norm of a point is never negative. For any choice of the real numbers α and β, $0 \leq |\alpha p - \beta q|$. Squaring this and using the definition of norm and the rules in (1-1),

$$\begin{aligned} 0 \leq |\alpha p - \beta q|^2 &= (\alpha p - \beta q) \cdot (\alpha p - \beta q) \\ &= \alpha^2 p \cdot p - \alpha\beta p \cdot q - \alpha\beta q \cdot p + \beta^2 q \cdot q \end{aligned}$$

or, using $p \cdot q = q \cdot p$, and (1-1),

$$2\alpha\beta(p \cdot q) \leq \alpha^2|p|^2 + \beta^2|q|^2.$$

In this, we now choose $\alpha = |q|$ and $\beta = |p|$, getting

$$2|p|\,|q|p \cdot q \leq 2|p|^2|q|^2.$$

If $|p|\,|q| \neq 0$, then it is positive, and dividing by it, we obtain the Schwarz inequality. When $|p|\,|q| = 0$, $p \cdot q$ is also zero, and there is nothing to prove. ∎†

EXERCISES‡

1. When $p = (2, 0, -3)$ and $q = (-1, 3, 2)$, compute $p + q$, $p - q$, $p \cdot q$, $|p|$, $|p - q|$, $3p - 2q$.

2. Show that the properties given in formula (1-1) hold.

3. Show that the following properties of norm are true: (*a*) $|p| > 0$ unless $p = \mathbf{0}$; (*b*) $|\alpha p| = |\alpha|\,|p|$ for any real number α; (*c*) $|p - q| = |q - p|$.

***4.** (*a*) Prove the **triangle inequality for norms:**

$$|p + q| \leq |p| + |q|.$$

(*b*) Show that this can be extended to any finite number of points, i.e.,

$$|p_1 + p_2 + \cdots + p_m| \leq |p_1| + |p_2| + \cdots + |p_m|.$$

5. Prove the **triangle inequality for distances:**

$$\text{dist}\,[p, q] \leq \text{dist}\,[p, r] + \text{dist}\,[r, q].$$

6. Is $|p - q| \leq |p| - |q|$?

7. Show that the mid-point of the line segment joining p and q is $\frac{1}{2}(p + q)$. How is the point $\frac{1}{3}(p + q + r)$ related to the points p, q, and r?

8. How are the points $\lambda p + (1 - \lambda)q$ related to the points p and q?

9. For $n = 3$, 2, and 1 in turn, graph the set of all points p in E^n for which: (*a*) $|p| < 1$; (*b*) $|p| \leq 1$; (*c*) $|p| = 1$.

10. Let $A = (4, 2)$. Graph the set of points p in the plane for which: (*a*) $|p| < |p - A|$; (*b*) $|p| + |p - A| = 6$; (*c*) $|p| + |p - A| \leq 4$.

1.2. Sets of Points

Much of analysis deals with relationships between points and between sets of points. We introduce in this section some of the standard notation and terminology which is used. If S is a set or collection of points, we write $p \in S$ to mean that p is a **member** of S, or p **belongs** to S. If p is not a member of S, we write $p \notin S$. A **neighborhood** about a point p_0 is any of the sets N described by

$$N = \{\text{all } p \text{ with } |p - p_0| < \epsilon\}$$

for any choice of $\epsilon > 0$. Thus, in the plane, a neighborhood of a point p_0 is any disk having p_0 as center, and in space, a neighborhood of p_0 is any (solid) sphere with center at p_0. More precisely, we might refer to N as the ϵ neighborhood of p_0, or the neighborhood of radius ϵ about p_0. The role of neighborhoods will be to give precision to certain intuitive geometrical arguments involving "nearness."

With respect to a fixed set S, every point has one of three properties; for each, we use a familiar word but with a specialized meaning. We say

† Following the lead of Halmos, in his "Measure Theory," I have adopted the use of ∎ in place of Q.E.D to signify the end of a proof.

‡ A single star * indicates an exercise which requires a certain amount of ingenuity; those with a double star** are honor problems and pose a definite challenge.

that p is **interior** to S if p belongs to S and there is some neighborhood about p which contains only points of S. We say that p is **exterior** to S if p does not belong to S, and if there is some neighborhood about p which contains no point of S. We say that p is a **boundary point** for S if p is neither interior to S nor exterior to S. The set of all boundary points for S is called the **boundary** of S. In Fig. 1-2, p is exterior to S, q interior to S, and r a boundary point for S. In simple cases, the boundary of a set coincides with the intuitive notion of edge or circumference. It is important to keep in mind that a boundary point for a set may or may not belong to the set itself. However, every point belonging to S is either interior to S or is a boundary point, and every point not in S is either exterior to S or a boundary point. When all the boundary points for a set belong to the set, the set is called **closed**; a set that contains none of its boundary points is said to be **open.** Thus, a set is open if and only if each of its points is interior. As an illustration, let us prove that an "open" disk is in fact open. Let S be the set of all points p in the plane with $|p| < 1$. Let p_0 be any point of S. To show that p_0 is interior to S, we must construct a neighborhood around p_0 which lies in S. Let $r = |p_0|$,

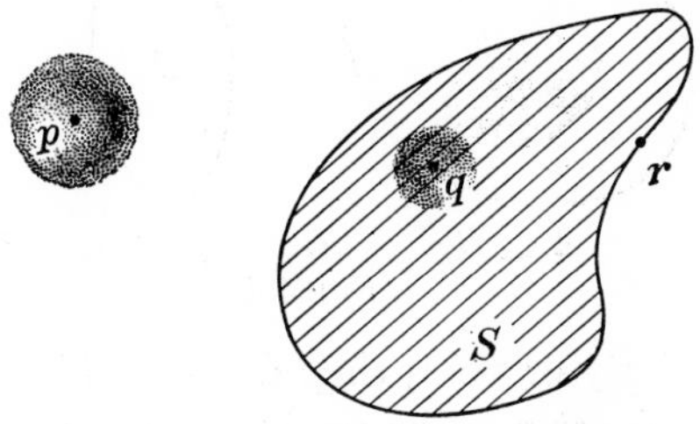

FIG. 1-2

$$\delta = \frac{(1 - r)}{2},$$

and let U be the neighborhood of radius δ about p_0. If p is any point of U, then $|p - p_0| < \delta$ so that

$$|p| = |p - p_0 + p_0| < |p - p_0| + |p_0| < \delta + r < 1$$

and $p \in S$. A similar argument could be used to prove that the "closed" disk, all p with $|p| \leq 1$, is a closed set. In everyday usage, the words "open" and "closed" are antonyms; this is no longer true since a set which contains some—but not all—of its boundary points would be neither open nor closed.

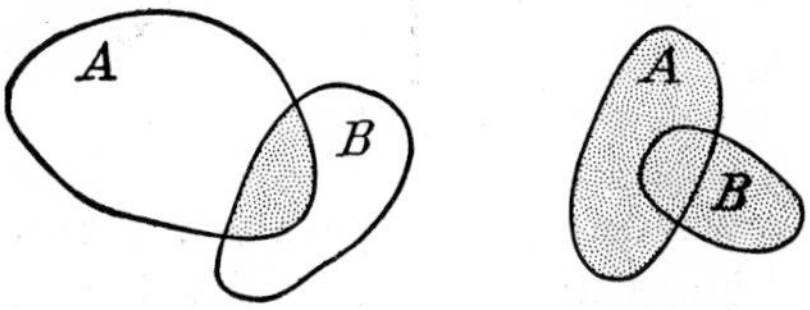

$A \cap B$ $\quad$ $A \cup B$

FIG. 1-3

If A and B are sets, then the **union** (or sum) of A and B is the set consisting of all the points p such that $p \in A$ or $p \in B$; notations for this set are $A \cup B$ or $A + B$. The **intersection** of A and B is the set $A \cap B$ consisting of all points p for which $p \in A$ and $p \in B$ (see Fig. 1-3). The union of a set S and its boundary is called the **closure** of S; it may be shown to be always a closed set. Thus, the closure of the *open* disk of radius R is the *closed* disk of radius R. When every point of a set A is also a point of B, we say that B **covers** A or that A is **included** in B, and write $A \subset B$. A collection of sets is said to cover a set A if every point of A is covered by at least one set of the collection. When two sets, B and C, have no common points, their intersection is said to be **empty** or void; they are also referred to as **disjoint** (see Fig. 1-4).

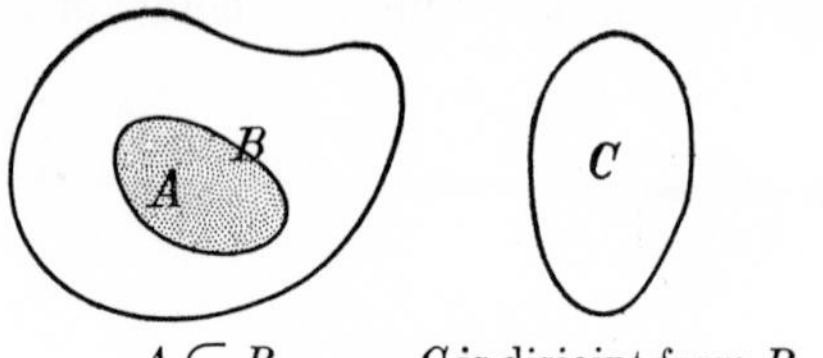

$A \subset B$ C is disjoint from B
FIG. 1-4

A set may be made up of a number of separate "pieces." For example, the set (Fig. 1-5)

$$H = \{\text{all } (x, y) \text{ with } x^2 - y^2 \geq 1\}$$

is the union of two disjoint hyperbolic regions. Putting the intuitive notion of "single piece" on a formal basis leads to the following definition: A set S is said to be **connected** if S cannot be covered by the union of two open sets, A and B, which are themselves disjoint, unless S itself is all included in A or all included in B. (Another way of looking at connectedness is given in Exercise 8 below. See also Exercise 7, Sec. 1.3.)

In ordinary usage, the words "finite" and "bounded" often have the same meaning. We shall use them to describe quite different aspects of a set. A set S is called **finite** if it contains only a finite number of points; a set is called **bounded** if it can be completely covered by a sufficiently large neighborhood of the origin. Thus, when the set S is bounded, there will be a number M such that $|p| \leq M$ for all $p \in S$. Any subset of a bounded set is bounded. A set that is not bounded is called **unbounded,** and one that is not finite is **infinite.** The set H of Fig. 1-5 is unbounded. The reader is warned to keep separate the term "boundary" and the terms "bounded" and "unbounded." A set such as H which is unbounded may well have a boundary.

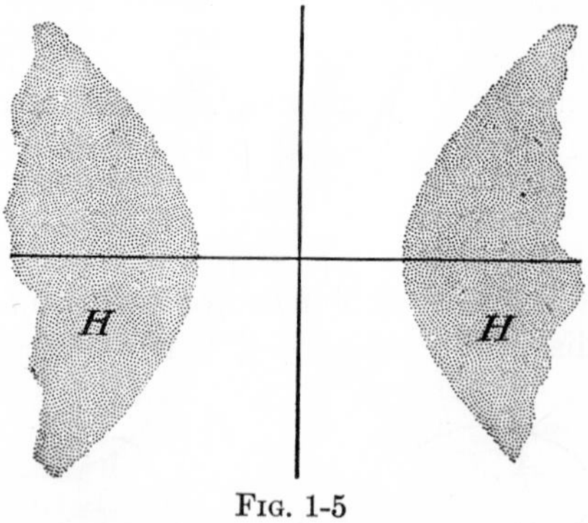

FIG. 1-5

The following examples may help to clarify the terminology that has been introduced.

(i) The set $S = \{\text{all } p = (x, y) \text{ with } 0 < |p| < 1\}$ is open, connected, bounded, and infinite; its boundary consists of the circumference

$$x^2 + y^2 = 1$$

and the origin (Fig. 1-6).

(ii) The set $S = \{\text{all } p = (x, y) \text{ with } x \geq 0\}$ is closed, unbounded, connected, and its boundary is the vertical axis (Fig. 1-7).

(iii) The set $S = \{\text{all } (x, y) \text{ with } |x| = |y|\}$ is closed, unbounded, connected, and its boundary is itself (Fig. 1-8).

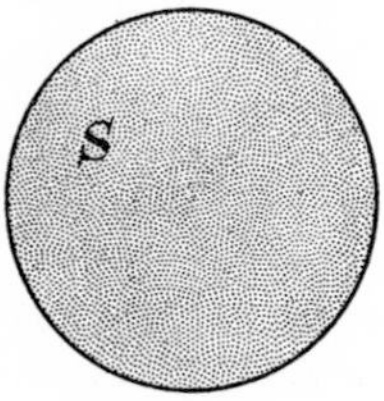

FIG. 1-6

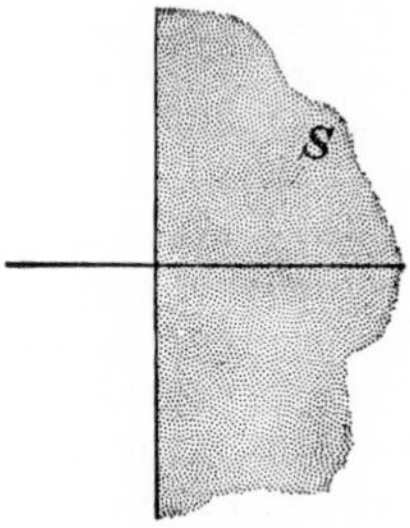

FIG. 1-7

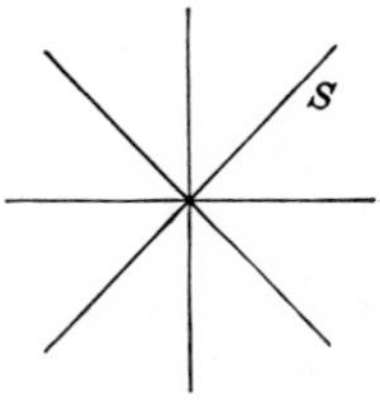

FIG. 1-8

(iv) The set H described above is closed, unbounded, disconnected, and its boundary is the hyperbola $x^2 - y^2 = 1$.

(v) The set $D = \{\text{all } (x, y) \text{ with } x \text{ and } y \text{ integers}\}$ is closed, infinite, unbounded, disconnected, and its boundary is itself (Fig. 1-9).

(vi) The whole plane is open, closed, connected, unbounded, and has no boundary points; the empty set is open, closed, connected, bounded, and has no boundary points.

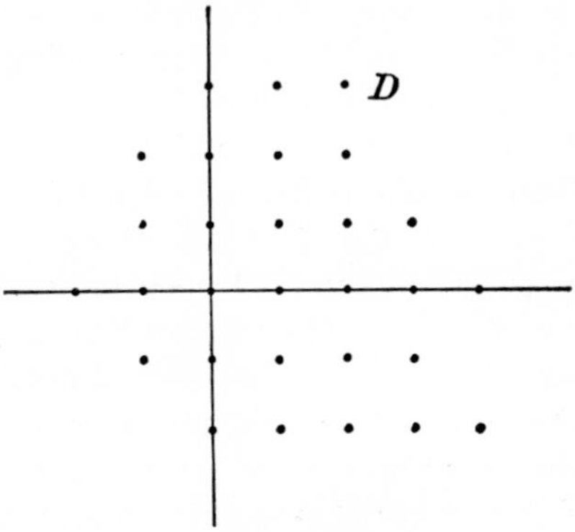

FIG. 1-9

The apparently paradoxical properties of the last example arise when the definitions of the terms are taken in their literal sense. For example, every point of the plane is interior, so that the plane is open; there are no points left over to be boundary points, so that every one of the boundary points of the plane belongs to the plane, and the plane is also closed. The reader may be relieved to know that the only sets in Euclidean spaces which have this property are the special ones such as those given in (vi).

EXERCISES

1. Tell which of the set properties described in this section apply to the set of all points (x, y) such that:

(a) $x^2 + y^2 = 1$
(b) $x^2 + y \geq 0$
(c) $x = y$
(d) $x > 1$
(e) $xy > 0$
(f) $y = |x - 1| + 2 - x$

2. Do the same for the set of points (x, y, z) such that:

(a) $x^2 + y^2 + z^2 > 4$
(b) $x^2 + y^2 \leq 4$
(c) $xy > z$
(d) $(x - y)^2 = z^2$

3. Applying the same definitions to the special case of sets on the line, what is meant by a neighborhood of -3? Is the set of all x such that $3 < x \leq 8$ open, or closed, or neither? Is the set of x with $-4 < x$ an open set?

4. What is the boundary of the set of all $p = (x, y)$ with x and y rational numbers?

5. Show that an equivalent definition is to say that p is a boundary point for a set S if and only if every neighborhood of p contains both a point of S and a point not in S.

6. The **complement** of a set S is the set of all points p with $p \notin S$. Prove that the complement of an open set is closed and that the complement of a closed set is open.

7. If A and B are closed sets, show that $A \cup B$ and $A \cap B$ are also closed.

****8.** Show that an open connected set S of the plane has the property that any two of its points can be joined by a polygonal line which lies entirely in S.

9. Show that any neighborhood is a bounded set.

***10.** Show that the complement of the set described in Exercise 4 is a set which is not open, but which also has the property given in Exercise 8.

1.3. Least Upper Bounds and the Nested Set Property

When we restrict our attention to sets of real numbers, the simplicity of 1-space allows us to give some of the previous definitions a more familiar form. For example, an **open interval** is the set of all x with $a < x < b$, and the corresponding **closed interval,** denoted by $[a, b]$, is the set of all x with $a \leq x \leq b$. The boundary of $[a, b]$ is the set composed of its two end points. A **neighborhood** of a point x_0 is any open interval centered at x_0. A set S is bounded if there is a number M such that $-M \leq x \leq M$ for all $x \in S$. The set of all x such that $c < x$ is called an **unbounded open interval,** and is sometimes also described by $c < x < \infty$. The symbol "∞" serves no purpose here; it does not represent a number. The interval does not have a right-hand end point, and the use of "∞" should not suggest this; it perhaps may help by emphasizing that x is unrestricted from above.

A number B is said to be an **upper bound** for a set S if $x \leq B$ for all $x \in S$, and b is a **lower bound** for S if $b \leq x$ for all $x \in S$. Not all sets have upper bounds or lower bounds. The set

$$\begin{aligned} S &= \{\text{all } x \text{ with } x \text{ a positive whole number}\} \\ &= \{1, 2, 3, 4, \ldots\} \end{aligned}$$

has lower bounds (e.g., -100, -1, or 1) but has no upper bounds.

Clearly, a set which has both an upper and a lower bound is a bounded set.

One of the characteristic properties of the real numbers is the **least upper bound property:**

Let S be a set of real numbers which is bounded from above; then, among all the upper bounds, there is one that is smallest. Similarly, if S is bounded from below, then among all the lower bounds, there is one that is greatest.

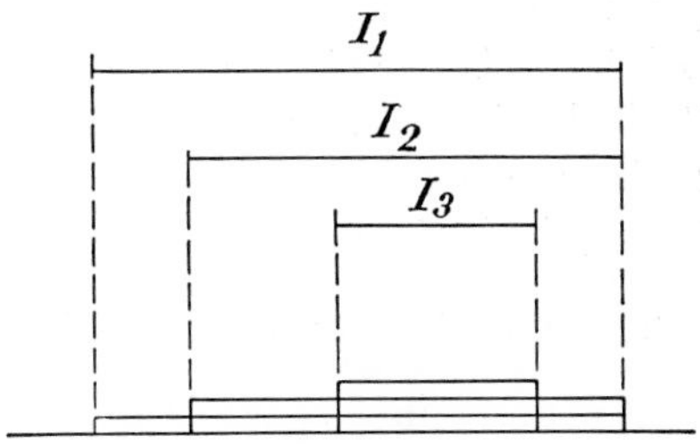

FIG. 1-10

A set that is bounded has both a least upper bound B and a greatest lower bound b such that $b \leq x \leq B$ for all $x \in S$, and such that B cannot be decreased, nor b increased. Common abbreviations for these are B = lub (S) = sup (S) and b = glb (s) = inf (S).† B and b need not be members of S. Whenever S has a largest member, it is of course lub (S). The word **maximum** is used with this sense. Similarly, the **minimum** of a set S is the word given to glb (S) when this number belongs to the set. When a set fails to have a maximum, the lub is often used to take its place. For example, the open interval I of x with $0 < x < 3$ has neither a maximum nor a minimum, but sup (I) = 3 and inf (I) = 0.

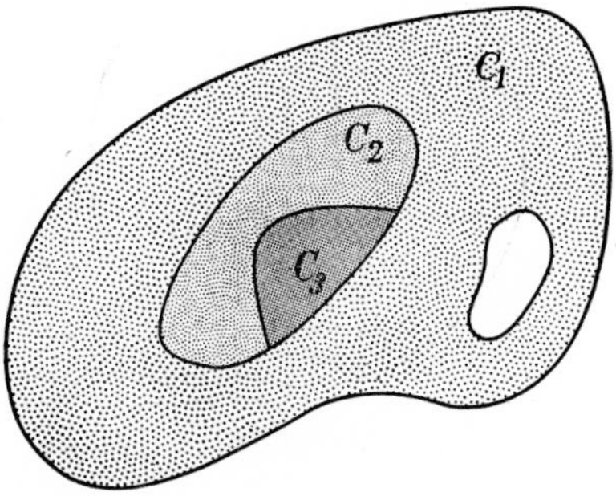

FIG. 1-11

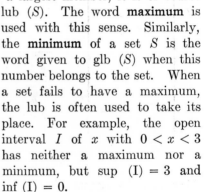

There are a number of other properties which are equivalent to or implied by the least upper bound property. Among these, one seems especially transparent, and is easily generalized to n-space. It is called the **nested interval property:**

Let I_1, I_2, I_3, . . . be a sequence of (nonempty) closed bounded intervals which are nested in the sense that each covers all that follow. Then, there is at least one point x_0 which lies in all the intervals (Fig. 1-10).

In n-space this becomes the **nested set property:**

Let C_1, C_2, C_3, . . . be a nested sequence of nonempty closed bounded sets. Then, there is at least one point $\bar{p}$ which belongs to all the sets C_n (Fig. 1-11).

† "sup" derives from "supremus" = "highest" and "inf" from "infimus" = "lowest."

(An indication of the method by which these properties may be proved is given in the Appendix.)

These properties are often used to prove other basic results in analysis. As an illustration, we choose the important **Bolzano-Weierstrass theorem** dealing with cluster points of a set. A point p is called a **cluster point** for the set S if every neighborhood of p contains infinitely many points of S.† Note that in order to have cluster points, the set S must itself be infinite. A cluster point for S need not belong to S. The notions of cluster point and boundary point are closely connected but not equivalent (see Exercises 1 and 2).

Theorem 2. *Every bounded infinite set has at least one cluster point.*

The proof in 2-space is easy to follow with the help of a diagram (Fig. 1-12). Let E be an infinite bounded set. We may assume that

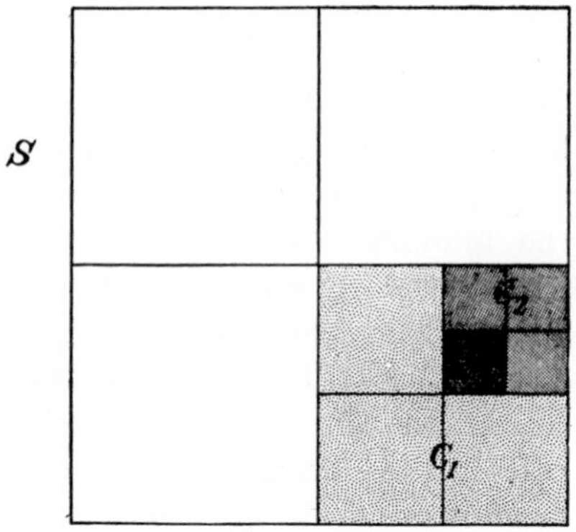

FIG. 1-12

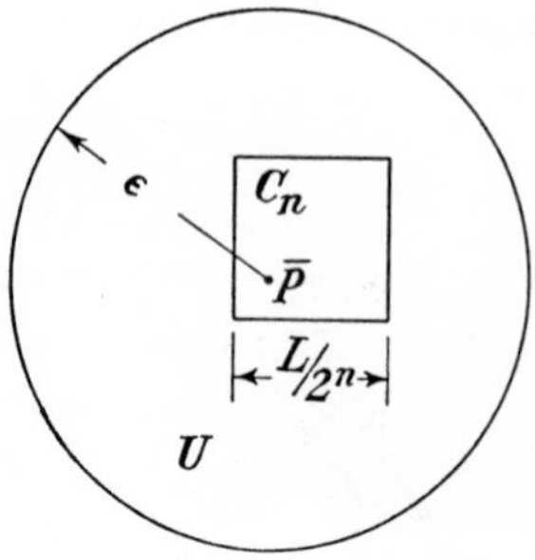

FIG. 1-13

E is covered by a square S with sides of length L. Divide S into quarters by a vertical and a horizontal line. One of these four squares must contain an infinite number of points of the set E, since otherwise E would itself have been finite. Choosing such a subsquare, divide it in turn into four pieces, and select one of them which contains an infinite number of points of E. By continuing this process, we generate a nested sequence of closed squares S, C_1, C_2, . . . such that the sides of C_n have length $L/2^n$ and each C_n contains infinitely many points of E. Using the nested set property, there is a point $\bar{p}$ which lies in all of the squares C_n. We show that $\bar{p}$ is a cluster point for E. Take any $\epsilon > 0$ and let U be an ϵ neighborhood of $\bar{p}$ (Fig. 1-13). If n is chosen so large that $L/2^n < \epsilon/2$, then the square C_n, which must contain $\bar{p}$, is covered by U. Since C_n contains infinitely many points of E, so must U. Thus, every neigh-

† The terms "limit point" and "point of accumulation" are also used.

borhood of $\bar{p}$ contains infinitely many points of E, and $\bar{p}$ is a cluster point for E. ▮

EXERCISES

1. If $S = \left\{\text{all } p = \left(\frac{1}{n}, \frac{1}{m}\right) \text{ for } n = 1, 2, \ldots, \text{ and } m = 1, 2, \ldots\right\}$, what are the cluster points for S? What is the boundary of S?

2. Show that a *boundary point* for a set S which is not a member of S must be a *cluster point* for S. Can you show that the boundary points which are not cluster points deserve the name "**isolated points** of S"?

3. Does an infinite set which is unbounded have to have a cluster point?

4. Show that the nested interval property fails if the intervals are allowed to be unbounded, or if they are allowed to be open.

5. The **diameter** of a set S is defined to be the least upper bound of the numbers $|p - q|$ for all choices of p and q in S. Let A and B be two sets with $A \subset B$; prove that diam $(A) \leq$ diam (B).

6. In the definition of cluster point for a set S, it was required that every neighborhood of the point $\bar{p}$ contain *infinitely* many points of S. Show that it is only necessary that each neighborhood contain *two* points of S. Is this the best you can do?

***7.** Prove that the unit interval [0, 1] is a connected set.

1.4. Sequences of Points

If to each positive integer $n = 1, 2, \ldots$ there is assigned a point, then these points form what is called an **infinite sequence** $\{p_n\}$ with **terms** $p_1, p_2, p_3, \ldots$. This notion differs from that of a set in that a particular order is assigned to the points by the subscripts and in that the same point may occur many times. The assignment $p_n = 1/n$ describes a sequence of points on the line (Fig. 1-14) and $p_n = (n, 1/n)$

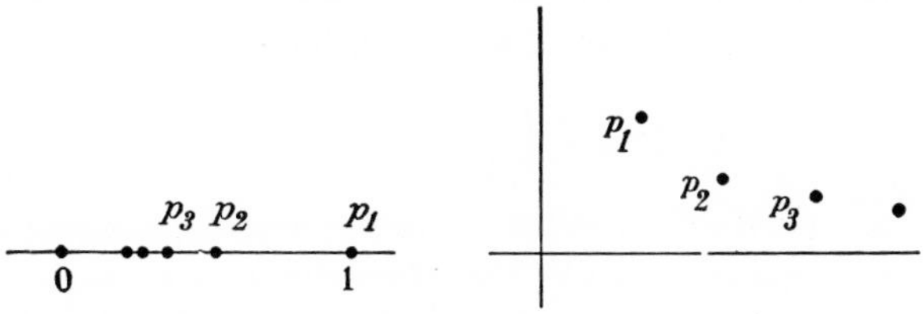

FIG. 1-14

describes a sequence of points in the plane (Fig. 1-14). The assignment $p_n = (-1)^n$ also describes a sequence of points on the line whose trace consists only of the points 1 and -1.

A sequence is said to be **bounded** if there is a bounded set which contains all the terms of the sequence. The first and third illustrations above were bounded, while the second was unbounded. The notion of **convergence** is basic to the study of sequences:

A sequence $\{p_n\}$ *is said to* **converge** *to a point* $\bar{p}$ *if and only if, given any neighborhood* U *of* $\bar{p}$*, we have* $p_n \in U$ *for all but a finite number of integers* n.

More generally, $\{p_n\}$ is said to be **convergent** if there is some point $\bar{p}$ to which it converges; we usually write $\lim_{n\to\infty} p_n = \bar{p}$. If we revert to the original description of neighborhood, this definition takes on the form:

$\lim_{n\to\infty} p_n = \bar{p}$ *means that corresponding to each positive number* $\epsilon > 0$, *a number* N *can be found such that* $|p_n - \bar{p}| < \epsilon$ *whenever* $n \geq N$.

This is the formal equivalent of the intuitive notion of limit: $\lim_{n\to\infty} p_n = \bar{p}$ means that as n increases, the terms p_n concentrate more and more closely around the point $\bar{p}$. The terms do not have to approach from a particular direction, nor does the distance from p_n to $\bar{p}$ have to decrease at each change in n. For example, the sequence described by

$$p_n = \frac{2 + (-1)^n}{n}$$

has terms 1, $\frac{3}{2}$, $\frac{1}{3}$, $\frac{3}{4}$, $\frac{1}{5}$, $\frac{3}{6}$, . . . and converges to 0.

Not all sequences are convergent. Neither 1, 2, 3, . . . (specified by $p_n = n$) nor 0, 1, 0, 1, . . . (given by $p_n = \frac{1}{2} + (-1)^n\frac{1}{2}$) converge. It is evident from the definition that the alteration of a finite number of terms of a sequence does not affect its convergence properties. In this sense, convergence is a property of the "last" terms of a sequence, rather than the first. In order to show that a specific sequence converges, the only method available at present requires a certain amount of computation; this will be diminished when we can make use of general theorems about limits. As an illustration, let us examine the sequence

$$p_n = \left(\frac{1}{n}, \frac{n}{n+1}\right).$$

We first select a candidate for the limit $\bar{p}$. By one process or another (for example, plotting the trace of the sequence) we are led to guess that $\bar{p}$ should be chosen as (0, 1). We then wish to show that $\lim_{n\to\infty} p_n = (0, 1)$. This means that if a number $\epsilon > 0$ is given, it must be shown that p_n lies in the ϵ neighborhood of (0, 1) for all sufficiently large n. Substituting the coordinates of p_n, we wish to have

$$\left|\left(\frac{1}{n}, \frac{n}{n+1}\right) - (0, 1)\right| < \epsilon$$

or

$$\left(\frac{1}{n}\right)^2 + \left(\frac{n}{n+1} - 1\right)^2 = \frac{1}{n^2} + \frac{1}{(n+1)^2} < \epsilon^2$$

for all n larger than some number N. This is "self-evident"; however, to give a formal argument, we must determine a value for N. Since $1/n^2 + 1/(n+1)^2 < 2/n^2$ we may choose N so that $2/N^2 \le \epsilon^2$ and this will surely be large enough. Thus, the choice $N = \sqrt{2}/\epsilon$ will serve; so would $N = 2/\epsilon$ or $N = 20/\epsilon^2$ or any number N that is always larger than $\sqrt{2}/\epsilon$ when ϵ is small.

We now turn to the first of several general theorems about limits.

Theorem 3. *Any convergent sequence is bounded.*

Let $\lim_{n\to\infty} p_n = \bar{p}$. Then, if U is any neighborhood of $\bar{p}$, there are at most a finite number of terms of $\{p_n\}$ which lie outside U. U is a bounded set; if we increase the radius of U and expand it to cover the finite number of omitted terms, the resulting set S is still bounded and contains *all* the terms of the sequence. ▌

Theorem 4. *If* $\lim_{n\to\infty} p_n = \bar{p}$ *and* $\lim_{n\to\infty} q_n = \bar{q}$, *then*

$$\lim_{n\to\infty} (p_n + q_n) = \bar{p} + \bar{q}.$$

Given $\epsilon > 0$, we may assume that numbers N' and N'' have been found such that $|p_n - \bar{p}| < \epsilon$ whenever $n \ge N'$ and $|q_n - q| < \epsilon$ whenever $n \ge N''$. Take N to be a number larger than both N' and N'', for example, $N = N' + N''$. If $n \ge N$, both of these inequalities hold. Since

$$\begin{aligned} |(p_n + q_n) - (\bar{p} + \bar{q})| &= |p_n - \bar{p} + q_n - \bar{q}| \\ &\le |p_n - \bar{p}| + |q_n - \bar{q}| \end{aligned}$$

(where we have used the fundamental *triangle inequality* for norms, Exercise 4, Sec. 1.1), we see that whenever $n \ge N$

$$|(p_n + q_n) - (\bar{p} + \bar{q})| < 2\epsilon.$$

This says that, except for a finite number at the beginning, *all* the terms of the sequence $\{p_n + q_n\}$ lie in the 2ϵ neighborhood of $\bar{p} + \bar{q}$. Since ϵ can be any positive number, we have shown that this property holds for *every* neighborhood of $\bar{p} + \bar{q}$, and proved $\lim_{n\to\infty} (p_n + q_n) = \bar{p} + \bar{q}$. ▌

The next result offers a way of proving convergence without first having to guess $\bar{p}$.

Theorem 5 *The sequence* $\{p_n\}$ *is convergent if, corresponding to any* $\epsilon > 0$, *a number* N *can be found such that* $|p_n - p_m| < \epsilon$ *whenever* n *and* m *are larger than* N.

A sequence of points which has the characteristic property described in the theorem is called a **Cauchy sequence**; thus, the theorem states that every Cauchy sequence is convergent. The property is often abbreviated: $\lim_{n,m\to\infty} |p_n - p_m| = 0$. It is also true that every convergent sequence is also a Cauchy sequence (Exercise 10).

The proof of this theorem uses the *nested set property* (Sec. 1.3). Since the number ϵ occurring in the hypothesis can be any positive number, we make special choices of it: first choosing $\epsilon = 1$. There is then an integer N_1 such that $|p_n - p_m| < 1$ for all $n, m \geq N_1$. In particular, $|p_{N_1} - p_m| < 1$ for all $m \geq N_1$. Next taking $\epsilon = \frac{1}{2}$, there is an integer $N_2 > N_1$ such that $|p_n - p_m| < \frac{1}{2}$ when $n, m \geq N_2$; again, $|p_{N_2} - p_m| < \frac{1}{2}$ for all $m \geq N_2$. Continuing, with $\epsilon = \frac{1}{3}, \frac{1}{4}, \ldots$, we obtain a sequence of integers $\{N_k\}$ with $N_1 < N_2 < N_3 < \cdots$ such that $|p_{N_k} - p_m| < 1/k$ for all $m \geq N_k$. In geometric language, this says that the neighborhood of radius $1/k$ about the point p_{N_k} contains all but a finite number of terms of the sequence $\{p_n\}$, namely, all p_m with $m \geq N_k$.

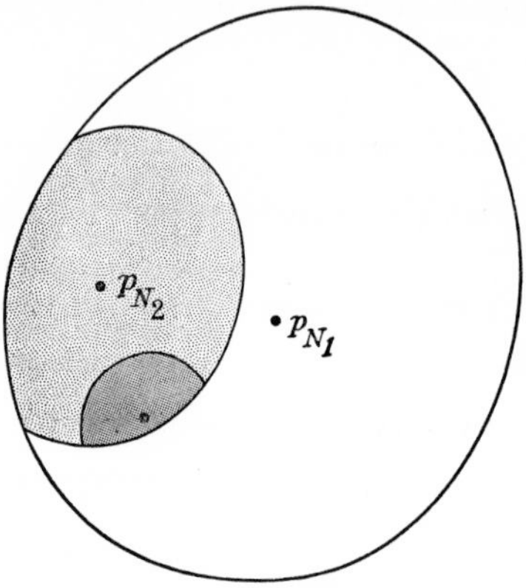

FIG. 1-15

We next construct a nested sequence of closed bounded sets. Let

$$\begin{aligned} C_1 &= \{\text{all } p \text{ with } |p - p_{N_1}| \leq 1\} \\ C_2 &= \{\text{all } p \in C_1 \text{ with } |p - p_{N_2}| \leq \tfrac{1}{2}\} \\ C_3 &= \{\text{all } p \in C_2 \text{ with } |p - p_{N_3}| \leq \tfrac{1}{3}\} \end{aligned}$$

and so on (Fig. 1-15). There is then a point $\bar{p}$ which lies in all the sets C_k, so that for each $k = 1, 2, \ldots$ $|\bar{p} - p_{N_k}| \leq 1/k$. It remains to show that $\lim_{m\to\infty} p_m = \bar{p}$. By the triangle inequality,

$$\begin{aligned} |\bar{p} - p_m| &= |\bar{p} - p_{N_k} + p_{N_k} - p_m| \\ &\leq |\bar{p} - p_{N_k}| + |p_{N_k} - p_m| \\ &\leq \frac{1}{k} + \frac{1}{k} = \frac{2}{k} \end{aligned}$$

for any choice of $m \geq N_k$. This says that the neighborhoods of radius $2/k$ about $\bar{p}$ each contain all but a finite number of the terms of the sequence $\{p_n\}$ and $\lim_{n\to\infty} p_n = \bar{p}$. ∎

In the proof of this theorem we have also encountered the important notion of **subsequence.** The sequence $\{p_{N_k}\}$ whose terms are $p_{N_1}, p_{N_2}, \ldots$ is a subsequence of the sequence $\{p_n\}$. In general a subsequence of a sequence $\{p_n\}$ is obtained by selecting an infinite number of terms from it in the order in which they occur, obtaining a sequence $\{q_n\}$ with terms $q_k = p_{r_k}$, where $r_1, r_2, \ldots$ may be any increasing sequence of positive integers. The proof given above for Theorem 5 essentially involved two steps: (1) any Cauchy sequence has a convergent subsequence; (2) if $\{p_n\}$ has a convergent subsequence, and is a Cauchy sequence, then $\{p_n\}$ converges (see Exercise 11).

EXERCISES

1. Show that the sequence described by $p_n = (n, 1/n)$ does not converge.

2. Show that $p_n = \left(\frac{n+1}{n}, \frac{(-1)^n}{n}\right)$ defines a convergent sequence.

3. Suppose that the terms of an infinite sequence are selected only from a finite set of points. When will the sequence converge?

4. If $\bar{p}$ is a cluster point for a set E, show that there is a sequence of points of E which converges to $\bar{p}$.

5. Let $p_n = \sqrt{n}$. Show that $\lim_{n \to \infty} |p_{n+1} - p_n| = 0$. Is $\{p_n\}$ a Cauchy sequence?

6. Among the following sequences, some are subsequences of others; determine all those that are so related.†

(*a*) $1, -1, 1, -1, \ldots$
(*b*) $1, 1, -1, 1, 1, -1, \ldots$
(*c*) $1, \frac{1}{2}, \frac{1}{3}, \frac{1}{4}, \ldots$
(*d*) $1, \frac{1}{4}, \frac{1}{9}, \frac{1}{16}, \frac{1}{25}, \ldots$
(*e*) $1, 0, \frac{1}{2}, 0, \frac{1}{3}, 0, \frac{1}{4}, 0, \ldots$

7. A point $\bar{p}$ is called a **limit point** for a sequence $\{p_n\}$ if there is a subsequence which converges to $\bar{p}$. Can a sequence have two different limit points? An infinite number of limit points? No limit points?

***8.** Show that a sequence which is bounded always has at least one limit point.

***9.** Show that a bounded sequence with exactly *one* limit point is convergent.

10. Show that a convergent sequence $\{p_n\}$ always has the Cauchy property

$$\lim_{n,m \to \infty} |p_n - p_m| = 0.$$

11. (Alternative proof of Theorem 5.) Let $\{p_n\}$ be a Cauchy sequence. Show first that it is bounded, and then, using Exercises 8 and 9 above, prove that it converges.

12. Let $p_n = (a_n, b_n)$ define a sequence of points in the plane. Show that $\{p_n\}$ is convergent only if $\{a_n\}$ and $\{b_n\}$ are each convergent.

1.5. Real Sequences

If we turn from general sequences of points to sequences of real numbers, additional possibilities appear. In particular, we encounter the special class of **monotone** sequences. A sequence $\{a_n\}$ is said to be

† Strictly speaking, a description of a sequence is not complete until a formula for the general term is given. In practice, it may be sufficient merely to list off enough of the terms to make the law of formation evident. This brings in matters of experience and judgment which can sometimes lead to conflicting choices; the terms 2, 3, 5, 8 might equally well be followed by 12, 17, 23, 30, . . . or by 13, 21, 34, 55, ...

monotone increasing if $a_1 \leq a_2 \leq a_3 \leq \cdots$ and **monotone decreasing** if $a_1 \geq a_2 \geq a_3 \geq \cdots$; these are abbreviated $\{a_n\} \uparrow$ and $\{a_n\} \downarrow$.

Theorem 6. *A bounded monotone sequence is convergent.*

We discuss only the case in which $\{a_n\} \uparrow$. The first step is to select the correct value for $\lim_{n\to\infty} a_n$, and then prove that it *is* the limit. Consider the set of terms which form the sequence. This is a bounded set S of real numbers, and as such, it has a least upper bound L. Since L is an *upper* bound for S, we have $a_n \leq L$ for all n. If $\epsilon > 0$, $L - \epsilon$ is smaller than L; since L was the *least* upper bound, $L - \epsilon$ is not an upper bound for S, and there must be some member of S which is larger than $L - \epsilon$. We suppose that one such a_N is selected, so that $L - \epsilon < a_N \leq L$. Since $\{a_n\}$ is monotone increasing, we must also have $L - \epsilon < a_n \leq L$ for all $n \geq N$, and since ϵ is arbitrary, we have proved that $\lim_{n\to\infty} a_n = L$. ▌

This is one of the most useful general theorems about limits. It enables us to prove convergence for many sequences without having to first guess the limit; however, in applying the theorem, we do not obtain the value of the limit. Several examples will illustrate this.

The sequence $\{a_n\} = 2, 3/2, 4/3, \ldots, (n+1)/n, \ldots$ is decreasing. Since all the terms are positive, it is bounded from below by 0 and is therefore a bounded sequence. Hence, $\lim_{n\to\infty} a_n$ exists. (In this case, of course, it is trivial to show directly that $\lim_{n\to\infty} a_n = 1$.)

A more complicated example is furnished by the sequence $\{a_n\}$ with $a_n = n^{1/n}$. The first few terms are $1, \sqrt{2}, \sqrt[3]{3}, \sqrt[4]{4}$, or (approximately) 1, 1.41, 1.44, 1.41. This is certainly not a monotone sequence if we start with the first term; it seems possible that it may be monotone decreasing from the third term on. To verify this, we compare the size of $n^{1/n}$ and $(n+1)^{1/(n+1)}$; equivalently, and easier to work with, we compare the numbers n^{n+1} and $(n+1)^n$ which result from them by raising both to the exponent $n(n+1)$. Using the binomial theorem,

$$\begin{aligned}
(n+1)^n &= n^n + \frac{n}{1!}n^{n-1} + \frac{n(n-1)}{2!}n^{n-2} + \cdots \\
&\qquad + \frac{n(n-1)(n-2)\cdots(2)}{(n-1)!}n + 1 \\
&\leq n^n + \frac{1}{1!}n^n + \frac{1}{2!}n^n + \cdots + \frac{1}{n!}n^n \\
&\leq n^n\left(1 + \frac{1}{1!} + \frac{1}{2!} + \cdots + \frac{1}{n!}\right) \\
&\leq n^n(n) = n^{n+1},
\end{aligned}$$

when $n \geq 3$. Thus, $\{a_n\}$ is decreasing from the third term on; since the terms are all positive, and thus bounded from below, the theorem applies and $\lim_{n\to\infty} n^{1/n}$ exists. [In this case too, it can be shown that the value of the limit is 1; however, it is not trivial this time (see Sec. 2.6).]

Finally, let $a_n = (1 + 1/n)^n$. Computation gives the approximate values 2, 2.25, 2.37, 2.44, suggesting that this may be an increasing sequence. (This evidence, however, is worthless when we ask if the sequence $\{a_n\}$ is *bounded*.) To prove that $\{a_n\}$ is monotonic, we again compare a_n with a_{n+1}.

$$a_n = \left(1 + \frac{1}{n}\right)^n = 1 + \frac{n}{1!}\frac{1}{n} + \frac{n(n-1)}{2!}\frac{1}{n^2} + \frac{n(n-1)(n-2)}{3!}\frac{1}{n^3} + \cdots + \frac{n(n-1)\cdots(2)}{(n-1)!}\frac{1}{n^{n-1}} + \frac{1}{n^n}$$

$$= 1 + 1 + \frac{1}{2!}\left(1 - \frac{1}{n}\right) + \frac{1}{3!}\left(1 - \frac{1}{n}\right)\left(1 - \frac{2}{n}\right) + \cdots + \left[\frac{1}{n!}\left(1 - \frac{1}{n}\right)\cdots\left(\frac{2}{n}\right)\left(\frac{1}{n}\right)\right].$$

Replacing n by $n + 1$, we have

$$a_{n+1} = 1 + 1 + \frac{1}{2!}\left(1 - \frac{1}{n+1}\right) + \frac{1}{3!}\left(1 - \frac{1}{n+1}\right)\left(1 - \frac{2}{n+1}\right) + \cdots + \left[\frac{1}{n!}\left(1 - \frac{1}{n+1}\right)\cdots\left(\frac{3}{n+1}\right)\left(\frac{2}{n+1}\right)\right] + \left[\frac{1}{(n+1)!}\left(1 - \frac{1}{n+1}\right)\cdots\left(\frac{2}{n+1}\right)\left(\frac{1}{n+1}\right)\right],$$

the last term arising because the expansion of $[1 + 1/(n + 1)]^{n+1}$ has one more term than that of $(1 + 1/n)^n$. Comparing these expressions, term for term, we see that a_{n+1} is always larger than a_n, and $\{a_n\} \uparrow$. To prove boundedness, we again examine the expression for a_n and see that

$$a_n < 1 + 1 + \frac{1}{2!} + \frac{1}{3!} + \cdots + \frac{1}{n!} < 1 + 1 + \frac{1}{2} + \frac{1}{4} + \cdots + \frac{1}{2^n}.$$

This finite sum can be computed exactly since it is a geometric progression, and

$$a_n < 1 + \frac{1 - (\tfrac{1}{2})^{n+1}}{1 - (\tfrac{1}{2})} < 1 + \frac{1}{\tfrac{1}{2}} = 3.$$

Appealing to the theorem, $\lim_{n\to\infty} \{a_n\}$ exists. (Its value of course is the number $e = 2.71828\ 18285\ \ldots$.)

Any bounded sequence has, by Exercise 8, Sec. 1.4, one or more limit points. If the sequence is real, two of these limit points receive special names. The largest of all the limit points is called the **limit superior** (or **upper limit**) and the smallest, the **limit inferior** (or **lower limit**) for the sequence. For a sequence $\{a_n\}$, these are indicated by $\limsup_{n\to\infty} a_n$ or $\overline{\lim_{n\to\infty}}\, a_n$ and $\liminf_{n\to\infty} a_n$ or $\underline{\lim_{n\to\infty}}\, a_n$. These will coincide when the sequence converges. The technique of their use is somewhat more difficult than that of the ordinary limit (see Exercise 9 below), but one is not restricted to *convergent* sequences.

EXERCISES

1. Show that $\{a_n\}$ converges when

(*a*) $a_n = \dfrac{n}{2^n}$ (*b*) $a_n = \dfrac{1 \cdot 3 \cdot 5 \cdots (2n-1)}{2 \cdot 4 \cdot 6 \cdots (2n)}$

2. Let $a_1 = 1$, $a_2 = 3$, $a_3 = (a_1 + a_2)/2 = 2$, and in general $a_n = (a_{n-1} + a_{n-2})/2$. Is $\{a_n\}$ a monotone sequence? Does it converge?†

3. Investigate the convergence of the sequence $\{a_n\}$ described by

$$a_n = \sqrt{n^2 + n} - n.$$

4. If $\lim_{n\to\infty} a_n = A$ and $\lim_{n\to\infty} b_n = B$, prove that $\lim_{n\to\infty} a_n b_n = AB$.

5. If $\lim_{n\to\infty} a_n = A$ and $A \neq 0$, prove $\lim_{n\to\infty} \dfrac{1}{a_n} = \dfrac{1}{A}$.

6. Show that Theorem 6 can be used to prove the *nested interval property* (Sec. 1.3).

7. Find $\limsup_{n\to\infty} a_n$ and $\liminf_{n\to\infty} a_n$ when

(*a*) $a_n = (-1)^n$ (*b*) $a_n = (-1)^n \left(2 + \dfrac{3}{n}\right)$

(*c*) $a_n = \dfrac{n + (-1)^n(2n+1)}{n}$ (*d*) $a_n = \sin\left(\dfrac{n\pi}{3}\right)$

8. If $\limsup_{n\to\infty} a_n = A$ and $\limsup_{n\to\infty} b_n = B$, show by an example that it is not always the case that $\limsup_{n\to\infty} (a_n + b_n) = A + B$.

***9.** Show that for any bounded sequences $\{a_n\}$ and $\{b_n\}$

$$\liminf_{n\to\infty} a_n + \liminf_{n\to\infty} b_n \le \liminf_{n\to\infty} (a_n + b_n) \le \limsup_{n\to\infty} (a_n + b_n) \le \limsup_{n\to\infty} a_n + \limsup_{n\to\infty} b_n.$$

***10.** Let $\{a_n\}$ be a sequence converging to zero, and let $\{\sigma_n\}$ be the sequence of arithmetic means:

$$\sigma_n = \frac{a_1 + a_2 + \cdots + a_n}{n}$$

Prove that $\lim_{n\to\infty} \sigma_n = 0$.

† This is an example of a complete description of a sequence which specifies the law of formation of the terms, but does not contain a formula for the nth term; such a formula can be obtained: $a_n = (7 + 8(-1)^n 2^{-n})/3$.

CHAPTER 2

FUNCTIONS

2.1. Functions and Graphs

The notion of **function** is essentially the same as that of correspondence. A numerical-valued function f assigns to each point p in its **domain of definition** a single real number $f(p)$ called the **value** of f at p. The rule of correspondence may be described by a formula such as

$$f(p) = x^2 - 3xy \qquad \textit{when } p = (x, y)$$

or by several formulas, such as

$$f(p) = \begin{cases} x & \textit{when } x > y \\ x^2 + y & \textit{when } x \leq y \end{cases}$$

or by a geometrical description:

f(p) is the distance from p to the point (4, 7)

or even by an assumed physical relationship:

f(p) is the temperature at the point p.

In all of these instances, it is important to bear in mind that the rule or correspondence is the function f, whereas $f(p)$ is the numerical value which f assigns to p. A function may be thought of as a machine into which specific points may be fed, while the corresponding values emerge at the other end.

Real-valued functions are often classified according to the dimension of their domain of definition. If $f(p)$ is defined for all $p \in S$ and S is a subset of the plane, then we may write p as (x, y) and $f(p)$ as $f(x, y)$ and refer to f as a function of **two real variables.** Similarly, when S is a set in 3-space, we may write $f(x, y, z)$ for $f(p)$ and say that f is a function of **three real variables.** When S is a set on the line, we usually write $f(x)$ and call f a function of **one real variable.** In all these cases, however, f can still be thought of as a function defined for the single variable point p.

Other cases also arise. A function f may be defined only for points p which lie on a certain curve C in space. For example, if a thin wire were bent into the shape of C, $f(p)$ might be the temperature of the wire at p. Again, if Σ is a smooth surface in space, $f(p)$ might be the density of electric charge at the point p on Σ, and we would be led to consider a function which is defined only on Σ.

Side by side with the notion of a function as a correspondence or mapping between two sets (e.g., points and numbers), we have the concept of **graph.** If f is a function of one real variable, the graph of f is the set of points (x, y) in the plane for which $y = f(x)$. If f is a function of two real variables, the graph of f is the set of points (x, y, z) in 3-space for which $z = f(x, y)$. Conversely, it is possible to base the notion of function on that of graph. Let A and B be any two sets, and let E be any set composed of ordered pairs (a, b) with $a \in A$ and $b \in B$. By analogy, (a, b) may be called the "point" in an $A \times B$ space having coordinates a and b, regardless of the nature of the sets A and B. Any such set E can be called a graph or **relation,** and those that have the special property of being **single-valued** are called functions.† Although this approach has much value, it seems preferable to leave it at this point; a more complete treatment would require a discussion of the notion of ordered pair, and a considerable digression.

Many special properties of a function are reflected in simple geometrical properties of its graph. A function f defined on the line is said to be **monotonic increasing** if $f(x) \leq f(x')$ whenever $x < x'$; this means that the graph of f "rises" as we move along it from left to right. Again, a function of two variables is said to be **convex** if it obeys the condition

$$f(p_1) + f(p_2) \leq 2f\left(\frac{p_1 + p_2}{2}\right);$$

this says that Σ, the graph of f, is a surface with the property that if A and B are any two points on Σ, their mid-point lies on or below Σ. (A sketch will show the reason for calling such functions "convex.")

It is clear that the graph of a function of three or more real variables requires a space of dimension higher than three; the difficulty in visualizing this reduces the effectiveness of the graphical approach by decreasing the reliability of one's intuition. In such cases, other "pictures" for a function prove useful. For example, any function of three variables can be thought of—solely for the purposes of study—as specifying a temperature distribution throughout a region of space, and a function of four variables as specifying a temperature distribution which changes with time. Such visualizations will often help one to understand the behavior of a function as a whole; for example, it becomes easier to discuss the

† E is single-valued if and only if the fact that a point (a, b) is in E ensures that no other point with the same *first* coordinate is also in E.

function F given by

$$F(x, y, z) = [(x - 1)^2 + (y + 1)^2 + z^2]^{1/4}$$

if we call $F(p)$ the temperature at p, and observe that it is the square root of the distance from p to $(1, -1, 0)$. The surfaces of constant temperature—equithermal surfaces—are spheres with center at $(1, -1, 0)$, and at any point p, the direction in which $F(p)$ is increasing most rapidly is that directly *away* from $(1, -1, 0)$.

Sometimes it is said that *any* equation in x and y defines y as a function of x. This must both be explained and qualified. What is meant is that, given an equation $E(x, y) = 0$, one is generally able (at least in theory) to "solve for y," getting $y = f(x)$. Without *some* restrictions on E this is false; the equation $y^2 + (x - y)(x + y) - 1 = 0$ cannot possibly be "solved for y." Again, solution of the equation for y seldom gives a unique answer, while in writing $y = f(x)$, we require that exactly one value of y correspond to a given value of x. We must therefore modify the original statement and say that if the function E is suitably restricted, the equation $E(x, y) = 0$ defines a set of functions (possibly just one) such that if f is one of these, then $E(x, f(x)) = 0$ for all x in the domain of definition of f. The equation $x^2 + y^2 - 16 = 0$ yields two functions, $f(x) = \sqrt{16 - x^2}$ and $g(x) = -\sqrt{16 - x^2}$.

The geometric point of view is of assistance here. Let S be the graph of the equation $E(x, y) = 0$, that is, all the points (x, y) which satisfy it. This graph or relation may be single-valued, and in this case it is the sought for function; in general, S will not be single-valued so that some vertical lines will cut it more than once. However, S may then be cut apart into pieces, each of which *is* a function, and any of these is a function which is obtained from the equation by "solving for y." We shall discuss this topic in considerable detail in Chap. 5 when we take up the so-called *implicit function theorems*.

EXERCISES

1. Describe the domain of definition of each function f defined below, and sketch or describe its graph.

(*a*) $f(x) = 1/(1 + x^2)$

(*b*) $f(x, y) = 4 - x^2 - y^2$

(*c*) $f(x) = x/(x - 1)$

(*d*) $f(x, y) = 1/(x^2 - y^2)$

(*e*) $f(x, y) = \begin{cases} 1 & \text{for } x < y \\ 0 & \text{for } x = y \\ \frac{1}{2} & \text{for } x > y \end{cases}$

2. If f is a function which is defined only for points on a certain curve C in the plane what does its graph look like?

3. Let $f(x) = x^2 + x$, $g(x, y) = xy$ and $h(x) = x + 1$. What are:

(a) $f(g(1, 2))$
(b) $h(f(3))$
(c) $g(f(1), h(2))$
(d) $g(f(x), h(y))$
(e) $g(h(x), f(x))$
(f) $f(g(x, h(y)))$
(g) $f(f(x))$

4. (a) If $F(x) = x^2 + x$ and $G(s) = s + s^2$, are F and G different functions?
(b) If $F(x, y) = x^2 + y$ and $G(x, y) = x + y^2$, are F and G different functions?

5. A **level curve** or **contour line** of value k for a function f of two variables is the set of points p for which $f(p) = k$. Sketch the level curves of the function described by $f(x, y) = x^2 - y^2$ for various choices of k.

6. Sketch the level curves for f when

(a) $f(x, y) = y^2 - x$
(b) $f(p) = |p| - 1$
(c) $f(p) = \begin{cases} 1 & \text{when } |p| < 1 \\ x - y & \text{when } |p| \geq 1. \end{cases}$

7. For a function of three variables, the corresponding notion is that of **level surface**; sketch the level surfaces for the function: $f(x, y, z) = x^2 + y^2 - z^2$.

***8.** What can you say about the graph of a function f of two variables which has the property that, for any points p, q and any real numbers α, β,

$$f(\alpha p + \beta q) = \alpha f(p) + \beta f(q)?$$

2.2. Limits of Functions

A sequence of real numbers is defined to be a special type of function of one real variable, having the set of positive integers as its domain of definition. If f is the function, the terms of the sequence are the numbers $a_n = f(n)$ for $n = 1, 2, \ldots$. With this in mind, we take up the topic of limits for functions. By analogy with the definition given for sequences, we adopt a definition for the **limit of a function** "at infinity"; in applying this, it is assumed that $f(x)$ is defined for all positive x that are sufficiently large.

Definition 1. *A function f, defined on an unbounded interval $c < x < \infty$, is said to* **converge to** L *as x increases, written,*

$$\lim_{x \uparrow \infty} f(x) = L,$$

if and only if, corresponding to each $\epsilon > 0$, a number N may be found such that $|f(x) - L| < \epsilon$ whenever $x \geq N$.

For example, $\lim_{x \uparrow \infty} 1/x^2 = 0$ and $\lim_{x \uparrow \infty} \dfrac{x}{x - 1} = 1$, while $\lim_{x \uparrow \infty} \sin x$ and $\lim_{x \uparrow \infty} x^2 - x$ do not exist; the computations needed to establish these differ little from those for sequences (Sec. 1.4).

The definition of limit for approach to a (finite) point takes a slightly different form. We assume that $f(x)$ is defined for all points x in some neighborhood (= interval) about a point b, with the possible exception of b itself; whether or not f is defined at b is irrelevant.†

Definition 2. *We write*

$$\lim_{x \to b} f(x) = L$$

if and only if, corresponding to each $\epsilon > 0$, *a number* $\delta > 0$ *may be found such that* $|f(x) - L| < \epsilon$ *whenever* $0 < |x - b| < \delta$.

Comparing this with Definition 1, we see that the number δ plays a role analogous to that of N. Several examples will help to show this. Let $f(x) = x^2 + 3$ and $b = 2$; we show that $\lim_{x \to b} f(x) = 7$. As a first step, we write

$$f(x) - L = (x^2 + 3) - 7 = x^2 - 4 = (x - 2)(x + 2).$$

We wish to make this small by controlling the size of $|x - b| = |x - 2|$. Since only points x near 2 need be considered, we may decide from the start that δ will always be chosen less than 1; this limits us to points x in the interval [1, 3] and for these, $|x + 2| \leq 3 + 2 = 5$. Hence, for all x in this interval, $|f(x) - L| \leq 5|x - 2|$. Given $\epsilon > 0$, we choose δ as any positive number smaller than $\epsilon/5$, and then if $|x - 2| < \delta$,

$$|f(x) - L| < 5(\epsilon/5) = \epsilon.$$

Again, let f be described by

$$f(x) = \begin{cases} \dfrac{x^3 - 1}{x - 1} & \text{for } x \neq 1 \\ 2 & \text{when } x = 1. \end{cases}$$

and consider $\lim_{x \to 1} f(x)$. Computation gives

$$f(1.1) = 3.31, \qquad f(1.01) = 3.0301,$$

and we are led to guess that $\lim_{x \to 1} f(x) = 3$. To confirm this, we estimate the difference $f(x) - 3$. When $x \neq 1$, we have

$$\begin{aligned} f(x) - 3 &= \frac{x^3 - 1}{x - 1} - 3 = \frac{x^3 - 3x + 2}{x - 1} \\ &= x^2 + x - 2 = (x - 1)(x + 2). \end{aligned}$$

When $x = 1$, $f(x) - 3 = f(1) - 3 = 2 - 3 = -1$. However, our aim

† The term "deleted neighborhood of $\bar{p}$" is sometimes used to denote a neighborhood of $\bar{p}$ from which $\bar{p}$, the center, has been removed. In this terminology, we would say that f is defined in a deleted neighborhood of b.

is to make $f(x) - 3$ small whenever $0 < |x - 1| < \delta$, and this explicitly rules out $x = 1$; we therefore work only with the formula

$$f(x) - 3 = (x - 1)(x + 2).$$

As before, we will decide to use numbers δ smaller than 1, so that we need only discuss points x in the interval [0, 2], or since 1 may be deleted, the intervals $0 \leq x < 1$ and $1 < x \leq 2$. For such x, $|x + 2| \leq 4$, and $|f(x) - 3| \leq 4|x - 1|$. Given ϵ, choose δ as $\epsilon/4$; then, $|f(x) - 3| < \epsilon$ whenever $0 < |x - 1| < \delta$.

Another possible behavior for a function f is indicated by the expression "$\lim_{x \to b} f(x) = \infty$." A word of caution: The symbol "∞" as used here, and also in Definition 1, is not a number, or a point on the line; it is merely a part of the expression, and has no meaning out of context. A test of this is the fact that "∞" does not occur in the definition of "$\lim_{x \uparrow \infty} f(x) = L$," nor does it occur in the following formal definitions:

Definition 2′. *We write*

$$\lim_{x \to b} f(x) = \infty$$

if and only if, corresponding to each positive number B, a number $\delta > 0$ can be found such that $f(x) \geq B$ whenever $0 < |x - b| < \delta$.

Definition 2″. *We write*

$$\lim_{x \to b} f(x) = -\infty$$

if and only if, corresponding to each negative number $-B$, a number $\delta > 0$ can be found such that $f(x) \leq -B$ whenever $0 < |x - b| < \delta$.

As illustrations, $\lim_{x \to 1} (x - 1)^{-2} = \infty$, $\lim_{x \to 0} \log |x| = -\infty$. We cannot write $\lim_{x \to 0} 1/x = \infty$, since the behavior of this function is not the same for both positive and negative x; however, we can write $\lim_{x \to 0} 1/|x| = \infty$.

Following the pattern set above, one may also frame definitions for $\lim_{x \uparrow \infty} f(x) = \infty$ and $\lim_{x \uparrow \infty} f(x) = -\infty$. To illustrate their correct use, we would write $\lim_{x \uparrow \infty} e^x = \infty$, $\lim_{x \uparrow \infty} \log x = \infty$, and $\lim_{x \uparrow \infty} (x \sin x - x^2) = -\infty$, but *not* $\lim_{x \uparrow \infty} x \sin x = \infty$ or $\lim_{x \uparrow \infty} (x \sin x + x) = \infty$.

Several other modifications are also useful.

Definition 3. *We write*

$$\lim_{x \uparrow b} f(x) = L$$

if and only if, corresponding to each $\epsilon > 0$, *a number* $\delta > 0$ *can be found such that* $|f(x) - L| < \epsilon$ *whenever* $|x - b| < \delta$ *and* $x < b$; *that is, whenever* $b - \delta < x < b$.

This is often called the **left-hand limit** of f at b, or the limit of $f(x)$ as x approaches b **from below.**† A **right-hand limit** at b is defined in a similar fashion. Both may exist when the usual two-sided limit does not; the function described by $f(x) = [1 + e^{1/x}]^{-1}$ has at the origin the left-hand limit 1 and the right-hand limit 0 (see Fig. 2-1). (When both one-sided limits exist and have the same value, then the two-sided limit exists.)

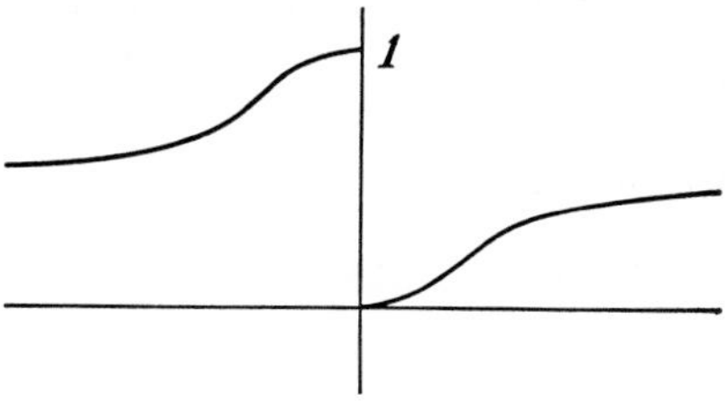

FIG. 2-1. $f(x) = \dfrac{1}{1 + e^{1/x}}$

The theorems concerning limits which were proved in Chap. 1 for sequences also hold for functions.

Theorem 1. *If* $\lim\limits_{x \to b} f(x) = A$, *and* $\lim\limits_{x \to b} g(x) = B$, *then*

$$\lim_{x \to b} (f(x) + g(x)) = A + B$$

and $\lim\limits_{x \to b} f(x)g(x) = AB$. *If* $A \neq 0$, *then* $\lim\limits_{x \to b} \dfrac{g(x)}{f(x)} = \dfrac{B}{A}$.

Corresponding statements can be given for the one-sided limits and limits at "infinity"; however, A and B must be understood to represent numbers. The operations of addition, multiplication, and division do not apply to the symbols "∞" and "$-\infty$" (see Appendix).

The **Cauchy condition** for convergence of a sequence (Theorem 5, Sec. 1.4) has an analogue for functions:

Theorem 2. $\lim\limits_{x \to b} f(x)$ *exists if, corresponding to each* $\epsilon > 0$, *a number* $\delta > 0$ *can be found such that* $|f(x_1) - f(x_2)| < \epsilon$ *whenever* x_1 *and* x_2 *obey the conditions* $0 < |x_1 - b| < \delta$, $0 < |x_2 - b| < \delta$.

This property of the function f may be abbreviated

$$\lim_{\substack{x_1 \to b \\ x_2 \to b}} |f(x_1) - f(x_2)| = 0.$$

A function f is said to be **bounded** on a set E if there is a number M such that $|f(x)| \leq M$ for all $x \in E$, and **monotone increasing (decreasing)** on E if $f(x_1) \leq f(x_2)$ $(f(x_1) \geq f(x_2))$ whenever $x_1 < x_2$ and $x_1 \in E$, $x_2 \in E$.

† It will be observed that this is analogous to the definition of $\lim\limits_{x \uparrow \infty} f(x)$.

Theorem 3. *If f is bounded and monotone increasing on the open interval $a < x < b$, then $\lim_{x \uparrow b} f(x)$ exists.*

EXERCISES

1. Formulate precise definitions for:

(a) $\lim_{x \downarrow -\infty} f(x) = L$ (b) $\lim_{x \uparrow \infty} f(x) = \infty$

(c) $\lim_{x \downarrow b} f(x) = L$

2. Discuss the existence of:

(a) $\lim_{x \to 0} (1 - x^2)$ (b) $\lim_{x \uparrow \infty} \dfrac{x}{1 + x}$

(c) $\lim_{x \downarrow 0} \sqrt{x}$ (d) $\lim_{x \uparrow 1} (1 - x)^{-1/2}$

3. Discuss the existence of:

(a) $\lim_{x \downarrow -\infty} \dfrac{x - 1}{\sqrt{1 + x^2}}$ (b) $\lim_{x \uparrow \infty} \dfrac{x - 1}{\sqrt{1 + x^2}}$

4. What are the forms which Theorem 2 and Theorem 3 take when "b" is replaced by "∞"?

5. State a theorem comparable to Theorem 3 which applies to monotonedecreasing functions.

6. Prove Theorem 1.

***7.** Prove Theorem 2.

8. Prove Theorem 3.

9. A function is bounded for large positive values if there are numbers x_0 and M such that $f(x)$ is defined and obeys $|f(x)| \leq M$ for all $x \geq x_0$. Suppose that f is bounded for large values, and $\lim_{x \uparrow \infty} g(x) = 0$. Prove $\lim_{x \uparrow \infty} f(x)g(x) = 0$. Is Theorem 1 helpful?

10. By proving appropriate monotonicity, show that $\lim_{x \downarrow 0} x^{1/x}$ and $\lim_{x \uparrow \infty} x^{1/x}$ exist. (For this problem, you may use knowledge of differentiation.)

2.3. Limits of Functions (General Case)

We turn now to the study of limits for functions of several variables. Let $f(p)$ be defined for all points p in a neighborhood of a point p_0, except possibly the point p_0 itself; as with functions of one variable, the nature of f *at* the point p_0 does not enter into the definition of $\lim_{p \to p_0} f(p)$.

Definition 4. *We write*

$$\lim_{p \to p_0} f(p) = L$$

if and only if, corresponding to each $\epsilon > 0$ a number $\delta > 0$ can be found such that $|f(p) - L| < \epsilon$ whenever $0 < |p - p_0| < \delta$.

As an illustration, let $f(x, y) = x + y^2$ and $p_0 = (2, 1)$. Assuming that a good guess for L is 3, we write

$$\begin{aligned} f(p) - 3 &= x + y^2 - 3 = (x - 2) + (y^2 - 1) \\ &= (x - 2) + (y + 1)(y - 1). \end{aligned}$$

When the point $p = (x, y)$ is near p_0, y will be near 1. If we decide that the numbers δ will always be chosen less than 1, then when $|p - p_0| < \delta$, y will certainly lie between 0 and 2, so that for any point p in the δ neighborhood of p_0, $|y + 1| \le 3$. Combining this with the fact that $|x - 2| \le |p - p_0|$ and $|y - 1| \le |p - p_0|$, we see that whenever $|p - p_0| < \delta$, then $|f(p) - 3| \le |x - 2| + 3|y - 1| \le \delta + 3\delta = 4\delta$. Given ϵ, we choose δ so that $\delta < \epsilon/4$; then, for any p with $0 < |p - p_0| < \delta$, one has $|f(p) - 3| \le 4\delta < \epsilon$.

In the one-variable case which we discussed in Sec. 2.2, there were only two directions from which the point x could approach the point b, and we were led to introduce left and right one-sided limits. When we turn to the two-variable case, we have an infinite number of possible "modes of approach" to a point p_0. The general case is covered by the following definition. Let S be a set on which f is defined, and let p_0 be a cluster point for S; for simplicity, we assume that p_0 is not itself in S.

Definition 5. *We say that $f(p)$ converges to L as p approaches p_0 in S, written*

$$\lim_{p \to p_0} f(p) = L \qquad [p \in S]$$

if and only if, corresponding to any $\epsilon > 0$ a number $\delta > 0$ can be found such that $|f(p) - L| < \epsilon$ whenever $|p - p_0| < \delta$ and $p \in S$.

An important special case of this arises when S is a line segment or an arc (curve) having p_0 as an end point. In these cases, the limit of $f(p)$ as p approaches p_0 from S reduces essentially to the computation of the limit of a function of one variable. For, let the arc be given by parametric equations: $x = \phi(t)$, $y = \psi(t)$, with $0 \le t \le 1$, and such that $\lim_{t \downarrow 0} \phi(t) = x_0$, $\lim_{t \downarrow 0} \psi(t) = y_0$, the coordinates of p_0. Then, setting $g(t) = f(\phi(t), \psi(t))$, we see that $\lim_{p \to p_0} f(p)$, $[p \in S]$, is exactly $\lim_{t \downarrow 0} g(t)$. As an illustration, the limit of $f(x, y)$ as (x, y) approaches the origin along the horizontal axis from the right becomes $\lim_{x \downarrow 0} f(x, 0)$, while the limit along the vertical axis from below is $\lim_{y \downarrow 0} f(0, y) = \lim_{t \downarrow 0} f(0, -t)$. If (x, y) approaches the origin along the ray of slope 1, we obtain $\lim_{t \downarrow 0} f(t, t)$. The following result, simple although it is, is often quite useful in discussing the existence of limits.

Theorem 4. *If $f(p)$ is defined for all points in a neighborhood of p_0, except possibly at p_0 itself, and $\lim_{p \to p_0} f(p) = L$, then the limit of $f(p)$ exists for p approaching p_0 in any set S and always has the value L.*

Since $\lim_{p \to p_0} f(p)$ exists, for a given ϵ a number δ can be chosen such that $|f(p) - L| < \epsilon$ whenever $0 < |p - p_0| < \delta$. This remains true if we further restrict p by the requirement $p \in S$, where S is any set having p_0 as a cluster point. Hence, it follows that $\lim_{p \to p_0} f(p) = L$, with $p \in S$, and the limiting value does not depend upon the mode of approach. ▌

The additional complexity introduced in going from functions of one variable to those of several variables can be seen from the following simple examples.

Consider first the function f defined everywhere in the plane, except at the origin, by $f(x, y) = xy/\sqrt{x^2 + y^2}$, and let us study the behavior of $f(p)$ as p approaches $\mathbf{0}$. When p is on either of the axes, then $xy = 0$ and $f(p) = 0$. Thus, $f(p)$ converges to 0 as p approaches $\mathbf{0}$ along the axes. Is it true that $\lim_{p \to \mathbf{0}} f(p) = 0$? As a first step, we observe that

$$|x| \leq |p| \quad \text{and} \quad |y| \leq |p|$$

so that

$$|xy| \leq |p|^2 \quad \text{and} \quad |f(p)| = \frac{|xy|}{|p|} \leq \frac{|p|^2}{|p|} = |p|.$$

Thus, given $\epsilon > 0$ we can make $|f(p) - 0| < \epsilon$ for all p with $0 < |p - \mathbf{0}| < \delta$ by choosing $\delta = \epsilon$, and we have shown that $\lim_{p \to \mathbf{0}} f(p) = \mathbf{0}$. Another way to show this is to transform to polar coordinates; putting $x = r \cos \theta$ and $y = r \sin \theta$, $f(p)$ is $r \cos \theta \sin \theta$, and $|f(p)| = |r \cos \theta \sin \theta| \leq r = |p|$.

Consider next the function g defined by $g(x, y) = xy/(x^2 + y^2)$. Again, $g(p) = 0$ when p lies on either axis, so that $g(p)$ converges to 0 as p approaches $\mathbf{0}$ along them. This time, however, $\lim_{p \to \mathbf{0}} g(p)$ fails to exist. To see this, we approach $\mathbf{0}$ along the line whose equation is $y = x$. We have $g(p) = g(x, x) = x^2/2x^2 = \frac{1}{2}$, so that the limiting value for this mode of approach is $\frac{1}{2}$, not 0. Polar coordinates may again be used; we obtain $g(p) = r^2 \sin \theta \cos \theta / r^2 = \sin \theta \cos \theta$, so that the limiting value clearly depends upon the direction of approach to the origin.

The final illustration will show that the behavior of a function may be considerably more complicated. Let $F(x, y) = xy^2/(x^2 + y^4)$. If p lies on either axis, $F(p) = 0$. On the line $y = x$,

$$F(p) = F(x, x) = \frac{x^3}{x^2 + x^4} = \frac{x}{1 + x^2}$$

and $\lim_{x\to 0} F(x, x) = 0$. In fact, $F(p)$ converges to 0 as p approaches the origin along *every* straight line. When $y = mx$,

$$F(p) = F(x, mx) = \frac{m^2x}{1 + m^4x^2}$$

and $\lim_{x\to 0} F(x, mx) = 0$. In spite of this, it is not true that $\lim_{p\to \mathbf{0}} F(p) = 0$. To show this, we produce a curve terminating at the origin along which $F(p)$ does not converge to 0; this curve is the parabola $y^2 = x$, and $F(p) = F(y^2, y) = y^4/2y^4 = \frac{1}{2}$.

When f is a function of two real variables, the notation $\lim_{\substack{x\to x_0\\ y\to y_0}} f(x, y)$ is often used in place of $\lim_{p\to p_0} f(p)$. This should not be confused with notion of an **iterated** limit, such as $\lim_{x\to x_0} \lim_{y\to y_0} f(x, y)$, in which we treat f as a function of x and y separately, rather than as a function of the point (x, y). For example,

$$\lim_{x\to 0} \lim_{y\to 0} \frac{x^2}{x^2 + y^2} = 1 \qquad \text{and} \qquad \lim_{y\to 0} \lim_{x\to 0} \frac{x^2}{x^2 + y^2} = 0$$

while $\lim_{\substack{x\to 0\\ y\to 0}} \frac{x^2}{x^2 + y^2}$ fails to exist.

We may also discuss the behavior of a function "at infinity," that is, when $|p|$ is large.

Definition 6. *We write*

$$\lim_{|p|\to\infty} f(p) = L$$

if and only if, corresponding to each $\epsilon > 0$, *a number* N *can be found such that* $|f(p) - L| < \epsilon$ *whenever* $|p| \geq N$.

For example, if $f(x, y) = 1/(x^2 + y^2 + 1)$, then we may write

$$\lim_{|p|\to\infty} f(p) = 0.$$

Again, if $f(x, y, z) = T + (x^2 + y^2 + z^2)^{-\frac{1}{2}}$ is the temperature at (x, y, z), we would say that the temperature "at infinity" is T, meaning that $\lim_{|p|\to\infty} f(p) = T$.

EXERCISES

✓**1.** Discuss the existence of the following limits:

(*a*) $\lim_{p\to\mathbf{0}} \frac{x + y}{x^2 + y^2}$ (*b*) $\lim_{|p|\to\infty} \frac{x + y}{x^2 + y^2}$

(*c*) $\lim_{p\to\mathbf{0}} \frac{xy - z^2}{x^2 + y^2 + z^2}$ (*d*) $\lim_{|p|\to\infty} \frac{xy - z^2}{x^2 + y^2 + z^2}$

2. If $\lim_{p \to p_0} f(p) = A$ and $\lim_{p \to p_0} g(p) = B$, prove that $\lim_{p \to p_0} (f(p) + g(p)) = A + B$, $\lim_{p \to p_0} f(p)g(p) = AB$, and, assuming that $A \neq 0$, $\lim_{p \to p_0} \dfrac{1}{f(p)} = \dfrac{1}{A}$.

3. Use Exercise 2 to compute $\lim_{p \to (1,2)} \dfrac{x + y^2}{xy}$.

4. A function f is said to be bounded near p_0 if there are numbers M and $\delta > 0$ such that $|f(p)| \leq M$ for all p with $0 < |p - p_0| < \delta$. Prove that if $\lim_{p \to p_0} f(p)$ exists, then f is bounded near p_0.

5. Let A and B be two points in space, and set

$$f(p) = |p - A| - |p - B|.$$

Is f a bounded function? Can you show that, for any p_0, $\lim_{p \to p_0} f(p) = f(p_0)$? Does $\lim_{|p| \to \infty} f(p)$ exist?

6. Following the pattern of Definition 5, formulate one for: "$f(p)$ converges to L as $|p|$ becomes infinite in the set S." Using this, discuss the behavior of

$$f(x, y) = \exp(x - y)$$

when $|p|$ is large. (*Hint:* You may assume knowledge of properties of the exponential function.)

*7. Show that $\lim_{p \to p_0} f(p) = L$ if and only if $\lim_{n \to \infty} f(p_n) = L$ for every sequence $\{p_n\}$ which converges to p_0.

2.4. Continuity

Let f be defined on a set E. If p_0 is an interior point of E, we say that f is **continuous** at p_0 whenever $\lim_{p \to p_0} f(p) = f(p_0)$. If p_0 is a boundary point of E and f is defined at p_0, then the same definition is used except that p is restricted to approach p_0 in the set E. We say that f is **continuous on** E if f is continuous at each point of E. Recasting this in the ϵ, δ form, we arrive at the following definition.

Definition 7. *A function f is continuous on a set E if and only if $f(p)$ is defined for each $p \in E$, and if corresponding to any $\epsilon > 0$ and $p_0 \in E$, a number $\delta > 0$ can be found such that $|f(p) - f(p_0)| < \epsilon$ whenever $p \in E$ and $|p - p_0| < \delta$.*

The term **discontinuity** is used in two ways. The first refers to a point at which a particular function is defined, but at which it is not continuous. For example, consider the function f described by

$$f(p) = f(x, y) = \begin{cases} x^2 + y^2 & \text{when } |p| \leq 1 \\ 0 & \text{when } |p| > 1. \end{cases}$$

This function is defined in the whole plane, and is continuous there except at the points p with $|p| = 1$; each point of this circumference is thus a discontinuity of f. If we consider f only on the set $E = \{$all p

with $|p| \leq 1\}$, then f is continuous on E; the points of the circumference would not be considered discontinuities this time. On the other hand, if we restrict f to the set consisting of points p with $1 \leq |p| \leq 2$, it is not continuous everywhere in the ring, since the points on the inner circumference are again discontinuities. In its second usage, the term discontinuity is often applied to points at which a function is not defined. For example, the function described by $f(x) = 1/x$ is said to be discontinuous (or to have a discontinuity) at the origin.

Discontinuities can be further classified as **removable** and **essential.** If $f(p_0)$ is defined, and $L = \lim_{p \to p_0} f(p)$ exists but $L \neq f(p_0)$, then p_0 is a discontinuity for f; however, it may be "removed" by altering the definition for f at p_0. If we construct a new function F by setting $F(p) = f(p)$ for all p in the domain of f, except p_0, and setting $F(p_0) = L$, then F is now continuous at p_0. Again, if a function f were not defined at p_0, but $L = \lim_{p \to p_0} f(p)$ exists, then we may define $f(p_0)$ to be L and thus extend the domain of f to include p_0 so that f is continuous at p_0. In both of these cases, we would say that p_0 was a removable discontinuity for f. When $\lim_{p \to p_0} f(p)$ does not exist, p_0 is said to be an essential discontinuity for f, since by no assignment of a value for $f(p_0)$ can we make f continuous there. For example, let

$$f(x) = x^x \qquad \text{when } x > 0$$

$$g(x) = \begin{cases} x & \text{when } x > 0 \\ 2 & \text{when } x = 0 \end{cases}$$

$$h(x) = \sin\left(\frac{1}{x}\right) \qquad \text{when } x > 0.$$

All are continuous on the open interval $0 < x$, and can be said to have discontinuities at the origin. However, this is a removable discontinuity for f and g, and an essential discontinuity for h (see Fig. 2-2). To explain this, we observe that f is not defined for $x = 0$, but that it may be shown that $\lim_{x \downarrow 0} f(x) = 1$; if we set $f(0) = 1$, the extended function is now continuous on the closed interval $0 \leq x$. The function g is defined at the origin, but $g(0) = 2 \neq 0 = \lim_{x \downarrow 0} g(x)$. If we alter g there so that $g(0) = 0$, then g too is continuous for $0 \leq x$. (Since this redefinition of g has produced a new function, a new letter such as "G" should be used to denote it; however, when the context is sufficiently clear, such precision is not usual.) The third function, h, is not defined at the origin, nor does $\lim_{x \downarrow 0} h(x)$ exist, and no choice for $h(0)$ will make h continuous there.

We did not verify the assertions of continuity made above. A proof based solely upon the definition of continuity would involve extensive and detailed computation. To see why this would be the case, let us verify that P given by $P(x) = x^2 - 2x + 3$, is continuous on the whole line. (By contrast, it should be observed that the continuity of P would follow at once from the continuity of I, where $I(x) = x$, and Theorem 6 (page 36); here, however, we shall gain considerable insight by carrying

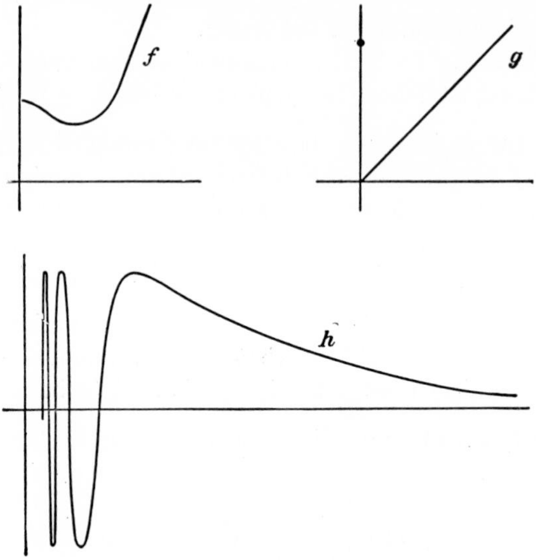

FIG. 2-2

out the detailed treatment which allows only the use of the definition.) Let x_0 be any point on the line, and suppose that $\epsilon > 0$ has been given. We must produce a number $\delta > 0$ such that $|P(x) - P(x_0)| < \epsilon$ whenever $|x - x_0| < \delta$. As a first step, we estimate the difference

$$\begin{aligned} P(x) - P(x_0) &= (x^2 - 2x + 3) - (x_0{}^2 - 2x_0 + 3) \\ &= x^2 - x_0{}^2 + 2x_0 - 2x \\ &= (x - x_0)(x + x_0 - 2). \end{aligned}$$

Suppose that $|x - x_0| < \delta$, where δ is yet to be determined. Then,

$$\begin{aligned} |x + x_0 - 2| &= |x - x_0 + 2x_0 - 2| \\ &\le |x - x_0| + 2|x_0| + 2 \\ &< \delta + 2|x_0| + 2 \end{aligned}$$

so that for all such points x,

$$|P(x) - P(x_0)| \le \delta(\delta + 2|x_0| + 2).$$

If we again agree to choose δ smaller than 1, then

$$\delta + 2|x_0| + 2 \leq 3 + 2|x_0|.$$

Thus, if $\delta \leq \epsilon/(3 + 2|x_0|)$, then

$$|P(x) - P(x_0)| < \delta(3 + 2|x_0|) \leq \epsilon,$$

and we have shown that P is continuous at x_0.

Several features of this example are worth noting. The choice which we have made for δ depends both upon ϵ and upon x_0; moreover, as we move x_0 to the right, δ decreases, and in fact tends to zero. This behavior can also be seen in the graph of P. The assertion that P is continuous at x_0 is equivalent to the following: *Take the point $(x_0, P(x_0))$ on the graph*

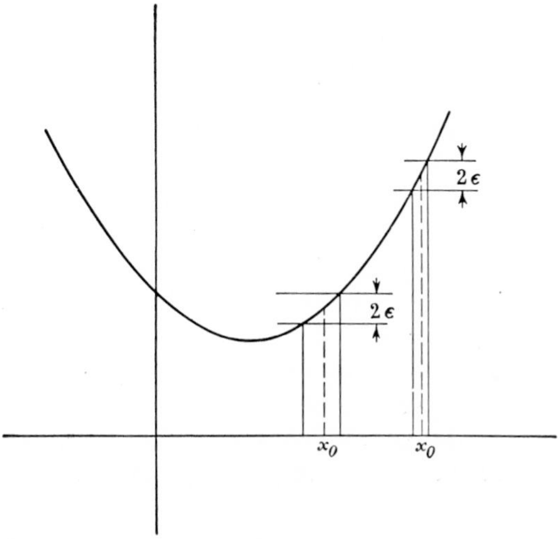

FIG. 2-3

of P and draw two horizontal lines, ϵ above and ϵ below the point; then, the point $(x, P(x))$ lies between these lines for every choice of x with $x_0 - \delta < x < x_0 + \delta$. As we move x_0 to the right, the graph becomes steeper and the number δ must be chosen smaller and smaller in order to maintain this relationship (see Fig. 2-3).

Suppose now that we restrict x_0 to the interval $[-3, 3]$. It is then always true that $3 + 2|x_0| \leq 9$ so that choosing $\delta = \epsilon/9$, we have $|P(x) - P(x_0)| < \epsilon$ for all x and x_0 with $|x - x_0| < \delta$ and x_0 in $[-3, 3]$. The number δ now depends only on ϵ and the interval. If we use the general interval $[-a, a]$, then $3 + 2|x_0| \leq 3 + 2a$ when $x_0 \in [-a, a]$ and δ might be choosen as $\epsilon/(3 + 2a)$, and again $|P(x) - P(x_0)| < \epsilon$. To this important property, a special name is given.

Definition 8. *We say that f is* **uniformly continuous** *on a set E if and only if, corresponding to each $\epsilon > 0$ a number $\delta > 0$ can be found such that $|f(p) - f(q)| < \epsilon$ whenever p and q are points in E and $|p - q| < \delta$.*

Comparing this with Definition 7, it should be noticed that the choice of δ can now be made independently of the location of the points p and q. The term "uniformly continuous" is always used in conjunction with a set which must be specified; in the illustration above, we have shown directly that P is uniformly continuous on the interval $[-3, 3]$. More generally, P is uniformly continuous on each bounded interval, but is not uniformly continuous on the whole line.

For another example, let $f(x) = 1/x$. We shall show that f is continuous on the open interval $0 < x < 1$ but is not uniformly continuous there. We first write

$$|f(x) - f(x_0)| = \left|\frac{1}{x} - \frac{1}{x_0}\right| = \frac{|x_0 - x|}{xx_0}.$$

To prove continuity at x_0, which may be any point with $0 < x_0 < 1$, we wish to make $|f(x) - f(x_0)|$ small by controlling $|x - x_0|$. If we decide to consider only numbers δ obeying $\delta < x_0/2$, then any point x such that $|x - x_0| < \delta$ must also satisfy $x > x_0/2$, and $xx_0 > x_0^2/2$. Thus, for such x, $|f(x) - f(x_0)| < \delta/xx_0 < 2\delta/x_0^2$. Given $\epsilon > 0$, we can ensure that $|f(x) - f(x_0)| < \epsilon$ by taking δ so that $\delta \leq (x_0^2/2)\epsilon$. Thus, f is continuous at each point x_0 with $0 < x_0 < 1$. If f were uniformly continuous there, then a number $\delta > 0$ could be so chosen that $|f(x) - f(x')| < 1$ for every pair of points x and x' between 0 and 1 with $|x - x'| \leq \delta$. To show that this is not the case, we consider the special pairs, $x = 1/n$ and $x' = \delta + 1/n$. For these, we have $|x - x'| = \delta$ and

$$|f(x) - f(x')| = \left|n - \frac{1}{\delta + 1/n}\right| = \frac{n\delta}{\delta + 1/n}.$$

No matter how small δ is, n can be chosen so that this difference is larger than 1; for example, any n bigger than both $1/\delta$ and 3 will suffice.

A plausible (but incorrect) graphical argument can also be given. Examination of the graph of f shows that its slope becomes arbitrarily steep as we move toward the vertical axis and this would seem to imply that f cannot be uniformly continuous. This reasoning has an analytical counterpart; the choice $\delta = (x_0^2/2)\epsilon$ which we have made above becomes arbitrarily small as x_0 moves toward 0, so that "no positive number can be found which works for all $x_0 > 0$." To see the flaw in these arguments, consider F, where $F(x) = \sqrt{x}$. Since the graph of F also becomes arbitrarily steep as we move toward the vertical axis, the first argument would seem to show that this function too is not uniformly continuous on the interval $0 < x < 1$. We seem to reach the same conclusion if we repeat the second line of reasoning. To see this, we first prove continuity. Given points x and x_0 with $0 < x < 1$, $0 < x_0 < 1$, we have

$$|F(x) - F(x_0)| = |\sqrt{x} - \sqrt{x_0}| = \left|\frac{(\sqrt{x} - \sqrt{x_0})(\sqrt{x} + \sqrt{x_0})}{\sqrt{x} + \sqrt{x_0}}\right|$$
$$= \frac{|x - x_0|}{\sqrt{x} + \sqrt{x_0}} \leq \frac{|x - x_0|}{\sqrt{x_0}}.$$

Given ϵ, we select δ so that $\delta \leq \sqrt{x_0}\,\epsilon$; then, if $|x - x_0| < \delta$, then $|F(x) - F(x_0)| < \delta/\sqrt{x_0} < \epsilon$. This shows that F is continuous on the interval $0 < x < 1$. The choice of δ as $\sqrt{x_0}\,\epsilon$ suggests that F is not uniformly continuous there, since this number becomes arbitrarily small as x_0 approaches 0. However, F in fact *is* uniformly continuous. To prove this, we must make a more careful choice of δ. Assume that we have chosen δ, and again estimate the difference $|F(x) - F(x_0)|$. Two cases arise, depending on the size of x_0. If $0 < x_0 < \delta$, and $|x - x_0| < \delta$, then $0 < x < 2\delta$, and we have

$$|F(x) - F(x_0)| = |\sqrt{x} - \sqrt{x_0}| \leq \sqrt{x} + \sqrt{x_0}$$
$$\leq \sqrt{2\delta} + \sqrt{\delta} < 3\sqrt{\delta}.$$

If $x_0 \geq \delta$, then, using the original estimate of the difference,

$$|F(x) - F(x_0)| \leq \frac{|x - x_0|}{\sqrt{x_0}} < \frac{\delta}{\sqrt{\delta}} = \sqrt{\delta} < 3\sqrt{\delta}.$$

No matter how δ is chosen, we have shown that if $|x - x_0| < \delta$, then $|F(x) - F(x_0)| < 3\sqrt{\delta}$. This at once proves that F is uniformly continuous, since given ϵ we may choose $\delta = \epsilon^2/9$ and have $|F(x) - F(x_0)| < \epsilon$ whenever x and x_0 obey $x > 0$, $x_0 > 0$ and $|x - x_0| < \delta$.

When is a continuous function also uniformly continuous? The following Theorem answers this; a proof is found in Exercises 5 and 6.

Theorem 5. *If S is a closed and bounded set of points and f is continuous on S, then f is uniformly continuous on S.*

The examples we have given above show the need for the words "closed" and "bounded" if the result is to be true in general; individual functions may be uniformly continuous on unbounded sets; $I(x) = x$ gives a function which is uniformly continuous on the whole line.

As we have seen, continuity of a function f at p_0 is equivalent to the assertion $\lim_{p \to p_0} f(p) = f(p_0)$. Thus, continuous functions are those for which such limits can be computed merely by substitution. The results of the preceding sections on limits lead at once to Theorem 6.

Theorem 6. *If f and g are continuous on a set E, then so are their sum $f + g$ and their product fg. The quotient f/g is continuous at all points $p \in E$ at which $g(p) \neq 0$.*

This enables one to construct continuous functions from simpler ones. The obvious continuity of I (where again $I(x) = x$) shows that the general rational function $R = P/Q$ (where P and Q are polynomials) is continuous everywhere except at the zeros of Q.

Composition or superposition of continuous functions also yields continuous functions. There are many special cases of this general principle; as samples, we give a one-variable and a two-variable form.

Theorem 7. (i) *Let f, g, and h be functions of one variable with*

$$h(x) = g(f(x)).$$

Let f be continuous at p_0 and g continuous at $q_0 = f(p_0)$. Then, h is continuous at p_0.

(ii) *Let F, G, H, and K be functions of two real variables, with*

$$K(x, y) = H(F(x, y), G(x, y)).$$

Let F and G be continuous at p_0 and H continuous at $q_0 = (F(p_0), G(p_0))$. Then, K is continuous at p_0.

If we assume that the sine function has been shown to be continuous for all real values, then it follows that the function described by $\sin(1/x)$ is continuous for all $x \neq 0$, that $x \sin xy$ is continuous for all points of the plane, and that $x^2y \csc(x + y)$ is continuous in the plane except on the lines $x + y = n\pi$, where n is an integer.

We have seen that the fact that a polynomial is continuous follows from Theorem 6. How do we know that a function such as sine or logarithm is continuous? The only honest reply is to say it depends upon the way in which the function itself is defined. For example, a traditional definition of sine is: *For any $x \geq 0$, $\sin(x)$ is the second coordinate of the point P on the unit circle whose distance from* (1, 0), *measured along the circumference, is x* (see Fig. 2-4). To show that the sine is continuous at 0, we must prove that $\lim_{x \downarrow 0} \sin x = 0$. Referring to the diagram, it is clear that as x approaches 0, P approaches (1, 0); writing $P = (u, v)$, $v = \sin x$ and $\lim v = 0$. Since it is sometimes felt that such a "proof by picture" needs analytical bolstering, the second diagram in the figure is used to show that for positive x, $0 \leq \sin x \leq H \leq x$, and thus $\lim_{x \downarrow 0} \sin x = 0$. This is no less a proof by picture than the former! In fact, quite a bit of additional work must be done to put this approach on a firm footing. The description of the sine function given above already presupposes the theory of arc length! Other approaches can be given which avoid these objections. One method defines the trigonometric functions by means of infinite series, and will be discussed in Sec. 4.3; another method constructs them from certain indefinite integrals, and will be explained in Chaps. 4 and 5. In both of these,

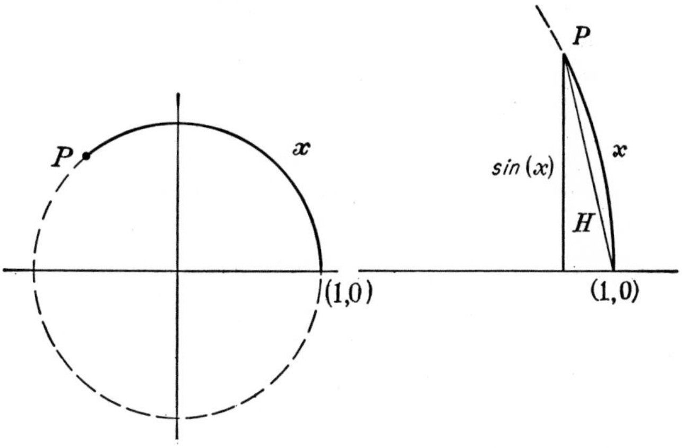

FIG. 2-4

continuity of the functions follows from certain general theorems, whereas some of the specific properties (e.g., addition formulas) require separate treatment.

The important property of uniform continuity described in Definition 8 has several equivalent formulations. One of these is concerned with the

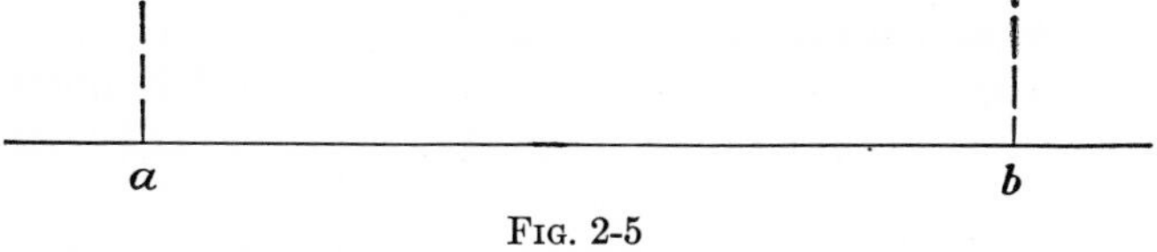

FIG. 2-5

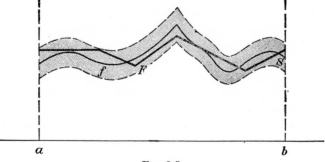

notion of **uniform approximation.** We say that a function F is a uniform approximation to within ϵ (or an ϵ-approximation) for a function f on a set E if $|F(p) - f(p)| < \epsilon$ for all $p \in E$. If f and F are functions of one variable and E is an interval $[a, b]$, this has a simple graphical interpretation. For a given ϵ, let S be the band which is obtained by moving a vertical line segment of length 2ϵ along f keeping its mid-point on the graph (Fig. 2-5). Then, F is an ϵ-approximation to f if the graph of F

lies in S. If a function f is somewhat complicated in structure, it is often convenient to work instead with a simpler function F which approximates it. In the general class of continuous functions of one variable, perhaps the simplest are the polynomials, and those that are **piecewise** polynomials, that is, described by polynomial formulas which may differ on adjoining intervals. Among the latter are the **piecewise linear** functions. The graph of such a function is a connected curve composed of a finite number of straight-line segments.

Theorem 8. *If f is continuous (and hence uniformly continuous) on the closed interval $[a, b]$ then it can be approximated to within ϵ on $[a, b]$ by a piecewise linear function, for any $\epsilon > 0$. Conversely, any function f which can be so approximated is necessarily uniformly continuous there.*

Given f and $\epsilon > 0$, we wish to construct a piecewise linear F such that $|F(x) - f(x)| < \epsilon$ for all $x \in [a, b]$. An obvious line of attack is to choose points $P_0, \ldots, P_N$ on the graph of f and let F be the function obtained by joining these in order. It seems reasonable that if the points are chosen close enough together, F will be the desired approximation. To formalize this, let the points be $(x_k, f(x_k))$ and set $F(x_k) = f(x_k)$ for $k = 0, 1, \ldots, N$. Between x_k and x_{k+1}, F is linear and is given by

$$F(x) = \frac{(x_{k+1} - x)f(x_k) + (x - x_k)f(x_{k+1})}{x_{k+1} - x_k}.$$

This is merely the familiar process of linear interpolation. To estimate the difference $|F(x) - f(x)|$, we observe that $F(x)$ lies between $f(x_k)$ and $f(x_{k+1})$ when x lies between x_k and x_{k+1}, so that $|F(x) - f(x)|$ is less than or equal to the larger of $|f(x_k) - f(x)|$ and $|f(x_{k+1}) - f(x)|$. We are now ready to choose the points x_k. Since f is uniformly continuous on $[a, b]$ we can select $\delta > 0$ so that $|f(x) - f(x')| < \epsilon$ whenever x and x' belong to $[a, b]$ and $|x - x'| < \delta$. Choose N sufficiently large so that $|b - a|/N < \delta$, and divide the interval $[a, b]$ into N equal intervals. Let the points of division be $a = x_0, x_1, \ldots, x_N = b$ in order of size. Clearly, $|x_{k+1} - x_k| < \delta$ so that if $x_k \le x \le x_{k+1}$, $|f(x_k) - f(x)|$ and $|f(x_{k+1}) - f(x)|$ are each smaller than ϵ, and $|F(x) - f(x)| < \epsilon$. This holds on each of the N subintervals so that F is a uniform ϵ-approximation to f on $[a, b]$. ▌

Conversely, if f is a function which admits such approximations for any $\epsilon > 0$, then f is uniformly continuous on $[a, b]$. For, given $\epsilon > 0$, we can choose a piecewise linear approximation F such that $|F(x) - f(x)| < \epsilon$ for all $x \in [a, b]$; since F itself is uniformly continuous, we may choose $\delta > 0$ so that $|F(x) - F(x')| < \epsilon$ whenever x and x' are in $[a, b]$ and $|x - x'| < \delta$. Then, for any such pair of points,

$$\begin{aligned}|f(x) - f(x')| &= |f(x) - F(x) + F(x) - F(x') + F(x') - f(x')| \\ &\leq |f(x) - F(x)| + |F(x) - F(x')| + |F(x') - f(x')| \\ &\leq \epsilon + \epsilon + \epsilon = 3\epsilon.\end{aligned}$$

We have found $\delta > 0$ such that $|f(x) - f(x')| < 3\epsilon$ whenever x and x' lie in $[a, b]$ and $|x - x'| < \delta$. This being true for each $\epsilon > 0$, f is uniformly continuous on $[a, b]$. ▌

Another theorem of similar nature is commonly known as the **Weierstrass approximation theorem**: *If f is continuous on the closed interval $[a, b]$, then it can be uniformly approximated to within ϵ on $[a, b]$ by a polynomial, for any $\epsilon > 0$.* This may be obtained from Theorem 8 by showing that any piecewise linear function can be approximated by a polynomial.†

EXERCISES

1. Discuss the continuity of the function f described by:

(*a*) $f(x) = \begin{cases} x \sin(1/x) & \text{for } x \neq 0 \\ 0 & \text{for } x = 0 \end{cases}$

(*b*) $f(x, y) = xy/(x^2 + y^2) \quad \text{for } (x, y) \neq (0, 0)$

(*c*) $f(x, y) = \begin{cases} xy^2/(x^2 + y^4) & \text{for } (x, y) \neq (0, 0) \\ 0 & \text{for } x = y = 0 \end{cases}$

(*d*) $f(x, y) = \begin{cases} (x^2 - y^2)/(x - y) & \text{for } x \neq y \\ x - y & \text{for } (x, y) \text{ when } x = y \end{cases}$

2. Let $f(x) = \begin{cases} 1 & \text{if } x \text{ is a rational number} \\ 0 & \text{if } x \text{ is an irrational number} \end{cases}$

Is f continuous anywhere?

***3.** Let $f(x) = \begin{cases} 0 & \text{if } x \text{ is irrational} \\ 1/q & \text{if } x \text{ is the rational number } p/q \text{ (in lowest terms)} \end{cases}$

Is f continuous anywhere?

4. Let f be continuous in an open set S and suppose that $\lim_{p \to p_0} f(p)$ exists for every boundary point p_0 of S, as p approaches p_0 in S. Extend the definition of f to the boundary of S by setting $f(p_0) = \lim_{p \to p_0} f(p)$. Then, show that f is now continuous on the closure of S, which is the union of S and its boundary.

***5.** Show that a function f is uniformly continuous on a set E if and only if

$$\lim_{n \to \infty} |f(p_n) - f(q_n)| = 0$$

for every pair of sequences $\{p_n\}$, $\{q_n\}$ of points of E such that $\lim_{n \to \infty} |p_n - q_n| = 0$.

6. Use Exercise 5 to prove Theorem 5.

***7.** Let f be uniformly continuous on the open interval $0 < x < 1$. Prove that $\lim_{x \downarrow 0} f(x)$ exists.

8. Let f be uniformly continuous on a bounded open set S. Prove that f can be extended to the boundary of S so as to be continuous in the closure of S.

† For a proof of this in a generalized form, see W. Rudin, "Principles of Mathematical Analysis," pp. 131–136, McGraw-Hill Book Company, Inc., New York, 1953.

2.5. Properties of Continuous Functions

In this section we take up a number of the implications of the continuity of a function. If one were to think of the general continuous function in terms of a smooth graph such as might be drawn with a pencil, most of these theorems would seem entirely obvious and to require no proof. However, continuous functions can be described whose graphs cannot be pictured in this fashion. (See page 138, or Rudin, "Principles of Mathematical Analysis," pp. 125–127.) It is therefore important to see that these properties follow from the precise notion of continuity, with no dependence upon intuition.

As a first example, it seems reasonable that if a function is continuous at p_0 and strictly positive there, then it must be strictly positive in some neighborhood of p_0. Putting this more precisely, we arrive at Theorem 9.

Theorem 9. *Let f be continuous on S and let $p_0 \in S$ with $f(p_0) > 0$. Then, there is a number $\epsilon > 0$ and a neighborhood U about p_0 such that $f(p) > \epsilon$ for all $p \in S \cap U$.*

Take $\epsilon = f(p_0)/2 > 0$. Since f is continuous at p_0, there is a number $\delta > 0$ such that $|f(p) - f(p_0)| < \epsilon$ whenever $p \in S \cap U$, where U is the neighborhood about p_0 of radius δ. For any such p, we therefore have

$$\begin{aligned} f(p) &= f(p) - f(p_0) + f(p_0) \\ &\geq f(p_0) - |f(p) - f(p_0)| \\ &> f(p_0) - \epsilon = 2\epsilon - \epsilon = \epsilon. \quad \blacksquare \end{aligned}$$

A function f is said to be **bounded** on a set S if there is a number M such that $|f(p)| \leq M$ for all $p \in S$. A function can be continuous on a set and unbounded there, for example, $f(x) = 1/x$ on the open interval $0 < x < 1$. This is not the case if the set is sufficiently restricted.

Theorem 10. *If the set S is closed and bounded and f is continuous on S, then f is bounded on S.*

Several proofs of this may be given. In one variable, we can give a simple direct argument. Since f is uniformly continuous on S, it has a piecewise linear approximation F such that $|f(x) - F(x)| < 1$ for all $x \in S$. Since the graph of F is a polynomial curve composed of a finite number of line segments, F is bounded on S; if $|F(x)| \leq M$, then $|f(x)| \leq 1 + M$, so that f is bounded on S. When f is a function of several real variables, an indirect proof is often given. If f were not bounded on S, there would be points $p_1, p_2, \ldots, p_n, \ldots$ in S with $|f(p_1)| > 1$, $|f(p_2)| > 2, \ldots, |f(p_n)| > n, \ldots$. By the Bolzano-Weierstrass theorem (or more exactly, Exercise 8, Sec. 1.4) the sequence $\{p_n\}$ has a limit point $\bar{p} \in S$ which is the limit of some particular converging subsequence

$\{p_{r_n}\}$. Since f is known to be continuous at $\bar{p}$, $\{f(p_{r_n})\}$ must converge to $f(\bar{p})$; this cannot happen since $|f(p_{r_n})| > r_n$ where $\lim_{n\to\infty} r_n = \infty$. The contradiction shows that f must have been bounded on S. ▌

A function can be bounded on a set without taking on a maximum or a minimum value on that set; this is true, for example, for I, where $I(x) = x$ on the open interval $0 < x < 1$, and on the closed interval $[0, 1]$ for the discontinuous function F described by

$$F(x) = \begin{cases} x & \text{when } 0 < x < 1 \\ \frac{1}{2} & \text{when } x = 0 \text{ or } x = 1. \end{cases}$$

However, this is not the case if the set is closed and bounded and the function continuous.

Theorem 11. *If S is closed and bounded, and f is continuous on S, then $f(p)$ takes a maximum and a minimum value for $p \in S$.*

By the previous theorem, f is bounded on S; we can then find numbers b and B such that $b \le f(p) \le B$ for all $p \in S$. Let M be the smallest such upper bound B and let m be the largest such lower bound b. We still have $m \le f(p) \le M$ for all $p \in S$, and M cannot be decreased, nor m increased. If there is a point $p \in S$ with $f(p) = M$, then M is the *maximum* value of f on S. If this is not the case, then $f(p) < M$ for all $p \in S$. Set $g(p) = 1/[M - f(p)]$; the function g is continuous on S and must therefore be bounded there. If $g(p) \le A$, then $f(p) \le M - 1/A$ for all $p \in S$; this contradicts the assumption that M was the smallest upper bound for f. Similarly, if there were no point of S with $f(p) = m$, then $h(p) = 1/[f(p) - m]$ would be continuous on S and therefore bounded; however, if $h(p) \le A$, then $f(p) \ge m + 1/A$ for every $p \in S$. ▌

Another important property of a continuous function is that set forth in the **intermediate value theorem.**

Theorem 12. *Let S be an open connected set and let f be continuous on S. Let a and b be two values of f and let $a < c < b$. Then, there is a point $p \in S$ with $f(p) = c$.*

The one-variable form of this is especially plausible; it asserts that if the graph of f starts off below the line $y = c$, and ends up above it, it must at some point cross it. To prove the theorem, we let A be the set of $p \in S$ with $f(p) < c$ and B the set of $p \in S$ with $f(p) > c$. If $p_0 \in B$, then Theorem 9 shows that $f(p) > c$ for all points p in some neighborhood of p_0, so that p_0 is the center of a neighborhood composed only of points of B. This shows that B is an open set. A similar argument shows that A is open. If $f(p)$ is never c for $p \in S$, then these two sets together cover S, and S could not be a connected set; we may therefore conclude that there is a point $p \in S$ with $f(p) = c$. ▌

EXERCISES

1. Show directly, without the use of Theorem 10, that the function described by

$$f(x, y) = \frac{3x + y^2}{1 + x^2}$$

is bounded on the disk $S = \{\text{all } (x, y) \text{ with } x^2 + y^2 \leq 3\}$. What is the maximum value there?

2. Prove that any polynomial with real coefficients and of odd degree has at least one real root.

***3.** Prove the following modification of Theorem 12: Let S be an open connected set and let f be continuous on S. Let P and Q be points of S with $f(P) = a$, $f(Q) = b$, and let $a < c < b$. Let Γ be any continuous curve joining P and Q and lying entirely in S. Then, there is a point p on the graph of Γ such that $f(p) = c$.

2.6. Mean Value Theorems and L'Hospital's Rule

Certain fundamental properties of functions of one variable involve differentiation. We recall that f is said to be **differentiable** at x_0 if f is defined on a neighborhood of x_0 and has a derivative at x_0 defined by

$$(2\text{-}1) \qquad f'(x_0) = \lim_{x \to x_0} \frac{f(x) - f(x_0)}{x - x_0} = \lim_{h \to 0} \frac{f(x_0 + h) - f(x_0)}{h}.$$

A frequent application of differential calculus is to so-called maximum-minimum problems. We say that f has a **local maximum** at x_0 if there is a neighborhood U about x_0 such that $f(x) \leq f(x_0)$ for all $x \in U$. The notion of a **local minimum** is defined similarly, and the term **extreme value** may be used to refer to either.

Theorem 13. *Let $f(x)$ be defined on a neighborhood of x_0 and have a local extreme value at x_0. If f is differentiable at x_0, then $f'(x_0) = 0$.*

We may assume that $f(x_0 + h) \leq f(x_0)$ for all h with $|h| < \delta$, and that $C = \lim_{h \to 0} \frac{f(x_0 + h) - f(x_0)}{h} = f'(x_0)$ exists. This limit may also be computed by letting h approach 0 first from above, and then from below. Since the numerator of the fraction is never strictly positive, we find that C obeys the conditions $C \leq 0$ and $C \geq 0$ so that necessarily $C = 0$. ▌

It is important to keep in mind that $f'(x_0)$ need not be zero if x_0 is an end point, rather than an interior point. Thus in using this theorem in the solution of a maximum-minimum problem, separate consideration must be given to the possibility of an end point extreme value.

One immediate consequence of Theorem 13 has acquired a special name.

Theorem 14 (*Rolle's Theorem*). *Let f be continuous on the interval $[a, b]$ and let $f'(x)$ exist for $a < x < b$. If in addition, $f(a) = f(b)$, then there is a point x_0 with $a < x_0 < b$ at which $f'(x_0) = 0$.*

If f is constant, any choice of x_0 will do. If f is not constant, then it has either an interior minimum or an interior maximum at some point x_0 of the open interval $a < x < b$, and since f is differentiable everywhere, $f'(x_0) = 0$. ▮

Corollary. *Let f be differentiable on the interval $[a, b]$. Then, the zeros of f are separated by zeros of f'.*

Rolle's theorem in turn has two generalizations.

Theorem 15 (*Mean Value Theorem*). *Let f be continuous on $[a, b]$ and let $f'(x)$ exist for $a < x < b$. Then, a point x_0 can be found with $a < x_0 < b$ such that*

$$f(b) = f(a) + (b - a)f'(x_0).$$

Theorem 16 (*General Mean Value Theorem*). *Let f and g be continuous on $[a, b]$, with $f'(x)$ and $g'(x)$ defined for $a < x < b$. Then, a point x_0 can be found with $a < x_0 < b$ such that*

$$[f(b) - f(a)]g'(x_0) = [g(b) - g(a)]f'(x_0). \tag{2-2}$$

If g is chosen as $g(x) = x$, Theorem 15 is implied by Theorem 16. To prove the latter, we construct a function F to which we apply Rolle's theorem. Let $F(x) = f(x) - Kg(x)$; this is continuous on $[a, b]$ and differentiable in its interior. We shall choose K so that $F(a) = F(b)$. To attain this, we want $f(a) - Kg(a) = f(b) - Kg(b)$, or equivalently, $f(b) - f(a) = K[g(b) - g(a)]$. If $g(a) \neq g(b)$, K can be found, and F satisfies the hypothesis of Rolle's theorem. There is then an x_0 with $a < x_0 < b$ such that $F'(x_0) = 0$, and $f'(x_0) = Kg'(x_0)$. Substituting for K its value, we obtain (2-2). If $g(a) = g(b)$, then (2-2) holds if we can find an x_0 with $[f(b) - f(a)]g'(x_0) = 0$; applying Rolle's theorem to g, we can choose x_0 so that $g'(x_0) = 0$. ▮

These mean value theorems have simple geometrical interpretations. For the first one, let $P = (a, f(a))$ and $Q = (b, f(b))$, both points on the graph of f. Then Theorem 15 asserts that there is some point $(x_0, f(x_0))$ on the graph between P and Q at which the slope is the same as that of the line from P to Q. The more general mean value theorem has a similar interpretation. Let Γ be the curve given parametrically by $x = f(t)$, $y = g(t)$ for $a \le t \le b$, and let $P = (f(a), g(a))$, $Q = (f(b), g(b))$. Then, Theorem 16 asserts that there is a point between P and Q on Γ at which the tangent is parallel to the line through P and Q. The analytical forms of these theorems can be modified. Since the point x_0 lies between a and b, we can write $x_0 = a + \theta h$ where $h = b - a$ and $0 < \theta < 1$. The conclusion of Theorem 15 would then read

$$f(a + h) = f(a) + hf'(a + \theta h). \tag{2-3}$$

The uses of the mean value theorems are of two sorts, one "practical" and the other "theoretical"; the distinctions here are quite subjective. As an example of the former, we shall use the mean value theorem to obtain a simple approximation to a special function.

Theorem 17. *When* $u > 0$ *and* $v \geq 0$, $\sqrt{u^2 + v}$ *may be replaced by* $u + v/2u$ *with an error of* $v^2/4u^3$ *at most.*

To illustrate this, $\sqrt{87} = \sqrt{81 + 6} \sim 9 + 6/18 = 9\frac{1}{3}$, with an error at most $36/(4)(9)^3 \sim .012$. To prove this, put $f(x) = \sqrt{u^2 + x}$ so that $f(0) = u$, while $f(v)$ is the value we wish to estimate. By the mean value theorem, there is an x_0, $0 < x_0 < v$, with

$$\begin{aligned} f(v) &= f(0) + (v - 0)f'(x_0) \\ &= u + \frac{v}{2\sqrt{u^2 + x_0}}. \end{aligned}$$

Since $x_0 > 0$, $\sqrt{u^2 + x_0} > u$ and we have shown that $f(v) < u + v/(2u)$. Thus, the approximation $u + v/(2u)$ is always larger than the true value of $\sqrt{u^2 + v}$. To estimate the error in the approximation, we observe that $x_0 < v$ so that $\sqrt{u^2 + x_0} < \sqrt{u^2 + v} < u + v/(2u)$. Hence,

$$\begin{aligned} f(v) &= u + \frac{v}{2\sqrt{u^2 + x_0}} \\ &> u + \frac{v}{2\left[u + \dfrac{v}{2u}\right]} = u + \frac{uv}{2u^2 + v} \end{aligned}$$

and thus

$$u + \frac{uv}{2u^2 + v} < \sqrt{u^2 + v} < u + \frac{v}{2u}.$$

The error made in using the right-hand term as the approximate value is less than the difference

$$\left[u + \frac{v}{2u}\right] - \left[u + \frac{uv}{2u^2 + v}\right] = \frac{v^2}{(2u)(2u^2 + v)} < \frac{v^2}{4u^3}. \quad \blacksquare$$

[The more exact methods made possible by Taylor's theorem, Sec. 3.3, show that the approximation $u + v/(2u)$ is accurate to within $v^2/(8u^3)$.]

An extremely useful result which arises from the general mean value theorem (Theorem 16) is known as L'Hospital's rule. It provides a simple procedure for the evaluation of limiting values of functions which are expressible as quotients.

Theorem 18 (*L'Hospital's Rule*). *Let f and g be differentiable on the interval $a \leq x < b$, with $g'(x) \neq 0$ there. If*

(i) $$\lim_{x \uparrow b} f(x) = 0 \qquad \lim_{x \uparrow b} g(x) = 0$$

or if

(ii) $$\lim_{x \uparrow b} f(x) = \infty \qquad \lim_{x \uparrow b} g(x) = \infty$$

and if $$\lim_{x \uparrow b} \frac{f'(x)}{g'(x)} = L$$

then $$\lim_{x \uparrow b} \frac{f(x)}{g(x)} = L.$$

The upper end point b may be finite or "∞", and L may be finite or "∞." Before proving the theorem, we give several illustrations of its use, and possible modifications.

To evaluate $\lim_{x \downarrow 0} \dfrac{1 - \cos(x^2)}{x^4}$, we consider instead

$$\lim_{x \downarrow 0} \frac{2x \sin(x^2)}{4x^3} = \lim_{x \downarrow 0} \frac{\sin(x^2)}{2x^2} = \frac{1}{2}.$$

By the theorem, this is also the value of the original limit.

Again, consider $\lim_{x \downarrow 0} x^x$. Since $\log(x^x) = x \log x$, we consider instead $\lim_{x \downarrow 0} x \log x = \lim_{x \downarrow 0} \dfrac{\log x}{1/x}$. We replace this by $\lim_{x \downarrow 0} \dfrac{1/x}{-1/x^2} = \lim_{x \downarrow 0} -x = 0.$ Since the exponential function is continuous, we conclude that

$$\lim_{x \downarrow 0} x^x = \lim_{x \downarrow 0} \exp(x \log x) = \exp(0) = 1.$$

We shall first prove the theorem under hypothesis (i). Because of the form of these conditions, the fraction $f(x)/g(x)$ is said to be "indeterminate of the form $0/0$." We consider only the case in which b is finite, and may therefore take $b = 1$. Since $\lim_{x \uparrow 1} f(x) = 0$ and

$$\lim_{x \uparrow 1} g(x) = 0$$

we may set $f(1) = 0$, $g(1) = 0$, and thus have f and g continuous on the closed interval $a \leq x \leq 1$. Applying the general mean value theorem, we see that for such a choice of x, with $a < x < 1$, there is a point x^* lying between x and 1, such that

$$\frac{f'(x^*)}{g'(x^*)} = \frac{f(1) - f(x)}{g(1) - g(x)} = \frac{f(x)}{g(x)}$$

Since $\lim_{x^* \uparrow 1} \dfrac{f'(x^*)}{g'(x^*)} = L$, we may choose $\delta_n > 0$ so that

$$\left| \frac{f(x)}{g(x)} - L \right| = \left| \frac{f'(x^*)}{g'(x^*)} - L \right| < \frac{1}{n}$$

whenever $1 - \delta_n < x < 1$; this proves that $\lim_{x \uparrow 1} \dfrac{f(x)}{g(x)} = L$. ▌

Under hypothesis (ii), the proof is somewhat more involved. Since we now have $\lim_{x \uparrow 1} f(x) = \infty$, $\lim_{x \uparrow 1} g(x) = \infty$, the fraction $f(x)/g(x)$ is said to be "indeterminate of the form ∞/∞" for $x = 1$. It is tempting to rewrite this as $\dfrac{f(x)}{g(x)} = \dfrac{1/g(x)}{1/f(x)}$, which is now indeterminate of the form $0/0$; however, application of the first form of the theorem does not lead to the desired proof, but only to the assertion that if $\lim_{x \uparrow 1} \dfrac{f(x)}{g(x)}$ exists, its value must be L. For, consider the quotient

$$\frac{(1/g)'}{(1/f)'} = \frac{-g'/g^2}{-f'/f^2} = \left(\frac{f}{g}\right)^2 \frac{g'}{f'}.$$

The mere fact that $\lim_{x \uparrow 1} \dfrac{f'(x)}{g'(x)} = L$ does not at once imply that this new quotient has a limit; if, however, we assume that $\lim_{x \uparrow 1} \dfrac{f(x)}{g(x)} = L'$ exists, and that $L \neq 0$, then we can apply case (i), and conclude that $L' = L$.

To obtain a valid proof of case (ii), we again use the mean value theorem. Given ϵ, we first choose δ so that whenever $1 - \delta < \bar{x} < 1$,

$$\left| \frac{f'(\bar{x})}{g'(\bar{x})} - L \right| < \epsilon$$

Set $x_0 = 1 - \delta$, and take any point x, with $x_0 < x < 1$. By the mean value theorem, there is a choice of $\bar{x}$ with $x_0 < \bar{x} < x$ such that

$$\frac{f(x) - f(x_0)}{g(x) - g(x_0)} = \frac{f'(\bar{x})}{g'(\bar{x})}.$$

Accordingly,

$$\left| \frac{f(x) - f(x_0)}{g(x) - g(x_0)} - L \right| < \epsilon.$$

Putting

$$h(x) = \left\{1 - \frac{f(x_0)}{f(x)}\right\} \Big/ \left\{1 - \frac{g(x_0)}{g(x)}\right\}$$

this becomes

$$\left| \frac{f(x)}{g(x)} h(x) - L \right| < \epsilon$$

valid for all x with $x_0 < x < 1$. Since $\lim_{x \uparrow 1} f(x) = \infty$ and $\lim_{x \uparrow 1} g(x) = \infty$, it follows that $\lim_{x \uparrow 1} h(x) = 1$. Choose x_1 between x_0 and 1 so that $|h(x) - 1| < \epsilon$ and $h(x) > \frac{1}{2}$ for all x with $x_1 < x < 1$. For such values of x, we have

$$\left| \left\{ \frac{f(x)}{g(x)} - L \right\} h(x) \right| = \left| \frac{f(x)}{g(x)} h(x) - Lh(x) \right|$$

$$\leq \left| \frac{f(x)}{g(x)} h(x) - L \right| + |L[1 - h(x)]| < \epsilon + |L|\epsilon$$

and

$$\left| \frac{f(x)}{g(x)} - L \right| < \frac{(1 + |L|)\epsilon}{h(x)} < 2(1 + |L|)\epsilon.$$

This proves that $\lim_{x \uparrow 1} \frac{f(x)}{g(x)} = L$. ∎

Proofs of the other modifications of the theorem are easily supplied. For example, the case where $b = \infty$ may be reduced to the preceding by considering instead the functions F and G defined by $F(x) = f(1/x)$, $G(x) = g(1/x)$. If f and g obey (i) or (ii) for $x \uparrow \infty$, F and G obey them for $x \downarrow 0$. Since $F'(x)/G'(x) = f'(1/x)/g'(1/x)$, we may apply the previously proved form and conclude that if $\lim_{x \uparrow \infty} \frac{f'(x)}{g'(x)} = L$, then $\lim_{x \uparrow \infty} \frac{f(x)}{g(x)} = L$.

EXERCISES

In these problems, you may use any formulas and techniques from elementary calculus.

1. A man is in a rowboat which is located 5 miles from the nearest point of a straight shore. His pier is located some distance down the shore, and is exactly 13 miles from the boat. He can row 3 miles per hour, and walk r miles per hour. Where should he land to reach the pier as quickly as possible?

2. Give a complete discussion of the problem of finding the right circular cone of greatest lateral area which may be inscribed upside down in the cone of radius 1 and altitude 3.

3. Left- and right-hand derivatives at a point x_0 for a function f are defined as

$$\lim_{x \uparrow x_0} \frac{f(x) - f(x_0)}{x - x_0} \quad \text{and} \quad \lim_{x \downarrow x_0} \frac{f(x) - f(x_0)}{x - x_0}$$

respectively. Show by examples that these may exist where the usual two-sided derivative does not. Can such a function be discontinuous at x_0?

4. If $f'(x) = 0$ for all x, $a < x < b$, show that f is constant there.

5. In the following, F is a function which obeys the condition $|F'(x)| \leq C < 1$ for all $x \geq 0$, and $F(0) > 0$.

(*a*) Prove that the equation $F(x) = x$ has one and only one positive root.

(*b*) Show that this root is the limit of the sequence $\{x_n\}$, where $x_1 = F(0)$, $x_2 = F(x_1)$, $x_{n+1} = F(x_n)$.

6. Use Exercise 5 to find an approximation to the positive root of the equation

$$\sin x - 2x + 2 = 0.$$

***7.** Let the sides of a right triangle be: longer leg $= B$, shorter leg $= b$, hypotenuse $= H$. Let the smallest angle of the triangle be θ. Show that θ is given approximately by $3b/(2H + B)$, within .02 (radians). (*Hint:* Express b and B in terms of θ, and estimate this expression.)

8. Let $f'(x)$ exist and f' be bounded, for all x. Prove that f is uniformly continuous on the whole line.

9. Let f'' exist and be negative on the interval [0, 1]. Show that the graph of f is convex, that is, if P and Q lie on the graph, then the line PQ is never above the graph between P and Q.

10. Evaluate:

(a) $\lim\limits_{x\to 0} \dfrac{1 - \cos(x^2)}{x^3 \sin x}$ (b) $\lim\limits_{x\downarrow 0} x^x$

(c) $\lim\limits_{x\to 0} \dfrac{\sin x + \cos x - e^x}{\log(1 + x^2)}$ *(d) $\lim\limits_{x\uparrow\infty} \dfrac{1}{x} e^{-x^2} \displaystyle\int_0^x t^2 e^{t^2}\, dt$

11. It is clear that $\lim\limits_{x\to\infty} e^{-\sin x}$ does not exist. Write this as

$$\lim_{x\to\infty} \frac{2x + \sin 2x}{(2x + \sin 2x)e^{\sin x}}$$

apply L'Hospital's rule, and obtain

$$\lim_{x\to\infty} \frac{4\cos x}{(2x + 4\cos x + \sin 2x)e^{\sin x}} = 0.$$

Explain this apparent contradiction.

CHAPTER 3

INTEGRATION

3.1. The Definite Integral

In this section, we develop the definition and some of the properties of the double integral $\iint_D f(x, y)\,dxdy$ of a function f over a bounded domain D in the plane. The methods apply also to the simpler case of the integral $\int_a^b f(x)\,dx$ of a function of one variable, and to the case of triple- or higher-dimensional multiple integrals.

Historically, the concept of integral had as its starting point, the notion of area. Let us take for granted the definition of area of rectangles, and seek a suitable definition of area which applies to more general sets. Let D be any bounded set in the plane and choose a fixed closed rectangle R which contains D, having its sides parallel to the coordinate axes. We shall use the term **grid** (or net) for any finite set of horizontal and vertical lines. Any grid N produces a collection of closed rectangles $R_{11}, R_{12}, R_{13}, \ldots, R_{mn}$ whose union is R and which together cover D. This collection is called the partition of R determined by the grid N. We separate the rectangles R_{ij} into three classes (see Fig. 3-1). Class (i), all the R_{ij} which contain only interior points of D; class (ii), all the R_{ij} which contain at least one boundary point of D; class (iii), all R_{ij} which contain only exterior points of D. The union of the rectangles of class (i) is called the **inner** or inscribed set for D determined by the grid N, while the union of the rectangles of class (i) and class (ii) is called the **outer** or circumscribing set. Let $\bar{S}(N, D)$ be the total area of the outer set, and $\underline{S}(N, D)$ the total area of the inner set. Clearly, $0 \le \underline{S}(N, D) \le \bar{S}(N, D) \le$ area of R. As N ranges over all possible grids, the values $\bar{S}(N, D)$ generate a bounded set which is determined solely by the set D. Let $\bar{A}(D)$ be the greatest lower bound (infimum) of this set. Similarly, the values $\underline{S}(N, D)$ generate another bounded set, and we let $\underline{A}(D)$ be its least upper bound (supremum). We call $\bar{A}(D)$ the **outer area** of D, and $\underline{A}(D)$ the **inner area** of D. If they have the same value, we denote it by $A(D)$ and call this the **area** of D. As a measure of the fineness of the mesh of a grid N, we use the number

$d(N)$ = largest diameter (diagonal) of any of the rectangles R_{ij}. If a set D has area, then the inner and outer sums, $\underline{S}(N, D)$ and $\bar{S}(N, D)$, will approach $A(D)$ as $d(N)$ decreases.†

This process defines a notion of area for certain sets D. Not all sets have an area. For example, let D be the set of points (x, y) with $0 \leq x \leq 1$, $0 \leq y \leq 1$, and both x and y rational. Since D has no

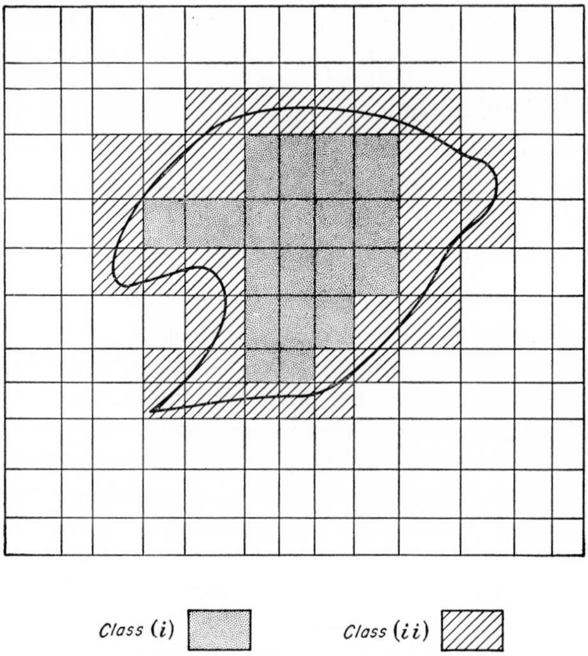

FIG. 3-1

interior points, class (i) is always empty so that $\underline{A}(D) = 0$. On the other hand, every point of the unit square is a boundary point for D, so that every circumscribing set has area 1, and $\bar{A}(D) = 1$. Since these are not equal, the set D does not have an area. (Note that this is distinctly different from saying that a set D has zero area, for this would mean $\underline{A}(D) = \bar{A}(D) = 0$.)

For any choice of N, the number $\bar{S}(N, D) - \underline{S}(N, D)$ is exactly the sum of the areas of the rectangles R_{ij} of the partition which are in class (ii). These are just the ones which form the circumscribing set for the boundary Γ of D. Thus, the number $\bar{A}(D) - \underline{A}(D)$ is exactly $\bar{A}(\Gamma)$, the outer area of the boundary of D. We have therefore shown that a set D is well behaved enough to have an area if and only if its boundary is a

† Since this seems intuitively obvious, we have omitted the proof. It is lengthy, but not difficult, and is quite similar to proofs which we discuss later on in this section.

set with zero area. This can be shown to be the case when the boundary is composed of polygonal curves, or more generally, piecewise smooth curves (Exercises 10 and 11). However, an example has been constructed of a region D, bounded by a simple closed curve, which does not have an area.†

Let us turn now to the definition of the Riemann integral of a function f over such a region D. We first do this for $D = R$. Let N be any grid partitioning R into rectangles R_{ij}. In each R_{ij}, choose a point p_{ij} and then form the **Riemann sum**

$$S(N, f, \{p_{ij}\}) = \Sigma f(p_{ij}) A(R_{ij}).$$

Definition. *The double integral* $\iint_R f$ *exists and has value* v *if and only if for any* $\epsilon > 0$ *there is a* $\delta > 0$ *such that*

$$|S(N, f, \{p_{ij}\}) - v| < \epsilon$$

for any choice of $\{p_{ij}\}$ *and any grid* N *with* $d(N) < \delta$.

By analogy with preceding definitions, this is often written

$$\lim_{d(N)\to 0} S(N, f, \{p_{ij}\}) = \iint_R f.$$

However, as a limit operation, it differs in many essentials from those that we have discussed earlier. The system of grids is not a sequence tending toward some limit, and the number $d(N)$ does not serve to identify the grid N; this is an example of what is called a directed system, and which is a generalization of the notion of sequence.‡

Theorem 1. *If* f *is continuous on* R, *then* $\iint_R f$ *exists.*

To make easier the proof of the next theorem, we will only assume that f is bounded on R in the first stages of the present proof. Associated with each rectangle R_{ij} in the partition of R determined by a grid N are two numbers

$$M_{ij} = \sup_{p \in R_{ij}} f(p)$$
$$m_{ij} = \inf_{p \in R_{ij}} f(p)$$

We set

$$\bar{S}(N) = \Sigma M_{ij} A(R_{ij}) = \text{upper Riemann sum}$$
$$\underline{S}(N) = \Sigma m_{ij} A(R_{ij}) = \text{lower Riemann sum}.$$

† See the paper by W. F. Osgood, *Trans. Am. Math. Soc.*, vol. 4, pp. 107–112, 1903.

‡ An elementary discussion of these concepts may be found in "Universal Mathematics," Part I, Chap. IV, an experimental textbook published by the University of Kansas, 1954, or in E. J. McShane, Partial Ordering and Moore-Smith Limits, *Am. Math. Monthly*, vol. 59, pp. 1–11, 1952.

It is clear that $\underline{S}(N) \leq S(N, f, \{p_{ij}\}) \leq \bar{S}(N)$ for any choice of the points p_{ij}, and if f is continuous, equality at either end can be obtained by proper choices. We separate the proof into several simple steps. In order to be able to compare two different grids and their upper and lower sums, we introduce the notion of a **refinement** of a grid.

Definition. *A grid N' is said to be a refinement of the grid N if N' is obtained by adding one or more lines to those which form N.*

We note that it is possible to have two grids, neither of which is a refinement of the other.

Lemma 1. *If N' is a refinement of N, then*

$$\underline{S}(N) \leq \underline{S}(N') \leq \bar{S}(N') \leq \bar{S}(N).$$

Let us examine the effect of the refinement on a single term $M_{ij}A(R_{ij})$ of the upper sum $\bar{S}(N)$. Under the new partition scheme, R_{ij} will be broken up into a collection of smaller rectangles $r_1, r_2, \ldots, r_m$. Thus, corresponding to this single term of $\bar{S}(N)$, there will be in $\bar{S}(N')$ a block of terms $M^{(1)}A(r_1) + M^{(2)}A(r_2) + \cdots + M^{(m)}A(r_m)$, where $M^{(k)}$ is the least upper bound of f in r_k. Since each r_k lies in R_{ij}, $M^{(k)} \leq M_{ij}$, and

$$\sum_1^m M^{(k)}A(r_k) \leq M_{ij} \sum_1^m A(r_k) = M_{ij}A(R_{ij}).$$

Repeating this argument for each term of $\bar{S}(N)$, we find that $\bar{S}(N') \leq \bar{S}(N)$. An analogous argument shows that $\underline{S}(N) \leq \underline{S}(N')$. ▌

Every grid is a refinement of the empty grid which does not partition R at all, so that for any N,

$$mA(R) \leq \underline{S}(N) \leq \bar{S}(N) \leq MA(R)$$

where $m = \inf_{p \varepsilon R} f(p)$ and $M = \sup_{p \varepsilon R} f(p)$. The set of lower sums $\underline{S}(N)$ forms a bounded set of numbers as N ranges over all possible grids N; let s be its least upper bound. The set of all upper sums $\bar{S}(N)$ is also bounded; let S be its greatest lower bound.

Lemma 2. *$s \leq S$ and for any N, $S - s \leq \bar{S}(N) - \underline{S}(N)$.*

This asserts that the four numbers mentioned have the relative position shown below:

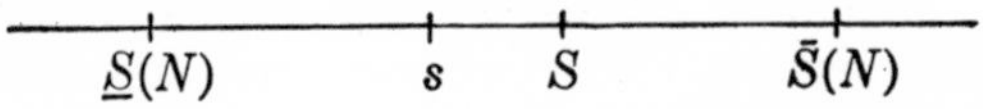

Since $\underline{S}(N)$ is always to the left of s, and $\bar{S}(N)$ to the right of S, it is always true that $S - s \leq \bar{S}(N) - \underline{S}(N)$, regardless of the relative positions of s and S. Let N_1 and N_2 be any two grids, and construct a third grid N by forming the union of N_1 and N_2. N will therefore have all of the lines that make up N_1, and will be a refinement of N_1. It will also be a refinement of N_2. Applying Lemma 1,

$$\begin{matrix}\underline{S}(N_1)\\ \underline{S}(N_2)\end{matrix} \leq \underline{S}(N) \leq \bar{S}(N) \leq \begin{matrix}\bar{S}(N_1)\\ \bar{S}(N_2).\end{matrix}$$

In particular, $\underline{S}(N_1) \leq \bar{S}(N_2)$. Since N_1 and N_2 were arbitrary grids, this shows that every lower sum is smaller than each upper sum, $\bar{S}(N_2)$. Since s is the least upper bound for the set of lower sums, $s \leq \bar{S}(N_2)$. This holds for every N_2, so that $s \leq S$. ▮

Up to this point, we have not assumed that f was continuous. The numbers s and S are therefore defined for any bounded function f; they are called the **lower** and **upper** integrals of f over R.

Lemma 3. *If f is continuous on R, then* $\lim_{d(N)\downarrow 0} |\bar{S}(N) - \underline{S}(N)| = 0.$

Since R is closed and bounded, f is uniformly continuous on R. Given ϵ, we may choose $\delta > 0$ so that $|f(p) - f(q)| < \epsilon$ whenever p and q lie in R and $|p - q| < \delta$. Let N be any grid which partitions R with mesh diameter $d(N) < \delta$. Since $M_{ij} = f(p)$ and $m_{ij} = f(q)$ for a particular choice of p and q in R_{ij}, and since R_{ij} has diameter less than δ, we have $M_{ij} - m_{ij} < \epsilon$ for all i and j. This gives

$$\begin{aligned}0 \leq \bar{S}(N) - \underline{S}(N) &= \Sigma(M_{ij} - m_{ij})A(R_{ij})\\ &\leq \epsilon\Sigma A(R_{ij}) = \epsilon A(R).\end{aligned}$$

This shows that $|\bar{S}(N) - \underline{S}(N)|$ can be made arbitrarily small merely by requiring that $d(N)$ be small. ▮

We now complete the proof of the theorem. Lemma 2 and Lemma 3 combined show that $s = S$. Call the common value v. Given ϵ, choose δ so that $\bar{S}(N) - \underline{S}(N) < \epsilon$ whenever N obeys $d(N) < \delta$. The closed interval $[\underline{S}(N), \bar{S}(N)]$ contains v and also the value of the general Riemann sums $S(N, f, \{p_{ij}\})$. Thus $|S(N, f, p_{ij}) - v| < \epsilon$ whenever the grid N obeys $d(N) < \delta$, so that $\iint_R f$ exists. ▮

We next weaken the requirement that f be continuous everywhere in R.

Theorem 2. *Let R be a closed rectangle, and let f be bounded in R and continuous at all points of R except those in a set E of zero area. Then, $\iint_R f$ exists.*

Since E has zero area, we can partition R into rectangles so that those covering E have arbitrarily small total area. Given $\epsilon > 0$ we choose such a set R_0 with $A(R_0) < \epsilon$. The remaining rectangles form a closed set R_1 containing no points of E, and in which f is continuous. Since f is then uniformly continuous in R_1, we may choose $\delta_1 > 0$ so that

$|f(p) - f(q)| < \epsilon$ whenever p and q lie in R_1 and $|p - q| < \delta_1$. Take any grid N, and form the difference

$$\bar{S}(N) - \underline{S}(N) = \Sigma(M_{ij} - m_{ij})A(R_{ij}).$$

Divide the collection of rectangles R_{ij} into two classes. Into class $\mathcal{C}_1$ we put all R_{ij} which are subsets of R_1, and into the class $\mathcal{C}_2$ we put all

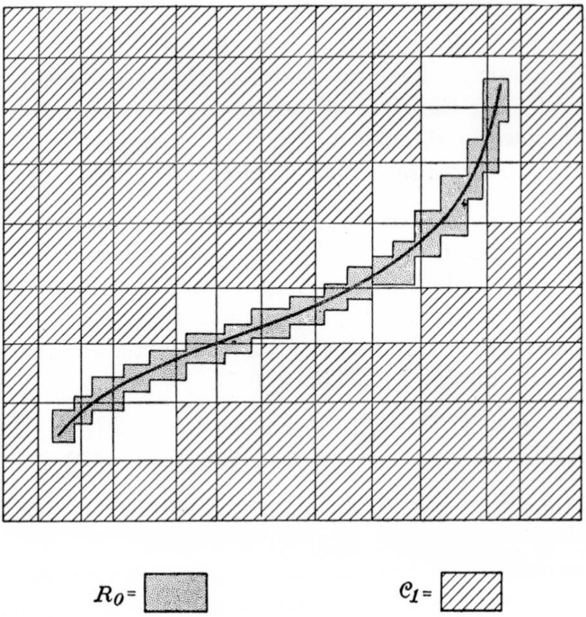

FIG. 3-2

that remain (see Fig. 3-2). We split the expression for $\bar{S}(N) - \underline{S}(N)$ in a corresponding way:

$$\bar{S}(N) - \underline{S}(N) = \sum_{R_{ij} \in \mathcal{C}_1} (M_{ij} - m_{ij})A(R_{ij}) + \sum_{R_{ij} \in \mathcal{C}_2} (M_{ij} - m_{ij})A(R_{ij})$$

If $d(N) < \delta_1$, we have $M_{ij} - m_{ij} < \epsilon$ whenever $R_{ij} \subset R_1$, so that

$$\sum_{R_{ij} \in \mathcal{C}_1} (M_{ij} - m_{ij})A(R_{ij}) \leq \epsilon \sum_{R_{ij} \in \mathcal{C}_1} A(R_{ij}) \leq \epsilon A(R).$$

By assumption, f is bounded in R so that $|f(p)| < B$ for all $p \in R$. Let R_0' be the union of the rectangles in $\mathcal{C}_2$. Then,

$$\sum_{R_{ij} \in \mathcal{C}_2} (M_{ij} - m_{ij})A(R_{ij}) \leq 2B \sum_{R_{ij} \in \mathcal{C}_2} A(R_{ij}) = 2BA(R_0').$$

The set R'_0 is exactly the circumscribing set for R_0 in the partition determined by N. We can therefore choose δ_2 so that $A(R'_0) \leq A(R_0) + \epsilon < 2\epsilon$ whenever $d(N) < \delta_2$. Letting δ be the smaller of δ_1 and δ_2, we have shown that whenever N is a grid which partitions R with $d(N) < \delta$, $\bar{S}(N) - \underline{S}(N) < \epsilon A(R) + 4B\epsilon = (4B + A(R))\epsilon$. This reestablishes Lemma 3 with our weakened hypothesis, and the theorem follows as before. ▌

We use a simple device to define $\iint_D f$ when D is not a rectangle. Let D be bounded, and choose any closed rectangle R containing D. Define a new function F on R by

$$F(p) = \begin{cases} f(p) & \text{for } p \in D \\ 0 & \text{for } p \notin D, \end{cases}$$

and then define $\iint_D f$ to be $\iint_R F$ when the latter exists.

Theorem 3. *If D is a bounded set having an area, and f is bounded on D and continuous at all interior points of D, then $\iint_D f$ exists, and the value is independent of the choice of the containing rectangle R.*

The function F is continuous at all points of R exterior to D, and at all points interior to D. The boundary of D must contain all the discontinuities of F. Since D has area, the boundary of D is a set with zero area, and, by Theorem 2, $\iint_R F$ exists. Suppose that R' is another closed rectangle containing D and F' is the corresponding function. Form $R'' = R \cap R'$ which is also a closed rectangle containing D. Then,

$$\iint_R F = \iint_{R''} F = \iint_{R''} F' = \iint_{R'} F',$$

and we obtain the same value for $\iint_D f$ from both R and R'. ▌

What we have said about the double integral is also valid for the general n-fold multiple integral. Because of the importance of the special case $n = 1$, we restate some of the treatment. A grid is now just a finite set of division points. If we impose a grid N on the closed interval $I = [a, b]$, we obtain a partition of I into closed intervals $I_k = [x_k, x_{k+1}]$, where $a = x_0 < x_1 < x_2 < \cdots < x_n = b$. The general Riemann sum becomes

$$S(N, f, \{p_k\}) = \Sigma f(p_k)\, \Delta x_k,$$

where $p_k \in I_k$ and $\Delta x_k = x_{k+1} - x_k$ is the length of I_k. The number $d(N)$ is now the largest of the lengths Δx_k.

Definition. *The integral* $\int_I f$ *of* f *over the interval* I *exists and has the value* v *if and only if (in the sense defined on page 51)*

$$\lim_{d(N)\to 0} S(N, f, \{p_k\}) = v.$$

Instead of $\int_I f$, it is customary to write $\int_a^b f$ or $\int_a^b f(x)\,dx$. Corresponding to Theorem 2, we have Theorem 2′.

Theorem 2′. *If* f *is bounded on* $[a, b]$ *and if* f *is continuous on* $[a, b]$ *except on a set of zero length, then* $\int_a^b f$ *exists.*

A set on the line has zero length if it can be covered by a finite collection of intervals of arbitrarily small total length. In particular, a finite set of points has zero length. As an instance of the theorem,

$$\int_{-1}^{1} \sin^2\left(\frac{1}{x}\right) dx$$

exists, since the integrand is bounded and continuous except at the single point $x = 0$.

Some of the familiar properties of the definite integral are set forth in the next theorem as they would be stated for double integrals. The sets D, D_1, and D_2 are assumed to have area.

Theorem 4. *Let* f *and* g *be continuous and bounded on* D. *Then,*

(i) $\iint_D (f + g)$ *exists and is* $\iint_D f + \iint_D g$.

(ii) *For any constant* C, $\iint_D Cf = C \iint_D f$.

(iii) *If* $f(p) \geq 0$ *for all* $p \in D$, $\iint_D f \geq 0$.

(iv) $\iint_D |f|$ *exists and* $\left|\iint_D f\right| \leq \iint_D |f|$.

(v) *If* $D = D_1 \cup D_2$ *and* D_1 *and* D_2 *intersect in a set with zero area, then*

$$\iint_D f = \iint_{D_1} f + \iint_{D_2} f.$$

Most of these follow directly from corresponding properties of the Riemann sums. Take a rectangle R containing D and define f and g to vanish off D. Then, the relations

$$\Sigma[f(p_{ij}) + g(p_{ij})]A(R_{ij}) = \Sigma f(p_{ij})A(R_{ij}) + \Sigma g(p_{ij})A(R_{ij})$$
$$\Sigma Cf(p_{ij})A(R_{ij}) = C\Sigma f(p_{ij})A(R_{ij})$$

lead at once to (i) and (ii). For (iii), we observe that if $f(p) \geq 0$ for all $p \in D$, then $S(N, f, \{p_{ij}\}) \geq 0$. In turn, (iii) leads to (iv); since $|f| + f$ and $|f| - f$ are each positive on D, and continuous, $\iint_D |f| + \iint_D f \geq 0$ and $\iint_D |f| - \iint_D f \geq 0$. To prove (v), we define a special function F by

$$F(p) = \begin{cases} f(p) & \text{for } p \in D_1 \\ 0 & \text{for } p \notin D_1. \end{cases}$$

Then $\displaystyle\iint_D f = \iint_D F + \iint_D (f - F) = \iint_{D_1} f + \iint_{D_2} (f - F)$

$$= \iint_{D_1} f + \iint_{D_2} f. \quad \blacksquare$$

With functions of one variable, the last property is usually stated differently. When $a \leq b$, $\int_a^b f$ is an alternative notation for $\int_{[a,b]} f$. When $a > b$, we define $\int_a^b f$ to mean $-\int_{[b,a]} f$.

Corollary. *Let f be continuous on an interval I, and let a, b, and c be any three points of I. Then,*

$$\int_a^b f + \int_b^c f = \int_a^c f.$$

EXERCISES

Where nothing is said, assume that the sets D mentioned below have positive area.

1. If $D_1 \subset D_2$, then $A(D_1) \leq A(D_2)$.

2. Show that a finite set has zero area.

3. Let D be the set of all points $(1/n, 1/m)$ where n and m are positive integers. Does D have area?

4. Formulate corresponding definitions for volume and the triple integral $\iiint_D f$ where D is a bounded set in 3-space.

5. The *characteristic function* of a set D is the function k defined by $k(p) = 1$ for $p \in D$, $k(p) = 0$ for $p \notin D$. Show that $\iint_R k$ exists and is $A(D)$ when D has an area, and R is a rectangle containing D. Discuss the existence of the integral when D does not have an area.

6. If f is continuous on D and $m \leq f(p) \leq M$ for all $p \in D$, show that

$$mA(D) \leq \iint_D f \leq MA(D).$$

7. If $\iint_D f$ exists, and if $f(p) = g(p)$ for all $p \in D$ except those in a set of zero area, show that $\iint_D g$ exists, and that $\iint_D f = \iint_D g$.

8. (*Mean Value Theorem.*) Let D be open and connected. Let f and g be continuous and bounded on D, with $g(p) \geq 0$ for all $p \in D$. Then, there is a point $\bar{p} \in D$ such that $\iint_D fg = f(\bar{p}) \iint_D g$.

9. If D is open, and if f is continuous, bounded, and obeys $f(p) \geq 0$ for all $p \in D$, then $\iint_D f = 0$ implies $f(p) = 0$ for all p.

10. Let $f(x)$ be continuous for $a \leq x \leq b$. Show that the graph of f has zero area.

***11.** Let $f(t)$ be continuous for $0 \leq t \leq 1$. Let $g(t)$ be continuous for $0 \leq t \leq 1$ with $|g'(t)| \leq B$. Show that the set of points (x, y) with $x = f(t)$, $y = g(t)$, $0 \leq t \leq 1$, has zero area.

***12.** Let f be continuous and positive on $[a, b]$. Let D be the set of all points (x, y) with $a \leq x \leq b$ and $0 \leq y \leq f(x)$. Show that D has area $A(D) = \int_a^b f$.

***13.** A general subdivision $\mathcal{S}$ of a closed rectangle R is a collection $D_1, D_2, \ldots, D_m$ of a finite number of domains D_j, each having area, which together cover R, and such that no pair have common interior points. The norm $d(\mathcal{S})$ of such a subdivision is the largest of the diameters of the sets D_j. Let f be continuous on R. Show that for any ϵ there is a δ such that whenever $\mathcal{S}$ is a general subdivision of R, and

$$S(\mathcal{S}, f, \{p_j\}) = \Sigma f(p_j) A(D_j)$$

with $p_j \in D_j$, then

$$\left| \iint_R f - S(\mathcal{S}, f, \{p_j\}) \right| < \epsilon$$

whenever $d(\mathcal{S}) < \delta$.

3.2. Evaluation of Definite Integrals

Several comments about notation are in order. It will be noticed that in most instances, we use $\int_a^b f$ and $\iint_D f$ rather than $\int_a^b f(x)\,dx$ and $\iint_D f(x, y)\,dxdy$. When the second form is used, it must be recalled that the occurrence of "x" in $\int_a^b f(x)\,dx$ or of "x" and "y" in $\iint_D f(x, y)\,dxdy$ is that of a dummy letter, and that one could equally well write $\int_a^b f(u)\,du$ or $\int_a^b f(t)\,dt$, or $\iint_D f(u, v)\,dudv$ or $\iint_D f(s, t)\,dsdt$. The same is true for the letter "j" in $\sum_{j=1}^n a_j$ and both "i" and "j" in $\sum_{i,j=1}^n i^2j^3$. While the notation $\int_a^b f$ is thus preferable from some points of view, it also has some disadvantages. Without introducing additional notations, it is difficult to indicate $\int_0^1 (x^3 - 4x^2 - 1)\,dx$ except in this way; again, when f is a function of several variables, and we wish to indicate the result of integration with respect to only one, it is convenient to write $\int_a^b f(x, y)\,dy$. No simple and usable substitute suggests itself for these, which does not also have dummy letters. It is also important to realize that in all of these, the letter "d" is irrelevant and serves merely to block off the letter which follows it from the function which is the integrand. In place of $\int_a^b f(x, y)\,dy$, we might write $\int_a^b f(x, y)\,\boxed{y}$ or even $\boxed{y}\int_a^b f(x, y)$ where the presence of "y" in the square is to inform us that in carrying out the integration, we must regard $f(x, y)$ as a function of the second variable alone. In the language of logic, "x" is free, while "y" is bound and "$\boxed{y}$" serves as a quantifier. There is a reason for the conventional choice of "dy" in place of the suggested "$\boxed{y}$"; this will be indicated when we discuss the rule for "change of variable" in integration.

If it is known that $\iint\limits_D f$ exists, then its value can often be obtained by the use of special subdivision schemes. If $N_1, N_2, \ldots$ is a sequence of grids such that $\lim\limits_{k\to\infty} d(N_k) = 0$, then the corresponding sequence of Riemann sums will converge to the value of the integral. To illustrate this, we first evaluate $\iint\limits_R xy^2\,dxdy$, where R is the square: $0 \le x \le 1$, $0 \le y \le 1$. Let N_k be the grid which partitions R into k^2 equal squares each of side $1/k$. Choosing the point p_{ij} in R_{ij} to be $\left(\frac{i}{k}, \frac{j}{k}\right)$, we have

$$\bar{S}(N_k) = \sum f(p_{ij})A(R_{ij}) = \sum_{i,j=1}^{k} \frac{i}{k}\left(\frac{j}{k}\right)^2 \frac{1}{k^2}$$

$$= \frac{1}{k^5}\sum_{i=1}^{k} i \sum_{j=1}^{k} j^2.$$

Since $\displaystyle\sum_1^k i = \frac{k(k+1)}{2}$ and $\displaystyle\sum_1^k j^2 = \frac{k(k+1)(2k+1)}{6}$

$$\bar{S}(N_k) = \frac{1}{k^5}\left(\frac{k(k+1)}{2}\right)\left(\frac{k(k+1)(2k+1)}{6}\right)$$

and

$$\iint\limits_R xy^2\,dxdy = \lim_{k\to\infty} \bar{S}(N_k) = 1/6.$$

As another illustration, let us compute from the definition $\int_1^2 \sqrt{x}\,dx$.

If we again use equal subdivisions, we arrive at the Riemann sums

$$\bar{S}(N_n) = \sum_{j=1}^{n} \sqrt{1 + \frac{j}{n}\frac{1}{n}} = \frac{1}{n\sqrt{n}} \sum_{j=1}^{n} \sqrt{j+n}$$

However, it is not easy to compute $\lim_{n\to\infty} \bar{S}(N_n)$. Instead, we use a different type of subdivision with unequal intervals. Choose

$$r = 2^{1/n} > 1,$$

and let N_n be the grid with division points

$$1 = r^0 < r < r^2 < \cdots < r^{n-1} < r^n = 2.$$

The longest of the intervals determined by this grid is the last, so that $d(N_n) = 2 - r^{n-1} = 2(1 - 1/r)$. Since $\lim_{n\to\infty} r = \lim_{n\to\infty} 2^{1/n} = 1$,

$$\lim_{n\to\infty} d(N_n) = 0.$$

This time

$$\begin{aligned}
\bar{S}(N_n) &= \sqrt{r}\,(r-1) + \sqrt{r^2}\,(r^2 - r) + \cdots + \sqrt{r^n}\,(r^n - r^{n-1}) \\
&= \sqrt{r}\,(r-1)(1 + r\sqrt{r} + [r\sqrt{r}]^2 + \cdots + [r\sqrt{r}]^{n-1}) \\
&= \sqrt{r}\,(r-1)\,\frac{r^{3n/2} - 1}{r^{3/2} - 1} \\
&= (2\sqrt{2} - 1)\sqrt{r}\,\frac{r-1}{r^{3/2} - 1}
\end{aligned}$$

so that

$$\int_1^2 \sqrt{x}\,dx = \lim_{n\to\infty} \bar{S}(N_n) = (2\sqrt{2} - 1)\lim_{r\to 1} \sqrt{r}\,\frac{r-1}{r^{3/2}-1} = \frac{(4\sqrt{2} - 2)}{3}.$$

If this direct method were the only available procedure for computing the value of an integral, only the simplest of integrands could be used. We next prove the **fundamental theorem of integral calculus,** which justifies the process of evaluating the integral of a function of one variable by means of antidifferentiation.

Definition. *A function F is an antiderivative (or primitive or indefinite integral) of f on an interval I if $F'(x) = f(x)$ for all $x \in I$.*

Theorem 5. *If f is continuous on the interval $I = [a, b]$ then f has an antiderivative on I.*

Define a function F_0 on I by

$$F_0(x) = \int_a^x f \qquad \text{for } a \le x \le b.$$

If x and $x + h$ both lie in I, then

$$\begin{aligned} F_0(x + h) - F_0(x) &= \int_a^{x+h} f - \int_a^x f \\ &= \int_x^{x+h} f = f(\bar{x})h \end{aligned}$$

where $\bar{x}$ lies between x and $x + h$. Letting h approach 0, and using the fact that f is continuous,

$$F_0'(x) = \lim_{h \to 0} \frac{F_0(x + h) - F_0(x)}{h} = f(x)$$

so that F_0 is an antiderivative of f on I. ▌ (When x is a or b, we have shown that the appropriate one-sided derivative of F_0 has the correct value.)

A function which is discontinuous may have no antiderivative; however, a function which has one antiderivative, has an infinite number, since any constant may be added.

Theorem 6. *If F_1 and F_2 are both antiderivatives of the same function f on an interval I, then $F_1 - F_2$ is constant on I.*

For, $(F_1 - F_2)' = F_1' - F_2' = f - f = 0$ on I, and Exercise 4, Sec. 2.6, applies. ▌

Theorem 7. *If f is continuous on $[a, b]$ and F is any antiderivative of f, then*

$$\int_a^b f = F(b) - F(a).$$

Let F_0 be the particular antiderivative of f which was constructed in Theorem 5. By Theorem 6, we may write $F = F_0 + C$. Referring back to the definition of F_0, we have $F_0(a) = 0$ so that $C = F(a)$. Then,

$$\int_a^b f = F_0(b) = F(b) - C = F(b) - F(a). \quad ▌$$

One consequence of this is the familiar procedure for "change of variable" in integration. (We postpone the analogous procedure for multiple integrals until Chap. 6.)

Corollary. *Let ϕ' exist and be continuous on the interval $[\alpha, \beta]$ with $\phi(\alpha) = a$ and $\phi(\beta) = b$. Let f be continuous at all points $\phi(u)$ for $\alpha \le u \le \beta$. Then,*

$$\int_a^b f(x)\, dx = \int_\alpha^\beta f(\phi(u))\phi'(u)\, du.$$

The rule may also be stated: To make the substitution $x = \phi(u)$ in an integral $\int_a^b f(x)\, dx$, replace $f(x)$ by $f(\phi(u))$, replace dx by $\phi'(u)\, du$, and replace the limits a and b by u values which correspond to them. It might seem that this is obviously true, since if $x = \phi(u)$,

$$dx = \frac{dx}{du}\,du = \phi'(u)\,du.$$

However, we are misled by a matter of notation. Using the alternate square notation, the theorem asserts that

$$\int_a^b f(x)\boxed{x} = \int_\alpha^\beta f(\phi(u))\phi'(u)\boxed{u}$$

and the rule requires us to replace $\boxed{x}$ by $\phi'(u)\boxed{u}$; analogously, the differentiation rule $\frac{dy}{dx} = \frac{dy}{ds}\frac{ds}{dx}$ is not proved by canceling the two occurrences of "ds". It is a virtue of the notation used in differentiation and integration that such formalism is consistent with the truth, and serves as a guide in the correct application of theorems.

To give a valid proof of the theorem, let $F' = f$ and define G on $[\alpha, \beta]$ by $G(u) = F(\phi(u))$. Then, $G'(u) = F'(\phi(u))\phi'(u) = f(\phi(u))\phi'(u)$ so that

$$\begin{aligned}\int_\alpha^\beta f(\phi(u))\phi'(u)\,du &= \int_\alpha^\beta G'(u)\,du = \int_\alpha^\beta G' \\ &= G(\beta) - G(\alpha) = F(\phi(\beta)) - F(\phi(\alpha)) \\ &= F(b) - F(a) = \int_a^b f. \quad \blacksquare\end{aligned}$$

For fixed a and b, there may be a number of possible choices of α and β; any of these may be used if ϕ is continuous and differentiable on the entire interval $[\alpha, \beta]$. For example, with $x = u^2 = \phi(u)$, we have

$$\int_1^4 f(x)\,dx = \int_1^2 f(u^2)2u\,du = \int_{-1}^2 f(u^2)2u\,du = \int_1^{-2} f(u^2)2u\,du.$$

This requires care in its use, as may be seen from the special choices $f(x) = x$ and $f(x) = \sqrt{x}$.

The following examples should be studied carefully. The first contains an incorrect application of Theorem 7, and the second an incorrect application of the corollary.

(i) To compute $\int_{-2}^2 x^{-2}\,dx$, we observe that an antiderivative is $-x^{-1}$, so that

$$\int_{-2}^2 x^{-2}\,dx = -x^{-1}\Big|_{-2}^2 = -(1/2) - (1/2) = -1.$$

(ii) Let $C = \int_{-1}^1 \left[\sin\frac{1}{x}\right]^2 dx$. Since the integrand is bounded and continuous on $[-1, 1]$ except at the point $x = 0$, the integral exists. Moreover, since the integrand is never negative, $C > 0$. Put $u = 1/x$ so that $f(x)$ becomes $(\sin u)^2$ and $dx = -u^{-2}\,du$. When $x = 1$, $u = 1$, and when $x = -1$, $u = -1$. Thus,

$$C = \int_{-1}^{1} (\sin u)^2(-u^{-2})\,du = -\int_{-1}^{1} \left[\frac{\sin u}{u}\right]^2 du.$$

The integrand in this integral is continuous on $[-1, 1]$ since the discontinuity at $u = 0$ is removable; thus, the new integral exists, and is negative!

Turning now to multiple integrals, we show that these may be replaced by equivalent iterated (repeated) single integrals.

Theorem 8. *Let R be the rectangle described by $a \le x \le b$, $c \le y \le d$ and let f be continuous on R. Then*

$$\iint_R f = \int_a^b dx \int_c^d f(x, y)\,dy.$$

For fixed x, $f(x, y)$ is continuous in y, so that we may write

$$F(x) = \int_c^d f(x, y)\,dy.$$

The theorem asserts that $\int_a^b F$ exists and is $\iint_R f$. We shall prove this by showing that any one-dimensional Riemann sum computed for a partition of the interval $[a, b]$ and the function F, has the same value as a special two-dimensional Riemann sum for R and f.

Let N be any grid which partitions $[a, b]$ with division points

$$a = x_0 < x_1 < \cdots < x_n = b$$

and choose any point p_i in the interval $[x_i, x_{i+1}]$. The corresponding sum is

$$S(N, F, \{p_i\}) = \sum_{i=0}^{n-1} F(p_i)\,\Delta x_i.$$

Let $d(N) = \delta$ and choose any division points for the interval $[c, d]$, $c = y_0 < y_1 < \cdots y_m = d$ so that $\Delta y_j = y_{j+1} - y_j \le \delta$ for each j (see Fig. 3-3). Then, for any x,

$$\begin{aligned} F(x) &= \int_c^d f(x, y)\,dy = \int_{y_0}^{y_m} f(x, y)\,dy \\ &= \int_{y_0}^{y_1} f(x, y)\,dy + \int_{y_1}^{y_2} f(x, y)\,dy + \cdots + \int_{y_{m-1}}^{y_m} f(x, y)\,dy. \end{aligned}$$

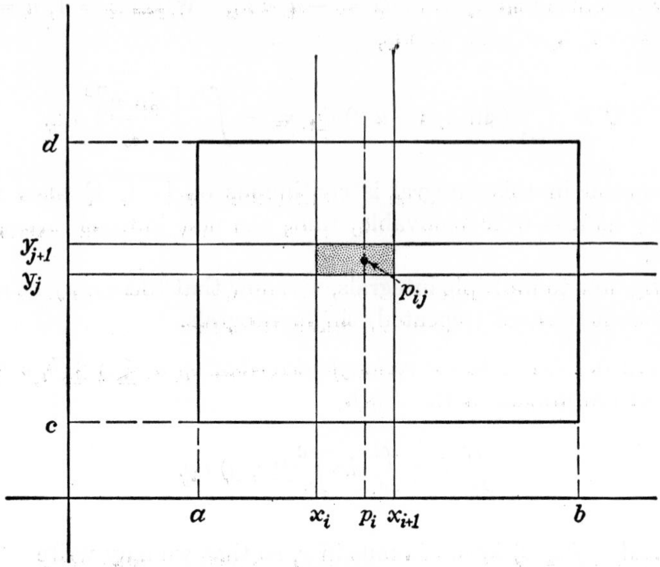

FIG. 3-3

To each of these, we apply the mean value theorem for integrals. A point $\bar{y}_j$ can be chosen in the interval $[y_j, y_{j+1}]$ so that

$$\int_{y_j}^{y_{j+1}} f(x, y)\, dy = f(x, \bar{y}_j)[y_{j+1} - y_j]$$
$$= f(x, \bar{y}_j)\, \Delta y_j.$$

In general, the choice of $\bar{y}_j$ depends upon the value of x so that we should write $\bar{y}_j = Y_j(x)$. Summing for $j = 0, 1, \ldots, m - 1$, we have

$$F(x) = f(x, Y_0(x))\, \Delta y_0 + \cdots + f(x, Y_{m-1}(x))\, \Delta y_{m-1}.$$

When x is chosen as the particular point p_i, $(x, Y_j(x))$ becomes a point

$$p_{ij} = (p_i, Y_j(p_i))$$

in R, and

$$F(p_i) = \sum_{j=0}^{m-1} f(p_{ij})\, \Delta y_j.$$

Returning to the original one-dimensional Riemann sum for F,

$$S(N, F, \{p_i\}) = \sum_{i=0}^{n-1} \left\{ \sum_{j=0}^{m-1} f(p_{ij})\, \Delta y_j \right\} \Delta x_i$$
$$= \sum_{i=0}^{n-1} \sum_{j=0}^{m-1} f(p_{ij})\, \Delta x_i\, \Delta y_j.$$

The vertical lines $x = x_i$, $i = 0, 1, \ldots, n$, and the horizontal lines $y = y_j$, $j = 0, 1, \ldots, m$, define a grid N^* which partitions R into rectangles R_{ij} in such a fashion that $p_{ij} \in R_{ij}$ and $A(R_{ij}) = \Delta x_i \, \Delta y_j$; moreover, since $\Delta x_i \leq \delta$ and $\Delta y_j \leq \delta$, $d(N^*) < 2\delta = 2d(N)$. We have therefore shown that corresponding to any grid N which partitions $[a, b]$ we can find a grid N^* which partitions R such that

$$S(N, F, \{p_i\}) = S(N^*, f, \{p_{ij}\}).$$

Since $\iint_R f$ exists, the two-dimensional Riemann sums converge and $\int_a^b F$ exists and is equal to $\iint_R f$. ∎

We remark that in this proof, we could have obtained the existence of $\int_a^b F$ at the outset from the easily proven fact that F is continuous (see Exercise 13). However, if we extend the theorem to functions f which may have discontinuities in R, then F may be discontinuous. In fact, if f is bounded and continuous on R except at points of a set E of zero area, it may happen that for individual values of x, $\int_c^d f(x, y)\, dy$ does not exist, and the set of x for which this is true can fail to be a set of zero length. Since the introduction of the Lebesgue integral overcomes all these defects of the Riemann integral, we do not discuss the general case further, but treat instead an important special case.†

Theorem 9. *Let f be bounded in a closed rectangle R, and continuous there except in a set E of zero area. Suppose that every vertical line meets E in at most k points. Then,*

$$\iint_R f = \int_a^b dx \int_c^d f(x, y)\, dy.$$

The proof of this requires only slight modifications from that for Theorem 8. As before, we consider F defined on $[a, b]$ by

$$F(x) = \int_c^d f(x, y)\, dy.$$

Since $f(x, y)$ is continuous in y in $[c, d]$ except for at most k points, and since f is bounded, this integral exists and F is defined. Again take a general one-dimensional Riemann sum $S(N, F, \{p_i\}) = \sum_{i=0}^{n-1} F(p_i)\, \Delta x_i$ and choose division points y_j on $[c, d]$. These determine a grid N^* which

† See, for example, M. E. Munroe, "Introduction to Measure and Integration," Addison-Wesley Publishing Company, Cambridge, Mass., 1953.

partitions R into rectangles R_{ij}. Let R_0 be the union of those which contain points of E, and let R_1 be the union of the remaining rectangles. We may again write

$$F(p_i) = \int_{y_0}^{y_m} f(p_i, y)\, dy = \sum_{j=0}^{m-1} \int_{y_j}^{y_{j+1}} f(p_i, y)\, dy.$$

Since $f(p_i, y)$ is continuous as a function of y in all but k of the intervals $[y_j, y_{j+1}]$, we may apply the mean value theorem as before, and replace these by terms of the form $f(p_{ij})\, \Delta y_j$. For the remaining k terms, we have bounds of the form $B\, \Delta y_j$, where B is an upper bound for $|f|$ in R. Adding these estimates for $F(p_i)\, \Delta x_i$, we arrive at

$$\left| S(N, F, \{p_i\}) - \sum_{R_{ij} \subset R_1} f(p_{ij}) A(R_{ij}) \right| \le B \sum_{R_{ij} \subset R_0} A(R_{ij}).$$

Since $\iint_R f$ exists, and since R_0 is the circumscribing set for E and E has zero area, we have $\lim_{d(N) \to 0} S(N, F, \{p_i\}) = \iint_R f$. ▮

Further specialization of this yields the familiar result.

Corollary. *Let D be the set described by the inequalities $a \le x \le b$, $\phi(x) \le y \le \psi(x)$, where ϕ and ψ are continuous on $[a, b]$. Let f be continuous on D. Then,*

$$\iint_D f = \int_a^b dx \int_{\phi(x)}^{\psi(x)} f(x, y)\, dy.$$

The expression on the right is commonly called an **iterated integral,** and may often be evaluated by means of the antidifferentiation process and the fundamental theorem of calculus. As an example, let D be the region between the line $y = x$ and the parabola $y = x^2$, and let

$$f(x, y) = xy^2.$$

Then,

$$\iint_D f = \int_0^1 dx \int_{x^2}^{x} xy^2\, dy = \int_0^1 dx \left[\frac{xy^3}{3} \right]_{x^2}^{x}$$

$$= \int_0^1 \frac{x^4 - x^7}{3}\, dx = \frac{1}{40}.$$

Since this region D is such that every horizontal line cuts the boundary at most twice, $\iint_D f$ can also be evaluated by an iterated integral in which the order of the variables is reversed.

$$\iint_D f = \int_0^1 dy \int_y^{\sqrt{y}} xy^2\, dx = \int_0^1 dy \left[\frac{x^2y^2}{2}\right|_y^{\sqrt{y}}$$

$$= \tfrac{1}{2} \int_0^1 (y^3 - y^4)\, dy = \tfrac{1}{40}.$$

In the cases which are usually encountered, the evaluation of a double integral can be reduced to the computation of a number of such iterated integrals. As an example, consider the region D bounded by the line $y = -1$, and the curves

$$x = \sin(\pi y) \qquad \text{and} \qquad y = (x+1)^2\left(\frac{5}{12}x + 1\right) = C(x)$$

(see Fig. 3-4). To evaluate $\iint_D f$, it is convenient to split D into four regions as shown, so that

$$\iint_D f = \iint_{D_1} f + \iint_{D_2} f + \iint_{D_3} f + \iint_{D_4} f$$

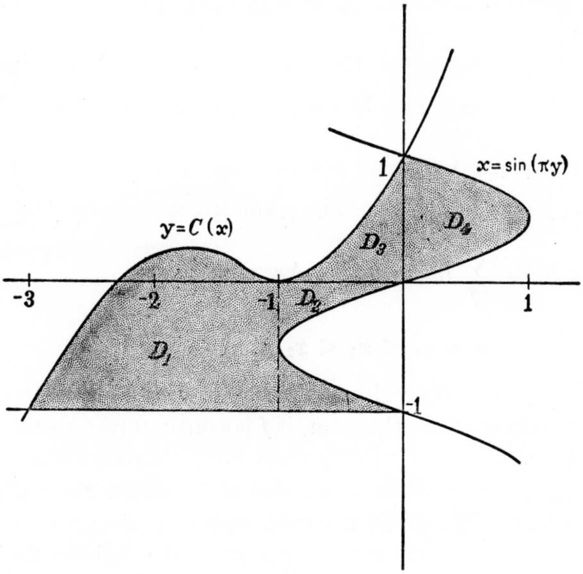

FIG. 3-4

where we have

$$\iint_{D_1} f = \int_{-3}^{-1} dx \int_{-1}^{C(x)} f(x, y)\, dy$$

$$\iint_{D_2} f = \int_{-1}^{0} dy \int_{-1}^{\sin(\pi y)} f(x, y)\, dx$$

$$\iint_{D_3} f = \int_{-1}^{0} dx \int_{0}^{C(x)} f(x, y)\, dy$$

$$\iint_{D_4} f = \int_{0}^{1} dy \int_{0}^{\sin(\pi y)} f(x, y)\, dx$$

The last two could be combined and written as

$$\iint_{D_3 \cup D_4} f = \int_{0}^{1} dy \int_{\gamma(y)}^{\sin(\pi y)} f(x, y)\, dx$$

where $x = \gamma(y)$ is the particular solution of the cubic equation $y = C(x)$ valid for $-1 \leq x \leq 0$. In cases such as these, it is often more efficient to apply some method of approximate integration; this is particularly true when the final numerical answer in the "exact" method must be obtained by reference to the tabulated approximate values of one or more standard functions. One such scheme which is easily applied is to construct a grid N covering the region D, and then compute the upper and lower Riemann sums $\bar{S}(N)$ and $\underline{S}(N)$ for f. The exact value of $\iint_D f$ must then lie between these numbers, and their difference is a measure of the accuracy of the approximation. Any other Riemann sum $\sum_{i,j} f(p_{ij}) A(R_{ij})$ may also be used as an approximation. In practice, a number of simple formulas are commonly used in the approximate evaluation of single integrals. The general Riemann sum for $\int_a^b f$ can be put into the form $\sum_0^{n-1} f_i\, \Delta x_i$, where $\Delta x_i = x_{i+1} - x_i$,

$$a = x_0 < x_1 < x_2 < \cdots x_n = b,$$

and where $f_i = f(p_i)$ is the value of f at some point of the interval $[x_i, x_{i+1}]$. By the intermediate value theorem, if f is continuous on such an interval and A and B are values of f there, then every number between A and B, and in particular $(A + B)/2$, is a value of f. More generally, if $A_1, A_2, \ldots, A_r$ are values of f on an interval, so is $c_1 A_1 + \cdots + c_r A_r$, where $c_j \geq 0$ and $\Sigma c_j = 1$. (This is merely a general weighted average of the numbers A_j.) Two special cases of this lead to the **trapezoidal rule** and

Simpson's rule. For the first, we take $f_i = [f(x_i) + f(x_{i+1})]/2$, and for the latter, we take $f_i = [f(x_i) + 4f(\bar{x}) + f(x_{i+1})]/6$, where $\bar{x}$ is the mid-point $\bar{x} = (x_i + x_{i+1})/2$. The reason behind the second choice lies in the result of Exercise 18 which shows that Simpson's rule is exact whenever f is a polynomial of degree at most 3; application of the formula therefore amounts to approximating f on each of the intervals $[x_i, x_{i+1}]$ by such a polynomial, chosen to fit f at the end points and the mid-point. Other methods for estimating the value of an integral will be found in the exercises.

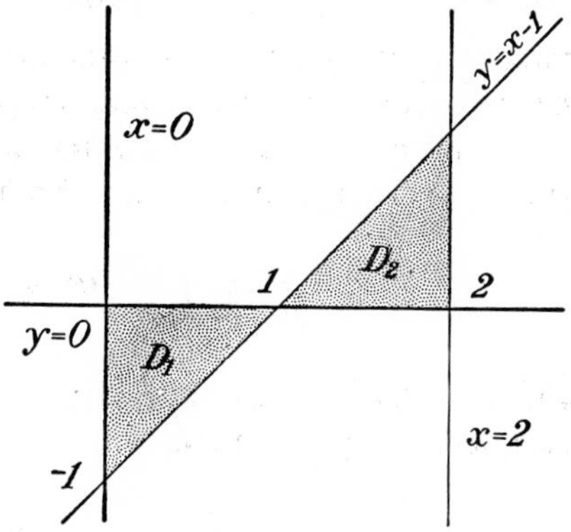

FIG. 3-5

Although iterated integrals appear thus in connection with the evaluation of double integrals, these are quite distinct concepts. Iterated integrals often arise independently and cannot always be converted directly into double integrals. For example $\int_0^2 dx \int_0^{x-1} f(x, y)\, dy$ has the form of an iterated integral, obtained from the double integral of f over some region D bounded by the curves $y = 0$, $y = x - 1$, $x = 0$, $x = 2$. However, there is a point $(1, 0)$ at which the curves cross, so that *two* regions are formed (see Fig. 3-5). The integral of f over the union of these can be written as

$$\int_0^1 dx \int_{x-1}^0 f(x, y)\, dy + \int_1^2 dx \int_0^{x-1} f(x, y)\, dy$$

which is different from the original iterated integral. If we define a new function F by setting $F(p) = f(p)$ for $p \in D_2$ and $F(p) = -f(p)$ for $p \in D_1$, then

$$\begin{aligned}\iint_D F &= \iint_{D_1} F + \iint_{D_2} F = -\iint_{D_1} f + \iint_{D_2} f \\ &= -\int_0^1 dx \int_{x-1}^0 f(x, y)\, dy + \int_1^2 dx \int_0^{x-1} f(x, y)\, dy \\ &= \int_0^1 dx \int_0^{x-1} f(x, y)\, dy + \int_1^2 dx \int_0^{x-1} f(x, y)\, dy \\ &= \int_0^2 dx \int_0^{x-1} f(x, y)\, dy.\end{aligned}$$

By such devices as these, any iterated integral of the form

$$\int_a^b dx \int_{\phi(x)}^{\psi(x)} f(x, y)\, dy$$

can be replaced by the double integral of some function F over the set of regions determined by the curves $y = \phi(x)$, $y = \psi(x)$, $x = a$, $x = b$.

When such an iterated integral has been converted into a double integral, it is often possible to represent it as the sum of one or more iterated integrals of the form $\int_c^d dy \int_{\alpha(y)}^{\beta(y)} g(x, y)\, dx$. This process is known as "reversing the order of integration in an iterated integral." We illustrate this with several simple examples.

Let us first reverse the order of integration in the iterated integral that we have just discussed. We have

$$\int_0^2 dx \int_0^{x-1} f(x, y)\, dy = -\iint_{D_1} f + \iint_{D_2} f$$

where D_1 and D_2 are again the triangles shown in Fig. 3-5. Treating each separately, we have

$$\iint_{D_1} f = \int_{-1}^0 dy \int_0^{y+1} f(x, y)\, dx$$

$$\iint_{D_2} f = \int_0^1 dy \int_{y+1}^2 f(x, y)\, dx$$

so that we obtain

$$\int_0^2 dx \int_0^{x-1} f(x, y)\, dy = \int_0^1 dy \int_{y+1}^2 f(x, y)\, dx - \int_{-1}^0 dy \int_0^{y+1} f(x, y)\, dx.$$

It should be noticed that the nature of f does not enter into this calculation, except to ensure the existence of the appropriate integrals.

As another illustration, we have the useful formula

$$\int_a^b dx \int_a^x f(x, y)\, dy = \int_a^b dy \int_y^b f(x, y)\, dx \tag{3-1}$$

which follows at once from the observation that both sides reduce to the double integral of f over the triangle with vertices (a, a), (b, a), (b, b).† The following is a special application of this which is often used. Consider the n-fold iterated integral

$$\int_0^b dx_1 \int_0^{x_1} dx_2 \int_0^{x_2} dx_3 \ldots \int_0^{x_{n-1}} f(x_n)\, dx_n.$$

† It should be observed that the same technique is used in working with discrete sums. For example, the analogue of (3-1) is

$$\sum_{i=r}^{n} \sum_{j=r}^{i} a_{ij} = \sum_{j=r}^{n} \sum_{i=j}^{n} a_{ij}.$$

The last two inner integrals have the form

$$\int_0^{x_{n-2}} dx_{n-1} \int_0^{x_{n-1}} f(x_n)\, dx_n$$

to which the relation (3-1) may be applied, obtaining

$$\int_0^{x_{n-2}} dx_n \int_{x_n}^{x_{n-2}} f(x_n)\, dx_{n-1} = \int_0^{x_{n-2}} f(x_n)(x_{n-2} - x_n)\, dx_n.$$

We have thus reduced the original integral to an $(n - 1)$-fold iterated integral. Repeating this process,

$$\int_0^{x_{n-3}} dx_{n-2} \int_0^{x_{n-2}} f(x_n)(x_{n-2} - x_n)\, dx_n$$

becomes

$$\int_0^{x_{n-3}} dx_n \int_{x_n}^{x_{n-3}} f(x_n)(x_{n-2} - x_n)\, dx_{n-2} = \int_0^{x_{n-3}} f(x_n) \frac{(x_{n-3} - x_n)^2}{2!}\, dx_n$$

and the original integral can finally be reduced to the single integral $\int_0^b f(x_n) \frac{(b - x_n)^{n-1}}{(n-1)!}\, dx_n$.

As a final illustration of this technique, let us prove a theorem dealing with differentiation of a function defined by means of an integral. As we have mentioned, if $f(x, y)$ is continuous for $a \le x \le b$, and $c \le y \le d$, then

$$F(x) = \int_c^d f(x, y)\, dy \tag{3-2}$$

is continuous for x in $[a, b]$ (Exercise 13). It is reasonable to suppose that if f is differentiable as a function of x alone, with y fixed, so that the partial derivative

$$f_1(x, y) = \frac{\partial f}{\partial x} = \lim_{h \to 0} \frac{f(x + h, y) - f(x, y)}{h}$$

exists for each x in $[a, b]$ and y in $[c, d]$, then we may differentiate (3-2) under the integral sign, obtaining

$$F'(x) = \int_c^d \frac{\partial f}{\partial x}\, dy = \int_c^d f_1(x, y)\, dy. \tag{3-3}$$

We justify this under the hypothesis that f_1 is continuous.

Theorem 10. *Let f and f_1 be defined and continuous for $x \in [a, b]$, $y \in [c, d]$, and F defined by (3-2). Then, $F'(x)$ exists on the interval $[a, b]$ and is given by (3-3).*

Since f_1 is continuous, $\phi(x) = \int_c^d f_1(x, y)\, dy$ is continuous for $x \in [a, b]$. Take any x_0 in $[a, b]$ and consider the integral

$$\int_a^{x_0} \phi = \int_a^{x_0} dx \int_c^d f_1(x, y)\, dy.$$

Reverse the order of integration, obtaining

$$\begin{aligned}\int_a^{x_0} \phi &= \int_c^d dy \int_a^{x_0} f_1(x, y)\, dx = \int_c^d dy \int_a^{x_0} \frac{\partial f}{\partial x}\, dx \\ &= \int_c^d [f(x_0, y) - f(a, y)]\, dy = F(x_0) - F(a).\end{aligned}$$

This shows that F is an antiderivative for ϕ, so that F' exists and is ϕ. ∎

For example, if $F(x) = \int_0^1 \frac{\sin (xy)}{y}\, dy$, then

$$F'(x) = \int_0^1 \cos (xy)\, dy = \frac{\sin (xy)}{x}\Big|_0^1 = \frac{\sin x}{x}.$$

This technique is sometimes useful in the evaluation of special types of definite integrals. For example, let us show that for $x > 0$,

$$\begin{aligned}F(x) &= \int_0^{\pi/2} \log (\sin^2 \theta + x^2 \cos^2 \theta)\, d\theta \\ &= \pi \log \frac{x + 1}{2}.\end{aligned}$$

Differentiating the integral which defines F, we have

$$F'(x) = \int_0^{\pi/2} \frac{2x \cos^2 \theta\, d\theta}{\sin^2 \theta + x^2 \cos^2 \theta}$$

so that

$$\begin{aligned}\frac{F'(x)(x^2 - 1)}{2x} &= \int_0^{\pi/2} \frac{(x^2 - 1) \cos^2 \theta\, d\theta}{\sin^2 \theta + x^2 \cos^2 \theta} \\ &= \int_0^{\pi/2} \frac{x^2 \cos^2 \theta + \sin^2 \theta - 1}{\sin^2 \theta + x^2 \cos^2 \theta}\, d\theta \\ &= \frac{\pi}{2} - \int_0^{\pi/2} \frac{d\theta}{\sin^2 \theta + x^2 \cos^2 \theta}.\end{aligned}$$

Now
$$\begin{aligned}\int \frac{d\theta}{\sin^2 \theta + x^2 \cos^2 \theta} &= \int \frac{\sec^2 \theta\, d\theta}{\tan^2 \theta + x^2} \\ &= x^{-1} \arctan [x^{-1} \tan \theta]\end{aligned}$$

so that for $x > 0$ and $x \neq 1$,

$$F'(x) = \frac{2x}{x^2 - 1}\left\{\frac{\pi}{2} - \frac{\pi}{2x}\right\} = \frac{\pi}{x+1}.$$

We have established this for all $x > 0$ except $x = 1$. When $x = 1$, we have directly $F'(1) = 2\int_0^{\pi/2} \cos^2\theta\, d\theta = \frac{\pi}{2}$, or we may argue that F' is continuous, so that $F'(1) = \lim_{x\to 1} F'(x) = \frac{\pi}{2}$. Integrating F', we have $F(x) = \pi \log (x + 1) + C$. To determine C, we observe that

$$F(1) = \int_0^{\pi/2} \log (1)\, d\theta = 0$$

so that $C = -\pi \log 2$, and $F(x) = \pi \log \frac{x+1}{2}$.

If a function is defined by a definite integral in which the limits also contain the free variable, such as

$$F(x) = \int_{\alpha(x)}^{\beta(x)} f(x, y)\, dy,$$

then the preceding rule for computing $F'(x)$ must be extended. If α and β are differentiable on an interval $[a, b]$ and $f_1(x, y)$ exists and is continuous for $x \in [a, b]$ and y between $\alpha(x)$ and $\beta(x)$, then

$$\text{(3-4)}\quad F'(x) = \beta'(x)f(x, \beta(x)) - \alpha'(x)f(x, \alpha(x)) + \int_{\alpha(x)}^{\beta(x)} f_1(x, y)\, dy.$$

We postpone the proof of this formula until Chap. 5 since it requires further use of partial differentiation. As an illustration, if

$$F(x) = \int_{x^2}^{e^x} \frac{\sin (xu)}{u}\, du$$

then

$$F'(x) = e^x \frac{\sin (xe^x)}{e^x} - 2x\frac{\sin x^3}{x^2} + \int_{x^2}^{e^x} \cos (xu)\, du = (1 + x^{-1}) \sin (xe^x) - 3x^{-1} \sin (x^3).$$

EXERCISES

1. By choosing an appropriate grid and computing $\bar{S}(N)$ and $\underline{S}(N)$, estimate the value of $\int_0^1 \frac{dx}{1+x^3}$ to within .05. Compare this with the work of computing the exact value by the usual process.

2. By choosing an appropriate grid, estimate the value of $\int_0^2 dy \int_0^1 \frac{dx}{x+y+10}$ to within .02, and again compare by computing the exact value.

3. Find the antiderivatives (indefinite integrals)

(a) $\displaystyle\int \frac{x^2 + 4x + 2}{2x^3 + x^2}\, dx$ (b) $\displaystyle\int \frac{dx}{(x^2 + 2x + 2)^2}$

4. If possible, give an explicit formula for a function F such that for all x,

(a) $F'(x) = x + |x - 1|$ (b) $\log F'(x) = 2x + e^x$

5. Let F be defined by

$$F(x) = \int_1^x \exp\left(\frac{u^2 + 1}{u}\right) \frac{du}{u}.$$

Show that $F(1/x) = -F(x)$.

6. Let f be continuous on $[0, 1]$ and suppose that for all x, $0 < x < 1$,

$$\int_0^x f = \int_x^1 f.$$

Can you determine f?

7. Evaluate the double integral $\displaystyle\iint_D x^2y\, dxdy$ when D is the region bounded by (a) the line $y = x$ and the parabola $y = x^2$; (b) the line $y = x - 2$ and the parabola $x = 4 - y^2$.

8. Express the following iterated integral as a double integral, and then as an iterated integral with the order of integrations reversed.

$$\int_1^2 dx \int_0^x f(x, y)\, dy.$$

9. Express the following iterated integral as a triple integral, and then rewrite it in the other five possible orders of integration as iterated integrals.

$$\int_0^2 dx \int_1^{2-\frac{1}{2}x} dy \int_x^2 f(x, y, z)\, dz.$$

10. Evaluate the preceding integral with $f(x, y, z) = x + yz$.

11. Evaluate:

(a) $\displaystyle\int_0^1 dy \int_y^1 e^{y/x}\, dx$ (b) $\displaystyle\int_1^2 dx \int_{1/x}^2 ye^{xy}\, dy$

12. Reverse the order of integration in the following iterated integral, and compute its value.

$$\int_{-6}^8 dx \int_{x^{1/3}}^{(x+6)/7} xy\, dy.$$

13. Let $f(x, y)$ be defined and continuous for $a \le x \le b$, $c \le y \le d$. Let

$$F(x) = \int_c^d f(x, y)\, dy.$$

Prove that F is continuous on $[a, b]$.

14. Let f and g be continuous on $[a, b]$. Show that

$$\left[\int_a^b fg\right]^2 \le \int_a^b f^2 \int_a^b g^2.$$

(This is the integral form for the Schwarz inequality, given in Chap. 1 for finite sums.)

15. Using Exercise 14, show that

$$\int_0^1 \sqrt{x}\, e^{-x}\, dx < .47.$$

16. Use the same method to estimate the value of

(a) $\int_0^1 \sqrt{1 + x^3}\, dx$ (b) $\int_0^\pi \sqrt{\sin x}\, dx$

17. Extending Exercise 14, formulate a corresponding inequality applying to functions of two variables, and use this to show that

$$\iint_D \sqrt{4x^2 - y^2}\, dx\, dy < \frac{\sqrt{15}}{6}$$

where D is the triangle with vertices at (0, 0), (1, 0), (1, 1).

18. Show that

$$\int_a^b P = (b - a)\,\frac{P(a) + P(b) + 4P([a + b]/2)}{6}$$

whenever P is a polynomial of degree at most 3.

19. Verify the following statements:

(a) If $F(x) = \int_{-1}^1 \log\,(1 + xe^u)\, du,$

then $$F'(x) = x^{-1} \log\left(\frac{1 + ex}{1 + e^{-1}x}\cdot\right)$$

(b) If $F(x) = \int_1^x u^{-1} \cos\,(xu^2)\, du,$

then $$F'(x) = \frac{3 \cos\,(x^3)}{2x} - \frac{\cos x}{2x}.$$

(c) If $F(x) = \int_0^\pi u^{-1} e^{xu} \sin u\, du,$

then $$F'(x) = \frac{e^{\pi x} + 1}{x^2 + 1}.$$

3.3. Taylor's Theorem

This important and useful result can be regarded either as a statement about the approximation of functions by polynomials, or as a generalization of the mean value theorem.

Suppose that a function f is given to us, and we wish to find a polynomial P which approximates f in a specified sense, for example, uniformly on some interval I. One familiar procedure is that of interpolation, or curve fitting. We choose points $x_1, x_2, \ldots, x_n$ on I, and determine P so that $P(x_i) = f(x_i)$, $i = 1, 2, \ldots, n$. If P has degree m, then there will be $m + 1$ coefficients to be determined, so that in general a polynomial of degree $n - 1$ must be used to fit f at n points.

Once P has been computed, it remains a separate problem to study the accuracy of the approximation at points x of the interval I other than the points x_i. Another method for choosing a suitable polynomial P is to select one point x_0 in the interval (e.g., the mid-point) and then choose P to match f very closely at the point x_0. We first introduce a convenient notation.

Definition. *A function f of one variable is said to be of class C^n on $[a, b]$ if $f^{(n)}(x)$ exists and is continuous for all x with $a \leq x \leq b$.*

For $n = 1$ and $n = 2$, we write C' and C''; C^∞ is the class of functions having derivatives of all orders. Any polynomial is infinitely differentiable, as are e^x and $\sin x$, but $x^{5/3}$ is not so on any interval containing 0.

Let $f \varepsilon C^n$ on an interval I about x_0. Among all the polynomials of degree n, there is exactly one which matches f at x_0 up through the nth derivative, so that

$$P^{(k)}(x_0) = f^{(k)}(x_0) \qquad k = 0, 1, \ldots, n. \tag{3-5}$$

We shall call this the **Taylor polynomial** of degree n at x_0, and denote it by P_{x_0}. When $n = 1$, P_{x_0} is the first-degree polynomial which goes through $(x_0, f(x_0))$ and has there the same slope as does f; it is therefore just the line tangent to the graph of f, and

$$P(x) = f(x_0) + f'(x_0)(x - x_0).$$

When $n = 2$, P is a parabola which is tangent to f at $(x_0, f(x_0))$ and there has the same curvature as does f. Writing

$$P(x) = A + B(x - x_0) + C(x - x_0)^2$$

and imposing conditions (3-5), we see that

$$P(x) = f(x_0) + f'(x_0)(x - x_0) + f''(x_0)\frac{(x - x_0)^2}{2}.$$

In general,

$$P_{x_0}(x) = f(x_0) + f'(x_0)(x - x_0) + \cdots + f^{(n)}(x_0)\frac{(x - x_0)^n}{n!}$$

We are concerned with the accuracy with which this polynomial approximates f at points of the interval I away from x_0; therefore we study the remainder $R_n(x) = f(x) - P_{x_0}(x)$. Taylor's theorem expresses this remainder in terms of the function f.

Theorem 11. *Let $f \varepsilon C^{n+1}$ on an interval I about x_0. Then,*

$$R_n(\bar{x}) = \frac{1}{n!}\int_{x_0}^{\bar{x}} f^{n+1}(t)(\bar{x} - t)^n \, dt$$

where $\bar{x} \varepsilon I$.

We have $R_n(\bar{x}) = f(\bar{x}) - P_{x_0}(\bar{x})$. Consider the function $g(t) = P_t(\bar{x})$. This is the value at $\bar{x}$ of the Taylor polynomial for f at t; when $t = x_0$, $g(x_0) = P_{x_0}(\bar{x})$, and when $t = \bar{x}$, $g(\bar{x}) = P_{\bar{x}}(\bar{x}) = f(\bar{x})$. Hence,

$$R_n(\bar{x}) = g(\bar{x}) - g(x_0) = \int_{x_0}^{\bar{x}} g'.$$

We have

$$g(t) = f(t) + f'(t)(\bar{x} - t) + f''(t)\frac{(\bar{x} - t)^2}{2!} + \cdots + f^{(n)}(t)\frac{(\bar{x} - t)^n}{n!}$$

so that

$$\begin{aligned} g'(t) &= f'(t) + \{f''(t)(\bar{x} - t) - f'(t)\} \\ &\quad + \left\{f'''(t)\frac{(\bar{x} - t)^2}{2!} - f''(t)\frac{\bar{x} - t}{1!}\right\} + \cdots \\ &\quad + \left\{f^{(n+1)}(t)\frac{(\bar{x} - t)^n}{n!} - f^{(n)}(t)\frac{(\bar{x} - t)^{n-1}}{(n-1)!}\right\} \\ &= f^{(n+1)}(t)\frac{(\bar{x} - t)^n}{n!} \end{aligned}$$

since the sum telescopes. Using this expression for g' in $\int_{x_0}^{\bar{x}} g'$ we have the theorem. ▌

There are many alternate forms for R_n.

Corollary 1. $R_n(\bar{x}) = f^{(n+1)}(\tau)\dfrac{(\bar{x} - x_0)^{n+1}}{(n+1)!}$ *where* τ *is a point between* x_0 *and* $\bar{x}$.

We obtain this by applying a mean value theorem to the integral expression for $R_n(\bar{x})$, using the form given in Exercise 8, Sec. 3.1.

$$\begin{aligned} R_n(\bar{x}) &= \frac{1}{n!}\int_{x_0}^{\bar{x}} f^{(n+1)}(t)(\bar{x} - t)^n\,dt \\ &= \frac{f^{(n+1)}(\tau)}{n!}\int_{x_0}^{\bar{x}} (\bar{x} - t)^n\,dt \\ &= \frac{f^{(n+1)}(\tau)}{n!}\,\frac{(\bar{x} - x_0)^{n+1}}{n+1}. \end{aligned}$$

Using this form of the remainder, we may write Taylor's theorem in another fashion which is perhaps more familiar.

Corollary 2. *If* $f \in C^{n+1}$ *in a neighborhood of* x_0, *then for some choice of* τ *between* x_0 *and* x

$$f(x) = f(x_0) + f'(x_0)\frac{x - x_0}{1!} + \cdots + f^{(n)}(x_0)\frac{(x - x_0)^n}{n!} + f^{(n+1)}(\tau)\frac{(x - x_0)^{n+1}}{(n+1)!}. \tag{3-6}$$

When $n = 0$, this becomes the usual mean value theorem for differential calculus:

$$f(x) = f(x_0) + f'(\tau)(x - x_0).$$

For the Taylor polynomial to be a good approximation to f, uniformly on an interval I, the remainder R_n must be uniformly small there. The importance of the theorem lies in the fact that by having a formula for R_n, we are thereby able to estimate its size. For example, let us find a polynomial which approximates e^x on the interval $[-1, 1]$ accurately to within .005. Using (3-5) with $x_0 = 0$, we have†

$$P(x) = f(0) + f'(0)x + f''(0)\frac{x^2}{2!} + \cdots + f^{(n)}(0)\frac{x^n}{n!}$$

which in our case is

$$P(x) = 1 + x + \frac{x^2}{2!} + \cdots + \frac{x^n}{n!}.$$

The remainder, using the formula of Corollary 1, is

$$e^x - P(x) = R_n(x) = f^{(n+1)}(\tau)\frac{x^{n+1}}{(n+1)!} = e^\tau \frac{x^{n+1}}{(n+1)!}.$$

For x and τ in $[-1, 1]$, $|R_n(x)| \le e/(n+1)!$. Since we desire accuracy to within .005, we must choose n so that $e = 2.718 \cdots < (.005)(n+1)!$ Trial shows that $n = 5$ is sufficiently large, so that the polynomial $1 + x + x^2/2 + x^3/6 + x^4/24 + x^5/120$ has the desired property.

In this case, it is clear that by increasing the degree of the Taylor polynomial, we can attain a polynomial approximation to e^x on $[-1, 1]$— or in fact, on any bounded interval—with arbitrarily small error. This is a special property of the exponential function, and is shared by an important class of functions.

Definition. *A function f is said to be analytic at a point x_0 if there is an open interval I about x_0 on which f is of class C^∞ and such that* $\lim_{n\to\infty} R_n(x) = 0$ *for each $x \in I$.*

The functions e^x, $\sin x$, and $\cos x$ are analytic everywhere; $\sqrt{x}$ is analytic for each point $x_0 > 0$, and $x/(x^2 - 1)$ is analytic at each point of the intervals $x < -1$, $-1 < x < 1$, and $1 < x$. Since

$$R_n(x) = f(x) - P_{x_0}(x),$$

this property is equivalent to saying that the sequence of Taylor polynomials for f at x_0 converge to f in a neighborhood of x_0; as we shall see in Chap. 4, this enables us to say that analytic functions are those that

† This special case is often called the Maclaurin expansion.

are sums of their **Taylor series.** The theory of analytic functions is a separate and highly evolved branch of analysis and one which has been adequately treated in a variety of texts.†

There are functions of class C^∞ which are not analytic, and for which the Taylor polynomials are very poor approximations. An often used example is $f(x) = \exp(-1/x^2)$. When $x \neq 0$, f is continuous and infinitely differentiable. In fact, $f'(x) = 2x^{-3}\exp(-1/x^2)$, and induction shows that $f^{(n)}(x)$ has the form $x^{-3n}Q(x)\exp(-1/x^2)$, where Q is a polynomial of degree $2(n-1)$. Since $\lim_{x\to 0} f(x) = 0$, the discontinuity at the origin may be removed by setting $f(0) = 0$; the formula for $f^{(n)}$ shows that it is also true that $\lim_{x\to 0} f^{(n)}(x) = 0$ for $n = 1, 2, \ldots$. This allows us to show that f is also infinitely differentiable at $x = 0$, with $f^{(n)}(0) = 0$ for $n = 1, 2, \ldots$. For $n = 1$, $f'(0) = \lim_{h\to 0} \frac{f(h)}{h}$; applying L'Hospital's rule, we replace this by $\lim_{h\to 0} f'(h)$, which exists and has the value 0. Induction establishes the general result. The function f can be shown to be analytic for all $x \neq 0$. However, it is not analytic at $x = 0$, even though it is infinitely differentiable there. The Taylor polynomial of degree n at 0 is $0 + 0x + 0x^2/2 + \cdots + 0x^n/n!$ so that $R_n(x) = \exp(-1/x^2)$, which does not tend to zero as n increases, on any neighborhood of 0. For this function, then the Taylor polynomials at the origin do not converge to the function. Of course, since f is continuous everywhere, it is possible to approximate it uniformly on any bounded interval by a polynomial with arbitrary accuracy. This points up the fact that while the Taylor polynomials have the advantage that they are easily defined and computed, they need not be the best approximation to use. For example, the Taylor polynomial of degree 2 at the origin for e^x is $1 + x + x^2/2$ which approximates it uniformly on $[-1, 1]$ within .22; however, there are other polynomials of degree 2 which are better approximations; $.99 + 1.175x + .543x^2$ approximates e^x uniformly on $[-1, 1]$ within .04.

As an illustration of the application of these results in the evaluation of an integral, let us consider

$$C = \int_0^1 \sqrt{x}\, e^{\sqrt{x}}\, dx.$$

Instead of applying the expansion process to the integrand directly, we first recall that

$$e^x \sim 1 + x + \frac{x^2}{2} + \frac{x^3}{6} + \frac{x^4}{24} + \frac{x^5}{120}$$

† For example, L. V. Ahlfors, "Complex Analysis," McGraw-Hill Book Company, Inc., New York, 1953.

within .005 on $[-1, 1]$. On $[0, 1]$, we may write

$$\sqrt{x}\, e^{\sqrt{x}} \sim \sqrt{x}\left[1 + x^{1/2} + \cdots + \frac{x^{5/2}}{120}\right]$$
$$\sim x^{1/2} + x + \cdots + \frac{x^3}{120}$$

also good to .005. Making this replacement in the integral,

$$C \sim \int_0^1 \left(x^{1/2} + x + \frac{x^{3/2}}{2} + \cdots + \frac{x^3}{120}\right) dx = 1.4357$$

with an error of at most $\int_0^1 (.005)\, dx = .005$. Our estimate is actually better than that, for the substitution $u = \sqrt{x}$ gives

$$C = \int_0^1 2u^2 e^u\, du = (4 - 4u + 2u^2)e^u \Big|_0^1 = 1.4366.$$

EXERCISES

1. Show that $\sin x$ can be approximated by $x - x^3/6$ within .01 on the interval $[-1, 1]$.

2. Determine the accuracy of the approximation

$$\cos x \sim 1 - \frac{x^2}{2} + \frac{x^4}{24}$$

on the interval $[-1, 1]$.

3. Determine the accuracy of the approximation

$$\log (1 + x) \sim x - \frac{x^2}{2} + \frac{x^3}{3} - \frac{x^4}{4}$$

on the interval $[-\tfrac{1}{2}, \tfrac{1}{2}]$.

4. Determine the accuracy of the approximation

$$\sqrt{x} \sim 1 + \frac{(x - 1)}{2} - \frac{(x - 1)^2}{8}$$

on the interval $[\tfrac{1}{2}, \tfrac{3}{2}]$.

5. How many terms of the Taylor expansion for $\sin x$ about a conveniently chosen point are needed to obtain a polynomial approximation accurate to .01 on the interval $[0, \pi]$? On the interval $[0, 2\pi]$?

6. Estimate the values of the following integrals within .05.

(*a*) $\displaystyle\int_0^1 e^{-x^2}\, dx$ (*b*) $\displaystyle\int_0^1 \frac{\sin x}{x}\, dx$ (*c*) $\displaystyle\int_1^2 \frac{dx}{1 + \log x}$

7. Show that for all $x \geq 1$, $\log x \leq \sqrt{x} - 1/\sqrt{x}$.

8. Show that for all $x \geq 0$, $e^x \geq \tfrac{3}{2}x^2$. Can you replace $\tfrac{3}{2}$ by a larger number?

9. Let f obey the condition $|f^{(n)}(x)| \leq B^n$ for all x in an open interval I, and all n. Show that f is analytic on I.

***10.** Let f be of class C'' on $[0, 1]$ with $f(0) = f(1) = 0$, and suppose that $|f''(x)| \leq A$ for all x, $0 < x < 1$. Show that $|f'(\frac{1}{2})| \leq A/4$ and that $|f'(x)| \leq A/2$ for $0 < x < 1$.

****11.** Let f belong to class C^∞ on $[-1, 1]$ and obey there the condition $f^{(n)}(x) \geq 0$ for all n. Prove that f is analytic for $-1 < x < 1$.

3.4. Improper Integrals

As outlined in Sec. 3.1, the notion of **area** applied only to bounded sets. If we seek to extend this to unbounded sets, a simple procedure suggests itself. Let $R_1 \subset R_2 \subset \cdots$ be an expanding sequence of closed rectangles whose union is the whole plane; for example, we may

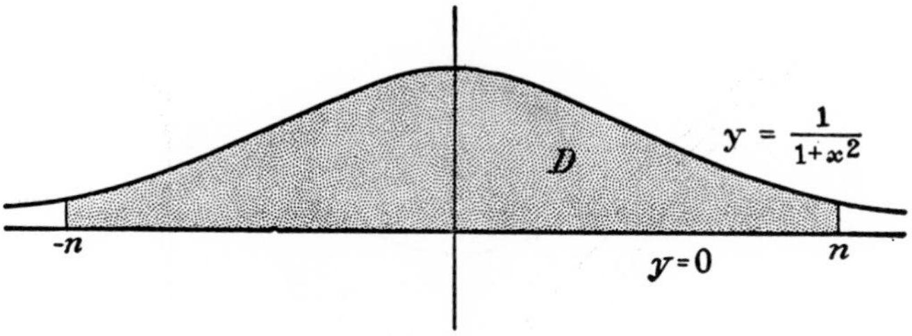

FIG. 3-6

choose R_n as the square with center at the origin, and one vertex at (n, n). Let D be an unbounded set whose area we wish to measure. We form the bounded set $D_n = R_n \cap D$, the part of D in R_n, and assume that the boundary of D is nice enough so that each of these has an area. Since the sets $\{D_n\}$ form an expanding sequence, the sequence of their areas $\{A(D_n)\}$ is a monotone sequence. If it is bounded, it converges, and we write $A(D) = \lim_{n \to \infty} A(D_n)$; if it is unbounded, the sequence diverges, and we write $A(D) = \infty$.

To see how this process works, let D be the set of all points (x, y) with $0 \leq y \leq (1 + x^2)^{-1}$ (see Fig. 3-6). Choosing R_n as above, we have

$$\begin{aligned} A(D_n) &= \int_{-n}^{n} dx \int_0^{1/(1+x^2)} dy = \int_{-n}^{n} \frac{dx}{1 + x^2} \\ &= 2 \arctan (n), \end{aligned}$$

and

$$A(D) = \lim_{n \to \infty} A(D_n) = \pi.$$

Again, let D be the set of all points (x, y) with $|x^2 - y^2| \leq 1$ (see Fig. 3-7). We have

$$\begin{aligned} A(D_n) &= 8 \int_0^1 dx \int_0^x dy + 8 \int_1^n dx \int_{\sqrt{x^2-1}}^{x} dy \\ &= 4 + 8 \int_1^n (x - \sqrt{x^2 - 1})\, dx. \end{aligned}$$

Since $x - \sqrt{x^2 - 1} = 1/(x + \sqrt{x^2 - 1}) \geq \frac{1}{2}x$,

$$A(D_n) \geq 4 + 8 \int_1^n \frac{dx}{2x} = 4 + 4 \log n$$

and $A(D) = \infty$.

It is natural to ask if the choice of the rectangles $\{R_n\}$ affects the final value of $A(D)$. We shall show that it does not; we first prove an important result which has nothing to do with integration, but is a fundamental theorem dealing with coverings of bounded sets by open sets.†

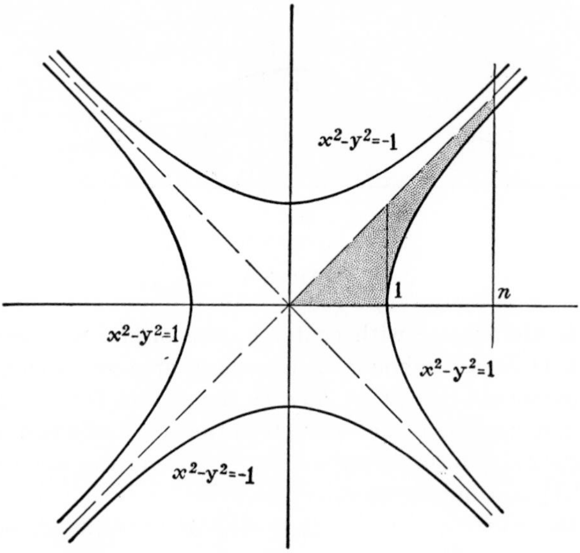

FIG. 3-7

Lemma (Heine-Borel Theorem). *Let E be a closed and bounded set in the plane (or in E^n). Let $U_1, U_2, \ldots$ be any collection of open sets whose union covers E. Then, some finite subcollection also cover E.*

Let $V_1 = U_1$, $V_2 = U_1 \cup U_2$, and in general let V_n be the union of the sets $U_1, U_2, \ldots, U_n$. The sets V_j form an expanding sequence of open sets whose union is the same as that of the sets U_j, and which therefore also cover E. We shall show that an integer k can be chosen so that $V_k \supset E$; the finite subcollection $\{U_1, \ldots, U_k\}$ will therefore cover E. Let $C_n = E - V_n = \{\text{all } p \in E \text{ with } p \notin V_n\}$. These sets are closed, bounded, and $C_1 \supset C_2 \supset C_3 \supset \cdots$. If these were all non-empty, then by the nested set property (Sec. 1.3) there would be a

† This result is another of the assertions which may be taken as a starting point in the study of the real number system. We derive it here from the nested set property; conversely, the nested set property easily follows from it (see Appendix).

point q which lies in each of the sets C_n. But, q would then be a point of E which lies in none of the sets V_n, in contradiction to the fact that the sets $\{V_n\}$ together cover all of E. We conclude that the sets C_n must be empty from some index on. If C_k is empty, then V_k contains E, proving the lemma. ▌

We now show that the number $A(D)$ is independent of the choice of the expanding sequence of rectangles; we require, however, that any such sequence share with the special sequence used above the property that their interiors cover the plane, i.e., each point of the plane is interior to R_n when n is sufficiently large.

Theorem 12. *Let $\{R'_n\}$ and $\{R_n\}$ be two expanding sequences of closed rectangles whose interiors cover the plane. Let D be a set such that*

$$D_n = D \cap R_n \qquad \text{and} \qquad D'_n = D \cap R'_n$$

have area for each $n = 1, 2, 3, \ldots$. Then,

$$\lim_{n\to\infty} A(D_n) = \lim_{n\to\infty} A(D'_n).$$

Let U_n be the set of interior points of R_n and set $E = R'_j$. The open sets U_n cover the plane, and thus E; by the Heine-Borel theorem, there is a k such that $E \subset U_k$. This implies that for each j, there is a corresponding k such that $R'_j \subset R_k$. Intersecting both with D, $D'_j \subset D_k$ and $A(D'_j) \le A(D_k) \le \lim_{n\to\infty} A(D_n)$. Since this holds for any j, $\lim_{n\to\infty} A(D'_n) \le \lim_{n\to\infty} A(D_n)$. By an analogous argument, we obtain the reversed inequality, and thus equality of the limits. ▌

Having extended the notion of area, we may similarly seek to extend the notion of the definite integral

$$I(f, D) = \iint_D f.$$

Regarded as a function of the pair (f, D), we have shown that it is defined when D is a bounded set having area, and f is bounded and continuous on D, except for a set of zero area. In both cases, the word "bounded" cannot be deleted. For example, if f were not bounded above on D, then for any grid N partitioning D, the upper Riemann sum $\bar{S}(N)$ would have the value ∞, since $\operatorname{lub}_{p \in R_{ij}} f(p)$ would be infinite for some choice of i and j. In particular, the previous definition fails to give meaning to the integrals $\int_0^1 \log x\, dx$ and $\int_0^1 1/\sqrt{x}\, dx$. Guided by our discussion of area for unbounded sets, let us attempt to extend $I(f, D)$ so that it will be defined for some unbounded regions D and some unbounded functions f. To distinguish these from the original notion of integral, we call them **improper** integrals.

What meaning should be attached to $\int_c^\infty f$ when f is continuous on the unbounded interval $c \leq x < \infty$? If f is positive-valued, we can fall back on the notion of area, and define the value of this to be the area of the plane region $D = \{\text{all } (x, y) \text{ with } c \leq x < \infty \text{ and } 0 \leq y \leq f(x)\}$. Applying the previous discussion,

$$\int_c^\infty f = A(D) = \lim_{n\to\infty} \int_c^n dx \int_0^{f(x)} dy$$
$$= \lim_{n\to\infty} \int_c^n f(x)\, dx.$$

Modifying this slightly, we adopt the following definition to be applied also when the integrand takes on positive and negative values.

Definition. *Let $f(x)$ be continuous for $c \leq x < \infty$. Then,*

$$\int_c^\infty f = \lim_{r\uparrow\infty} \int_c^r f$$

when this limit exists.

To illustrate this,

$$\int_0^\infty e^{-x}\, dx = \lim_{r\uparrow\infty} \int_0^r e^{-x}\, dx = \lim_{r\uparrow\infty} - e^{-x}\Big|_0^r = 1.$$

$$\int_0^\infty \sin x\, dx = \lim_{r\uparrow\infty} - \cos x \Big|_0^r$$

which does not exist. Since the final step in the computation is the evaluation of a limit, it is customary to use the terms "convergent" and "divergent" in place of "exist" and "not exist." Thus $\int_0^\infty e^{-x}\, dx$ converges and $\int_0^\infty \sin x\, dx$ diverges. Following the same pattern, we shall understand $\int_{-\infty}^c f$ to mean $\lim_{r\uparrow\infty} \int_{-r}^c f$.

For the expression $\int_{-\infty}^\infty f$ two distinct definitions are used.

(i)
$$\int_{-\infty}^\infty f = \lim_{r\to\infty} \int_c^r f + \lim_{r\to\infty} \int_{-r}^c f$$
$$= \int_c^\infty f + \int_{-\infty}^c f.$$

(ii)
$$\int_{-\infty}^\infty f = \lim_{r\to\infty} \int_{-r}^r f.$$

To distinguish these, we call the first the (ordinary) value of the improper integral, and the second the **Cauchy principal value.** These agree whenever both exist, but the Cauchy value may exist in some cases where the ordinary value does not. The reason for this lies in the fact that the limit calculations in the ordinary case must be computed separately, and if either diverges, so does the integral. However, in the Cauchy principal value, the limit operations are combined and divergence of one may be offset by the other. For example, consider the improper integral

$$\int_{-\infty}^{\infty} \frac{(1+x)\,dx}{1+x^2}.$$

We have

$$\int_0^r \frac{(1+x)\,dx}{1+x^2} = \left[\arctan x + \frac{1}{2}\log(1+x^2)\right]_0^r$$
$$= \arctan r + \frac{1}{2}\log(1+r^2),$$

and since $\lim_{r\to\infty} \log(1+r^2) = \infty$, the original integral is a divergent improper integral. However,

$$\int_{-r}^{0} \frac{(1+x)\,dx}{1+x^2} = -\arctan(-r) - \frac{1}{2}\log(1+r^2)$$

so that

$$\int_{-r}^{r} \frac{(1+x)\,dx}{1+x^2} = 2\arctan r$$

and

$$(\text{C.P.V.}) \int_{-\infty}^{\infty} \frac{(1+x)\,dx}{1+x^2} = \pi.$$

Unless there is some indication (such as the prefix (C.P.V.)) that the Cauchy value is meant, the ordinary value is always to be understood, and is usually the one which is appropriate to the problem. The rather arbitrary nature of choice (ii) may be seen from the fact that

$$\lim_{r\to\infty} \int_{-r}^{2r} \frac{(1+x)\,dx}{1+x^2} = \pi + \log 2.$$

One important case in which both choices agree is that in which the integrand is always positive, or always negative.

Let us consider now the case in which the range of integration is a bounded set, but the integrand is unbounded. For example, can we attach a meaning to $\int_0^1 \frac{1}{\sqrt{x}}\,dx$? We may again consider the set D bounded by the horizontal axis and the graph (see Fig. 3-8). This set is unbounded, and computing its area, we have

$$A(D) = \lim_{n\to\infty} \int_0^n dy \int_0^{\text{minimum of } y^{-2} \text{ and } 1} dx$$
$$= \lim_{n\to\infty} \left\{\int_0^1 dy \int_0^1 dx + \int_1^n dy \int_0^{y^{-2}} dx\right\}$$
$$= \lim_{n\to\infty} \left\{1 + \int_1^n y^{-2}\,dy\right\} = \mathbf{2}$$

so that we are led to write

$$\int_0^1 x^{-1/2}\,dx = 2.$$

More generally, if f is continuous on $[a, b]$ except at a finite number of points, with $f(x) \geq 0$ for all x, let f_n be the function defined on $[a, b]$ by

$$f_n(x) = \text{minimum of } f(x) \text{ and } n.$$

If D is the set of points lying above the horizontal axis, below the graph of f, and between the lines $x = a$, $x = b$, then the area of this unbounded set is given by

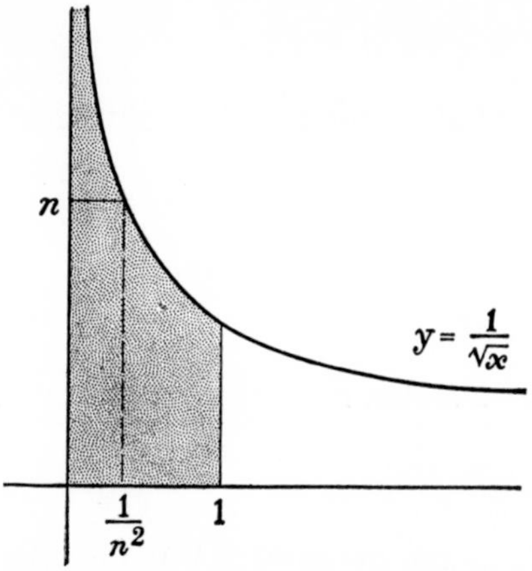

Fig. 3-8

$$A(D) = \lim_{n\to\infty} \int_a^b f_n.$$

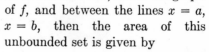

Were we to take this as our definition for $\int_a^b f$, we would find that it is not too easily applied, even when f is uncomplicated. Moreover, this would have to be modified to treat integrands taking both positive and negative values. Instead, we adopt a different definition which overcomes some of these objections, and which leads to the same results. We first isolate the discontinuities of f by splitting the interval of integration into subintervals in each of which f is continuous, except possibly for one end point. For example, if $f(x) = 1/(x^2 - 1)$ and the interval of integration is $[-1, 2]$, we would first write

$$\int_{-1}^{2} f(x)\,dx = \int_{-1}^{0} f(x)\,dx + \int_0^1 f(x)\,dx + \int_1^2 f(x)\,dx$$

since the discontinuities are at 1 and -1. We may therefore assume that we are considering a function f which is continuous on a half-open interval $a < x \leq b$ and unbounded there; we do not require that f be positive.

Definition. *Let $f(x)$ be continuous for $a < x \leq b$. Then,*

$$\int_a^b f = \lim_{r \downarrow a} \int_r^b f$$

whenever this limit exists.

Using this for the integral $\int_0^1 x^{-1/2}\,dx$, we obtain

$$\int_0^1 x^{-1/2}\,dx = \lim_{r\downarrow 0} \int_r^1 x^{-1/2}\,dx$$
$$= \lim_{r\downarrow 0} 2\sqrt{x}\,\Big|_r^1 = 2$$

in agreement with the former calculation. This agreement is of course not accidental.

Theorem 13. *Let f be continuous for $a < x \le b$ with $f(x) \ge 0$. Let D be the region bounded by the line $y = 0$, by $x = a$ and $x = b$, and the curve $y = f(x)$. Then, $A(D) = \int_a^b f$.*

This asserts that $\lim_{n\to\infty} \int_a^b f_n$ and $\lim_{r\downarrow a} \int_r^b f$ are either both infinite, or both finite and equal. First, choose $r > a$ and let $M_r = \max_{x\varepsilon[r,b]} f(x)$. When $n > M_r$, $f_n(x) = f(x)$ on $[r, b]$ so that

$$\int_a^b f_n = \int_a^r f_n + \int_r^b f_n \ge \int_r^b f$$

using the fact that f is positive. Letting n increase, we find that for any $r > a$,

$$\lim_{n\to\infty} \int_a^b f_n \ge \int_r^b f$$

and

$$\lim_{n\to\infty} \int_a^b f_n \ge \lim_{r\downarrow a} \int_r^b f.$$

To obtain the opposite inequality, choose any n; since $f(x) \ge f_n(x)$ for all x, while $f_n(x) \le n$,

$$\int_r^b f_n \le \int_r^b f \qquad \text{and} \qquad \int_a^r f_n \le n(r - a).$$

Combining these, we have

$$\int_a^b f_n \le n(r - a) + \int_r^b f$$

and letting r approach a, we see that for any choice of n,

$$\int_a^b f_n \le \lim_{r\downarrow a} \int_r^b f$$

and thus

$$\lim_{n\to\infty} \int_a^b f_n \le \lim_{r\downarrow a} \int_r^b f.$$

Equality must hold, and we have shown that the alternate definition is consistent with the original area definition. ▌

The examples which follow show how the definition is to be modified if the discontinuity of the integrand occurs at the upper end point, and if there is more than one discontinuity in the interval of integration.

(i)
$$\int_0^1 \frac{dx}{\sqrt{1-x^2}} = \lim_{r\uparrow 1} \int_0^r \frac{dx}{\sqrt{1-x^2}} = \lim_{r\uparrow 1} \arcsin r$$
$$= \frac{\pi}{2}$$

(ii)
$$\int_0^1 \frac{dx}{\sqrt{x}\,(1-x)} = \int_0^{1/2} \frac{dx}{\sqrt{x}\,(1-x)} + \int_{1/2}^1 \frac{dx}{\sqrt{x}\,(1-x)}$$

Standard integration procedure shows that

$$\int \frac{dx}{\sqrt{x}\,(1-x)} = \log \frac{1+\sqrt{x}}{1-\sqrt{x}}$$

so that

$$\int_0^{1/2} \frac{dx}{\sqrt{x}\,(1-x)} = \lim_{r\downarrow 0} \log \frac{1+\sqrt{x}}{1-\sqrt{x}}\Bigg|_r^{1/2} = \log \frac{\sqrt{2}+1}{\sqrt{2}-1}.$$

However,

$$\int_{1/2}^1 \frac{dx}{\sqrt{x}\,(1-x)} = \lim_{r\uparrow 1} \log \frac{1+\sqrt{x}}{1-\sqrt{x}}\Bigg|_{1/2}^{r} = \infty$$

so that the original improper integral is divergent.

So far, we have extended the definite integral by relaxing separately the restriction that the interval of integration be bounded, and that the integrand be bounded. These may also be combined. We interpret

$$\int_0^\infty x^{-1/2}e^{-x}\,dx \qquad \text{to mean} \qquad \int_0^1 x^{-1/2}e^{-x}\,dx + \int_1^\infty x^{-1/2}e^{-x}\,dx$$

and speak of the original improper integral as convergent only when both of these integrals are convergent.

If care is exercised, the techniques applicable to ordinary proper integrals may also be used in evaluating improper integrals. If $\phi(u)$ is of class C' for $\alpha \le u \le \beta$, and if $\phi(\alpha) = a$, and $\lim_{u\uparrow\beta} \phi(u) = b$, then the change of variable $x = \phi(u)$ converts an improper integral $\int_a^b f(x)\,dx$ into $\int_\alpha^\beta f(\phi(u))\phi'(u)\,du$. If this is now a proper integral, the original integral was convergent; if the new integral is also improper, then both are convergent or both divergent. For example, the substitution $x = u^2$ in $\int_0^1 x^{-1/2}\,dx$ gives

$$\int_0^1 \frac{2u\,du}{u} = \int_0^1 2\,du = 2.$$

This procedure is also valid for integrals with unbounded range of integration. The integral $\int_0^\infty \frac{dx}{(1+x^2)^2}$ becomes $\int_0^{\pi/2} (\cos\theta)^2\, d\theta$ under the substitution $x = \tan\theta$; likewise, $\int_1^\infty x^{-2}\sin x\, dx$ is convergent since the substitution $x = 1/u$ changes this into the proper integral

$$\int_1^0 -\sin\left(\frac{1}{u}\right) du = \int_0^1 \sin\left(\frac{1}{u}\right) du.$$

When the interval of integration is split into a union of subintervals, the original integral is represented as a sum of integrals, each having the same integrand, and it is divergent if any one of these diverges. A common error is to suppose that this is true whenever one integral is represented in any fashion as a sum of integrals. However, the integrals $\int_0^1 (1+x)/x\, dx$ and $\int_0^1 (2x-1)/x\, dx$ are each divergent, while their sum

$$\int_0^1 \frac{1+x}{x}\, dx + \int_0^1 \frac{2x-1}{x}\, dx = \int_0^1 \frac{1+x+2x-1}{x}\, dx = \int_0^1 3\, dx$$

is convergent.

The convergence of an improper integral such as $\int_0^\infty f(x)\, dx$ depends upon the behavior of $f(x)$ when x is large. The following simple comparison test is often used to show convergence or divergence. The functions f and g are assumed continuous on the interval $a \le x < b$, and b may be a number or ∞.

Theorem 14. *Let $0 \le f(x) \le g(x)$ for $a \le x < b$. Then, if $\int_a^b g$ converges, so does $\int_a^b f$ and $\int_a^b f \le \int_a^b g$.*

Let $F(r) = \int_a^r f$ and $G(r) = \int_a^r g$. The hypotheses imply that $F(r) \le G(r)$ for all $r < b$ and that $\lim_{r\uparrow b} G(r)$ exists. Since f is positive valued, F is monotone increasing as $r \uparrow b$; since it is bounded above by $\lim_{r\uparrow b} G(r)$, $\lim_{r\uparrow b} F(r)$ exists and is less than or equal to $\lim_{r\uparrow b} G(r)$. ▌

Corollary. *Let $f(x) \ge 0$ and $g(x) \ge 0$ for $a \le x < b$, and let*

$$\lim_{x\uparrow b} \frac{f(x)}{g(x)} = L$$

with $0 < L < \infty$. Then, the integrals $\int_a^b f$ and $\int_a^b g$ are either both convergent or both divergent.

If $\lim_{x \to b} \frac{f(x)}{g(x)} = L$, then there is a point x_0 between a and b such that whenever $x_0 < x < b$

$$\frac{L}{2} < \frac{f(x)}{g(x)} < 2L.$$

Thus, $f(x) < 2Lg(x)$ and $g(x) < \frac{2}{L} f(x)$ for all x, $x_0 < x < b$. Applying the theorem, we see that if $\int_a^b g$ converges, so does $\int_a^b f$, and conversely. ∎

To apply these tests, one must have at hand a collection of known integrals for comparison. Most frequently used are:

$$\int_1^\infty \frac{dx}{x^p} \quad \text{converges if and only if } p > 1$$

$$\int_0^1 \frac{dx}{x^p} \quad \text{converges if and only if } p < 1$$

$$\int_a^c \frac{dx}{|c - x|^p} \quad \text{converges if and only if } p < 1$$

For example, $\int_0^\infty \frac{dx}{\sqrt{x + x^3}}$ converges since the integrand is dominated by $1/\sqrt{x}$ on the interval $[0, 1]$ and by $1/x^{3/2}$ on $[1, \infty]$. The integral $\int_0^\infty \frac{dx}{\sqrt{x + x^2}}$ is divergent since $\lim_{x \uparrow \infty} \frac{x}{\sqrt{x + x^2}} = 1$ and $\int_1^\infty \frac{dx}{x}$ diverges.

These comparison tests apply directly only when the integrand is everywhere positive. However, the next result may often be used to reduce a general case to this special one.

Theorem 15. *$\int_a^b f$ always converges if $\int_a^b |f(x)|\, dx$ converges.*

Since $f(x)$ always lies between $-|f(x)|$ and $|f(x)|$,

$$0 \le |f(x)| + f(x) \le 2|f(x)|.$$

If $\int_a^b |f|$ converges, then so does $\int_a^b [f(x) + |f(x)|]\, dx$, and subtracting the convergent integral $\int_a^b |f(x)|\, dx$, $\int_a^b f(x)\, dx$ must converge.

The following examples illustrate the use of this in combination with the preceding theorems.

(i) $\int_1^\infty \frac{\sin x}{x^2}\, dx$ converges since $\left|\frac{\sin x}{x^2}\right| \le \frac{1}{x^2}$.

(ii) $\int_0^1 \frac{\cos(1/x)}{\sqrt{x}}\, dx$ converges since $\frac{|\cos(1/x)|}{\sqrt{x}} \le x^{-1/2}$.

(iii) $\int_0^\infty \frac{\sin x}{x\sqrt{x}}\,dx$ converges, since $|x^{-3/2}\sin x| \le x^{-3/2}$ on the interval $[1, \infty]$ and $\lim_{x\downarrow 0} \sqrt{x}\,\frac{\sin x}{x\sqrt{x}} = 1$.

A convergent improper integral $\int_a^b f$ is said to be **absolutely convergent** if $\int_a^b |f|$ is convergent, and **conditionally convergent** if $\int_a^b |f|$ is divergent. All the convergent examples that we have discussed so far are absolutely convergent. A sample of an integral which is only conditionally convergent is $\int_1^\infty x^{-1}\sin x\,dx$. The type of argument which was used above fails here; $\left|\frac{\sin x}{x}\right|$ is dominated by $1/x$, but $\int_1^\infty x^{-1}\,dx$ is divergent so that Theorem 15 does not apply, and this method gives no information about the convergence or divergence of either $\int_1^\infty x^{-1}\sin x\,dx$ or $\int_1^\infty x^{-1}|\sin x|\,dx$. To prove convergence of the first integral and divergence of the second, a different method must be used.

Recall the familiar formula for **integration by parts:**

$$\int_a^b f(x)\,dg(x) = f(x)g(x)\Big|_a^b - \int_a^b g(x)\,df(x).$$

We apply this to our integral, and have

$$\begin{aligned}\int_1^r \frac{\sin x}{x}\,dx &= \int_1^r \frac{1}{x}\,d(-\cos x)\\ &= -\frac{\cos x}{x}\Big|_1^r + \int_1^r \cos x\,d\left(\frac{1}{x}\right)\\ &= -\frac{\cos r}{r} + \cos(1) - \int_1^r \frac{\cos x}{x^2}\,dx.\end{aligned}$$

Since $\lim_{r\to\infty} r^{-1}\cos r = 0$, we have shown that

$$\int_1^\infty \frac{\sin x}{x}\,dx = \cos(1) - \int_1^\infty \frac{\cos x}{x^2}\,dx.$$

The technique of integration by parts has replaced the original improper integral with another; however, the new one is absolutely convergent, since $|x^{-2}\cos x| \le x^{-2}$. This shows that the original integral converges.

To show that $\int_1^\infty x^{-1}\sin x\,dx$ is itself not absolutely convergent, write

$$\int_1^{m\pi} \frac{|\sin x|}{x}\,dx = \int_1^\pi \frac{\sin x}{x}\,dx + \sum_1^{m-1} \int_{n\pi}^{(n+1)\pi} \frac{|\sin x|}{x}\,dx.$$

Since the minimum value of $1/x$ on $[n\pi, (n+1)\pi]$ is $1/(n+1)\pi$,

$$\int_{n\pi}^{(n+1)\pi} \frac{|\sin x|}{x}\,dx \geq \frac{1}{(n+1)\pi}\int_{n\pi}^{(n+1)\pi} |\sin x|\,dx$$
$$\geq \frac{2}{(n+1)\pi} \geq \frac{2}{\pi}\int_{n+1}^{n+2}\frac{dx}{x}$$

and
$$\sum_{1}^{m-1}\int_{n\pi}^{(n+1)\pi} \frac{|\sin x|}{x}\,dx \geq \frac{2}{\pi}\sum_{1}^{m-1}\int_{n+1}^{n+2}\frac{dx}{x}$$
$$\geq \frac{2}{\pi}\int_{2}^{m+1}\frac{dx}{x} = \frac{2}{\pi}\log\frac{m+1}{2}.$$

Hence,
$$\int_{1}^{m\pi} \frac{|\sin x|}{x}\,dx \geq \int_{1}^{\pi}\frac{\sin x}{x}\,dx + \frac{2}{\pi}\log\frac{m+1}{2},$$

and $\int_{1}^{\infty}\frac{|\sin x|}{x}\,dx$ diverges.

The device of integration by parts may be applied in other cases too. To study the improper integral $\int_{2}^{\infty}\frac{\cos x}{\log x}\,dx$, we first perform an integration by parts. (The use of "∞" is an abbreviation for the previous limit operations.)

$$\int_{2}^{\infty}\frac{\cos x}{\log x}\,dx = \int_{2}^{\infty}\frac{1}{\log x}\,d(\sin x)$$
$$= \frac{\sin x}{\log x}\bigg|_{2}^{\infty} - \int_{2}^{\infty}\sin x\,d\frac{1}{\log x}$$
$$= -\frac{\sin 2}{\log 2} + \int_{2}^{\infty}\frac{\sin x}{x(\log x)^2}\,dx.$$

Since $\int_{2}^{\infty}\frac{dx}{x(\log x)^2}$ converges, the new improper integral is (absolutely) convergent, and $\int_{2}^{\infty}\frac{\cos x}{\log x}\,dx$ converges.

The same procedure can be used to prove convergence for a general class of improper integrals.

Theorem 16 (*Dirichlet Test*). *Let f, g, and g' be continuous on the unbounded interval $c \leq x < \infty$. Then the integral $\int_{c}^{\infty} f(x)g(x)\,dx$ is convergent if f and g obey the following conditions:*

(i) $\lim_{x\to\infty} g(x) = 0$,

(ii) $\int_{c}^{\infty} g'$ *is absolutely convergent,*

(iii) $F(r) = \int_{c}^{r} f$ *is bounded for* $c \leq r < \infty$.

Take $$\int_c^r fg = \int_c^r g(x)\,dF(x) = F(x)g(x)\Big|_c^r - \int_c^r F(x)\,dg(x)$$
$$= F(r)g(r) - F(c)g(c) - \int_c^r F(x)g'(x)\,dx.$$

By assumption, $|F(r)| \le M$ for all $r \ge c$ so that $|F(r)g(r)| \le M|g(r)|$ and $\lim_{r\to\infty} F(r)g(r) = 0$. Also, $|F(x)g'(x)| \le M|g'(x)|$ and by hypothesis, $\int_c^\infty |g'(x)|\,dx$ converges, so that by comparison $\int_c^\infty F(x)g'(x)\,dx$ converges. This shows that $\lim_{r\to\infty} \int_c^r fg$ exists. ▮

Two special cases of this are used frequently.

Corollary 1. *$\int_c^\infty fg$ converges if f obeys condition* (iii) *and $g(x)$ decreases monotonically to zero as $x \uparrow \infty$.*

For, $g'(x)$ is always negative so that

$$\int_c^r |g'(x)|\,dx = -\int_c^r g'(x)\,dx = -g(x)\Big|_c^r = g(c) - g(r),$$

and $\lim_{r\to\infty} \int_c^r |g'(x)|\,dx$ exists and is $g(c)$. ▮

Corollary 2. *If g is of class C' for $c \le x < \infty$ and $g(x)$ decreases monotonically to zero as $x \uparrow \infty$, then the integrals $\int_c^\infty g(x) \sin x\,dx$ and $\int_c^\infty g(x) \cos x\,dx$ are convergent.*

This corollary covers both of the illustrations given above. It is often applied in combination with a change of variable.

In $\int_0^\infty \cos (x^2)\,dx$, set $x = \sqrt{u}$, obtaining the improper integral $\int_0^\infty \frac{\cos u}{2\sqrt{u}}\,du$. As $u \downarrow 0$, the integrand behaves like $1/\sqrt{u}$ so that $\int_0^1 \frac{\cos u}{2\sqrt{u}}\,du$ converges. Corollary 2 then shows at once that $\int_1^\infty \frac{\cos u}{2\sqrt{u}}\,du$ converges.†

Again, $\int_0^1 x^{-1} \sin (x^{-1})\,dx$ becomes $\int_1^\infty \frac{\sin u}{u}\,du$ after the substitution $x = 1/u$, and is therefore convergent.

The discussion of improper double and triple integrals follows somewhat the same pattern, allowing for the change in dimension. The most significant difference is the absence of an analogue for conditional convergence. The reason for this will appear later. For the present, only

† This example shows that $\int_0^\infty f(x)\,dx$ can converge without having $\lim_{x\to\infty} f(x) = 0$. See also Exercise 3b.

positive integrands will be considered. Let D be an unbounded plane set and f continuous and positive in D. If we agree that $\iint\limits_D f$ is to measure the volume of the region V in 3-space lying above D and below the surface $z = f(x, y)$, then we are led to the following definition.

Definition. *$\iint\limits_D f$ is $\lim\limits_{n\to\infty} \iint\limits_{D_n} f$ where $D_n = D \cap R_n$ and $\{R_n\}$ is an expanding sequence of closed rectangles whose interiors cover the plane.*

As in Theorem 12, the Heine-Borel theorem shows that the value obtained does not depend upon the choice of the sequence $\{R_n\}$. To illustrate this, let D be the first quadrant and $f(x, y) = xye^{-(x^2+y^2)}$. Choosing R_n as the square with center at the origin and vertices at $(\pm n, \pm n)$

$$\iint\limits_{D_n} f = \int_0^n \int_0^n xye^{-(x^2+y^2)}\,dxdy$$

$$= \int_0^n dx \int_0^n xe^{-x^2}ye^{-y^2}\,dy$$

$$= \int_0^n xe^{-x^2}\,dx \int_0^n ye^{-y^2}\,dy = \left[\frac{1 - e^{-n^2}}{2}\right]^2$$

and
$$\iint\limits_D f = \lim_{n\to\infty} \iint\limits_{D_n} f = 1/4.$$

When D is a bounded set, but f is unbounded, the region V above D and below the surface $z = f(x, y)$ is again an unbounded set in 3-space. Its volume is found by constructing the truncated functions f_n, where $f_n(p) = \min\{n, f(p)\}$. These are bounded and the volume of V is $\lim\limits_{n\to\infty} \iint\limits_D f_n$ which we may accept as the definition of $\iint\limits_D f$, when the limit exists. Even in simple cases, this process can be somewhat complicated to carry out. For example, let D be the unit square with vertices at $(0, 0)$, $(0, 1)$, $(1, 0)$, $(1, 1)$, and $f(x, y) = yx^{-1/2}$. Cutting f off at height n, we see that $f(p) \le n$ when $y \le n\sqrt{x}$ and

$$f_n(p) = \begin{cases} yx^{-1/2} & \text{for } y \le n\sqrt{x} \\ n & \text{for } y > n\sqrt{x}. \end{cases}$$

Thus (see Fig. 3-9),

$$\iint\limits_D f_n = \int_0^{1/n^2} dx \int_{n\sqrt{x}}^1 n\,dy + \int_0^{1/n^2} dx \int_0^{n\sqrt{x}} yx^{-1/2}\,dy$$
$$+ \int_{1/n^2}^1 dx \int_0^1 yx^{-1/2}\,dy = \frac{1}{3n} + \frac{1}{3n} + \left(1 - \frac{1}{n}\right)$$

and $\iint_D f = 1$. As in the case of single integrals, an alternative procedure may be used. The integrand $yx^{-1/2}$ is continuous in D except on the left edge, $x = 0$. Let D_r be the rectangle bounded by the lines $x = 1$, $x = r$, $y = 0$, and $y = 1$. As $r \downarrow 0$, D_r approaches D. Since f is continuous in D_r, we may integrate f over D_r, and define $\iint_D f$ to be $\lim_{r \downarrow 0} \iint_{D_r} f$. We have

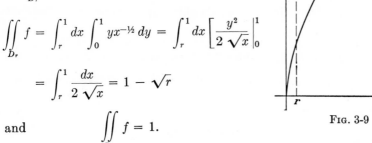

$$\iint_{D_r} f = \int_r^1 dx \int_0^1 yx^{-1/2}\, dy = \int_r^1 dx \left[\frac{y^2}{2\sqrt{x}}\right]_0^1$$

$$= \int_r^1 \frac{dx}{2\sqrt{x}} = 1 - \sqrt{r}$$

and
$$\iint_D f = 1.$$

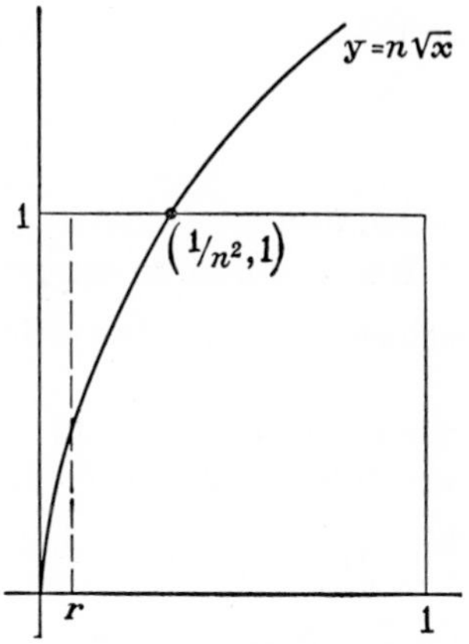

FIG. 3-9

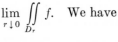

This suggests the following general definition.

Definition. *Let D be an open set whose boundary consists of a finite number of piecewise smooth curves and isolated points, and let f be continuous and positive-valued on D. Then, $\iint_D f$ converges and has value c if and only if there is an expanding sequence of closed sets $\{D_n\}$ which converges to D in the sense that every point of D is interior to some set D_k while each D_k lies in the closure of D, and such that f is bounded on each D_k and* $c = \lim_{n\to\infty} \iint_{D_n} f$.

As before, the existence of the limit and the value obtained are independent of the choice of the sequence $\{D_n\}$. To illustrate the definition, let us evaluate the integral of $(x^2 + y^2)^{-\lambda}$ over the unit disk. We take D to be the set of (x, y) with $0 < x^2 + y^2 < 1$ and D_n as the annulus $1/n = \rho \le \sqrt{x^2 + y^2} \le 1$, and compute $\iint_{D_n} (x^2 + y^2)^{-\lambda}\, dxdy$. To make this easier, we transform to polar coordinates, setting $x = r \cos \theta$, $y = r \sin \theta$, $dx\, dy = r\, dr\, d\theta$. (It should be noticed that we have not yet discussed these formulas or the general change-of-variable formula for multiple integrals; since the special case we are using is so familiar, we defer justification until later, and proceed.)

$$\iint_{D_n} (x^2 + y^2)^{-\lambda}\, dxdy = \int_\rho^1 dr \int_0^{2\pi} r^{-2\lambda} r\, d\theta$$

$$= 2\pi \int_\rho^1 r^{1-2\lambda}\, dr$$

so that

$$\iint_D (x^2 + y^2)^{-\lambda}\, dxdy = \lim_{\rho \downarrow 0} 2\pi \int_\rho^1 r^{1-2\lambda}\, dr$$

$$= 2\pi \int_0^1 r^{1-2\lambda}\, dr$$

which diverges when $\lambda \geq 1$ and converges to $\pi/(1 - \lambda)$ when $\lambda < 1$.

We turn now to integrands which take on both positive and negative values. As an illustration, let us consider $\iint_D f$, where D is the first quadrant, and $f(x, y) = \sin (x^2 + y^2)$. Following the same pattern, we choose a sequence of regions $\{D_n\}$ converging to D and examine $\lim_{n \to \infty} \iint_D f$. Suppose that D_n is the square with vertices at (0, 0), (0, n), (n, 0), (n, n). Then

$$\iint_{D_n} f = \int_0^n dx \int_0^n \sin (x^2 + y^2)\, dy$$

$$= \int_0^n \sin (x^2)\, dx \int_0^n \cos (y^2)\, dy + \int_0^n \cos (x^2)\, dx \int_0^n \sin (y^2)\, dy$$

$$= 2 \int_0^n \sin (x^2)\, dx \int_0^n \cos (x^2)\, dx$$

and

$$\lim_{n \to \infty} \iint_{D_n} f = 2 \int_0^\infty \sin (x^2)\, dx \int_0^\infty \cos (x^2)\, dx.$$

Combining Theorem 16 with a change of variable, as shown on page 93, both of these improper integrals are seen to converge. In fact, using the method of complex contour† integration, both may be shown to have the value $\sqrt{\pi/8}$. We are thus led to suggest $2(\sqrt{\pi/8})^2 = \pi/4$ as the value of $\iint_D f$. However, let us examine the effect of a different choice for the sequence $\{D_n\}$. Take D_n to be the quarter circle $0 \leq x$, $0 \leq y$, $\sqrt{x^2 + y^2} \leq n$. Using polar coordinates, we have

$$\iint_{D_n} f = \int_0^{\pi/2} d\theta \int_0^n r \sin (r^2)\, dr$$

$$= \frac{\pi}{4} [1 - \cos (n^2)]$$

and $\lim_{n \to \infty} \iint_{D_n} f$ does not exist!

† See L. V. Ahlfors, "Complex Analysis," McGraw-Hill Book Company, Inc., New York, 1953.

In this example, two equally natural choices of the sequence $\{D_n\}$ led to inconsistent results.

Theorem 17. *Let f be continuous on D and $\iint_D |f|$ converge. Then, $\lim_{n\to\infty} \iint_{D_n} f$ exists and has the same value for any choice of the sequence $\{D_n\}$ converging to D.*

This is the analogue for Theorem 15, and we prove it by means of the 2-space analogue of the comparison test, Theorem 14 (Exercise 7). For any $p \in D$, $0 \le f(p) + |f(p)| \le 2|f(p)|$, and thus $\iint_D \{f + |f|\}$ converges. Let its value be A and the value of $\iint_D |f|$ be B. Then, for any sequence $\{D_n\}$ converging to D, $\lim \iint_{D_n} \{f + |f|\} = A$ and $\lim \iint_{D_n} |f| = B$ so that

$$\lim_{n\to\infty} \iint_{D_n} f = \lim_{n\to\infty} \left\{ \iint_{D_n} f + |f| - \iint_{D_n} f \right\}$$

exists and is $A - B$. ▮

This result suggests that we agree to say that $\iint_D f$ exists only when $\lim \iint_{D_n} f$ exists and is independent of the choice of the sequence $\{D_n\}$, where $\{D_n\}$ converges to D. The only restriction this imposes on the shape of the sets D_n is that each closed and bounded set lying interior to D shall eventually be covered by the interior of one of the sets D_k. This is so broad that it is easily seen that whenever $\iint_D f$ exists, so does $\iint_D |f|$.† We are thus left with a theory of absolutely convergent improper multiple integrals which does not allow conditional convergence.

† Write f as $f_1 - f_2$, where f_1 and f_2 are nonnegative and $|f| = f_1 + f_2$. If $\iint_D |f|$ diverges, then either $\iint_D f_1$ or $\iint_D f_2$ must diverge; moreover, if one of these converges, then $\iint_D f$ must diverge; if both diverge, then a sequence $\{D_n\}$ converging to D can be chosen so that $\iint_{D_n} f_1$ increases much faster than $\iint_{D_n} f_2$ and thus obtain

$$\lim_{n\to\infty} \iint_{D_n} f = \lim_{n\to\infty} \iint_{D_n} f_1 - \iint_{D_n} f_2 = \infty.$$

So far, we have said little about the evaluation of improper integrals. The methods of approximate integration apply as before. One must first replace the original interval or set over which the integration is to be carried out by a bounded set. For example, if we wish to find the approximate value of $\int_0^\infty e^{-t^2}\,dt$, accurate to .001, we first observe that

$$\left|\int_R^\infty e^{-t^2}\,dt\right| \le \int_R^\infty e^{-t}\,dt = e^{-R}.$$

Choose R sufficiently large so that $e^{-R} < .0005$. Then, calculate the value of $\int_0^R e^{-t^2}\,dt$ by Simpson's rule, with an accuracy of .0005. This will be the desired answer. Many times, however, a special device may enable one to find an expression for the exact value in terms of known constants and functions. In Secs. 4.4 and 4.5, we shall give a number of illustrations. Such a device can be used to evaluate the integral we have just discussed. Let us replace the dummy letter "t" by "x" and by "y", and consider the product

$$\int_0^R e^{-x^2}\,dx \int_0^R e^{-y^2}\,dy = \int_0^R \int_0^R e^{-x^2}e^{-y^2}\,dxdy.$$

As R increases, this converges, and we see that

$$I^2 = \left\{\int_0^\infty e^{-t^2}\,dt\right\}^2 = \int_0^\infty \int_0^\infty e^{-(x^2+y^2)}\,dxdy.$$

Since the integrand is positive, the value of the improper double integral does not depend upon the nature of the approximating regions D_n. Let us evaluate it by integrating over an expanding sequence of quarter circles, using polar coordinates.

$$\begin{aligned} I^2 &= \lim_{R\to\infty} \int_0^R dr \int_0^{\pi/2} e^{-r^2} r\,d\theta \\ &= \lim_{R\to\infty} \frac{\pi}{2} \int_0^R re^{-r^2}\,dr = \frac{\pi}{4}. \end{aligned}$$

Thus, I being positive, we have found that

$$I = \int_0^\infty e^{-t^2}\,dt = \tfrac{1}{2}\sqrt{\pi}.$$

EXERCISES

1. What is the area of the region bounded by $y = e^x$, $y = 2\cosh x$, with $x \ge 0$?

2. Discuss the convergence of the following integrals:

(a) $\int_0^\infty \frac{dx}{x^2 - 1}$ (b) $\int_{-\infty}^\infty \frac{dx}{x^3 + 1}$

(c) $\int_0^\infty \sin 2x\, dx$ (d) $\int_{-\infty}^\infty \frac{e^x}{1+e^{2x}}\, dx$

(e) $\int_0^1 \frac{x^2\, dx}{\sqrt{1-x^4}}$ (f) $\int_0^\infty \sqrt{x}\, e^{-x}\, dx$

(g) $\int_0^\infty \frac{1-\cos x}{x^2}$ (h) $\int_0^\infty \frac{dx}{\sqrt{x^3+x^2}}$

3. Discuss the convergence of the following integrals:

(a) $\int_0^\infty e^x \sin e^x\, dx$ (b) $\int_0^\infty x \sin e^x\, dx$

(c) $\int_0^{\pi/2} \sin(\sec x)\, dx$ (d) $\int_0^1 \frac{\sin(1/x)}{x}\, dx$

(e) $\int_0^1 x \log x\, dx$ (f) $\int_0^{\pi/2} \sqrt{\tan\theta}\, d\theta$

(g) $\int_0^{\pi/2} \frac{d\theta}{\sqrt{1-\sin\theta}}$ (h) $\int_0^{\pi/2} x\sqrt{\sec x}\, dx$

4. For what values of α and β does $\int_0^\infty \frac{dx}{x^\alpha + x^\beta}$ converge?

5. For what values of α and β does $\int_0^\infty x^\alpha |x-1|^\beta\, dx$ converge?

6. Let D be the unbounded triangular region in the right half plane bounded by the lines $y = 0$ and $y = x$, and let $f(x, y) = x^{-3/2}e^{y-x}$. Does $\iint_D f$ converge?

7. Let $0 \le f(p) \le g(p)$ for all p in a set D, and suppose that $\iint_D g$ converges. Prove that $\iint_D f$ converges.

3.5. Set Functions

By the term **set function** we mean a function F which assigns a number $F(S)$ to each set S in some specified class of sets. By contrast, the term point functions might be used for the functions f which have been discussed up until now, and which assign a number $f(p)$ to each point p in a specified set of points. Examples of set functions are common in pure and in applied mathematics, embracing such diverse notions as area, force, mass, moment of inertia, and probability. To illustrate this, let $\mathcal{A}$ be the class of bounded sets in the plane which have area. Then, the area function A, which assigns to each set $S \in \mathcal{A}$ its area $A(S)$, is a set function defined on the class $\mathcal{A}$. Taking an example from physics, we suppose we are given a specific distribution of matter throughout space, which in some places may be continuous, and in others, discrete. With this, we may associate a particular set function M by taking $M(S)$ to be the total mass of the matter lying within the set S. In particular, if the distribution of matter is taken to be only a single particle of mass 1 located at the origin, then $M(S) = 0$ whenever S fails to contain the origin, and $M(S) = 1$ if S contains the origin. Again, if a horizontal plate is subjected to a variable load distribution, we may obtain a set function F by choosing $F(S)$ to be the total force pressing down on each region S of the plate. Finally, if an experiment involves dropping shot from a height onto a target board, then to each region S of the target we can associate a number $P(S)$ which is the probability that an individual shot will land in S.

All the examples presuppose that one starts with a prior knowledge (e.g., the meaning of area, mass, force, or probability). Reversing the procedure, one might postulate the existence of the set functions, together with certain appropriate properties, and then use them to develop the corresponding physical notions. Among the additional properties that a set function may possess, one is particularly important, and is shared by the examples given above.

Definition. *A set function F is said to be finitely additive on a class $\mathcal{S}$ if and only if*

$$F(S_1 \cup S_2) = F(S_1) + F(S_2)$$

whenever S_1, S_2, and their union $S_1 \cup S_2$ are in $\mathcal{S}$ and S_1 and S_2 are disjoint.

An extensive category of finitely additive set functions can be constructed by means of integration. Let ϕ be a point function which is defined and continuous on the whole plane. Define a set function F on the class $\mathcal{A}$ by

$$F(S) = \iint_S \phi \tag{3-7}$$

The fact that F is finitely additive is merely a restatement of a familiar property of integration.

The central result of this section will show that every finitely additive set function which obeys certain simple continuity conditions is of the form (3-7); the point function ϕ will be obtained from F by a process of differentiation, and the entire result may be regarded as the analogue for multiple integrals of the fundamental theorem relating the operations of differentiation and integration of functions of one variable.

We first introduce a special limit process.

Definition. *If F is an arbitrary set function, defined at least for the class of all closed rectangles, we write* $\lim_{S \downarrow p_0} F(S) = L$ *if and only if for any $\epsilon > 0$ a number $\delta > 0$ can be found such that*

$$|F(S) - L| < \epsilon$$

whenever S is a set containing p_0 with diam $(S) < \delta$ *and S is in the domain of F.*

The sets S may be thought of as "closing down" on the point p_0; as an example, $\lim_{S \downarrow p_0} A(S) = 0$ for any point p_0, where A is the area function.

If $\lim_{S \downarrow p_0} F(S)$ exists for each point p_0 in a region D, it defines a point function g on D such that $g(p) = \lim_{S \downarrow p} F(S)$ for all $p \in D$.

Definition. *We write*

$$\lim_{S \downarrow p} F(S) = g(p), \text{ uniformly for } p \in D,$$

if and only if for any $\epsilon > 0$, *there is a* $\delta > 0$ *such that*

$$|F(S) - g(p)| < \epsilon$$

whenever $p \in D$ *and* S *is a set containing* p *with* diam $(S) < \delta$.

Using these notions of limit for set functions, we introduce a two-dimensional derivative for set functions F which are defined on the class $\mathcal{A}$. Corresponding definitions can be framed for higher-dimensional spaces.

Definition. *A set function* F *is said to be differentiable on a set* D *if* $\lim_{S \downarrow p} \dfrac{F(S)}{A(S)}$ *exists for each* $p \in D$, *and to be uniformly differentiable on* D, *if the convergence is uniform on* D.

This is not a new concept, especially in the case of the examples of set functions which we have given above. Taking F as the mass function M, the value of the quotient $M(S)/A(S)$ is the average mass per unit area (or volume, if we take the corresponding three-dimensional derivative) in the region S. As S closes down on p, the limit can be interpreted as the *density* of matter at p. Similarly, the derivative of the set function *force* is the point function *pressure* (= force per unit area). Not all set functions have a derivative; the mass function produced by an isolated unit point mass at the origin fails to have a derivative there since $M(S) = 1$ for any S containing $\mathbf{0}$, while $A(S) \downarrow 0$ (see also Exercise 3).

Theorem 18. *Let* D *be an open set whose boundary has zero area, and let* ϕ *be a point function which is bounded and continuous on* D, *and zero off* D. *Define a set function* F *on* $\mathcal{A}$ *by*

$$F(S) = \iint_S \phi.$$

Then, F *is uniformly differentiable on any closed rectangle lying in* D, *and the derivative of* F *is the point function* ϕ.

Let R be a closed rectangle lying in D. Since D is open, we may enlarge R slightly, obtaining a rectangle R_1 which contains R and also lies in D. ϕ is continuous in R_1, and therefore uniformly continuous. Given $\epsilon > 0$, choose $\delta > 0$ so that $|\phi(p) - \phi(q)| < \epsilon$ whenever p and q lie in R_1 and $|p - q| < \delta$. Since R lies interior to R_1 we may decrease δ if necessary so that $|\phi(p) - \phi(q)| < \epsilon$ whenever $p \in R$, and $|p - q| < \delta$. Let S be any set in $\mathfrak{A}$ which contains $p_0 \in R$ and has diam $(S) < \delta$. Let $M = \sup_{q \in S} \phi(q)$, and $m = \inf_{q \in S} \phi(q)$. Then $|M - \phi(p_0)| < \epsilon$ and $|m - \phi(p_0)| < \epsilon$. Since $F(S) = \iint_S \phi$, $F(S)$ lies between $mA(S)$ and $MA(S)$, and therefore

$$\left| \frac{F(S)}{A(S)} - \phi(p_0) \right| < \epsilon.$$

This holds for any set S containing p_0 with diam $(S) < \delta$ and any $p_0 \in R$. Thus, F is uniformly differentiable in R, with derivative ϕ. ▮

Our main result is the converse of this.

Theorem 19. *Let F be an additive set function, defined at least for all rectangles. Let F be uniformly differentiable on a closed rectangle E, with derivative a point function f. Then, f is continuous in E, and for any rectangle $R \subset E$,*

$$F(R) = \iint_R f$$

Given $\epsilon > 0$, choose $\delta > 0$ so that $\left| \dfrac{F(R)}{A(R)} - f(p) \right| < \epsilon$ for every $p \in E$ and every rectangle R which contains p and has diam $(R) < \delta$. Let p_1 and p_2 be points of E with $|p_1 - p_2| < \delta$. Choose R so as to contain both p_1 and p_2 and to have diam $(R) < \delta$. Then,

$$\begin{aligned} |f(p_1) - f(p_2)| &= \left| f(p_1) - \frac{F(R)}{A(R)} + \frac{F(R)}{A(R)} - f(p_2) \right| \\ &\leq \left| f(p_1) - \frac{F(R)}{A(R)} \right| + \left| f(p_2) - \frac{F(R)}{A(R)} \right| \\ &< \epsilon + \epsilon = 2\epsilon \end{aligned}$$

proving that f is uniformly continuous on E.

Now, define a set function on subsets of E by

$$F_0(S) = \iint_S f$$

The set function F_0 is defined on the class of sets $S \in \mathfrak{A}$ including, of course, the rectangles. By the previous theorem, F_0 is uniformly differentiable on any closed rectangle interior to E, and its derivative is also f. Define a third set function H by $H(R) = F(R) - F_0(R)$. This is again additive, and is uniformly differentiable inside E with derivative $f - f = 0$. We shall show that $H(R) = 0$ for every rectangle R lying interior to E. Given ϵ, choose $\delta > 0$ so that

$$\left|\frac{H(R)}{A(R)} - 0\right| = \left|\frac{H(R)}{A(R)}\right| < \epsilon$$

whenever R is interior to E and has diam $(R) < \delta$. Given *any* rectangle R_0 interior to E, we may express it as a union of disjoint rectangles $R_1, R_2, \ldots, R_n$ each of diameter less than δ. Since H is additive, $H(R_0) = \sum_1^n H(R_j)$. However, applying the general estimate above, $|H(R_j)| \leq \epsilon A(R_j)$ for each j, so that $|H(R_0)| \leq \epsilon \sum_1^n A(R_j) = \epsilon A(R_0)$. This holds for any choice of $\epsilon > 0$, and we must have $H(R_0) = 0$. Recalling the definition of H and of F_0, we obtain

$$F(R_0) = \iint_{R_0} f. \quad \blacksquare$$

Corollary. *If, in addition to the hypotheses above, F is monotone (that is, $A \subset B$ implies $F(A) \leq F(B)$) and is defined on the class of all $S \in \mathcal{A}$ with $S \subset E$, then*

$$F(S) = \iint_S f.$$

To prove this, construct a sequence $\{S_n\}$ of subsets of S such that $A(S_n) \to A(S)$, and such that each S_n is a finite union of rectangles. Since F is monotone, $F(S_n) \leq F(S)$; since F agrees with F_0 on rectangles, and therefore on unions of rectangles,

$$F_0(S_n) = \iint_{S_n} f \leq F(S)$$

for each $n = 1, 2, \ldots$. However, $\lim_{n\to\infty} \iint_{S_n} f = \iint_S f$ so that we have shown that

$$\iint_S f \leq F(S).$$

A similar argument, using a sequence of "circumscribed" sets whose areas converge to $A(S)$, yields the reversed inequality; accordingly,

$$F(S) = \iint_S f. \quad \blacksquare$$

In most applications of this, we shall employ the corollary, rather than the theorem. (See, for example, the discussion in Sec. 6.1.) These results may be regarded as the formal justification for the process of obtaining the mass of a body by integrating a density function over the corresponding set, or a force by integrating a pressure.

The material of this section can be considered an introduction to some of the basic notions of general measure theory. The interested reader will do well to turn to such books as "Measure Theory" by Halmos (D. Van Nostrand Company, Inc., New York, 1950) or "Theory of the Integral" by Saks (Warszawa-Lwów, 1937) for the general treatment. In this connection, it should be pointed out that we have chosen to present a portion of the theory of Jordan content in this chapter, rather than enter into the more general subject of countably additive measures.

EXERCISES

1. Do the following describe set functions that are finitely additive?

(*a*) $F(S)$ is the square of the area of the plane set S.

(*b*) $F(S)$ is the area of the smallest closed circular disk which contains the closed set S.

(*c*) $F(S)$ is the moment of inertia of the plane set S about an axis through the origin, and perpendicular to the plane.

(*d*) $F(S)$ is the diameter of the closed set S.

2. By considering the one-dimensional case, show that Theorems 18 and 19 are analogous to the fundamental theorem of calculus (See Theorems 5, 6, and 7, Sec. 3.2.)

3. Let f be a bounded function which is continuous everywhere in the plane except at the origin. Define F by $F(S) = \iint_S f$. Is F differentiable at the origin? (Your answer will depend upon the nature of the discontinuity of f.)

CHAPTER 4

CONVERGENCE

4.1. Infinite Series

An infinite series is often defined to be "an expression of the form $\sum_1^\infty a_n$." It is recognised that this has many defects. In order to avoid some of these, we adopt the following formal definition.

Definition. *An infinite series of real numbers is a pair of real sequences* $\{a_n\}$ *and* $\{A_n\}$ *whose terms are connected by the relations:*

$$
\begin{aligned}
A_n &= \sum_1^n a_k = a_1 + a_2 + \cdots + a_n \\
a_1 &= A_1 \qquad a_n = A_n - A_{n-1} \qquad n \geq 2.
\end{aligned}
\tag{4-1}
$$

The first sequence is called the **sequence of terms** of the series, and the second is called the **sequence of partial sums.** If either is given, the other can be found from the relations (4-1). To denote the series as a single entity, one might use the expression $\langle\{a_n\}, \{A_n\}\rangle$; it is more customary to use $\sum_1^\infty a_n$ or $a_1 + a_2 + \cdots$. Although the sequence of terms is given a dominant place in these expressions, the series itself is still the pair of sequences; we may speak of the sixth term of the series $\sum_1^\infty 1/(n^2 + n)$ (which is $1/42$) as well as the sixth partial sum (which is $6/7$). The index "n" is a dummy letter, and may be replaced by any other convenient choice. As with sequences, it is not necessary that the initial term of a series be labeled with index "1". It is often convenient to vary this, and use for example $a_0 + a_1 + a_2 + \cdots$.

Certain algebraic operations are defined for series.

Definition. (i) *The sum of the series* Σa_n *and* Σb_n *is the series* $\Sigma(a_n + b_n)$.
(ii) *The product of the series* Σa_n *by the number* c *is the series* $\Sigma(ca_n)$.

(iii) *The (Cauchy) product of the series* $\sum_0^\infty a_n$ *and* $\sum_0^\infty b_n$ *is the series* $\sum_0^\infty c_n$ *where*

$$c_n = a_0b_n + a_1b_{n-1} + \cdots + a_nb_0.$$

For example, if $a_n = 1/(n+1)$ and $b_n = -1/(n+2)$ then

$$\begin{aligned}\sum_0^\infty a_n + \sum_0^\infty b_n &= (1 + \tfrac{1}{2} + \cdots) + (-\tfrac{1}{2} - \tfrac{1}{3} - \tfrac{1}{4} - \cdots) \\ &= (1 - \tfrac{1}{2}) + (\tfrac{1}{2} - \tfrac{1}{3}) + \cdots \\ &= \tfrac{1}{2} + \tfrac{1}{6} + \tfrac{1}{12} + \cdots.\end{aligned}$$

It is *not* the series $1 - \frac{1}{2} + \frac{1}{2} - \frac{1}{3} + \frac{1}{3} - \cdots$ which is obtained by removing the parentheses. If the series $\sum_0^\infty a_n$ is multiplied by $\frac{1}{2}$, we have

$$\begin{aligned}(\tfrac{1}{2})\sum_0^\infty a_n &= (\tfrac{1}{2})(1 + \tfrac{1}{2} + \tfrac{1}{3} + \cdots) \\ &= \tfrac{1}{2} + \tfrac{1}{4} + \tfrac{1}{6} + \cdots.\end{aligned}$$

The product of $\sum_0^\infty a_n$ and $\sum_0^\infty b_n$ is

$$\begin{aligned}-\frac{1}{2} + \left(\frac{-1}{3} - \frac{1}{2}\frac{1}{2}\right) + \left(\frac{-1}{4} - \frac{1}{2}\frac{1}{3} - \frac{1}{3}\frac{1}{2}\right) + \cdots \\ = -\frac{1}{2} - \frac{7}{12} - \frac{7}{12} - \frac{101}{180} - \cdots.\end{aligned}$$

The adjective "Cauchy" is used in connection with this particular method for multiplying series to emphasize that this is only one of many possible definitions; the reason for this choice will be made clear when we discuss power series.

Definition. *A series Σa_n is said to converge to the sum A whenever the sequence of partial sums $\{A_n\}$ converges to A. A series that does not converge is said to diverge.*

We note that the algebraic operations described above may be performed on either divergent or convergent series. We shall see that both $\sum_0^\infty a_n$ and $\sum_0^\infty b_n$ of the example above are divergent; however, their sum is a convergent series, for the nth partial sum is

$$\left(1 - \frac{1}{2}\right) + \left(\frac{1}{2} - \frac{1}{3}\right) + \cdots + \left(\frac{1}{n} - \frac{1}{n+1}\right) = 1 - \frac{1}{n+1}$$

which converges to 1.

A frequent cause for confusion in discussions about series is the unfortunate habit mathematicians have of using the expression "Σa_n" to stand both for the series and (when convergent) for its sum, letting the context distinguish between these meanings. In "Σa_n is divergent" or "Σa_n is alternating" it is clear that the series itself is intended, while in "Σa_n is larger than 3," the sum is meant. However, in "Σa_n is positive," either is possible, since it may be intended to mean that each of the terms is positive. A worse case is the statement: $\Sigma a_n + \Sigma b_n = \Sigma(a_n + b_n)$. If this is a statement about series, it is simply the definition for addition of two series; if this is a statement about sums, it is the theorem which asserts that the sum of two convergent series is itself convergent, and its sum is the sum of the numbers Σa_n and Σb_n. Another source for confusion stems from the fact that in English, the words "series" and "sequence" are used with almost identical meanings, whereas their mathematical meanings are quite distinct.†

Much of the theory of infinite series bears a strong resemblance to that for improper integrals with the integrand $f(x)$ in $\int_0^\infty f(x)\,dx$ corresponding to the term a_n in Σa_n, and the partial sum $A_n = \sum_1^n a_k$ corresponding to $F(x) = \int_0^x f(u)\,du$. This analogy is not accidental, but arises from the fact that both can be treated as special cases of the general Stieltjes integral.‡ For this reason, some of the proofs of the theorems to follow have been abbreviated. The analogy between series and integrals is not perfect, however, as the first theorem shows (see footnote, p. 93).

Theorem 1. *If Σa_n converges, then* $\lim_{n\to\infty} a_n = 0$.

For
$$\lim_{n\to\infty} a_n = \lim_{n\to\infty} (A_n - A_{n-1}) = A - A = 0. \quad \blacksquare$$

Theorem 2 (*Comparison Test*). *If $0 \le a_n \le b_n$ for all sufficiently large n, and Σb_n converges, then Σa_n converges.*

The terms $\{a_n\}$ are positive from some index on, and at this point the

† Other languages are somewhat better here. *Folge* = *suite* = sequence and *reihe* = *série* = series.

‡ See D. V. Widder, "The Laplace Transform," Chap. I, Princeton University Press, Princeton, N.J., 1941.

sequence $\{A_n\}$ of partial sums becomes monotone increasing. They are bounded above so that $\lim_{n\to\infty} A_n$ exists. ▌

A corollary of this that is often easier to apply directly is:

Corollary. *If* $0 \le a_n$ *and* $0 \le b_n$ *and* $\lim_{n\to\infty} \frac{a_n}{b_n} = L$ *where* $0 < L < \infty$, *then* Σa_n *and* Σb_n *are either both convergent or both divergent.*

The next result is sometimes called the ratio comparison test.

Theorem 3. *If* $0 < a_n$, $0 < b_n$, *and* Σb_n *converges, and if for all sufficiently large* n, $\frac{a_{n+1}}{a_n} \le \frac{b_{n+1}}{b_n}$, *then* Σa_n *converges.*

Writing the inequality as $\frac{a_{n+1}}{b_{n+1}} \le \frac{a_n}{b_n}$, we see that $\{a_n/b_n\}$ is an ultimately decreasing sequence, and is therefore bounded. Thus, $a_n \le Mb_n$ for all n, and Σa_n converges by the simple comparison test. ▌

In order to apply either of these comparison tests, some known examples of divergent or convergent series must be at hand.

Theorem 4. *The geometric series* $\sum_0^\infty x^n = 1 + x + x^2 + \cdots$ *converges to* $1/(1 - x)$ *for* $|x| < 1$ *and diverges when* $|x| \ge 1$.

The partial sums are given by $A_n = (1 - x^{n+1})/(1 - x)$ when $x \ne 1$ and by $A_n = n + 1$ when $x = 1$. ▌

Combining this with Theorem 3 gives the **ratio test.**

Theorem 5. *If* $0 < a_n$, *let* $L = \limsup_{n\to\infty} \frac{a_{n+1}}{a_n}$ *and* $l = \liminf_{n\to\infty} \frac{a_{n+1}}{a_n}$. *Then* Σa_n *converges if* $L < 1$, *and diverges if* $l > 1$; *if* $l \le 1 \le L$, *no conclusion can be reached about the behavior of* Σa_n.

If $L < 1$, then a number x can be chosen so that $L < x < 1$ and $\frac{a_{n+1}}{a_n} \le x$ for all but a finite number of indices n. Since $x = \frac{x^{n+1}}{x^n}$, this takes the form given in Theorem 3 with $b_n = x^n$, and since $\Sigma b_n = \Sigma x^n$ converges, so does Σa_n. On the other hand, when $l > 1$, then for all sufficiently large n, $\frac{a_{n+1}}{a_n} \ge 1$ so that $\{a_n\}$ is an ultimately increasing sequence; as such, it cannot converge to zero, and Σa_n must diverge. ▌

In many cases, the sequence of ratios $\{a_{n+1}/a_n\}$ is convergent; when this happens, the statement of the theorem is simpler.

Corollary. *If* $\lim_{n\to\infty} \frac{a_{n+1}}{a_n} = r$, *then* Σa_n *is convergent if* $r < 1$, *and is divergent if* $r > 1$; *if* $r = 1$, Σa_n *may do either.*

Another test which arises by comparison with the geometric series is the **root test.**

Theorem 6. *Let* $a_n \geq 0$ *and* $\limsup_{n\to\infty} [a_n]^{1/n} = r$. *Then,* Σa_n *converges if* $r < 1$ *and diverges if* $r > 1$; *when* $r = 1$, *no conclusion can be reached.*

If $r < 1$, choose x with $r < x < 1$ and have $a_n{}^{1/n} \leq x$ for all sufficiently large n. Thus $a_n \leq x^n$ for $n \geq N$, and since Σx^n converges, so does Σa_n. If $r > 1$, then from the definition of limit superior, $[a_n]^{1/n} \geq 1$ for infinitely many indices n. We therefore have $a_{k_1} \geq 1$, $a_{k_2} \geq 1$, . . . , $a_{k_j} \geq 1$, . . . so that the sequence of terms $\{a_n\}$ is not convergent to zero; Σa_n must then diverge. ∎

These two tests are closely connected. The ratio test is often easier to apply; however, if a series can be shown convergent by the ratio test, it could also be treated by the root test (see Exercise 6). There are, however, series to which the root test applies, but which escape the ratio test. Consider for example the series

$$\tfrac{1}{4} + \tfrac{1}{2} + \tfrac{1}{8} + \tfrac{1}{4} + \tfrac{1}{16} + \tfrac{1}{8} + \tfrac{1}{32} + \cdots$$

whose terms are given by

$$a_{2k} = \frac{1}{2^k}, \qquad a_{2k-1} = \frac{1}{2^{k+1}}.$$

The sequence of term ratios is

$$\frac{1/2}{1/4} = 2, \qquad \frac{1/8}{1/2} = 1/4, \qquad \frac{1/4}{1/8} = 2$$

and in general

$$\frac{a_{n+1}}{a_n} = \begin{cases} 2 & \text{when } n \text{ is odd} \\ 1/4 & \text{when } n \text{ is even.} \end{cases}$$

Since

$$\limsup_{n\to\infty} \frac{a_{n+1}}{a_n} = 2 > 1 \qquad \text{and} \qquad \liminf_{n\to\infty} \frac{a_{n+1}}{a_n} = \frac{1}{4} < 1,$$

the ratio test is inconclusive. However, the root test may be used, and $\lim_{n\to\infty} [a_n]^{1/n} = 1/\sqrt{2} < 1$ so that the series converges.

The next theorem shows the close connection between improper integrals and infinite series; it also provides a large class of useful series for comparison purposes. It is called the **integral test.**

Theorem 7. *If* f *is continuous on the interval* $1 \leq x < \infty$ *and monotonic decreasing with* $\lim_{x\uparrow\infty} f(x) = 0$, *then the series* $\sum_1^\infty f(n)$ *and the improper integral* $\int_1^\infty f$ *are either both convergent or both divergent.*

Let $a_n = f(n)$ and $b_n = \int_n^{n+1} f$. Since f is monotone,

$$f(n+1) \leq \int_n^{n+1} f(x)\,dx \leq f(n)$$

or $a_{n+1} \leq b_n \leq a_n$. By the comparison test, Σa_n converges if Σb_n converges, and Σb_n converges if Σa_n converges, so that Σa_n and Σb_n converge or diverge together. But, Σb_n converges exactly when the integral $\int_1^\infty f$ converges. ∎

Corollary. *The series* $\sum_1^\infty \frac{1}{n^p}$ *and* $\sum_2^\infty \frac{1}{n(\log n)^p}$ *converge when* $p > 1$ *and diverge when* $p \leq 1$.

Using the first of these as the series Σb_n in Theorem 3, we obtain **Raabe's test** (see also Exercise 2).

Theorem 8. *If* $0 < a_n$ *and* $\frac{a_{n+1}}{a_n} \leq 1 - \frac{p}{n}$ *for all sufficiently large* n, *where* $p > 1$, *then* Σa_n *converges.*

We separate out a part of the proof which has nothing to do with series.

Lemma. *If* $p > 1$ *and* $n > 0$, *then* $1 - \frac{p}{n} < \left(1 - \frac{1}{n}\right)^p$.

If $x < 1$, then, by the mean value theorem,

$$1 - x^p = (1)^p - x^p = (1 - x)\,p\,(\bar{x})^{p-1}$$

for some point $\bar{x}$ with $x < \bar{x} < 1$. Thus, $1 - x^p \leq (1 - x)p$, and setting $x = 1 - \frac{1}{n}$, we obtain $1 - \left(1 - \frac{1}{n}\right)^p < \frac{p}{n}$. ∎

Using this, we prove the theorem as follows. By assumption, $a_{n+1}/a_n \leq 1 - p/n$ which by the lemma is smaller than $\left(1 - \frac{1}{n}\right)^p = \left(\frac{n-1}{n}\right)^p$. However, this is exactly b_{n+1}/b_n with $b_{n+1} = \frac{1}{n^p}$, so that Theorem 3 applies, and Σa_n converges. ∎

As an illustration of the last test, consider the series

$$\frac{1}{4} + \frac{1\cdot 3}{4\cdot 6} + \frac{1\cdot 3\cdot 5}{4\cdot 6\cdot 8} + \cdots + \frac{1\cdot 3\cdot \cdots \cdot (2n-1)}{4\cdot 6\cdot \cdots \cdot (2n+2)} + \cdots.$$

The successive ratios $\frac{a_{n+1}}{a_n}$ are $\frac{3}{6}, \frac{5}{8}, \ldots, \frac{2n-1}{2n+2}$ and $\lim_{n\to\infty} \frac{a_{n+1}}{a_n} = 1$ so that the simple ratio test fails. However,

$$\frac{2n-1}{2n+2} = \frac{2n+2-3}{2n+2} = 1 - \frac{3}{2n+2}$$

and since this has the form $1 - \dfrac{p}{n+1}$ with $p = 3/2 > 1$ the series is convergent by Raabe's test.

All the tests so far given are stated for series having positive terms. The next result makes it possible to apply these also to a wide class of general series.

Theorem 9. *If $\Sigma|a_n|$ converges, so does Σa_n.*

The Cauchy criterion for convergence (Theorem 5, Sec. 1.4) applied to the sequence of partial sums of a series shows that Σa_n converges if and only if $\lim\limits_{n,m\to\infty} \left|\sum_n^m a_k\right| = 0$. For any choice of n and m,

$$\left|\sum_n^m a_k\right| \le \sum_n^m |a_k|;$$

since $\Sigma|a_n|$ converges, the right side approaches 0 as n and m independently increase. This is also true of the left side, so that Σa_n is convergent. ▌

The first step in investigating the convergence of a series Σa_n with both positive and negative terms is to study the series $\Sigma|a_n|$, to which any of the preceding tests may be applied. It should be emphasized that *divergence* of $\Sigma|a_n|$ does not automatically imply divergence of Σa_n, unless the proof of the divergence of $\Sigma|a_n|$ lay in showing that $\{a_n\}$ did not converge to 0. In particular, we observe that Σa_n *does* diverge if $\liminf\limits_{n\to\infty} \dfrac{|a_{n+1}|}{|a_n|} > 1$ or if $\limsup\limits_{n\to\infty} |a_n|^{1/n} > 1$.

A convergent series Σa_n for which the series $\Sigma|a_n|$ is divergent is said to be **conditionally convergent;** if $\Sigma|a_n|$ is convergent, Σa_n is said to be **absolutely convergent.** The preceding theorems show that each of the following series is absolutely convergent.

$$1 - 1/4 + 1/9 - 1/16 + 1/25 - \cdots = \sum_1^\infty (-1)^{n+1} \frac{1}{n^2}$$

$$1 + 1/2 - 1/4 - 1/8 + 1/16 + 1/32 - \cdots = \sum_0^\infty (-1)^{n(n-1)/2} \frac{1}{2^n}$$

$$1 + 1/2 + 1/5 - 1/10 + 1/17 + 1/26 + 1/37 - 1/50 + \cdots$$
$$= \sum_0^\infty (-1)^{n(n-1)(n-2)/2} \frac{1}{n^2+1}$$

One may also use Theorem 1 to prove that a series having both positive and negative terms is divergent. For example, the series $1 - 2/5 + 3/9 - 4/13 + 5/17 - \cdots$ which has the general term

$$a_n = (-1)^{n+1} \frac{n}{4n - 3}$$

is divergent since it is not true that $\lim_{n\to\infty} a_n = 0$.

The methods given so far for testing a series do not apply to the (convergent) alternating harmonic series

$$1 - 1/2 + 1/3 - 1/4 + 1/5 - \cdots.$$

Since $\sum_1^\infty 1/n$ diverges, this series is not absolutely convergent, while $\lim_{n\to\infty} (-1)^{n+1} \frac{1}{n} = 0$, so that Theorem 1 cannot be used to show divergence. The next result contains as a special case the alternating series test and is the analogue for series of Theorem 16 in Chap. 3, which dealt with conditionally convergent improper integrals.

Theorem 10. *Let $\{a_n\}$ and $\{b_n\}$ be two sequences which obey the requirements:*

(i) $\lim_{n\to\infty} a_n = 0$.

(ii) $\Sigma|a_{n+1} - a_n|$ *converges.*

(iii) *The partial sums of the series Σb_n are bounded, so that*

$$|b_1 + b_2 + \cdots + b_n| = |B_n| \le M$$

for all n.

Then, the series $\Sigma a_n b_n$ converges.

In proving this, we use the analogue of integration by parts which is called partial summation.

$$\begin{aligned}\sum_1^n a_k b_k &= a_1 b_1 + a_2 b_2 + \cdots + a_n b_n \\ &= a_1 B_1 + a_2(B_2 - B_1) + \cdots + a_n(B_n - B_{n-1}) \\ &= (a_1 - a_2)B_1 + (a_2 - a_3)B_2 + \cdots + (a_{n-1} - a_n)B_{n-1} + a_n B_n \\ &= a_n B_n - \sum_1^{n-1} (a_{k+1} - a_k)B_k.\end{aligned}$$

Because of (i) and (iii), $\lim_{n\to\infty} a_n B_n = 0$. Since

$$|(a_{k+1} - a_k)B_k| \le M|a_{k+1} - a_k|$$

and (ii) holds, the series $\sum_{1}^{\infty}(a_{k+1} - a_k)B_k$ is convergent. These together prove that $\lim_{n\to\infty} \sum_{1}^{n} a_k b_k$ exists and $\sum_{1}^{\infty} a_n b_n$ converges. ▮

This theorem takes a simpler form when $\{a_n\}$ is monotonic.

Corollary 1. *If the sequence $\{a_n\}$ is monotonic decreasing with $\lim_{n\to\infty} a_n = 0$, and the partial sums of Σb_n are bounded, then $\Sigma a_n b_n$ converges.*

For

$$\sum_{1}^{n} |a_{k+1} - a_k| = (a_1 - a_2) + (a_2 - a_3) + \cdots + (a_n - a_{n+1})$$
$$= a_1 - a_{n+1}$$

and $\lim_{n\to\infty} \sum_{1}^{n} |a_{k+1} - a_k| = \lim_{n\to\infty} (a_1 - a_{n+1}) = a_1$ so that hypothesis (ii) is satisfied. ▮

A special choice of the sequence $\{b_n\}$ yields the usual **alternating series test.**

Corollary 2. *If $\{a_n\}$ is monotonic decreasing with $\lim_{n\to\infty} a_n = 0$, then $\sum_{1}^{\infty} (-1)^{n+1} a_n$ converges.*

With $b_n = (-1)^{n+1}$ the partial sums of $\sum_{1}^{\infty} b_n$ are always either 1 or 0, and are therefore bounded. ▮

The following examples illustrate the use of these tests; we note that none of the series is absolutely convergent.

The series $1 - \frac{1}{2} + \frac{1}{3} - \frac{1}{4} + \cdots$ is a simple alternating series and therefore converges. It should be noted that alternation of signs, and $\lim a_n = 0$ is not alone sufficient; the partial sums of the series $\frac{1}{3} - \frac{1}{2} + \frac{1}{5} - \frac{1}{2^2} + \frac{1}{7} - \frac{1}{2^3} + \frac{1}{9} - \frac{1}{2^4} + \cdots$ are unbounded since the positive terms form the divergent series $\frac{1}{3} + \frac{1}{5} + \frac{1}{7} + \cdots$, while the negative terms form a convergent geometric series $-\frac{1}{2} - \frac{1}{2^2} - \frac{1}{2^3} - \cdots$.

The series $1 + \frac{1}{2} - \frac{2}{3} + \frac{1}{4} + \frac{1}{5} - \frac{2}{6} + \frac{1}{7} + \cdots$ converges by appeal to Corollary 1; take $a_n = 1/n$ and let Σb_n be $1 + 1 - 2 + 1 + 1 - 2 + 1 + 1 - 2 + \cdots$ which has a bounded sequence of partial sums.

A somewhat more complicated example is the series

$$\sum_{1}^{\infty} \frac{\sin (nx)}{\sqrt{n}} = \sin x + \frac{\sin 2x}{\sqrt{2}} + \frac{\sin 3x}{\sqrt{3}} + \cdots .$$

We shall show that it converges for every value of the parameter x. Apply Corollary 1 with $a_n = 1/\sqrt{n}$ and $b_n = \sin nx$; it is only necessary to show that the partial sums of the series $\sum_{1}^{\infty} \sin nx$ are bounded.

Lemma. $$\sum_{1}^{n} \sin kx = \frac{\cos (x/2) - \cos (n + \frac{1}{2})x}{2 \sin (x/2)}$$

for all x with $\sin (x/2) \neq 0$.

We have

$$\sin\left(\frac{x}{2}\right) \sum_{1}^{n} \sin kx = \sin\left(\frac{x}{2}\right) \sin x + \sin\left(\frac{x}{2}\right) \sin 2x + \cdots + \sin\left(\frac{x}{2}\right) \sin nx.$$

Using the identity: $2 \sin A \sin B = \cos (B - A) - \cos (B + A)$, this may be written as

$$\begin{aligned} 2 \sin\left(\frac{x}{2}\right) \sum_{1}^{n} \sin kx &= \left(\cos \frac{x}{2} - \cos \frac{3x}{2}\right) + \left(\cos \frac{3x}{2} - \cos \frac{5x}{2}\right) \\ &\quad + \cdots + (\cos [n - \tfrac{1}{2}]x - \cos [n + \tfrac{1}{2}]x) \\ &= \cos\left(\frac{x}{2}\right) - \cos (n + \tfrac{1}{2})x, \end{aligned}$$

and the required relation follows. ▌

It is now clear that the partial sums of $\sum_{1}^{\infty} \sin (nx)$ are bounded by $1/|\sin (x/2)|$ so that Corollary 1 applies and $\sum_{1}^{\infty} \frac{\sin nx}{\sqrt{n}}$ converges for all x except possibly those for which $\sin (x/2) = 0$. However, these are the values $x = 0, \pm 2\pi, \ldots$, and the series is clearly convergent for these also.

The conditionally convergent series $\sum_{1}^{\infty} (-1)^{n+1} \frac{1}{n}$ is often used to illustrate a property which is shared by all conditionally convergent series, namely, that rearrangement of the order in which the terms appear may change the sum or even render the series divergent. Denoting the sum of this series by S (approximately .693), we write

$$S = 1 - \tfrac{1}{2} + \tfrac{1}{3} - \tfrac{1}{4} + \tfrac{1}{5} - \tfrac{1}{6} + \tfrac{1}{7} - \cdots .$$

Then

$$\tfrac{1}{2}S = \tfrac{1}{2} - \tfrac{1}{4} + \tfrac{1}{6} - \tfrac{1}{8} + \tfrac{1}{10} - \tfrac{1}{12} + \tfrac{1}{14} - \cdots .$$

Neither the convergence of a series nor the value of its sum is altered by the insertion or deletion of zero terms, so that

$$\tfrac{1}{2}S = 0 + \tfrac{1}{2} + 0 - \tfrac{1}{4} + 0 + \tfrac{1}{6} + 0 - \tfrac{1}{8} + \cdots$$

Adding this series to the first one, we have

$$\tfrac{3}{2}S = 1 + 0 + \tfrac{1}{3} - \tfrac{1}{2} + \tfrac{1}{5} + 0 + \tfrac{1}{7} - \tfrac{1}{4} + \tfrac{1}{9} + 0 + \cdots$$

or, dropping the zero terms,

$$\tfrac{3}{2}S = 1 + \tfrac{1}{3} - \tfrac{1}{2} + \tfrac{1}{5} + \tfrac{1}{7} - \tfrac{1}{4} + \tfrac{1}{9} + \tfrac{1}{11} - \tfrac{1}{6} + \cdots .$$

If the terms of this series are compared with those of the original series whose sum was S, it will be seen that these series are rearrangements of each other; each term of one appears exactly once somewhere among the terms of the other series. This emphasizes the fact that an infinite series is not merely the "sum" of an infinite set of numbers; if we return to the view that a series is a pair of related sequences, then we see that the two series are quite different, having entirely different sequences of terms, and that it should not be surprising, therefore, that they converge to different sums.

It is not difficult to see that more drastic rearrangements can convert the first series into a divergent series, or in fact, a series which converges to any desired sum. Our next theorem shows that this property does not hold for absolutely convergent series.

Theorem 11. *If $\sum_{1}^{\infty} a_n$ is an absolutely convergent series with sum A, then every rearrangement of $\sum_{1}^{\infty} a_n$ converges* to A.

Let the series $\sum_{1}^{\infty} a'_n$ result from an arbitrary rearrangement of the series $\sum_1^\infty a_n$. This means that $a'_n = a_{r_n}$ where the sequence $\{r_n\}$ is some ordering of the sequence of positive integers 1, 2, ... Given ϵ, choose N so that $\sum_{k>N} |a_k| < \epsilon$. This is possible since $\Sigma|a_k|$ converges. Each of the integers 1, 2, . . . , N appears once somewhere among the integers $r_1, r_2, \ldots$. Choose n_0 so that all are contained in the set $\{r_1, r_2, \ldots, r_{n_0}\}$. Write

$$\left| A - \sum_1^n a'_k \right| = \left| A - \sum_1^N a_k + \sum_1^N a_k - \sum_1^n a'_k \right|$$
$$\leq \left| A - \sum_1^N a_k \right| + \left| \sum_1^n a'_k - \sum_1^N a_k \right|.$$

The first is dominated by $\sum_{k>N} |a_k|$; if $n \geq n_0$ then $\sum_1^n a'_k - \sum_1^N a_k$ can be written as a sum of terms a_j with $j > N$ since each term a_k with $k = 1$, 2, . . . , N already appears in the sum $\sum_1^n a'_k$. Thus, for $n > n_0$,

$$\left| A - \sum_1^n a'_k \right| \leq \sum_{k>N} |a_k| + \sum_{j>N} |a_j| < 2\epsilon$$

and $\sum_1^\infty a'_k$ converges to A. ▮

Another operation on series which can sometimes alter sums is the removal of brackets. If the series Σa_n has partial sums $\{A_n\}$, then the partial sums of the series $(a_1 + a_2) + (a_3 + a_4 + a_5) + (a_6 + a_7) + (a_8 + a_9 + a_{10}) + \cdots$ are $A_2, A_5, A_7, A_{10}, \ldots$, a subsequence of the original sequence A_n. Any subsequence of a convergent sequence converges to the same limit, so that any convergent series may have its terms grouped in brackets without altering the sum. If the original series is divergent, grouping terms may render it convergent. The series $\sum_1^\infty (-1)^{n+1}$ diverges, while $(1 - 1) + (1 - 1) + \cdots$ converges to 0, and $1 - (1 - 1) - (1 - 1) - \cdots$ converges to 1.

The method which was used to establish the integral test (Theorem 7) may also be used to estimate the rate of divergence of a series. If f is continuous for $1 \leq x < \infty$ and is positive and decreasing, then

$$f(m + 1) \leq \int_m^{m+1} f(x)\, dx \leq f(m)$$

so that $$\sum_{2}^{n} f(k) \le \int_1^n f(x)\,dx \le \sum_{1}^{n-1} f(k)$$

and

$$f(n) \le \sum_{1}^{n} f(k) - \int_1^n f(x)\,dx \le f(1). \tag{4-2}$$

Applying this, for example, to the series $\sum_{1}^{\infty} \frac{1}{n}$, we see that

$$\sum_{1}^{n} \frac{1}{k} = \log n + C_n$$

where $0 < C_n < 1$. If f is monotone increasing (4-2) again holds with the inequality signs reversed. If this is used to estimate $\sum_{1}^{n} \sqrt{k}$ with $f(x) = x^{1/2}$, we obtain

$$\sum_{1}^{n} \sqrt{k} \le \frac{2}{3} n \sqrt{n} + \sqrt{n}.$$

With a little more care, we can improve this. The following general result is often useful.

Theorem 12. *Let f be of class C^2 on the interval $1 \le x < \infty$ with $f(x) \ge 0, f'(x) \ge 0, f''(x) \le 0$ there. Then,*

$$\left| \sum_{1}^{n} f(k) - \int_1^n f(x)\,dx - \frac{f(n)}{2} \right|$$

is bounded for all $n = 1, 2, \ldots$.

The conditions on f ensure that its graph is convex (see Fig. 4-1). In particular, between any two lines $x = a$ and $x = b$, the curve lies above the chord joining $(a, f(a))$ and $(b, f(b))$, and below the tangent at any intermediate point $(c, f(c))$. The first of these properties has already been shown as an exercise (Exercise 9, Sec. 2.6). For the second, we need only observe that by Taylor's theorem,

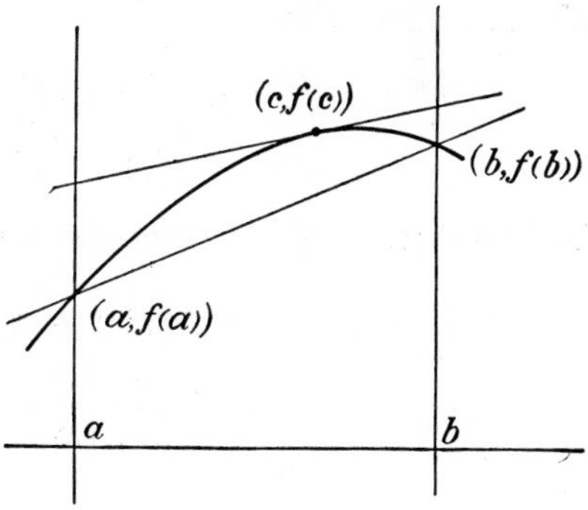

FIG. 4-1

$$\begin{aligned} f(x) &= f(c) + f'(c)(x - c) + f''(\tau)\frac{(x - c)^2}{2} \\ &\le f(c) + f'(c)(x - c). \end{aligned}$$

Using these bounds on f and choosing $c = (a + b)/2$, we have

$$\frac{f(a) + f(b)}{2}(b - a) \le \int_a^b f \le (b - a)f\left(\frac{a + b}{2}\right). \tag{4-3}$$

We use this to estimate $\int_1^n f$. First, we write

$$\begin{aligned}\int_1^n f &= \int_1^2 f + \int_2^3 f + \cdots + \int_{n-1}^n f \\ &\ge \frac{f(1) + f(2)}{2} + \frac{f(2) + f(3)}{2} + \cdots + \frac{f(n-1) + f(n)}{2} \\ &\ge \frac{f(1)}{2} + \sum_2^{n-1} f(k) + \frac{f(n)}{2} = \sum_1^n f(k) - \frac{f(n)}{2} - \frac{f(1)}{2}\end{aligned}$$

Then
$$\sum_1^n f(k) - \int_1^n f - \frac{f(n)}{2} \le \frac{f(1)}{2}.$$

To obtain a lower bound for this, we split up the integral in a different manner. Suppose that n is odd. Then, using the right side of (4-3),

$$\begin{aligned}\int_1^n f &= \int_1^3 f + \int_3^5 f + \cdots + \int_{n-2}^n f \\ &\le 2f(2) + 2f(4) + 2f(6) + \cdots + 2f(n-1).\end{aligned}$$

We may also write

$$\begin{aligned}\int_1^n f &= \int_1^2 f + \int_2^4 f + \int_4^6 f + \cdots + \int_{n-3}^{n-1} f + \int_{n-1}^n f \\ &\le f(2) + 2f(3) + 2f(5) + \cdots + 2f(n-2) + f(n).\end{aligned}$$

Adding these two estimates, we have

$$2\int_1^n f \le f(2) + 2\left\{f(2) + f(3) + \cdots + f(n-1)\right\} + f(n)$$

so that
$$\int_1^n f \le \sum_1^n f(k) - \frac{f(n)}{2} + \frac{f(2)}{2} - f(1).$$

If n were even, a similar computation leads to the same estimation, and for any n, we have

$$-\left\{\frac{f(2)}{2} - f(1)\right\} \le \sum_1^n f(k) - \int_1^n f - \frac{f(n)}{2}$$

and the theorem is proved. ▌

Applying this to the example $\sum_1^\infty \sqrt{k}$ we have

$$\sum_1^n \sqrt{k} = \frac{2}{3} n\sqrt{n} + \tfrac{1}{2}\sqrt{n} - C_n,$$

where $\frac{1}{6} \le C_n \le \frac{1}{2}\sqrt{2} - \frac{1}{3}$.

As another illustration, choose $f(x) = \log x$; since $\int_1^n \log x\, dx = n \log n - n + 1$, the theorem yields

$$\log (n!) = \sum_1^n \log k = n \log n + \tfrac{1}{2} \log n - n + C_n$$

where $1 \ge C_n \ge 1 - \frac{1}{2} \log 2$. This gives a weak form of Stirling's approximation: $n! = n^n e^{-n} \sqrt{n}\, e^{C_n}$.

The analogue of an improper double integral is a **double series** $\Sigma\Sigma a_{ij}$. There are several possible and acceptable definitions for convergence of double series. We select a simple one which is often used.

Definition. *The double series $\Sigma\Sigma a_{ij}$ converges to the sum A if and only if for any $\epsilon > 0$ there is a number N such that*

$$\left| A - \sum_{i=1}^{i=n} \sum_{j=1}^{j=m} a_{ij} \right| < \epsilon$$

whenever $n \ge N$ and $m \ge N$.

If we arrange the terms a_{ij} in a square array with a_{ij} in the ith row and jth column,

$$[a_{ij}] = \begin{bmatrix} a_{11} & a_{12} & a_{13} & \cdots & a_{1N} & \cdots & a_{1m} & \cdots \\ a_{21} & a_{22} & a_{23} & \cdots & a_{2N} & \cdots & a_{2m} & \cdots \\ \cdots & \cdot & \cdot & \cdots & \cdot & \cdots & \cdot & \cdots \\ a_{N1} & a_{N2} & a_{N3} & \cdots & a_{NN} & \cdots & a_{Nm} & \cdots \\ \cdots & \cdot & \cdot & \cdots & \cdot & \cdots & \cdot & \cdots \\ a_{n1} & a_{n2} & a_{n3} & \cdots & a_{nN} & \cdots & a_{nm} & \cdots \\ \cdots & \cdot & \cdot & \cdots & \cdot & \cdots & \cdot & \cdots \end{bmatrix}$$

we see that this definition amounts to summing $\Sigma\Sigma a_{ij}$ by rectangles. As with single series, the behavior of series with positive terms is particularly simple, and comparison theorems may be proved. Again, if $\Sigma\Sigma|a_{ij}|$ converges, so does $\Sigma\Sigma a_{ij}$; such a series is said to be absolutely convergent, and it can be shown that an absolutely convergent series can be arbitrarily rearranged without altering its convergence or its sum. In particular.

any absolutely convergent double series $\Sigma\Sigma a_{ij}$ can be rearranged as a convergent single series

$$a_{11} + a_{12} + a_{21} + a_{13} + a_{22} + a_{31} + a_{14} + a_{23} + \cdots .$$

One immediate application of this observation is the following important result dealing with multiplication of absolutely convergent single series.

Theorem 13. *Let* $\sum_0^\infty a_n$ *and* $\sum_0^\infty b_n$ *be absolutely convergent, with sums* A *and* B. *Then, their product series*

$$\sum_0^\infty c_n = \sum_0^\infty (a_0b_n + a_1b_{n-1} + \cdots + a_nb_0)$$

converges to AB.

Put $a_{ij} = a_ib_j$. Then,

$$\sum_{i=0}^{i=n} \sum_{j=0}^{j=m} |a_{ij}| = \sum_0^n |a_i| \sum_0^m |b_j|$$

so that $\sum_0^\infty \sum_0^\infty |a_{ij}|$ is a convergent double series. The series $\sum_0^\infty \sum_0^\infty a_{ij}$ is then absolutely convergent, and its sum is

$$\begin{aligned} \lim_{\substack{n\to\infty \\ m\to\infty}} \sum_{i=0}^{i=n} \sum_{j=0}^{j=m} a_{ij} &= \lim_{n\to\infty} \sum_0^n a_i \lim_{m\to\infty} \sum_0^m b_j \\ &= AB. \end{aligned}$$

Rewriting the double series as a simple series, and inserting brackets, we have

$$\begin{aligned} AB &= (a_0b_0) + (a_0b_1 + a_1b_0) + (a_0b_2 + a_1b_1 + a_2b_0) + \cdots \\ &= \sum_0^\infty c_n. \quad \blacksquare \end{aligned}$$

This theorem is also true if one of the series Σa_n or Σb_n is absolutely convergent and the other is conditionally convergent. A proof of this, together with many other refinements and additional results, may be found in more advanced books dealing with infinite series.† However,

† For example, K. Knopp, "Theory and Application of Infinite Series," Blackie & Son, Ltd., Glasgow, 1928.

if both series are conditionally convergent, the product may diverge (see Exercise 5).

The following result on reversal of the order of summation in an iterated double sum $\sum_{n=1}^{\infty} \left\{ \sum_{k=1}^{\infty} a_{nk} \right\}$ is often used.

Theorem 14. *If* $a_{nk} \geq 0$ *and* $\sum_{n=1}^{\infty} \left\{ \sum_{k=1}^{\infty} a_{nk} \right\}$ *converges to* S, *then* $\sum_{k=1}^{\infty} \left\{ \sum_{n=1}^{\infty} a_{nk} \right\}$ *also converges to* S.

The hypothesis asserts that each of the series $\sum_{k=1}^{\infty} a_{nk} = \alpha_n$ is convergent, and that $S = \sum_{1}^{\infty} \alpha_n$. For any k, $a_{nk} \leq \alpha_n$; invoking the comparison theorem, $\sum_{n=1}^{\infty} a_{nk}$ converges to a sum β_k for $k = 1, 2, \ldots$. Take any integer N and write

$$\begin{aligned}
\sum_{1}^{N} \beta_k = \beta_1 + \beta_2 + \cdots + \beta_N &= \sum_{n=1}^{\infty} a_{n,1} + \cdots + \sum_{n=1}^{\infty} a_{n,N} \\
&= \sum_{n=1}^{\infty} \{a_{n,1} + a_{n,2} + \cdots + a_{n,N}\} \\
&\leq \sum_{n=1}^{\infty} \alpha_n = S.
\end{aligned}$$

Since this bound is independent of N, $\sum_{1}^{\infty} \beta_k$ converges with sum less than or equal to S, and we have proved that

$$\sum_{k=1}^{\infty} \left\{ \sum_{n=1}^{\infty} a_{nk} \right\} \leq \sum_{n=1}^{\infty} \left\{ \sum_{k=1}^{\infty} a_{nk} \right\}.$$

We could now start over again with the series on the left, and obtain the opposite inequality; this shows that the two sides are actually equal. ▌

This result need not hold if the terms a_{nk} are not all positive. In the array given below, the sum of each row is 0 so that $\sum_{n=1}^{\infty} \left\{ \sum_{k=1}^{\infty} a_{nk} \right\} = 0$;

however, the sum of each column is 1 so that $\sum_{k=1}^{\infty} \left\{ \sum_{n=1}^{\infty} a_{nk} \right\}$ is divergent.

$$[a_{nk}] = \begin{bmatrix} 1 & -1 & 0 & 0 & 0 & 0 & \cdots \\ 0 & 2 & -2 & 0 & 0 & 0 & \cdots \\ 0 & 0 & 3 & -3 & 0 & 0 & \cdots \\ 0 & 0 & 0 & 4 & -4 & 0 & \cdots \\ \cdots & \cdots & \cdots & \cdots & \cdots & \cdots & \cdots \end{bmatrix}$$

The methods of the present section may also be used to discuss series whose terms are functions of one or more parameters; in such cases, we seek all the values of the parameters for which the resulting series converges. As instances of this, we have seen that the series $\sum_1^{\infty} 1/n^p$ is convergent when $p > 1$ and divergent when $p \le 1$, and that $\sum_0^{\infty} x^n$ is convergent when $|x| < 1$ and divergent when $|x| \ge 1$. A number of other examples follow:

(i) $\sum_1^{\infty} \dfrac{(x+1)^n}{n(3^n+1)}$ converges for $-4 \le x < 2$ and diverges for all other real x.

For, using the ratio test on the absolute values of the terms,

$$\frac{|a_{n+1}|}{|a_n|} = \frac{|x+1|^{n+1}}{(n+1)(3^{n+1}+1)} \frac{n(3^n+1)}{|x+1|^n} = \frac{n}{n+1} \frac{3^n+1}{3^{n+1}+1} |x+1|$$

and

$$\lim_{n\to\infty} \left| \frac{a_{n+1}}{a_n} \right| = \frac{|x+1|}{3}.$$

We may conclude that the series is convergent when $|x+1| < 3$ and divergent when $|x+1| > 3$. This gives convergence for all x with $-4 < x < 2$, with the end point values of the parameter in doubt. Testing each separately, we see that for $x = 2$ we obtain the divergent series

$$\sum_1^{\infty} \frac{3^n}{n(3^n+1)} = \sum_1^{\infty} \frac{1}{n(1+3^{-n})},$$

while for $x = -4$, we obtain the convergent alternating series

$$\sum_1^{\infty} \frac{(-3)^n}{n(3^n+1)} = \sum_1^{\infty} (-1)^n \frac{1}{n(1+3^{-n})}.$$

(ii) The series $1 + \frac{r}{1 + r^2} + \frac{r^2}{1 + r^4} + \cdots + \frac{r^n}{1 + r^{2n}} + \cdots$ converges for all values of r except $r = 1$ and $r = -1$.

The ratio test might again be used. However, it is easier to observe that if $|r| < 1$,

$$\frac{|r^n|}{1 + r^{2n}} \leq |r^n|,$$

and if $|r| > 1$,

$$\frac{|r^n|}{1 + r^{2n}} \leq \frac{|r^n|}{r^{2n}} = \left|\frac{1}{r}\right|^n$$

so that in both of these cases, the series converges. When $r = 1$ or $r = -1$, the terms are constantly ½ in absolute value and the series diverges.

(iii) The series $\frac{\alpha}{\beta} + \frac{\alpha(\alpha + 1)}{\beta(\beta + 1)} + \frac{\alpha(\alpha + 1)(\alpha + 2)}{\beta(\beta + 1)(\beta + 2)} + \cdots$, for $\alpha > 0$, $\beta > 0$, converges when $\beta > 1 + \alpha$ and diverges when $\beta \leq 1 + \alpha$.

The term ratios are $\frac{\alpha}{\beta}, \frac{\alpha + 1}{\beta + 1}, \frac{\alpha + 2}{\beta + 2}$, and in general $\frac{\alpha + n}{\beta + n}$ so that

$$\lim_{n \to \infty} \frac{a_{n+1}}{a_n} = 1,$$

which indicates nothing about convergence or divergence. Raabe's test is applicable, however, and writing $\frac{\alpha + n}{\beta + n} = 1 - \frac{\beta - \alpha}{n + \beta}$ we see that the series converges when $\beta - \alpha > 1$. If $\beta - \alpha = 1$, the series becomes

$$\frac{\alpha}{\alpha + 1} + \frac{\alpha(\alpha + 1)}{(\alpha + 1)(\alpha + 2)} + \frac{\alpha(\alpha + 1)(\alpha + 2)}{(\alpha + 1)(\alpha + 2)(\alpha + 3)} + \cdots$$
$$= \frac{\alpha}{\alpha + 1} + \frac{\alpha}{\alpha + 2} + \frac{\alpha}{\alpha + 3} + \cdots + \frac{\alpha}{\alpha + n} + \cdots$$

which is divergent. If $\beta < 1 + \alpha$, then the terms become even larger and the series is also divergent.

EXERCISES

1. Investigate the convergence of the following series:

(*a*) $\frac{1}{3} + \frac{2}{6} + \frac{3}{11} + \frac{4}{18} + \frac{5}{27} + \cdots$

(*b*) $\frac{1}{2} - \frac{2}{20} + \frac{3}{38} - \frac{4}{56} + \frac{5}{74} - \cdots$

(*c*) $\frac{1}{3} + \frac{1 \cdot 2}{3 \cdot 5} + \frac{1 \cdot 2 \cdot 3}{3 \cdot 5 \cdot 7} + \cdots$

(*d*) $\frac{1}{4} + \frac{1 \cdot 3}{4 \cdot 6} + \frac{1 \cdot 3 \cdot 5}{4 \cdot 6 \cdot 8} + \cdots$

(*e*) $2/1 - 3/2 + 2/3 - 1/4 + 2/5 - 3/6 + 2/7 - 1/8 + \cdots$

(*f*) $1 + \frac{1}{\sqrt{3}} - \frac{1}{\sqrt{2}} + \frac{1}{\sqrt{5}} + \frac{1}{\sqrt{7}} - \frac{1}{\sqrt{4}} + \frac{1}{\sqrt{9}} + \frac{1}{\sqrt{11}} - \frac{1}{\sqrt{6}} + \frac{1}{\sqrt{13}} + \cdots$

2. (*a*) Let $0 < a_n$ and $0 < b_n$ and $\frac{a_{n+1}}{a_n} \geq \frac{b_{n+1}}{b_n}$ for all sufficiently large n. Show that if Σb_n diverges, so does Σa_n.

(*b*) Prove: If $0 < a_n$ and $\frac{a_{n+1}}{a_n} \geq 1 - \frac{p}{n}$ for some $p \leq 1$ and all large n, then Σa_n diverges.

(*c*) Prove: If $0 < a_n$ and $\frac{a_{n+1}}{a_n} \geq 1 - \frac{1}{n} - \frac{A}{n^2}$ for all large n, then Σa_n diverges.

3. Determine the values of the parameters for which the following series converge.

(*a*) $\frac{r}{2} + \frac{4r^2}{9} + \frac{9r^3}{28} + \frac{16r^4}{65} + \cdots$

(*b*) $1 + \frac{x}{3} + \frac{2x^2}{9} + \frac{(2 \cdot 3)x^3}{27} + \frac{(2 \cdot 3 \cdot 4)x^4}{81} + \cdots$

(*c*) $\sum_1^\infty \frac{(x+2)^n}{n\sqrt{n+1}}$ (*d*) $\sum_1^\infty \frac{(2n)!\,x^n}{n(n!)^2}$

(*e*) $\sum_1^\infty \frac{(x-1)^{2n}}{n^2\,3^n}$ (*f*) $\sum_1^\infty ne^{-ns}$

(*g*) $\sum_1^\infty \frac{(\beta n)^n}{n!}$

(*h*) $\frac{\alpha\beta}{\gamma} + \frac{\alpha(\alpha+1)\beta(\beta+1)}{2!\,\gamma(\gamma+1)} + \frac{\alpha(\alpha+1)(\alpha+2)\beta(\beta+1)(\beta+2)}{3!\,\gamma(\gamma+1)(\gamma+2)} + \cdots$

(*i*) $\sum_1^\infty \frac{x^n(1-x^n)}{n}$ (*j*) $\sum_1^\infty \frac{nx^n}{n^3 + x^{2n}}$

(*k*) $\sum_1^\infty \frac{\sqrt{n}}{(n+1)(2x+3)^n}$ (*l*) $\sum_1^\infty \frac{1}{\sqrt{n}}\left[\frac{x+1}{2x-1}\right]^n$

(*m*) $\sum_1^\infty \sin\left(\frac{x}{n^2}\right)$

4. Let $\{a_n\} \downarrow 0$; show that $\sum_1^\infty a_n$ converges if and only if $\sum_0^\infty 2^n a_{2^n}$ converges.

5. Show that the Cauchy product of the convergent series $1 - \frac{1}{\sqrt{2}} + \frac{1}{\sqrt{3}} - \frac{1}{\sqrt{4}} + \cdots$ with itself gives a divergent series.

***6.** Show directly that if $\lim_{n\to\infty} \left|\frac{a_{n+1}}{a_n}\right| = L$, then $\lim_{n\to\infty} |a_n|^{1/n} = L$.

7. Some of the following statements are true and some are false; prove those that are true, and disprove those that are false.

(a) If Σa_n and Σb_n converge, so does $\Sigma(a_n + b_n)$.
(b) If Σa_n and Σb_n diverge, so does $\Sigma(a_n + b_n)$.
(c) If Σa_n is absolutely convergent, so is Σa_n^2.
(d) If Σa_n converges, and $\lim c_n = 0$, then $\Sigma a_n c_n$ converges.
(e) If Σb_n converges, and $\lim_{n\to\infty} \dfrac{a_n}{b_n} = 1$, then Σa_n converges.
(f) If Σa_n and Σb_n converge absolutely, so does $\Sigma a_n b_n$.
(g) If $\sum_1^\infty a_n^2$ converges, so does $\sum_1^\infty \dfrac{a_n}{n}$.
*(h) If $\{a_n\} \downarrow 0$ and Σa_n converges, then $\lim_{n\to\infty} na_n = 0$.

***8.** Let f and f' be continuous on the interval $1 \le x < \infty$ with $f(x) > 0$ and

$$\int_1^\infty |f'(x)|\,dx$$

convergent. Show that the series $\sum_1^\infty f(k)$ and the improper integral $\int_1^\infty f(x)\,dx$ are either both convergent or both divergent.

9. Since $\sum_2^\infty \dfrac{1}{n \log n}$ diverges, $\lim_{n\to\infty} \sum_2^n \dfrac{1}{k \log k} = \infty$. How many terms must be taken before the partial sums exceed 10?

10. Estimate:

(a) $\sum_1^n \dfrac{\log k}{k}$ (b) $\sum_1^n (\log k)^2$

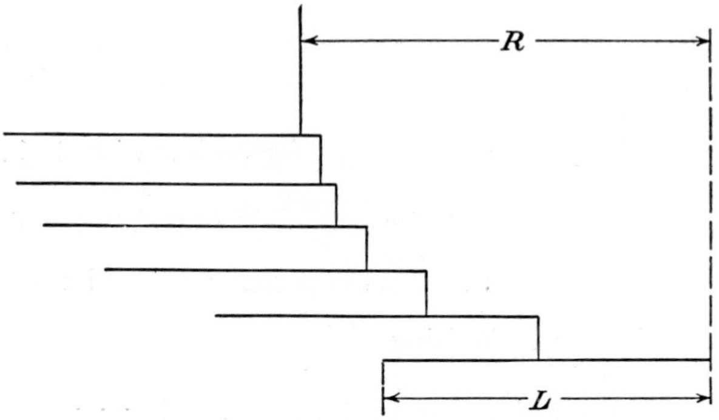

FIG. 4-2

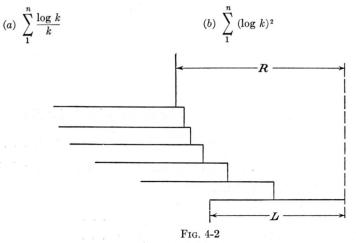

11. A mobile is to be made from 50 uniform sticks of length L by hanging each by a thread 1 in. long and of negligible mass from the end of the stick above it (see Fig. 4-2). When all are balanced in a horizontal position, the whole is supported by a thread from the top stick to the ceiling. How much space must be allowed for the rotation of the mobile?

12. Show that the sum of an alternating series lies between any pair of successive partial sums, so that the error made in stopping at the nth term does not exceed the absolute value of the next term.

13. Apply the previous exercise to show that the number $S = \sum_0^\infty (-1)^n/(n+1)^2$ lies between .818 and .828. (*Remark:* the average of two successive partial sums of an alternating series is often very accurate; in this example, two such sums are .8179 and .8279, and their average is .8229, while the true value of S is $\pi^2/12 = .82246 \ldots$.)

4.2. Uniform Convergence

At the end of the last section, we discussed the convergence of series whose terms involved one or more parameters or variables. In essence, we were there dealing with a particular notion of convergence of a series of functions which can be formalized as follows.

Definition. *Let each of the functions u_n be defined for points of a set D. Then, the series Σu_n is said to converge pointwise on a set $E \subset D$ if and only if $\Sigma u_n(p)$ converges for each $p \in E$.*

If we denote the sum of $\Sigma u_n(p)$ by $F(p)$, then we say that Σu_n converges pointwise to F on E. For sequences, a similar definition is used; $\{f_n\}$ converges pointwise to F on E if for each point $p \in E$, $\lim_{n\to\infty} f_n(p) = F(p)$. In the illustrative examples at the end of Sec. 4.1, and in Exercise 3, Sec. 4.1, pointwise convergence was established.

There are also a number of other important and useful notions of convergence for series and sequences of functions; before introducing these, let us observe some of the shortcomings of pointwise convergence. Each of the following examples represents a plausible, but unfortunately invalid, argument dealing with series or sequences of functions.

(i) The series $\sum_0^\infty x(1-x)^n$ converges for each x with $0 \le x \le 1$ to a sum $F(x)$. We observe that $\lim_{x\downarrow 0} x(1-x)^n = 0$ for $n = 0, 1, \ldots$. Is it true that $\lim_{x\downarrow 0} F(x) = 0$? This is perhaps plausible; however, it is easily shown to be false. Writing

$$\begin{aligned} F(x) &= x + x(1-x) + x(1-x)^2 + \cdots \\ &= x\{1 + (1-x) + (1-x)^2 + \cdots\} \end{aligned}$$

and using the formula for the sum of a geometric series, we have

$$F(x) = \frac{x}{1-(1-x)} = 1$$

holding for all x with $0 < x \leq 1$. In particular, then, $\lim_{x \downarrow 0} F(x) = 1$.

(ii) The series $\sum_1^\infty \frac{nx^2}{n^3 + x^3} = \frac{x^2}{1 + x^3} + \frac{2x^2}{8 + x^3} + \cdots$ converges for each x with $0 \leq x < \infty$ since $\frac{nx^2}{n^3 + x^3} \leq \frac{nx^2}{n^3} = \frac{x^2}{n^2}$ and $\sum_1^\infty \frac{x^2}{n^2}$ converges. Denote the sum of the series by $F(x)$. We observe that $\lim_{x \uparrow \infty} \frac{nx^2}{n^3 + x^3} = 0$ so that each term of the series approaches 0 as x increases. Is it true that $\lim_{x \uparrow \infty} F(x) = 0$? This is again plausible, and again false; in fact, $\lim_{x \uparrow \infty} F(x) = \infty$. To see this, choose any $x > 0$. Then, for any n with $\frac{1}{2} x < n < 2x$,

$$\frac{nx^2}{n^3 + x^3} \geq \frac{(x/2)x^2}{(2x)^3 + x^3} = \frac{1}{18}.$$

In the series for $F(x)$, there are therefore $(2x) - (x/2)$ terms, each larger than $\frac{1}{18}$, so that since all the terms of the series are positive, $F(x) \geq (3x/2)(\frac{1}{18}) = (x/12)$. Since this is true for any x,

$$\lim_{x \uparrow \infty} F(x) = \infty.$$

(iii) Set $f_n(x) = n^2 x e^{-nx}$. For each x with $0 \leq x \leq 1$, $\lim_{n \to \infty} f_n(x) = 0$. Is it true that $\lim_{n \to \infty} \int_0^1 f_n = 0$? Again, this is plausible, but untrue, for

$$\int_0^1 f_n = \int_0^1 n^2 x e^{-nx}\, dx = \int_0^n u e^{-u}\, du$$

so that

$$\lim_{n \to \infty} \int_0^1 f_n = \int_0^\infty u e^{-u}\, du = 1.$$

(iv) Set $f_n(x) = x e^{-nx^2}$ so that $\lim_{n \to \infty} f_n(x) = 0$ for all x, $-\infty < x < \infty$. Is it true that $\lim_{n \to \infty} f_n'(x) = 0$? No, for in particular, $f_n'(0) = 1$ for all n.

Again, the series $\sum_1^\infty \frac{\sin(n^2 x)}{n^2}$ converges for every x, but the series obtained by termwise differentiation, $\sum_1^\infty \cos(n^2 x)$, is divergent for every x.

All of these examples involve the reversal of order of two limit processes. In (i), for instance, we are concerned with the possible equality of

$$\lim_{x \downarrow 0} \lim_{n \to \infty} \sum_1^n u_k(x) \qquad \text{and} \qquad \lim_{n \to \infty} \lim_{x \downarrow 0} \sum_1^n u_k(x).$$

In circumstances such as these, the notion of **uniform convergence** of series or sequences of functions is especially useful. To simplify the discussion, we introduce a special notation. If f is a function which is defined on a set E, then $\|f\|_E$ will denote the least upper bound of the set of values $|f(p)|$ for $p \in E$; when f is continuous on E and E is closed and bounded, this is the maximum value of $|f(p)|$ on E. If f and g are both defined on E, then $\|f - g\|_E$ is a measure of the distance between f and g over the set E. If $\|f - g\|_E < \epsilon$, then $|f(p) - g(p)| < \epsilon$ for all $p \in E$ so that f approximates g within ϵ uniformly on E (see page 37).

Definition. *A sequence of functions* $\{f_n\}$ *is uniformly convergent to a function* F *on a set* E *if and only if* $\lim_{n \to 0} \|F - f_n\|_E = 0$.

If we restate this without using the special notation, it becomes: $\{f_n\}$ *converges to* F *uniformly on* E *if and only if, for any* ϵ *there is an* N *such that for any* $n \geq N$ *and any* $p \in E$, $|F(p) - f_n(p)| < \epsilon$. If a sequence $\{f_n\}$ is uniformly convergent on a set E, then it is certainly pointwise convergent for at least all points of E. However, it may converge pointwise on E and not uniformly on E. Examine again the sequence

$$f_n(x) = n^2 x e^{-nx}$$

As we saw, this sequence converges pointwise to zero on the interval $E = [0, 1]$. The convergence is not uniform on E. The maximum of f_n on E occurs for $x = 1/n$ and is $f_n(1/n) = n/e$, so that $\lim_{n \to \infty} \|f_n\|_E$ is not 0. This behavior is also evident from the graphs of the functions f_1, f_2, . . . (see Fig. 4-3). The definition of pointwise convergence can also be given as follows: $\{f_n\}$ *converges to* F *pointwise on* E *if and only if for any* $\epsilon > 0$ *and any point* $p \in E$, *there is an* N *such that whenever* $n \geq N$, $|F(p) - f_n(p)| < \epsilon$. Comparing this with the corresponding definition of uniform convergence, we see that the essential difference lies in the fact that in uniform convergence, N depends only upon ϵ, while in pointwise convergence, N depends upon both ϵ and p.

Uniform convergence of series is defined by throwing it back onto the sequence of partial sums: $\sum_1^\infty u_n$ *converges to* F *uniformly on* E *if and only if*

$\{f_n\}$ converges to F uniformly on E, where $f_n = \sum_1^n u_k$. An alternative statement is: *Σu_n converges uniformly on E if and only if Σu_n converges pointwise on E and* $\lim_{n\to\infty} \left\| \sum_n^\infty u_k \right\|_E = 0$.

By analogy with sequences of points, a sequence of functions $\{f_n\}$ is said to have the **Cauchy property** uniformly on a set E if for any $\epsilon > 0$

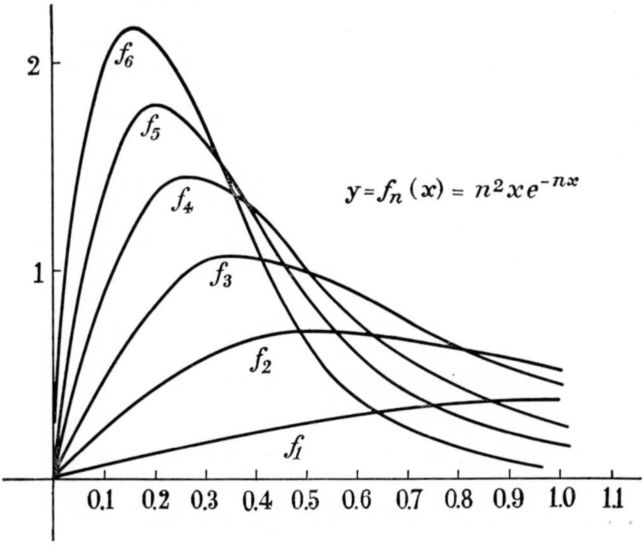

FIG. 4-3. Nonuniform convergence.

there is an N such that $\|f_n - f_m\|_E < \epsilon$ whenever $n \geq N$ and $m \geq N$ (see Sec. 1.4). As before, this is often written $\lim_{n,m\to\infty} \|f_n - f_m\|_E = 0$. Any uniformly convergent sequence has the Cauchy property; for, if $\{f_n\} \to F$ uniformly on E, then for any point $p \,\varepsilon\, E$,

$$\begin{aligned} |f_n(p) - f_m(p)| &= |f_n(p) - F(p) + F(p) - f_m(p)| \\ &\leq \|f_n - F\|_E + \|F - f_m\|_E \end{aligned}$$

so that $\lim_{n,m\to\infty} \|f_n - f_m\|_E = 0$. The converse also holds.

Theorem 15. *If* $\lim_{n,m\to\infty} \|f_n - f_m\|_E = 0$, *then there is a function F to which the sequence $\{f_n\}$ converges uniformly on E.*

Since $|f_n(p) - f_m(p)| \leq \|f_n - f_m\|_E$ for each point $p \,\varepsilon\, E$, $\{f_n(p)\}$ is a Cauchy sequence of numbers and is therefore convergent. Define F by $F(p) = \lim_{n\to\infty} f_n(p)$. F is then the pointwise limit of f_n on E. To show that the convergence is actually uniform, take any $p \in E$ and write

$$\begin{aligned} |F(p) - f_n(p)| &= |F(p) - f_k(p) + f_k(p) - f_n(p)| \\ &\leq |F(p) - f_k(p)| + |f_k(p) - f_n(p)| \\ &\leq |F(p) - f_k(p)| + \|f_k - f_n\|_E. \end{aligned}$$

Given $\epsilon > 0$, choose N so that $\|f_k - f_n\|_E < \epsilon$ whenever $n \geq N$, $k \geq N$. For each $p \in E$, $\lim_{k \to \infty} f_k(p) = F(p)$; we may then choose k larger than N and dependent upon p and ϵ, so that $|F(p) - f_k(p)| < \epsilon$. Making this choice of k in the inequality above, we have

$$|F(p) - f_n(p)| < \epsilon + \epsilon = 2\epsilon$$

holding now for each $n \geq N$ and each point $p \in E$. Hence, $\|F - f_n\|_E < 2\epsilon$ for all $n \geq N$, and $\{f_n\}$ is uniformly convergent to F on E. ∎

The following corollary gives the corresponding statement for series of functions.

Corollary. *If* $\lim_{n,m \to \infty} \left\| \sum_n^m u_k \right\|_E = 0$, *then* Σu_k *is uniformly convergent on* E.

The most frequently used test for uniform convergence is the following simple comparison test.

Theorem 16 (*Weierstrass Comparison Test*). *If* $\|u_k\|_E \leq M_k$ *for* $k = 1, 2, \ldots$ *and* $\sum M_k$ *converges, then* $\sum_1^\infty u_k$ *converges uniformly on* E.

For any $p \in E$, $|u_k(p)| \leq M_k$ so that by the simple comparison test, $\Sigma u_k(p)$ converges. Moreover, $\left| \sum_n^\infty u_k(p) \right| \leq \sum_n^\infty M_k$ for each $p \in E$ and thus $\lim_{n \to \infty} \left\| \sum_n^\infty u_k \right\|_E = 0$, proving uniform convergence. ∎

As an illustration, $\sum_1^\infty \frac{\sin(nx)}{n^2}$ converges uniformly for all x, $-\infty < x < \infty$, since $\left| \frac{\sin(nx)}{n^2} \right| \leq \frac{1}{n^2}$ and $\sum \frac{1}{n^2}$ converges.

We take up next a very important property of uniform convergence.

Theorem 17. *If* $\{f_n\}$ *converges to* F, *uniformly on* E, *and each function* f_n *is continuous on* E, *then* F *is continuous on* E.

We prove that F is continuous at an arbitrary point $p_0 \in E$. Given

$\epsilon > 0$, first choose N so that $\|F - f_N\|_E < \epsilon$. For any point p in E we may write

$$\begin{aligned}|F(p) - F(p_0)| &= |F(p) - f_N(p) + f_N(p) - f_N(p_0) + f_N(p_0) - F(p_0)| \\ &\leq |F(p) - f_N(p)| + |f_N(p) - f_N(p_0)| + |f_N(p_0) - F(p_0)| \\ &\leq 2\|F - f_N\|_E + |f_N(p) - f_N(p_0)| \\ &\leq 2\epsilon + |f_N(p) - f_N(p_0)|.\end{aligned}$$

Since f_N is continuous on E, we may now choose δ so that $|f_N(p) - f_N(p_0)| < \epsilon$ whenever $p \in E$ and $|p - p_0| < \delta$. We thus obtain

$$|F(p) - F(p_0)| < 3\epsilon$$

whenever $p \in E$ and $|p - p_0| < \delta$, proving that F is continuous at p_0. ▌

Stated for series, this becomes:

Corollary. *If each of the functions u_n is continuous on a set E, and Σu_n converges to F uniformly on E, then F is continuous on E.*

In particular, this shows that $F(p_0)$ is $\lim_{p \uparrow p_0} F(p)$ so that

$$\lim_{p \to p_0} \sum_1^\infty u_n(p) = \sum_1^\infty u_n(p_0).$$

Returning to the examples which opened this section, the series

$$\sum_0^\infty x(1 - x)^n$$

was a series of continuous functions, but its sum is the discontinuous function described by $F(x) = 1$, $0 < x \leq 1$, $F(0) = 0$. The series is therefore not uniformly convergent on $[0, 1]$. In fact, it cannot be uniformly convergent on the open interval $0 < x < 1$, even though F is continuous there. This is shown by the following general theorem.

Theorem 18. *Let E be the closure of an open set. Let $\{f_n\}$ converge uniformly in the interior of E. Suppose that each function f_n is continuous on E. Then, $\{f_n\}$ is uniformly convergent on E.*

Given $\epsilon > 0$, choose N so that $|f_n(p) - f_m(p)| < \epsilon$ whenever $n \geq N$, $m \geq N$, and p is an interior point of E. Since f_n and f_m are both continuous on E, so is $\phi(p) = |f_n(p) - f_m(p)|$, and since ϕ is bounded by ϵ on the interior of E, it is bounded by ϵ on all of E. This shows that $\|f_n - f_m\|_E \leq \epsilon$ for all n and m with $n \geq N$, $m \geq N$, and $\{f_n\}$ converges uniformly on E, by Theorem 15. ▌

A useful application of this to series is:

Corollary. *Let* $\sum_1^\infty u_n(x)$ *converge to* $F(x)$, *uniformly for all* x *with* $c \le x < \infty$. *Let* $\lim_{x\uparrow\infty} u_n(x) = b_n < \infty$ *for* $n = 1, 2, \ldots$. *Then,* $\sum_1^\infty b_n$ *converges, and* $\lim_{x\uparrow\infty} F(x) = \sum_1^\infty b_n$.

Setting $x = 1/t$, we obtain a series of functions which converges uniformly for $0 < t \le a$. Since $\lim_{t\downarrow 0} u_n\left(\frac{1}{t}\right) = b_n$, we can define the terms so as to be continuous at $t = 0$. Applying the theorem, the series is uniformly convergent for $0 \le t \le a$, and we can evaluate

$$\lim_{t\downarrow 0} F\left(\frac{1}{t}\right) = \lim_{x\uparrow\infty} F(x)$$

termwise. ∎

Returning again to the examples that opened this section, the series $F(x) = \sum_1^\infty \frac{nx^2}{n^3 + x^3}$ converges uniformly on each of the intervals $[0, R]$ since $\left|\frac{nx^2}{n^3 + x^3}\right| \le \frac{nR^2}{n^3} = \frac{R^2}{n^2}$ and $\sum_1^\infty \frac{1}{n^2}$ converges. However, it cannot converge *uniformly* on the whole unbounded interval $0 \le x < \infty$ since $\lim_{x\uparrow\infty} F(x) = \infty$ although $\lim_{x\uparrow\infty} \frac{nx^2}{n^3 + x^3} = 0$ for each n.

The next theorem is the fundamental result dealing with integration of uniformly convergent series or sequences. We state it in a two-dimensional form.

Theorem 19. *Let* D *be a closed bounded set in the plane which has area, and let the functions* f_n *be continuous on* D. *Then, if* $\{f_n\}$ *converges to* F *uniformly on* D, $\lim_{n\to\infty} \iint_D f_n = \iint_D F$.

$\iint_D F$ exists since F is continuous on D. For any n, we have

$$\left|\iint_D F - \iint_D f_n\right| = \left|\iint_D (F - f_n)\right| \le \iint_D |F - f_n| \le \|F - f_n\|_D\, A(D)$$

since $\|F - f_n\|_D$ is the maximum of $|F(p) - f_n(p)|$ for $p \in D$. Since $\lim_{n\to\infty} \|F - f_n\|_D = 0$, $\lim_{n\to\infty} \iint_D f_n = \iint_D F$. ∎

If $\{f_n\}$ is the sequence of partial sums of a series $\sum_1^\infty u_k$, then

$$\iint_D f_n = \iint_D (u_1 + u_2 + \cdots + u_n) = \iint_D u_1 + \iint_D u_2 + \cdots + \iint_D u_n,$$

leading to the following corollary.

Corollary. *If each of the functions u_n is continuous on D and $\sum_1^\infty u_n$ converges to F uniformly on D, then* $\iint_D F = \sum_1^\infty \iint_D u_n$.

This is usually abbreviated to the statement that a uniformly convergent series may be integrated termwise. As an illustration, consider the series $\sum_0^\infty (-t)^n$. This converges to $1/(1+t)$ uniformly on any interval $-r \le t \le r$, for $r < 1$. Integrating the series termwise between 0 and x, $|x| < 1$,

$$\int_0^x \frac{dt}{1+t} = \log(1+x) = \sum_0^\infty (-1)^n \int_0^x t^n \, dt = \sum_0^8 (-1)^n \frac{x^{n+1}}{n+1}.$$

Thus, for any x with $|x| < 1$,

$$\log(1+x) = x - \frac{x^2}{2} + \frac{x^3}{3} - \cdots + (-1)^{n-1}\frac{x^n}{n} + \cdots.$$

We can also extend this to the end point $x = 1$ by a special argument. If $x > 0$, the series $\sum_1^\infty (-1)^{n-1}\frac{x^n}{n}$ is an alternating series and converges for $0 \le x \le 1$. Using the fact (see Exercise 12, Sec. 4.1) that the partial sums of an alternating series constantly approach the sum and alternatively lie above and below, so that the error at any stage does not exceed the next term, we may write

$$\left| \log(1+x) - \sum_1^n (-1)^{k-1}\frac{x^k}{k} \right| \le \frac{x^{n+1}}{n+1} \le \frac{1}{n+1}$$

for any x with $0 \le x \le 1$. The series is then uniformly convergent on the whole closed interval [0, 1] so that term-by-term integration is valid for all x with $0 \le x \le 1$. In particular, setting $x = 1$, we have

$$\log 2 = 1 - \tfrac{1}{2} + \tfrac{1}{3} - \tfrac{1}{4} + \tfrac{1}{5} - \tfrac{1}{6} + \cdots .$$

The functions $f_n(x) = n^2xe^{-nx}$ of Example (iii), page 127, converge to zero pointwise on [0, 1] but do not converge uniformly on [0, 1], and their integrals $\int_0^1 f_n$ converge to 1, not 0. Examining their graphs (Fig. 4-3) we see that f_n has a peak near the origin which becomes narrower but higher as n increases, leaving the total area underneath the curve about constant. In contrast, if we divide by n, getting $g_n(x) = nxe^{-nx}$, these also converge to zero pointwise but not uniformly on [0, 1]. This time, none of the peaks reach higher than $1/e$ and $\lim_{n\to\infty} \int_0^1 g_n = 0$. This is an illustration of a very general theorem on termwise integration which is called the Osgood-Lebesgue bounded convergence theorem. Although this result is quite useful, its proof is so difficult that we state it here without proof.†

Theorem 20. *If the functions f_n and F are integrable on a bounded closed set E, and $\{f_n\} \to F$ pointwise on E, and if $\|f_n\|_E \le M$ for some M and all $n = 1, 2, \ldots$, then* $\lim_{n\to\infty} \int_E f_n = \int_E F$.

This may often be used when uniform convergence does not occur. Let g be continuous (and therefore bounded) on $[-1, 1]$. Then, the sequence $\{f_n\}$ with $f_n(x) = e^{-nx^2}g(x)$ is uniformly bounded on $[-1, 1]$ and converges pointwise to the function F

$$F(x) = \begin{cases} 0 & x \ne 0 \\ g(0) & x = 0. \end{cases}$$

This is not continuous if $g(0) \ne 0$ so that $\{f_n\}$ does not in general converge uniformly. However, Theorem 20 applies, so that

$$\lim_{n\to\infty} \int_{-1}^{1} \exp(-nx^2)\, g(x)\, dx = 0.$$

The process of differentiation is not as well behaved as that of integration. A series may be uniformly convergent, and still not allow termwise differentiation. However, if the series of derivatives is uniformly convergent, the termwise differentiation was justified.

† Those interested may find a proof in any book which treats the Lebesgue integral, for example, W. Rudin, "Principles of Mathematical Analysis," pp. 207–210, McGraw-Hill Book Company, Inc., New York, 1953.

Theorem 21. *Let* $\sum_1^\infty u_n(x)$ *converge to* $F(x)$ *for each* x *in* $[a, b]$. *Let* $u_n'(x)$ *exist and be continuous for* $a \le x \le b$ *and let* $\Sigma u_n'(x)$ *converge uniformly on* $[a, b]$. *Then,* $\sum_1^\infty u_n'(x) = F'(x)$.

Setting $g(x) = \Sigma u_n'(x)$, integrate termwise between a and x, so that

$$\begin{aligned} \int_a^x g &= \sum_1^\infty \int_a^x u_n' = \sum_1^\infty [u_n(x) - u_n(a)] \\ &= F(x) - F(a). \end{aligned}$$

This shows that F is an antiderivative (indefinite integral) of g so that $F'(x) = g(x)$ for all x in $[a, b]$. ∎

As an illustration of this, consider the series $F(x) = \sum_1^\infty e^{-n^2x}$ which converges for all $x > 0$. We shall show that F is continuous and of class C^∞ on this interval, that is, $F^{(k)}(x)$ exists for all $x > 0$. The termwise derivative of the series is $(-1)\sum_1^\infty n^2 \exp(-n^2x)$. If $\delta > 0$, then for all $x \ge \delta$, $|n^2 \exp(-n^2x)| \le n^2 \exp(-n^2\delta)$ so that the derived series is uniformly convergent for all x, $\delta \le x < \infty$. This shows that $F'(x)$ exists and is given by $(-1)\sum_1^\infty n^2 \exp(-n^2x)$, for all $x > 0$. Repetition of this process leads to

$$F^{(k)}(x) = (-1)^k \sum_1^\infty n^{2k} \exp(-n^2x), \qquad k = 1, 2, \ldots$$

where the series is uniformly convergent for $\delta \le x < \infty$ and any $\delta > 0$.

We conclude this section with a number of special examples.

(i) Let $F(x) = \sum_1^\infty \frac{x}{n(x+n)}$. Since $\left|\frac{x}{n(x+n)}\right| \le \frac{1}{n^2}$ for all x in $[0,1]$, this series is uniformly convergent there, and may be integrated termwise. The resulting series, $\sum_1^\infty \int_0^1 \frac{x\,dx}{n(x+n)}$, must converge. Denote its sum by γ, so that

$$\begin{aligned}\gamma &= \sum_1^\infty \int_0^1 \left\{\frac{1}{n} - \frac{1}{x+n}\right\} dx \\ &= \sum_1^\infty \left\{\frac{1}{n} - \log\frac{n+1}{n}\right\} \\ &= \lim_{N\to\infty} \left\{\sum_1^N \frac{1}{n} - \log(N+1)\right\}.\end{aligned}$$

Since $\lim_{N\to\infty} [\log(N+1) - \log N] = 0$, we have thus shown that there is a positive number γ such that

$$\sum_1^N \frac{1}{n} = \log N + \gamma + \sigma_N$$

where $\lim \sigma_N = 0$. The number γ is called Euler's constant, and is approximately .57721 . . . .

(ii) Let $F(x) = \sum_1^\infty \frac{1}{1+n^2x^2}$, converging for all $x \neq 0$. For any $\delta > 0$, and $x \geq \delta$, we see that $(1+n^2x^2)^{-1} \leq 1/n^2\delta^2$, so that the series is uniformly convergent for all x, $x \geq \delta$. Appealing to the corollary to Theorem 18, $\lim_{x\uparrow\infty} F(x) = 0$. How does F behave near the origin? When $x = 0$, the series becomes $1 + 1 + 1 + \cdots$, which suggests that $\lim_{x\downarrow 0} F(x) = \infty$. This conjecture is correct. For any N,

$$F(x) \geq \sum_1^N \frac{1}{1+n^2x^2} = g(x) \qquad \text{and} \qquad g(0) = N$$

so that

$$\liminf_{x\downarrow 0} F(x) \geq N,$$

and letting N increase, we see that $\lim_{x\downarrow 0} F(x) = \infty$. This approach cannot always be used, and depends upon the fact that the terms of the present series are positive. Consider, for example, the series

$$g(x) = \sum_0^\infty [1 + n(x-1)]x^n$$

which converges for all x with $-1 < x < 1$. Setting $x = 1$, this series also becomes $1 + 1 + 1 + \cdots$, but the conjecture that $\lim_{x \uparrow 1} g(x) = \infty$ is false. To see this, we write the series out as

$$\begin{aligned} g(x) &= 1 + [1 + (x - 1)]x + [1 + 2(x - 1)]x^2 + \cdots \\ &= 1 + x^2 + (2x - 1)x^2 + (3x - 2)x^3 + \cdots \\ &= 1 + x^2 + (2x^3 - x^2) + (3x^4 - 2x^3) + \cdots \\ &= 1, \qquad \text{for all } x, \ -1 < x < 1. \end{aligned}$$

(The series telescopes.) In particular, $\lim_{x \uparrow 1} g(x) = 1$.

Returning to our study of the function F, let us consider now

$$x^2F(x) = \sum_1^\infty \frac{x^2}{1 + n^2x^2}.$$

Since $\dfrac{x^2}{1 + n^2x^2} \le \dfrac{1}{n^2}$ for all x, $-\infty < x < \infty$, this series is uniformly convergent on the whole axis. In particular, $\lim_{x \to 0} x^2F(x) = \Sigma 0 = 0$, and

$$\lim_{x \uparrow \infty} x^2F(x) = \sum_1^\infty \lim_{x \uparrow \infty} \frac{x^2}{1 + n^2x^2} = \sum_1^\infty \frac{1}{n^2}.$$

Finally, consider $xF(x) = \sum_1^\infty \dfrac{x}{1 + n^2x^2}$. This converges uniformly on the intervals $\delta \le x < \infty$, for any $\delta > 0$. Does it converge uniformly for $0 \le x \le \delta$? If so, then $\lim_{x \downarrow 0} xF(x)$ would have to be 0; we shall show that instead, $\lim_{x \downarrow 0} xF(x) = \pi/2$. For any n,

$$\frac{x}{1 + (n + 1)^2x^2} \le \int_n^{n+1} \frac{x}{1 + t^2x^2}\, dt \le \frac{x}{1 + n^2x^2}$$

and adding,

$$\sum_{n=0}^\infty \frac{x}{1 + (n + 1)^2x^2} \le \int_0^\infty \frac{x}{1 + t^2x^2}\, dt \le \sum_{n=0}^\infty \frac{x}{1 + n^2x^2}$$

or

$$xF(x) \le \int_0^\infty \frac{x}{1 + x^2t^2}\, dt \le x + xF(x).$$

However,

$$\int_0^\infty \frac{x\, dt}{1 + x^2t^2} = \int_0^\infty \frac{du}{1 + u^2} = \frac{1}{2}\pi,$$

so that $\frac{1}{2}\pi - x \leq xF(x) \leq \frac{1}{2}\pi$, for all $x > 0$. Letting x approach 0, we have $\lim_{x \downarrow 0} xF(x) = \frac{1}{2}\pi$. Summarizing what we have found, the function F behaves near the origin like $\pi/2x$ and for large x, like Ax^{-2} where $A = \Sigma 1/n^2$ $(= \pi^2/6)$.

(iii) The methods of the present section allow us to construct a simple example of a nowhere differentiable continuous function. Let K be the special function defined by saying that $K(x)$ is the distance from x to the nearest integer; K is continuous everywhere, and periodic with period 1 (see Fig. 4-4). We note that K also has the property that

$$|K(b) - K(a)| = |b - a|$$

whenever a and b both lie in the same half of any interval $[m, m + 1]$. Set $u_j(x) = 10^{-j}K(10^j x)$ for $j = 0, 1, \ldots,$ and let $H(x) = \sum_0^\infty u_j(x)$ for all x. (Graphs of u_0, u_1, and $u_0 + u_1$ are given in Fig. 4-4.) Since $0 \leq u_j(x) \leq 10^{-j}$ for all x, the series for $H(x)$ is uniformly convergent for all x. Since each term u_j is everywhere continuous and satisfies the relation $u_j(x + 1) = u_j(x)$, H is everywhere continuous, and has period 1.

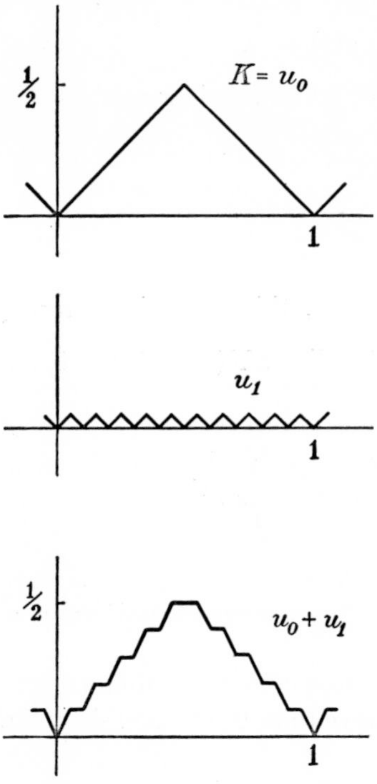

Fig. 4-4

We shall show that for any point b in $[0, 1]$,

$$H'(b) = \lim_{x \to b} \frac{H(x) - H(b)}{x - b}$$

fails to exist. We choose a special sequence $\{x_n\}$ approaching b for which this is easy to prove. Let b have the decimal representation

$$.b_1 b_2 b_3 \cdots = \sum_1^\infty \frac{b_j}{10^j}$$

To achieve uniqueness, we adopt the convention of using terminations

. . . 0000000 . . . rather than . . . 999999 . . . , so that, for example, we write .24100000 . . . in place of the equivalent .24099999 . . . . Given any positive integer $n = 1, 2, \ldots$, we define a real number x_n near b by

$$x_n = \begin{cases} b + 10^{-n} & \text{if } b_n \text{ is different from 4 and 9} \\ b - 10^{-n} & \text{if } b_n \text{ is either 4 or 9.} \end{cases}$$

So chosen, the pairs x_n and b, $10x_n$ and $10b$, . . . , $10^{n-1}x_n$ and $10^{n-1}b$, will always lie in the same half of any interval $[m, m + 1]$ which contains one of the pair. Moreover, for $j \geq n$, $10^j x_n$ and $10^j b$ will differ by some integer. The special properties of $K(x)$ then show that

$$|u_j(x_n) - u_j(b)| = \begin{cases} 10^{-n} = |x_n - b| & \text{for } j = 0, 1, \ldots, n-1 \\ 0 & \text{for } j \geq n. \end{cases}$$

and adding,

$$\frac{H(x_n) - H(b)}{x_n - b} = \overbrace{\pm 1 \pm 1 \cdots \pm 1 \pm 1}^{n \text{ terms}}$$

where the signs are determined by the particular digits in the decimal representation of b. However, regardless of the signs, we see that this quotient is an *even* integer for $n = 2, 4, 6, 8, \ldots$ and an *odd* integer for $n = 1, 3, 5, \ldots$. This shows that $\lim_{n \to \infty} \dfrac{H(x_n) - H(b)}{x_n - b}$ does not exist, and that H does not have a derivative at b.

As a final example, we prove the following important result which is frequently used in analysis. By virtue of it, a function which is continuous on a closed and bounded set may always be assumed to be continuous everywhere, and in fact zero-valued outside a sufficiently large disk.

Tietze's Extension Theorem. *Let E be a closed set in the plane (or in E^n), and let f be any function which is continuous and bounded on E. Then, there exists a function F which is continuous and bounded in the whole plane, and such that $F(p) = f(p)$ for all $p \in E$.*

It is first necessary to prove a preliminary result.

Lemma. *If C is a closed set, and $\phi(p) = d(p, C)$, the distance from p to C, then ϕ is everywhere continuous, and strictly positive off C.*

Let p, q, and c be three points with $c \in C$. The triangle property for distances shows that $|p - c| \leq |p - q| + |q - c|$. Since

$$d(p, C) = \inf_{c \in C} |p - c|,$$

we have $\phi(p) \leq |p - q| + |q - c|$. This holds in turn for every $c \in C$, so that $\phi(p) \le |p - q| + \phi(q)$. By symmetry, $\phi(q) \le |q - p| + \phi(p)$ so that, putting these together, $|\phi(p) - \phi(q)| \le |p - q|$. This shows that ϕ is everywhere (uniformly) continuous. If $\phi(p) = 0$, then

$$p = \lim c_n$$

for a sequence $\{c_n\}$ of points of C. Since C is closed, $p \in C$. ▌

To prove the theorem, we produce a series $\sum_1^\infty F_n$ of continuous functions which converges uniformly in the whole plane, and whose sum on the set E is f. Suppose that $|f(p)| \le M$ for $p \in E$. Divide E into three sets

$$A = \left\{\text{all } p \in E \quad \text{where } \frac{M}{3} \le f(p) \le M\right\}$$

$$C = \left\{\text{all } p \in E \quad \text{where } \frac{-M}{3} < f(p) < \frac{M}{3}\right\}$$

$$B = \left\{\text{all } p \in E \quad \text{where } -M \le f(p) \le \frac{-M}{3}\right\}$$

and construct a function F_1 by the definition

$$F_1(p) = \frac{M}{3}\,\frac{d(p, B) - d(p, A)}{d(p, B) + d(p, A)}$$

Since A and B are disjoint closed sets, F_1 is everywhere defined and is everywhere continuous. For any point p in the plane, $|F_1(p)| \le M/3$. On E, F_1 behaves as follows:

If $p \in A$, $d(p, A) = 0$ and $F_1(p) = \dfrac{M}{3}$.

If $p \in B$, $d(p, B) = 0$ and $F_1(p) = \dfrac{-M}{3}$.

If $p \in C$, then $\dfrac{-M}{3} \le F(p) \le \dfrac{M}{3}$.

An examination of the values of f on E shows that

$$|f(p) - F_1(p)| \le \tfrac{2}{3}M$$

for all $p \in E$. Repeat this argument with $f - F_1$ playing the role of f. On E, $f - F_1$ is bounded by $(2M)/3$. We can therefore construct a function F_2 which is everywhere continuous and such that $|F_2(p)| \le (\tfrac{1}{3})(2M/3)$ for all p, while $|[f(p) - F_1(p)] - F_2(p)| \le (\tfrac{2}{3})(2M/3)$ for $p \in E$. Continuing this, we arrive at a sequence of continuous functions $\{F_n\}$ which obey the two conditions:

$$|F_n(p)| \le \tfrac{1}{3}(\tfrac{2}{3})^{n-1}M, \qquad \text{all } p$$

$$|f(p) - \{F_1(p) + \cdots + F_n(p)\}| \le (\tfrac{2}{3})^n M, \qquad \text{all } p \in E.$$

The first condition assures us that the series $\sum_1^\infty F_n$ is uniformly convergent for all p. The sum F is then, by Theorem 17, continuous everywhere in the plane. The second condition shows that $F(p) = \sum_1^\infty F_n(p) = f(p)$ for all $p \in E$. Finally, for any p

$$|F(p)| \le \sum_1^\infty |F_n(p)| \le \frac{M}{3}\left(1 + \frac{2}{3} + \left(\frac{2}{3}\right)^2 + \cdots\right) \le \frac{M}{3}\frac{1}{1 - (2/3)} = M,$$

so that F is bounded on the whole plane by the same bound that applied to f on E. ▌

EXERCISES

1. Let $f_n(x) = x^n$ for $0 \le x \le 1$. Does $\{f_n\}$ converge pointwise on [0, 1]? Does it converge uniformly on [0, 1]? Does it converge uniformly on [0, ½]?

2. Let $f_n(x) = nx^n(1 - x)$ for $0 \le x \le 1$. Show that $\{f_n\}$ converges pointwise, but not uniformly, on [0, 1]. Does $\lim_{n\to\infty} \int_0^1 f_n = \int_0^1 \lim_{n\to\infty} f_n$?

3. Let $F(x) = \sum_1^\infty \dfrac{x^2}{x^2 + n^2}$. Study the uniform convergence of this series, and investigate the existence of $\lim_{x\downarrow 0} F(x)$, $\lim_{x\downarrow 0} \dfrac{F(x)}{x}$, $\lim_{x\downarrow 0} \dfrac{F(x)}{x^2}$, $\lim_{x\uparrow \infty} F(x)$, $\lim_{x\uparrow \infty} \dfrac{F(x)}{x^2}$, $\lim_{x\uparrow \infty} \dfrac{F(x)}{x}$.

4. Let f be continuous on the interval $0 \le x < \infty$, and let $\lim_{x\to\infty} f(x) = L$. What can you say about $\lim_{n\to\infty} \int_0^2 f(nx)\,dx$?

5. Let g be continuous on [0, 1] with $g(1) = 0$. Show that $\{g(x)x^n\}$ converges uniformly for x in [0, 1].

***6.** Let $\phi_n(x)$ be positive-valued and continuous for all x in $[-1, 1]$ with

$$\lim_{n\to\infty} \int_{-1}^1 \phi_n = 1.$$

Suppose further that $\{\phi_n\}$ converges to 0 uniformly on the intervals $[-1, -c]$ and $[c, 1]$ for any $c > 0$. Let g be any function which is continuous on $[-1, 1]$. Show that $\lim_{n\to\infty} \int_{-1}^1 g(x)\phi_n(x)\,dx = g(0)$.

***7.** Let f_n be continuous on a closed and bounded set E, for each n, and let $\{f_n\}$ converge pointwise to a continuous function F. Suppose that for any $p \in E$, the sequence $\{f_n(p)\}$ is an increasing sequence of real numbers. Prove that $\{f_n\}$ in fact converges uniformly on E. (*Hint:* For a given ϵ, consider the set

$$C_n = \{\text{all } p \in E \text{ with } F(p) - f_n(p) \geq \epsilon\},$$

and apply the nested set property.)

8. A sequence of functions $\{f_n\}$ is said to *converge in the mean*—or in L^2—to a function F on the interval $[a, b]$ whenever

$$\lim_{n \to \infty} \int_a^b |F(x) - f_n(x)|^2 \, dx = 0.$$

(*a*) Show that $\{f_n\}$ converges in the mean if it converges uniformly on $[a, b]$.

(*b*) Show that if $\{f_n\}$ converges in the mean to F on $[a, b]$, then $\lim_{n \to \infty} \int_a^b f_n = \int_a^b F$.

*(*c*) Show by an example that a sequence can converge in the mean to 0, without converging pointwise.

4.3. Power Series

Among all series of functions, the special class known as **power series** deserves particular attention. A general power series in x has the form $\sum_0^\infty a_n x^n$, and a power series in $x - c$ (or about $x = c$) has the form $\sum_0^\infty a_n (x - c)^n$. The behavior of power series with respect to pointwise convergence is especially simple.

Theorem 22. *With any power series* $\sum_0^\infty a_n x^n$ *is associated a radius of convergence* R, $0 \leq R \leq \infty$, *such that the series converges (absolutely) for all* x *with* $|x| < R$, *and diverges for all* x *with* $|x| > R$. *Moreover,* R *may be calculated from the relation*

$$\frac{1}{R} = \limsup_{n \to \infty} |a_n|^{1/n}$$

or

$$\frac{1}{R} = \lim_{n \to \infty} \left| \frac{a_{n+1}}{a_n} \right|$$

when the latter exists.

We have only to apply the root test for convergence. Let

$$L = \limsup |a_n|^{1/n}.$$

Then, $\limsup |a_n x^n|^{1/n} = L|x|$ so that $\Sigma a_n x^n$ converges whenever $L|x| < 1$, and diverges whenever $L|x| > 1$. If $L = 0$, we see that the series converges for all x; if $L = \infty$, then it converges only for $x = 0$. Setting $R = 1/L$, and interpreting $L = 0$ to correspond to $R = \infty$, and $L = \infty$

to $R = 0$, we see that $\Sigma a_n x^n$ converges for all x with $|x| < R$. The final statement of the theorem comes from the fact that when $\lim \left| \frac{a_{n+1}}{a_n} \right|$ exists, its value is always the same as $\lim |a_n|^{1/n}$. ▮ (See Exercise 6, Sec. 4.1.)

The corresponding facts for more general power series can be obtained from this by substitution. The series $\sum_0^\infty a_n[g(x)]^n$ may be called a power series in $g(x)$. If we set $g(x) = y$, this becomes $\sum_0^\infty a_n y^n$. If this power series in y has radius of convergence R, then $\sum_0^\infty a_n[g(x)]^n$ converges for all x with $|g(x)| < R$. In particular, this gives the corollary.

Corollary. *If $1/R = \limsup |a_n|^{1/n}$, then $\sum_0^\infty a_n(x - c)^n$ converges for all x with $|x - c| < R$, and diverges when $|x - c| > R$.*

The convergence set is thus an interval of length $2R$ centered at the point c, with end points $c - R$ and $c + R$. The behavior of power series with respect to uniform convergence is equally simple.

Theorem 23. *A power series $\sum_0^\infty a_n x^n$ with radius of convergence R is uniformly convergent in every closed interval $-b \leq x \leq b$ for $b < R$.*

The series $\Sigma a_n b^n$ is absolutely convergent. If $|x| \leq b$, then $|a_n x^n| \leq |a_n b^n|$. By the Weierstrass comparison theorem, $\Sigma a_n x^n$ converges uniformly for all x with $|x| \leq b$. ▮

If this is combined with Theorem 21, it follows that a power series can always be differentiated termwise within its interval of convergence.

Theorem 24. *Let $f(x) = \sum_0^\infty a_n x^n$ converge for $|x| < R$. Then, f' exists, and $f'(x) = \sum_1^\infty n a_n x^{n-1}$ for all x with $|x| < R$.*

Consider $x \sum_1^\infty n a_n x^{n-1} = \sum_1^\infty n a_n x^n$. Since multiplication by x does not affect convergence properties, the differentiated series has radius of convergence $1/L$, where $L = \limsup_{n\to\infty} |n a_n|^{1/n} = \limsup_{n\to\infty} |a_n|^{1/n}$, using the fact that $\lim_{n\to\infty} n^{1/n} = 1$. Thus, the original power series and its termwise derivative always have the same radius of convergence. The derived series is then uniformly convergent for $|x| \le b$, and any $b < R$, and, by Theorem 21, the differentiation was justified. ▌

Repeating this argument, we see that a function given by a convergent power series may be differentiated as many times as desired, and the derivatives computed termwise, within the interval of convergence.

Corollary 1. *If* $f(x) = \sum_0^\infty a_n(x - c)^n$, *convergent for some interval about* c, *then* $a_n = f^{(n)}(c)/n!$.

For we have

$$f^{(n)}(x) = n!a_n + 2 \cdot 3 \cdots (n + 1)a_{n+1}(x - c) \\ + 3 \cdot 4 \cdots (n + 2)a_{n+2}(x - c)^2 + \cdots$$

in an interval about c, and setting $x = c$, we have $f^{(n)}(c) = n!a_n$. ▌

Corollary 2. *If* $\sum_0^\infty a_n(x - c)^n = \sum_0^\infty b_n(x - c)^n$ *for all* x *in a neighborhood of* c, *then* $a_n = b_n$ *for* $n = 0, 1, \ldots$.

If the common value is $f(x)$, then a_n and b_n are of necessity both given by $f^{(n)}(c)/n!$. ▌

It should be observed that this shows that a function that is analytic on a neighborhood of c can have only one power series expansion of the form $\Sigma a_n(x - c)^n$, and that this one is the Taylor series which is obtained as the limit of the Taylor polynomials. Conversely, any function which is given by a convergent power series is analytic within the interval of convergence.

A power series can converge or fail to converge at either end point of its interval of convergence. Consider the series

$$f(x) = \sum_1^\infty \frac{x^n}{n^2}$$

which has radius of convergence $R = 1$. This converges in fact for all x with $-1 \le x \le 1$. If we differentiate this, we obtain

$$f'(x) = \sum_1^\infty \frac{x^{n-1}}{n}$$

which converges only for $-1 \le x < 1$. If we again differentiate it, we obtain

$$f''(x) = \sum_{2}^{\infty} \frac{n-1}{n} x^{n-2}$$

which now converges only for $-1 < x < 1$. The first of the three series converges uniformly for all x with $-1 \le x \le 1$ since its terms are dominated there by $1/n^2$. Theorem 23 shows that the second series converges uniformly in intervals $|x| \le b$ with $b < 1$; since it is (pointwise) convergent on the larger interval $-1 \le x \le b$, it might be conjectured that it is uniformly convergent there as well. The truth of this follows from a general result, due to Abel.

Theorem 25. *Let $\sum_{0}^{\infty} a_n x^n$ have radius of convergence R, and let it also converge for $x = R$ [for $x = -R$]. Then, it is uniformly convergent on the interval $0 \le x \le R$ [the interval $-R \le x \le 0$].*

Without loss of generality, we may assume that $R = 1$, and that $\Sigma a_n x^n$ converges when $x = 1$. Put $B_n = \sum_{n}^{\infty} a_k$ so that $\lim_{n\to\infty} B_n = 0$. Then, for any x, $0 \le x < 1$,

$$\begin{aligned}\sum_{n}^{\infty} a_k x^k &= a_n x^n + a_{n+1}x^{n+1} + \cdots \\ &= (B_n - B_{n+1})x^n + (B_{n+1} - B_{n+2})x^{n+1} + \cdots \\ &= B_n x^n + B_{n+1}(x^{n+1} - x^n) + B_{n+2}(x^{n+2} - x^{n+1}) + \cdots \\ &= B_n x^n + (x-1)x^n\{B_{n+1} + B_{n+2}x + \cdots\}.\end{aligned}$$

Given ϵ, choose N so that $|B_j| < \epsilon$ whenever $j \ge N$. Then, for $0 \le x < 1$, and $n \ge N$,

$$\begin{aligned}\left|\sum_{n}^{\infty} a_k x^k\right| &\le \epsilon x^n + (1-x)x^n\{\epsilon + \epsilon x + \epsilon x^2 + \cdots\} \\ &\le \epsilon x^n + \epsilon x^n(1-x)\{1 + x + x^2 + \cdots\} \\ &\le 2\epsilon x^n < 2\epsilon.\end{aligned}$$

This also holds when $x = 1$, since $|B_n| < \epsilon < 2\epsilon$. Thus, $\left|\sum_{n}^{\infty} a_k x^k\right| < 2\epsilon$ uniformly for all x with $0 \le x \le 1$, and all $n \ge N$, proving uniform convergence. ▮

Corollary. *If $\sum_{0}^{\infty} a_n R^n$ converges to S, then $\lim_{x \uparrow R} \sum_{0}^{\infty} a_n x^n = S$.*

Since power series are always uniformly convergent in closed intervals which lie in the interval of convergence, they can be integrated termwise over any such interval. The process of integration, or differentiation, is often combined with algebraic operations and with substitution to obtain the power series expansion of special functions; although the coefficients of the expansion of a function f can always be obtained from the formula $a_n = f^{(n)}(c)/n!$, this is often a long and complicated task. The following examples will illustrate these remarks.

Let us start from the simple geometric series

$$\frac{1}{1-x} = 1 + x + x^2 + x^3 + \cdots \tag{4-4}$$

which converges for $-1 < x < 1$. Repeated differentiation of this yields

$$\frac{1}{(1-x)^2} = 1 + 2x + 3x^2 + 4x^3 + \cdots + (n+1)x^n + \cdots$$

$$\frac{2}{(1-x)^3} = 2 + 6x + 12x^2 + \cdots + (n+1)(n+2)x^n + \cdots$$

and in general

$$\frac{k!}{(1-x)^{k+1}} = k! + \frac{(k+1)!}{1!}x + \frac{(k+2)!}{2!}x^2 + \cdots$$

with convergence for $-1 < x < 1$. If we choose instead to integrate the first series, we obtain

$$-\log(1-x) = x + \frac{x^2}{2} + \frac{x^3}{3} + \cdots \tag{4-5}$$

convergent for $-1 < x < 1$. Since the series is also convergent for $x = -1$, the corollary to Theorem 25 shows that (4-5) holds also for $x = -1$, with uniform convergence for $-1 \le x \le b$, $b < 1$. In (4-5), replace x by $-x$, obtaining

$$\log(1+x) = x - \frac{x^2}{2} + \frac{x^3}{3} - \frac{x^4}{4} + \cdots .$$

Divide by x, and integrate again on the interval $[0, x]$, $x \le 1$

$$\int_0^x \frac{\log(1+t)}{t}\,dt = x - \frac{x^2}{4} + \frac{x^3}{9} - \cdots (-)^{n+1}\frac{x^n}{n^2} + \cdots .$$

In the first series (4-4), replace x by $-x^2$, getting

$$\frac{1}{1+x^2} = 1 - x^2 + x^4 - x^6 + x^8 - \cdots$$

convergent for $-1 < x < 1$. Integrate from 0 to x, $|x| < 1$, obtaining

$$\arctan x = x - \frac{x^3}{3} + \frac{x^5}{5} - \cdots .$$

Since this converges for $x = 1$ and $x = -1$, it converges uniformly for $-1 \le x \le 1$. In particular, setting $x = 1$,

$$\frac{\pi}{4} = 1 - \frac{1}{3} + \frac{1}{5} - \frac{1}{7} + \cdots ,$$

where we have again used the corollary of Theorem 25. Let us define the exponential function E by the power series

$$E(x) = \sum_0^\infty \frac{x^n}{n!} = 1 + x + \frac{x^2}{2!} + \cdots . \tag{4-6}$$

Then, since this converges for all x, it converges uniformly in every interval $|x| \le R$, $R < \infty$. Differentiating, we obtain

$$E'(x) = \sum_1^\infty \frac{nx^{n-1}}{n!} = \sum_1^\infty \frac{x^{n-1}}{(n-1)!} = E(x).$$

This shows that the function E is a solution of the differential equation $y' = y$. The other properties of the exponential function can also be obtained from the series definition. To verify the relation

$$E(a)E(b) = E(a + b),$$

we form the Cauchy product of the series for $E(a)$ and $E(b)$, obtaining

$$\begin{aligned} E(a)E(b) &= \sum_0^\infty \frac{a^n}{n!} \sum_0^\infty \frac{b^n}{n!} = \sum_{n=0}^\infty \left\{ \frac{a^n b^0}{n!0!} + \frac{a^{n-1}b}{(n-1)!1!} + \cdots + \frac{a^0 b^n}{0!n!} \right\} \\ &= \sum_{n=0}^\infty \frac{1}{n!} \sum_{k=0}^n \frac{n!}{(n-k)!\,k!} a^{n-k} b^k \\ &= \sum_0^\infty \frac{1}{n!} (a+b)^n = E(a+b). \end{aligned}$$

With $e = E(1)$, $e^n = E(n)$, and we may define e^x for general real exponents as $E(x)$. Suppose we wish to expand e^x in a power series in powers of $x - c$. Write

$$\begin{aligned} e^x &= E(x - c + c) = E(x - c)E(c) \\ &= e^c \left\{ 1 + \frac{x-c}{1} + \frac{(x-c)^2}{2!} + \frac{(x-c)^3}{3!} + \cdots \right\} \end{aligned}$$

Replacing x by $-x^2$ in the series for E, we have

$$e^{-x^2} = 1 - x^2 + \frac{x^4}{2!} - \frac{x^6}{3!} + \cdots$$

convergent for all x. Integrating this, we have

$$\int_0^t e^{-x^2}\,dx = t - \frac{t^3}{3} + \frac{t^5}{10} - \frac{t^7}{42} + \cdots.$$

We note, however, that this expansion does not enable us to evaluate $\int_0^\infty e^{-x^2}\,dx$ since we cannot take the limit of the right side as t increases. On page 98, we have shown that the exact value of this is $\frac{1}{2}\sqrt{\pi}$.

EXERCISES

1. Determine the radius of convergence of the following series:

(a) $\sum_0^\infty n!x^n$ (b) $\sum_1^\infty \frac{n!}{n^n} x^n$

(c) $\sum_0^\infty c^{n^2}x^n$ where $0 < c < \infty$.

2. Define the trigonometric functions sine and cosine by

$$S(x) = \sum_0^\infty (-1)^n \frac{x^{2n+1}}{(2n+1)!}$$

and $C(x) = S'(x)$. Show directly that $S(2x) = 2S(x)C(x)$ by multiplying their power series.

3. Find power series representations for the following functions which converge in some interval containing the indicated point.

(a) $\sin(x^2)$ near $x = 0$ (b) $1/x$ near $x = 1$

(c) $\log(1 + x^2)$ near $x = 0$ (d) $\cosh(x)$ near $x = 0$

4. By integration, differentiation, or any other valid operation, find the functions which are given by the following power series.

(a) $\sum_1^\infty n^2x^n$ (b) $\sum_0^\infty \frac{x^n}{(2n)!}$

(c) $\sum_0^\infty \frac{x^{2n+1}}{2n+1}$ (d) $x + x^4 + x^7 + x^{10} + x^{13} + \cdots$

5. Can the following functions be expressed as power series in x which converge in a neighborhood of zero?

(a) $f(x) = |x|$ (b) $f(x) = \cos \sqrt{x}$

6. The Bessel function of zero order may be defined by $J_0(x) = \sum_0^\infty \frac{(-1)^n x^{2n}}{4^n (n!)^2}$.

Find its radius of convergence, and show that $y = J_0(x)$ is a solution of the differential equation: $xy'' + y' + xy = 0$.

***7.** Let $\lim_{n\to\infty} a_n = L$ and $f(x) = \sum_0^\infty a_n x^n$. Show that $\lim_{x\uparrow 1} (1 - x)f(x) = L$.

4.4. Improper Integrals with a Parameter

The notion of uniform convergence is not restricted to series and sequences. For example, if $\lim_{t\to t_0} f(p, t) = F(p)$ for each p in a set E, we say that the convergence is **uniform** on E if, given ϵ we can find a neighborhood N of t_0 such that $|f(p, t) - F(p)| < \epsilon$ for all $p \in E$ and all t in N, with $t \neq t_0$. As an illustration, let $f(x, t) = \frac{\sin(xt)}{t(1 + x^2)}$. Using L'Hospital's rule, we see that $\lim_{t\to 0} f(x, t) = \lim_{t\to 0} \frac{x\cos(xt)}{1 + x^2} = \frac{x}{1 + x^2}$ for all x, $-\infty < x < \infty$. Let us prove the convergence is uniform. For any x and any $t \neq 0 = t_0$, we have

$$|f(x, t) - F(x)| = \left| \frac{\sin xt}{t(1 + x^2)} - \frac{x}{1 + x^2} \right| = \frac{|x|}{1 + x^2} \left| \frac{\sin xt}{xt} - 1 \right|.$$

Since $\lim_{\theta\to 0} \frac{\sin\theta}{\theta} = 1$, we can choose β so that $\left|\frac{\sin\theta}{\theta} - 1\right| < \epsilon$ whenever $|\theta| < \beta$. For any R let $\delta = \beta/R$. Then, if $|x| \le R$ and $|t| < \delta$,

$$|xt| < R\left(\frac{\beta}{R}\right) = \beta,$$

so that

$$|f(x, t) - F(x)| \le R \left| \frac{\sin xt}{xt} - 1 \right| \le R\epsilon.$$

This shows that $\lim_{t\to 0} f(x, t) = \frac{x}{1 + x^2}$ uniformly on each of the intervals $[-R, R]$. To prove uniform convergence on the whole axis, we need an additional estimate. Since $|(\sin\theta)/\theta| \le 1$ for all θ, we see that for any x and t,

$$|f(x, t) - F(x)| \le \frac{2|x|}{1 + x^2}.$$

Since $\lim_{|x|\to\infty} \dfrac{2x}{1+x^2} = 0$, we can choose R_0 so that for any t

$$|f(x, t) - F(x)| < \epsilon$$

whenever $|x| \geq R_0$. Combining these inequalities, we have

$$|f(x, t) - F(x)| < \epsilon$$

for all x and any t with $|t| < \beta/R_0$.

The continuous analogue of an infinite series is an improper integral and the possibility of uniform convergence arises whenever the integrand contains a parameter.

Definition. *An improper integral $\int_c^\infty f(p, u)\,du$ is said to converge to $F(p)$, uniformly for $p \in E$, whenever*

$$\lim_{r\uparrow\infty} \int_c^r f(p, u)\,du = F(p),$$

uniformly for $p \in E$, that is, whenever corresponding to any $\epsilon > 0$ a number R may be found such that

$$\left| F(p) - \int_c^r f(p, u)\,du \right| = \left| \int_r^\infty f(p, u)\,du \right| < \epsilon$$

for all $p \in E$ and all $r \geq R$.

Each of the theorems of Sec. 4.2 has its analogue in a theorem dealing with uniform convergence and with the commutativity of certain limit operations. Since the proofs follow so closely the pattern of those for series, we point out only the essential differences, and leave the details to the reader.

Theorem 26 (*Comparison Test*). *The integral $\int_c^\infty f(p, u)\,du$ converges uniformly for $p \in E$ if f is continuous and obeys the condition $|f(p, u)| \leq g(u)$ for all $p \in E$ and u, $c \leq u < \infty$, and $\int_c^\infty g$ converges.*

Theorem 27. *The function $F(p) = \int_c^\infty f(p, u)\,du$ is continuous for $p \in E$ if the integral converges uniformly for $p \in E$, and f is continuous for all (p, u) with $p \in E$ and $c \leq u < \infty$.*

Write $F(p) = \int_c^r f(p, u)\,du + \int_r^\infty f(p, u)\,du$. By a previous result (Exercise 13, Sec. 3.2) the first integral is a continuous function of p. By hypothesis, the second is uniformly small if r is chosen sufficiently large. Thus, F can be approximated uniformly on E by continuous functions and is therefore continuous. ▌

Corollary. *If* $\int_c^\infty f(p, u)\,du$ *converges uniformly for* $p \in E$ *and* $f(p, u)$ *is continuous for* $p \in E$ *and* $c \leq u < \infty$, *and* $p_0 \in E$ *is a cluster point for* E, *then*

$$\lim_{p \to p_0} \int_c^\infty f(p, u)\,du = \int_c^\infty f(p_0, u)\,du.$$

As an illustration of these results, consider $F(x) = \int_1^\infty \frac{x^2\,du}{1 + x^2u^2}$. Since $\left|\frac{x^2}{1 + x^2u^2}\right| \leq \frac{1}{u^2}$ for all x, and $\int_1^\infty u^{-2}\,du$ converges, the integral defining F converges uniformly for all x. In consequence, F is continuous for all x, and

$$\lim_{x \uparrow \infty} F(x) = \int_1^\infty \lim_{x \uparrow \infty} \frac{x^2}{1 + x^2u^2}\,du = \int_1^\infty u^{-2}\,du = 1.$$

In this case, we can check the result directly. Making the substitution $xu = t$, $x > 0$,

$$\begin{aligned} F(x) &= x^2 \int_1^\infty \frac{du}{1 + x^2u^2} = x \int_x^\infty \frac{dt}{1 + t^2} \\ &= x \left\{\frac{\pi}{2} - \arctan x\right\} = \frac{\frac{1}{2}\pi - \arctan x}{1/x} \end{aligned}$$

so that, using L'Hospital's rule,

$$\lim_{x \uparrow \infty} F(x) = \lim_{x \uparrow \infty} \frac{-1/(1 + x^2)}{-x^{-2}} = 1.$$

Corresponding to Theorem 19 on termwise integration of series, we have a result which justifies the reversal of the order of integration in certain improper iterated integrals.

Theorem 28. $\int_a^b dx \int_c^\infty f(x, u)\,du = \int_c^\infty du \int_a^b f(x, u)\,dx$ *if* $f(x, u)$ *is continuous for* $a \leq x \leq b$, $c \leq u < \infty$ and $\int_c^\infty f(x, u)\,du$ *converges uniformly for* x *on* $[a, b]$.

Using Theorem 8, Sec. 3.2, to reverse the order of integration we have

$$\int_c^r du \int_a^b f(x, u)\,dx = \int_a^b dx \int_c^r f(x, u)\,du,$$

so that

$$\int_c^\infty du \int_a^b f(x, u)\,dx = \lim_{r \uparrow \infty} \int_a^b dx \int_c^r f(x, u)\,du.$$

On the other hand,

$$\int_a^b dx \int_c^\infty f(x, u)\, du = \int_a^b dx \int_c^r f(x, u)\, du + \int_a^b dx \int_r^\infty f(x, u)\, du.$$

Since $\int_c^\infty f(x, u)\, du$ converges uniformly,

$$\lim_{r \uparrow \infty} \int_r^\infty f(x, u)\, du = 0,$$

uniformly for $x \in [a, b]$ and

$$\lim_{r \uparrow \infty} \int_a^b dx \int_r^\infty f(x, u)\, du = 0. \quad \blacksquare$$

Without some restriction on the integrand, and on the mode of convergence of an improper integral, reversal of the order of integration is not valid. Consider, for example, a function F defined by

$$F(x) = \int_0^\infty (2xu - x^2u^2)e^{-xu}\, du. \tag{4-7}$$

For $x = 0, F(0) = 0$. With $x > 0$, we may evaluate F directly, obtaining

$$\begin{aligned} F(x) &= \lim_{R \to \infty} [xu^2e^{-xu}]_{u=0}^{u=R} \\ &= \lim_{R \to \infty} xR^2e^{-xR} = 0. \end{aligned}$$

Thus, $F(x) = 0$ for all $x \geq 0$. In particular, then,

$$\int_0^1 F(x)\, dx = \int_0^1 dx \int_0^\infty (2xu - x^2u^2)e^{-xu}\, du = 0.$$

Consider the effect of reversing the order of integration:

$$\begin{aligned} \int_0^\infty du \int_0^1 (2xu - x^2u^2)e^{-xu}\, dx &= \int_0^\infty du\, [x^2ue^{-xu}]_{x=0}^{x=1} \\ &= \int_0^\infty ue^{-u}\, du = 1. \end{aligned}$$

This discrepancy is explained by the fact that the original improper integral (4-7) is not uniformly convergent for x in the interval $[0, 1]$ over which we wish to integrate. We have

$$F(x) = \lim_{R \to \infty} xR^2e^{-xR} = \lim_{R \to \infty} g(x, R)$$

and the convergence is not uniform since $g(1/R, R) = R/e$, which is unbounded. (The graphs of these functions for several values of R are given in Fig. 4-3, page 129.)

When certain conditions are fulfilled, an improper integral containing a parameter can be differentiated with respect to that parameter underneath the integral sign.

Theorem 29. *If* $\int_c^\infty f(x, u)\,du$ *converges to* $F(x)$ *for all* x, $a \le x \le b$, *and if* f *and* $f_1 = \dfrac{\partial f}{\partial x}$ *are continuous for* $a \le x \le b$, $c \le u < \infty$, *and if* $\int_c^\infty f_1(x, u)\,du$ *is uniformly convergent for* x *in* $[a, b]$, *then for any* x *in* $[a, b]$,

$$F'(x) = \frac{d}{dx}\int_c^\infty f(x, u)\,du = \int_c^\infty f_1(x, u)\,du.$$

The proof is essentially the same as that of Theorem 10, Sec. 3.2. Set

$$g(x) = \int_c^\infty f_1(x, u)\,du.$$

Since this is uniformly convergent and f_1 is continuous, g is continuous, and for any $\bar{x}$, $a \le \bar{x} \le b$,

$$\begin{aligned}\int_a^{\bar{x}} g &= \int_a^{\bar{x}} g(x)\,dx = \int_a^{\bar{x}} dx \int_c^\infty f_1(x, u)\,du\\ &= \int_c^\infty du \int_a^{\bar{x}} f_1(x, u)\,dx.\end{aligned}$$

But

$$\int_a^{\bar{x}} f_1(x, u)\,dx = \int_a^{\bar{x}} \frac{\partial f}{\partial x}(x, u)\,dx = f(\bar{x}, u) - f(a, u)$$

and

$$\begin{aligned}\int_a^{\bar{x}} g &= \int_c^\infty [f(\bar{x}, u) - f(a, u)]\,du\\ &= F(\bar{x}) - F(a).\end{aligned}$$

Since g is continuous, this shows that F is differentiable, and that $F' = g$. ▌

We shall give a number of examples which illustrate these theorems and the manner in which they may be used in the evaluation of certain special definite integrals.

Let us start with the formula

$$\frac{1}{x} = \int_0^\infty e^{-xu}\,du, \tag{4-8}$$

valid for all $x > 0$. If we differentiate this, we obtain

$$\frac{1}{x^2} = \int_0^\infty ue^{-xu}\,du. \tag{4-9}$$

To check the validity of this process, we observe that $|ue^{-xu}| \le ue^{-\delta u}$

for all x with $x \geq \delta > 0$; since $\int_0^\infty ue^{-\delta u}\,du$ converges, the integral in (4-9) is uniformly convergent for all x with $\delta \leq x < \infty$. This justifies the differentiation and the formula (4-9) holds for every point x which can be included in one of these intervals, that is, for every x with $x > 0$.

More generally, the same argument may be used to show that for any $n = 1, 2, 3, \ldots$

$$\frac{n!}{x^{n+1}} = \int_0^\infty u^n e^{-xu}\,du. \tag{4-10}$$

As another illustration, consider the improper integral

$$\int_0^\infty \frac{e^{-x} - e^{-2x}}{x}\,dx. \tag{4-11}$$

Since the integrand may be expressed as $\int_1^2 e^{-xu}\,du$, we may write (4-11) as an iterated integral

$$\int_0^\infty dx \int_1^2 e^{-xu}\,du.$$

Reversing the order of integration, we obtain

$$\int_1^2 du \int_0^\infty e^{-xu}\,dx. \tag{4-12}$$

This does not alter the value, since the inner integral is uniformly convergent for all u with $1 \leq u \leq 2$. Using (4-8), we find that exact value of the original integral (4-11) is $\int_1^2 u^{-1}\,du = \log 2$.

Sometimes the operations of differentiation and integration are combined, as in the following illustration. On page 91, we saw that the improper integral $\int_0^\infty x^{-1} \sin x\,dx$ was conditionally convergent; we shall now show that its value is $\frac{1}{2}\pi$. Let

$$F(u) = \int_0^\infty e^{-xu} \frac{\sin x}{x}\,dx. \tag{4-13}$$

This converges for all $u \geq 0$ and $F(0)$ is the value we seek. If we differentiate (4-13), we obtain

$$F'(u) = -\int_0^\infty e^{-xu} \sin x\,dx \tag{4-14}$$

which may be integrated exactly, yielding $F'(u) = -(1 + u^2)^{-1}$. This is valid for all u with $u > 0$ since the integrand in (4-14) is dominated by e^{-xu} and, as we have seen, the integral of this is uniformly convergent for all u with $\delta \leq u < \infty$ and any $\delta > 0$. Integrating, we find that

$F(u) = C - \arctan u$, for all $u > 0$. Now, suppose we let u increase; from (4-13), it would seem that $\lim_{u \to \infty} F(u) = 0$, so that

$$0 = C - \lim_{u \to \infty} \arctan u = C - \tfrac{1}{2}\pi,$$

and $C = \frac{1}{2}\pi$. We then have $F(u) = \dfrac{\pi}{2} - \arctan u$, so that

$$F(0) = \int_0^\infty x^{-1} \sin x \, dx = \tfrac{1}{2}\pi.$$

There are two gaps in this argument. We have assumed that

$$\lim_{u \to \infty} \int_0^\infty e^{-xu} \frac{\sin x}{x} \, dx = 0$$

and

$$\lim_{u \downarrow 0} \int_0^\infty e^{-xu} \frac{\sin x}{x} \, dx = \int_0^\infty \frac{\sin x}{x} \, dx.$$

Both will follow from our general theorems if we can show that the integral in (4-13) which defines F is uniformly convergent for all u with $0 \le u < \infty$, since we are then justified in taking limits under the integral sign. We cannot use the Weierstrass comparison theorem to achieve this since $\int_0^\infty x^{-1}|\sin x| \, dx$ is divergent. Let us instead use integration by parts to improve the convergence. We have

$$\int_R^\infty e^{-xu}x^{-1} \sin x \, dx = \Big[-e^{-xu}x^{-1} \cos x \Big]_{x=R}^{x=\infty} - \int_R^\infty \frac{(1 + xu)e^{-xu} \cos x}{x^2} \, dx$$

choosing to integrate $\sin x$ and differentiate the remaining factor. The integrand in the second integral is always less than $1/x^2$ in absolute value, for any $u \ge 0$, so that

$$\left| \int_R^\infty e^{-xu}x^{-1} \sin x \, dx \right| \le \frac{e^{-uR}|\cos R|}{R} + \int_R^\infty x^{-2} \, dx$$
$$\le \frac{2}{R}$$

and therefore

$$\lim_{R \to \infty} \int_R^\infty e^{-xu}x^{-1} \sin x \, dx = 0$$

uniformly for all u with $0 \le u < \infty$. This, together with the previous remarks, completes the proof that

$$\int_0^\infty x^{-1} \sin x \, dx = \tfrac{1}{2}\pi.$$

Another specialized integral that can be treated by the same method is

$$\int_0^\infty \exp(-x^2 - x^{-2})\, dx. \tag{4-15}$$

Consider the related integral

$$F(u) = \int_0^\infty e^{-x^2}e^{-u^2/x^2}\, dx. \tag{4-16}$$

As partial motivation for this choice, we observe that $F(1)$ is the desired integral, while $F(0)$ is the familiar integral $\int_0^\infty e^{-x^2}\, dx$ which we have shown (Sec. 3.4) to have the value $\sqrt{\pi}/2$. Differentiate (4-16), getting

$$F'(u) = -2\int_0^\infty \left(\frac{u}{x^2}\right) e^{-x^2}e^{-u^2/x^2}\, dx. \tag{4-17}$$

To justify this, we must show that this integral converges uniformly. Writing the integrand in (4-17) as $u^{-1}(u/x)^2e^{-(u/x)^2}e^{-x^2}$ and using the fact that $s^2e^{-s^2}$ has maximum value e^{-1}, we see that the integrand is dominated by $(1/eu)e^{-x^2}$ so that the integral is uniformly convergent for all $u \geq \delta > 0$. We cannot easily integrate (4-17); however, let us make the substitution $t = u/x$, obtaining for any $u > 0$,

$$\begin{aligned} F'(u) &= -2\int_\infty^0 u^{-1}t^2e^{-t^2}e^{-(u/t)^2}\left(\frac{-u}{t^2}\right) dt \\ &= -2\int_0^\infty e^{-t^2}e^{-u^2/t^2}\, dt \\ &= -2F(u). \end{aligned}$$

Solving this differential equation, we find that $F(u) = Ce^{-2u}$, valid for all $u > 0$. However, the integral (4-16) which defines F is uniformly convergent for all u since $|e^{-x^2}e^{-u^2/x^2}| \leq e^{-x^2}$ for all u. In particular, F is then continuous at 0, and $\lim_{u \downarrow 0} F(u) = F(0)$. We know that $F(0)$ has the value $\sqrt{\pi}/2$, so that

$$C = \sqrt{\pi}/2, \quad \text{and} \quad F(1) = \int_0^\infty e^{-(x^2+1/x^2)}\, dx = \tfrac{1}{2}\sqrt{\pi}\, e^{-2}.$$

EXERCISES

1. Investigate the existence and uniformity of

$$\lim_{t\to 0} \frac{x \sin(xt)}{1 + x^2}.$$

2. Let f be continuous on the interval $0 \leq x < \infty$ with $|f(x)| \leq M$. Set

$$F(u) = \frac{2}{\pi} \int_0^\infty \frac{uf(x)\,dx}{u^2 + x^2}.$$

Show that $\lim\limits_{u \downarrow 0} F(u) = f(0)$.

3. Evaluate $\lim\limits_{r \to \infty} \int_0^{\pi/2} e^{-r \sin\theta}\,d\theta$.

4. Evaluate $\lim\limits_{x \to \infty} \int_0^\infty \frac{x^2u\,du}{x^3 + u^3}$.

5. Evaluate $\int_0^\infty \frac{\sin^2 (xu)\,du}{u^2}$.

6. Evaluate $\int_0^\infty \frac{1 - \cos x}{x^2}\,dx$.

7. Evaluate $\int_0^\infty e^{-u^2} \cos (xu)\,du$.

8. Evaluate $\int_0^\infty e^{-(x-1/x)^2}\,dx$.

4.5. The Gamma Function

In Sec. 4.4, we have discussed certain properties of functions which have been expressed as integrals. It is the exception when such functions can be expressed in terms of elementary functions; when this is not possible, the integral itself is often taken as the definition of the function, and additional properties of the function must be deduced from the integral representation. A simple and familiar instance of this procedure is the definition of the logarithm function by the formula

$$L(x) = \int_1^x \frac{dt}{t}, \qquad x > 0. \tag{4-18}$$

By making changes of variable, one may verify all the algebraic properties. For example, to prove that $L(1/x)$ is $-L(x)$, we set $t = 1/u$, and have

$$L\left(\frac{1}{x}\right) = \int_1^{1/x} \frac{dt}{t} = \int_1^x u(-u^{-2})\,du$$
$$= -\int_1^x \frac{du}{u} = -L(x).$$

A less familiar example is the approach to the trigonometric functions which starts with the definition

$$A(x) = \int_0^x \frac{dt}{1 + t^2}. \tag{4-19}$$

As an example of what may be done with this, let us make the variable change $t = 1/u$, and obtain

$$A(x) = \int_{\infty}^{1/x} \frac{-u^{-2}}{1 + u^{-2}}\,du = \int_{1/x}^{\infty} \frac{du}{1 + u^2}.$$

Let $K = \displaystyle\int_0^{\infty} \frac{dt}{1 + t^2} = \lim_{x \to \infty} A(x)$. Then, the last integral is

$$K - \int_0^{1/x} \frac{du}{1 + u^2} = K - A\left(\frac{1}{x}\right),$$

so that we have shown the identity $A(x) + A(1/x) = K$. In particular, $A(1) = K/2$; π may be defined as $2K$.

We devote this section to the study of some of the simpler properties of the **gamma function**, as defined by the improper integral

$$\Gamma(x) = \int_0^{\infty} u^{x-1}e^{-u}\,du. \tag{4-20}$$

This converges for all $x > 0$, and converges uniformly for all x in the interval $[\delta, L]$, for any $\delta > 0$ and $L < \infty$, so that $\Gamma(x)$ is continuous for all $x > 0$. If x is chosen as an integer, (4-19) becomes an integral which we can evaluate exactly, so that comparing this with Eq. (4-10) of Sec. 4.4,

$$\Gamma(n + 1) = \int_0^{\infty} u^n e^{-u}\,du = n!$$

If we write $x! = \Gamma(x + 1)$, we therefore obtain a definition of "factorial" applying to nonintegral values of x, which agrees with the customary definition when x is an integer. The gamma function also obeys the identity $(x + 1)! = (x + 1)(x!)$.

Theorem 30. $\Gamma(x + 1) = x\Gamma(x)$ *for any* $x > 0$.

Integrating by parts, we have

$$\Gamma(x + 1) = \int_0^{\infty} u^x e^{-u}\,du = \Big[-u^x e^{-u}\Big]_{u=0}^{u=\infty} + \int_0^{\infty} e^{-u}\,d(u^x)$$
$$= 0 + \int_0^{\infty} xe^{-u}u^{x-1}\,du = x\Gamma(x). \quad \blacksquare$$

By making appropriate changes of variable, many useful alternate definitions of the gamma function may be obtained. We list several below, together with the necessary substitution:

$$\Gamma(x) = 2\int_0^{\infty} t^{2x-1}e^{-t^2}\,dt \qquad \{u = t^2\} \tag{4-21}$$

$$\Gamma(x) = \int_0^1 \left[\log\left(\frac{1}{t}\right)\right]^{x-1} dt \qquad \{u = -\log t\}$$

$$\Gamma(x) = c^x \int_0^\infty t^{x-1}e^{-ct}\, dt \qquad \{u = ct\} \tag{4-22}$$

$$\Gamma(x) = \int_{-\infty}^\infty e^{xt} \exp(-e^t)\, dt \qquad \{u = e^t\} \tag{4-23}$$

The first of these, (4-21), makes it possible to determine the value of $\Gamma(x)$ when x is any multiple of $\frac{1}{2}$.

Theorem 31. $\Gamma(\frac{1}{2}) = \sqrt{\pi}$, $\Gamma(\frac{3}{2}) = \dfrac{\sqrt{\pi}}{2}$ *and in general,*

$$\Gamma(n + \tfrac{1}{2}) = \frac{(2n)!\sqrt{\pi}}{4^n n!}.$$

Putting $x = \frac{1}{2}$ in (4-21), we have $\Gamma(\frac{1}{2}) = 2\int_0^\infty e^{-t^2}\, dt = \sqrt{\pi}$. Using the functional equation $\Gamma(x + 1) = x\Gamma(x)$, we have

$$\Gamma(\tfrac{3}{2}) = (\tfrac{1}{2})\Gamma(\tfrac{1}{2}) = \frac{\sqrt{\pi}}{2}.$$

The general formula may be verified by an inductive argument. ▮

If we know the values of the gamma function on one interval $[k, k + 1]$, we can use the functional equation to compute the values on the adjacent intervals, and thus tabulate the function. Turning the formula around, we may write $\Gamma(x) = x^{-1}\Gamma(x + 1)$; since $\Gamma(1) = 1$, this shows that $\Gamma(x) \sim x^{-1}$ as x approaches 0. In this form, we can also use the functional equation to extend the definition of the gamma function to negative nonintegral values of x. For example, $\Gamma(-\frac{1}{2}) = (-2)\Gamma(\frac{1}{2}) = -2\sqrt{\pi}$, and $\Gamma(-\frac{3}{2}) = (-\frac{2}{3})\Gamma(-\frac{1}{2}) = (\frac{4}{3})\sqrt{\pi}$. $\Gamma(x)$ becomes unbounded as x approaches a negative integer since this is the case near 0. (An approximate graph of Γ is given in Fig. 4-5.)

As an illustration of the use of certain techniques for estimating the behavior of functions defined by an integral, we shall obtain a standard asymptotic formula for $\Gamma(x)$. When x is an integer n, this gives a form of Stirling's approximation for $n!$.

Theorem 32. *As x increases, $x! = \Gamma(x + 1) \sim x^x e^{-x}\sqrt{2\pi x}$.*

This means that

$$\lim_{x\to\infty} \frac{\Gamma(x + 1)}{x^x e^{-x}\sqrt{2\pi x}} = 1,$$

so that the approximation is in the sense of small percentage error, rather than small absolute error. For example, $100!$ is about $(9.3326)10^{157}$ while Stirling's formula gives $100^{100}e^{-100}\sqrt{200\pi}$ which is about $(9.3248)10^{157}$.

The relative error is thus $(9.3326)/(9.3248) - 1 = .0008$, or .08 per cent, while the absolute error is at least 10^{155}.

Starting from the original formula for $\Gamma(x + 1)$, we make the change of variable $u = xt$.

$$\Gamma(x + 1) = \int_0^\infty u^x e^{-u}\, du = x^{x+1} \int_0^\infty t^x e^{-xt}\, dt$$

so that

$$\frac{\Gamma(x + 1)}{(x^x)(x)} = \int_0^\infty (te^{-t})^x\, dt.$$

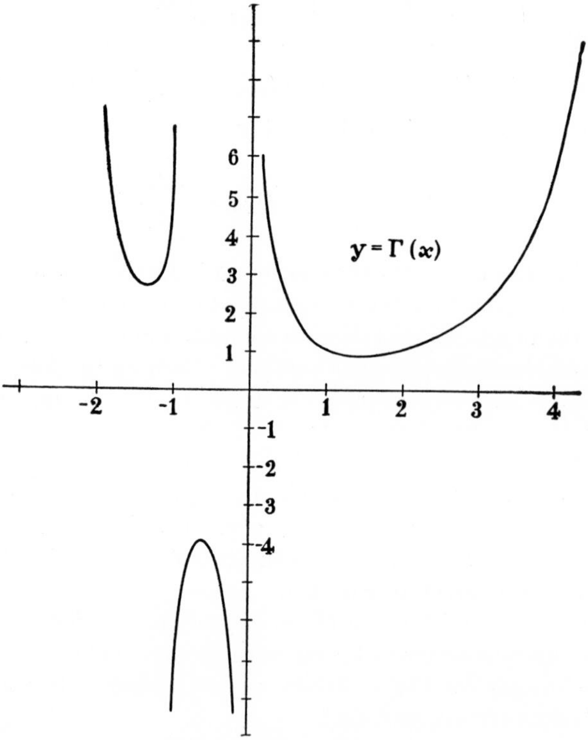

FIG. 4-5

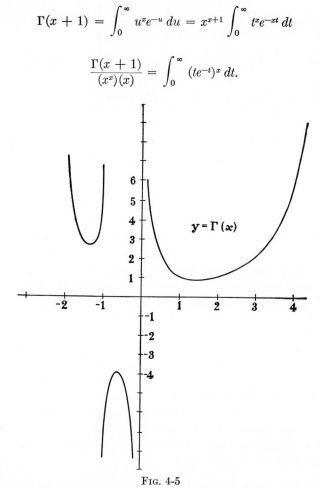

The maximum of the function $g(t) = te^{-t}$ occurs at $t = 1$ and is e^{-1}. This suggests splitting up the range of integration to emphasize the contribution around $t = 1$ (see Fig. 4-6). Choose numbers a and b with $a < 1 < b$ and write

$$\text{(4-24)} \qquad \frac{\Gamma(x + 1)}{(x^x)(x)} = \int_0^a [g(t)]^x\, dt + \int_a^b [g(t)]^x\, dt + \int_b^\infty [g(t)]^x\, dt.$$

We estimate each of these separately, beginning with the first and third. In the interval $[0, a]$, g has its maximum at a, and $A = g(a) < e^{-1}$. Thus,

$$\int_0^a [g(t)]^x \, dt \leq aA^x < A^x.$$

In the interval $[b, \infty]$, g has its maximum at b and $B = g(b) < e^{-1}$. Thus,

$$\int_b^\infty [g(t)]^x \, dt = \int_b^\infty g(t)[g(t)]^{x-1} \, dt$$
$$\leq B^{x-1} \int_0^\infty g(t) \, dt < 4B^x.$$

Thus, the first and third integrals decrease more rapidly than e^{-x}. To discuss the middle integral, we first specialize a and b by choosing $a = 1 - \delta$

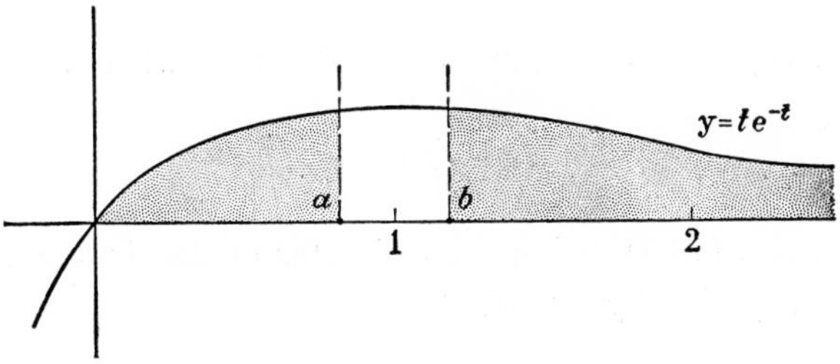

FIG. 4-6

and $b = 1 + \delta$, where $\delta > 0$. Putting $t = s + 1$ to shift the interval of integration, the middle integral becomes

$$I = \int_{-\delta}^{\delta} [(s + 1)e^{-(s+1)}]^x \, ds = e^{-x} \int_{-\delta}^{\delta} [(s + 1)e^{-s}]^x \, ds$$

We need an approximation for $(s + 1)e^{-s}$ for s near 0.

Lemma. $(1 + s)e^{-s} = e^{-s^2h(s)/2}$ *for* $|s| \leq \frac{1}{2}$ *where* $\lim_{s \to 0} h(s) = 1$.

Using the power series development of the logarithm function,

$$\log \{(1 + s)e^{-s}\} = \log (1 + s) - s = \left(s - \frac{s^2}{2} + \frac{s^3}{3} - \cdots\right) - s$$
$$= -\left(\frac{s^2}{2}\right)(1 - \tfrac{2}{3}s + \cdots) = -\frac{s^2h(s)}{2}. \quad \blacksquare$$

With this estimate, we have

$$e^xI = \int_{-\delta}^{\delta} [(1 + s)e^{-s}]^x \, ds = \int_{-\delta}^{\delta} e^{-xs^2h(s)/2} \, ds$$

Given $\epsilon > 0$, we may choose δ sufficiently small so that $1 - \epsilon < h(s) < 1 + \epsilon$ for all s, $|s| \leq \delta$, and have

$$\int_{-\delta}^{\delta} e^{-xs^2(1+\epsilon)/2} \, ds \leq e^xI \leq \int_{-\delta}^{\delta} e^{-xs^2(1-\epsilon)/2} \, ds \tag{4-25}$$

Each of these integrals has the form

$$\int_{-\delta}^{\delta} e^{-cxs^2}\,ds.$$

Lemma. *For any* $c > 0$, $\lim\limits_{x\to\infty} \sqrt{x} \int_{-\delta}^{\delta} e^{-cxs^2}\,ds = \sqrt{\dfrac{\pi}{c}}.$

Putting $t = s\sqrt{cx}$, we obtain

$$\sqrt{x}\int_{-\delta}^{\delta} e^{-cxs^2}\,ds = \sqrt{x}\int_{-\delta\sqrt{cx}}^{\delta\sqrt{cx}} e^{-t^2}\frac{dt}{\sqrt{cx}} = \frac{1}{\sqrt{c}}\int_{-\delta\sqrt{cx}}^{\delta\sqrt{cx}} e^{-t^2}\,dt$$

and
$$\lim_{x\to\infty}\sqrt{x}\int_{-\infty}^{\delta} e^{-cxs^2}\,ds = \frac{1}{\sqrt{c}}\int_{-\infty}^{\infty} e^{-t^2}\,dt = \sqrt{\frac{\pi}{c}}. \quad \blacksquare$$

Returning to Eq. (4-25), we can choose N so that whenever $x > N$,

$$\sqrt{\frac{2\pi}{1+\epsilon}} < \sqrt{x}\, e^x I < \sqrt{\frac{2\pi}{1-\epsilon}} \tag{4-26}$$

Returning to Eq. (4-24), using the estimates of the first and third integrals, and multiplying by $\sqrt{x}\, e^x$,

$$\frac{\Gamma(x+1)}{x^x e^{-x}\sqrt{x}} = \{\text{something smaller than } \sqrt{x}\,(eA)^x\} + \sqrt{x}\, e^x I$$
$$+ \{\text{something smaller than } \sqrt{x}\,(eB)^x\}.$$

Since A and B are each less than e^{-1}, the expressions in brackets approach 0 as x increases, so that for any $\epsilon > 0$ and for all sufficiently large x,

$$\sqrt{\frac{2\pi}{1+\epsilon}} < \frac{\Gamma(x+1)}{x^x e^{-x}\sqrt{x}} < \sqrt{\frac{2\pi}{1-\epsilon}}$$

proving that the limit of the inner function is $\sqrt{2\pi}$. ▮

If we admit the gamma function to the collection of functions which we may use, many otherwise intractable definite integrals can be evaluated exactly.

Theorem 33. $B(p, q) = \displaystyle\int_0^1 x^{p-1}(1-x)^{q-1}\,dx = \frac{\Gamma(p)\Gamma(q)}{\Gamma(p+q)}$ *where p and q are positive real numbers.*

The integral defines B as a function of two real variables; it is known as the **beta function.** When p and q are positive integers, the integrand is a polynomial, and $B(p, q)$ can be easily evaluated; the theorem makes the evaluation possible for all positive p and q.

We follow a procedure similar to that which we used in evaluating

$\int_0^\infty e^{-t^2}\,dt$ (page 98). Using the alternate formula (4-21) for the gamma function, and introducing different dummy letters for the variables of integration, we have

$$\Gamma(p) = 2\int_0^\infty y^{2p-1}e^{-y^2}\,dy$$
$$\Gamma(q) = 2\int_0^\infty x^{2q-1}e^{-x^2}\,dx.$$

The product of these can then be expressed as

$$\begin{aligned}\Gamma(p)\Gamma(q) &= \lim_{R\to\infty} 4\int_0^R y^{2p-1}e^{-y^2}\,dy \int_0^R x^{2q-1}e^{-x^2}\,dx \\ &= \int_0^\infty \int_0^\infty y^{2p-1}x^{2q-1}e^{-(x^2+y^2)}\,dxdy.\end{aligned}$$

Since the integrand of this improper double integral is positive, we can also integrate over the first quadrant by using quarter circles, and polar coordinates. Replace x by $r\cos\theta$, y by $r\sin\theta$, and $dxdy$ by $r\,drd\theta$. (We again defer the justification of this procedure until we discuss the general problem of change of variable in multiple integrals, and assume that this special case is sufficiently familiar.) Carrying this out, we have

$$\begin{aligned}\Gamma(p)\Gamma(q) &= \lim_{R\to\infty} 4\int_0^R dr \int_0^{\pi/2} (r\sin\theta)^{2p-1}(r\cos\theta)^{2q-1}e^{-r^2}r\,d\theta \\ &= 4\int_0^\infty r^{2p+2q-1}e^{-r^2}\,dr \int_0^{\pi/2} (\cos\theta)^{2q-1}(\sin\theta)^{2p-1}\,d\theta.\end{aligned}$$

In the first, put $u = r^2$ so that $dr = du/(2r)$; in the second, put $v = \sin^2\theta$ so that $d\theta = dv/(2\sin\theta\cos\theta)$. Then

$$\begin{aligned}\Gamma(p)\Gamma(q) &= 4\int_0^\infty \frac{u^{p+q-\frac{1}{2}}e^{-u}}{2u^{\frac{1}{2}}}\,du \int_0^1 \frac{(1-v)^{q-\frac{1}{2}}v^{p-\frac{1}{2}}}{2v^{\frac{1}{2}}(1-v)^{\frac{1}{2}}}\,dv \\ &= \int_0^\infty u^{p+q-1}e^{-u}\,du \int_0^1 v^{p-1}(1-v)^{q-1}\,dv \\ &= \Gamma(p+q)B(p,q). \quad \blacksquare\end{aligned}$$

Many integrals which are not originally in the form of a beta function can be converted into such a form, and thus evaluated. We give two samples of this.

$$\begin{aligned}\int_0^1 \frac{dx}{(1-x^4)^{\frac{1}{2}}} &= \int_0^1 \frac{u^{-\frac{3}{4}}\,du}{4(1-u)^{\frac{1}{2}}} = \tfrac{1}{4}B(\tfrac{1}{4},\tfrac{1}{2}) \\ &= \frac{\Gamma(\frac{1}{4})\Gamma(\frac{1}{2})}{4\Gamma(\frac{3}{4})}\end{aligned}$$

$$\int_0^{\pi/2} \sqrt{\sin\theta}\, d\theta = \int_0^1 \frac{v^{1/4}\, dv}{2v^{1/2}(1-v)^{1/2}} = \tfrac{1}{2}B(\tfrac{3}{4}, \tfrac{1}{2})$$

$$= \frac{\Gamma(\frac{3}{4})\Gamma(\frac{1}{2})}{2\Gamma(\frac{5}{4})} = \frac{2\Gamma(\frac{3}{4})\Gamma(\frac{1}{2})}{\Gamma(\frac{1}{4})}$$

(In the second, we have used the substitution $v = \sin^2\theta$, and in the last step, the functional equation for the gamma function.)

EXERCISES

1. Show directly from the integral definition in Eq. (4-18) that the function L has the property $L(xy) = L(x) + L(y)$.

2. Show that the function A, defined in (4-19), has the property that

$$A(2x/(1-x^2)) = 2A(x), \text{ for any } x,\ |x| < 1$$

3. Complete the induction argument in Theorem 31.

4. In terms of the gamma function, evaluate the following integrals:

(a) $\displaystyle\int_0^1 \frac{x^3\, dx}{\sqrt{1-x^3}}$ (b) $\displaystyle\int_0^1 \frac{dx}{\sqrt{x \log(1/x)}}$

(c) $\displaystyle\int_0^1 [1 - 1/x]^{1/3}\, dx$ (d) $\displaystyle\int_0^{\pi/2} \sqrt{\tan\theta}\, d\theta$

5. Show that $\Gamma(x)\Gamma(1-x) = \displaystyle\int_0^\infty \frac{u^{x-1}}{1+u}\, du$.

6. Evaluate $\displaystyle\int_0^\infty u^p e^{-u^q}\, du$.

7. Evaluate $\displaystyle\int_0^1 x^r[\log(1/x)]^s\, dx$.

CHAPTER 5

DIFFERENTIATION

5.1. Transformations

In Sec. 2.1, we discussed briefly the concept of a general function f as a mapping or correspondence between two sets A and B, which pairs each member a of A with a unique member $f(a) = b$ of B; the set A is called the **domain** of definition of f, and the set B is called the **range** of values of f. In all of the work which followed, however, we have dealt only with numerical-valued functions, i.e., functions whose ranges are sets of real numbers. In the present chapter, we shall consider functions whose range of values is a set of points in the plane (E^2) or, more generally, in n-space (E^n). To make it easier to refer to these, and to distinguish them from ordinary numerical-valued functions, we shall use the special term **transformation.** Thus, if A is a set in n-space and B a set in m-space, a transformation T of A onto B is a function whose domain is A, and whose range is B. We shall say that T carries a point p into the point $T(p) = q$ and call q the **image** of p under the transformation T. If p is a point in the plane and q a point in space, we may write $p = (x, y)$ and $q = (u, v, w)$ so that $T(x, y) = (u, v, w)$. In this case, we may also describe the transformation by specifying three coordinate functions, and writing

$$T: \begin{cases} u = f(x, y) \\ v = g(x, y) \\ w = h(x, y). \end{cases}$$

For brevity, we may also refer to such a transformation as a **mapping** from E^2 into E^3, even though its domain may not be all of the plane.

To illustrate these notions, let us begin with a particular transformation of the plane into itself:

$$T: \begin{cases} u = x^2 + y^2 \\ v = x + y. \end{cases} \tag{5-1}$$

Under T, the point (x, y) is sent into the point (u, v). For example, the image of $(1, 2)$ is $(5, 3)$, the image of $(0, 2)$ is $(4, 2)$, and the image of $(2, 0)$ is also $(4, 2)$. Any set of points in the XY plane is carried into a corresponding set of points in the UV plane. It often helps to compute the image of a number of selected curves and regions. To determine the image of the horizontal line $y = c$, make this substitution in the equations for T, obtaining

$$\begin{cases} u = x^2 + c^2 \\ v = x + c. \end{cases}$$

This can be regarded as parametric equations for the image curve in the UV plane, or x may be eliminated, resulting in the equation:

$$u = (v - c)^2 + c^2.$$

(In Fig. 5-1 these curves are shown for several choices of c.) Turning to regions, we first observe that the point (a, b) and the point (b, a) both have the same image. Thus, the line $y = x$ divides the XY plane into

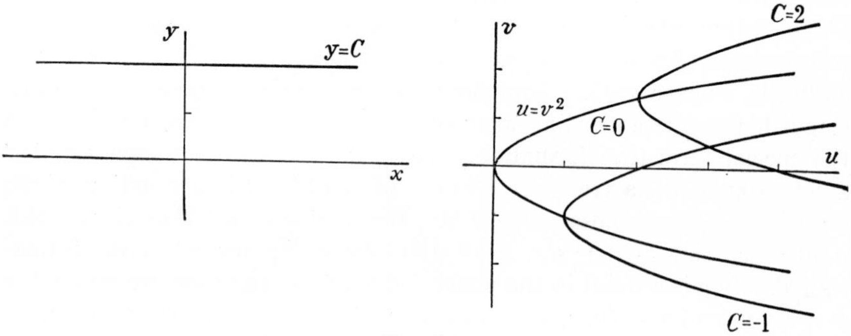

FIG. 5-1

two half planes which are mapped by T onto the same set in the UV plane. To determine this set, we first find the image of the line $y = x$. Substituting into (5-1), we obtain $u = 2x^2$, $v = 2x$ which are parametric equations for the parabola $v^2 = 2u$. The image of any point (x, y) lies within this curve, for

$$\begin{aligned} 2u - v^2 &= 2(x^2 + y^2) - (x + y)^2 \\ &= x^2 + y^2 - 2xy = (x - y)^2 \geq 0. \end{aligned}$$

Conversely, it is easy to see that every point (u, v) on or within this parabola is in turn the image of a point (x, y) (see Fig. 5-2). Accordingly, one may picture the effect of T approximately as follows: first, fold the XY plane along the line $y = x$, and then fit the folded edge along the parabola $v^2 = 2u$, and flatten out the rest to cover the inside of the parabola smoothly. (To permit the necessary distortion, think of the XY plane as a sheet of rubber.)

As another illustration, consider the following transformation of 2-space into 3-space.

$$(5\text{-}2) \qquad S: \begin{cases} u = x + y \\ v = x - y \\ w = x^2 \end{cases}$$

The image of (1, 2) under S is (3, −1, 1). The image of the line $y = x$ is the curve given in parametric form by

$$\begin{cases} u = 2x \\ v = 0 \\ w = x^2 \end{cases}$$

which is a parabola lying in the UW plane. The image of the whole XY plane is a parabolic cylinder resting on the UV plane (see Fig. 5-3).

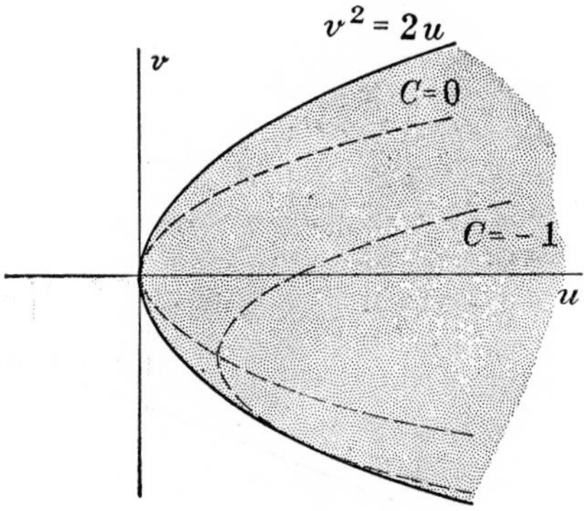

Since transformations belong to the general category of functions, one may also consider their graphs. Except in the simplest cases, this is usually difficult and of little help; for example, the graph of the transformation T described by (5-1) is the set of all points (x, y, u, v) in E^4 for which (5-1) holds, that is, the set of all points $(x, y, x^2 + y^2, x + y)$, $-\infty < x < \infty$, $-\infty < y < \infty$. Therefore, we usually adopt other

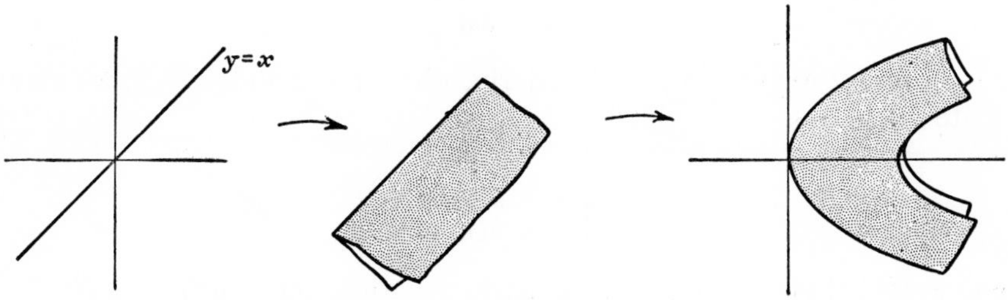

FIG. 5-2

devices in studying transformations. The general transformation from E^n to E^m can be described by means of the equations:

$$(5\text{-}3) \qquad T: \begin{cases} y_1 = f_1(x_1, x_2, \ldots, x_n) \\ y_2 = f_2(x_1, x_2, \ldots, x_n) \\ \cdots\cdots\cdots\cdots\cdots \\ y_m = f_m(x_1, x_2, \ldots, x_n) \end{cases}$$

where we have written $p = (x_1, x_2, \ldots, x_n)$ for the general point in n-space, and $q = (y_1, y_2, \ldots, y_m)$ for the general point in m-space. The labeling of the coordinates of p and q is quite arbitrary; convenience and habit are the guiding criteria. For example, the general transformation from 1-space to 3-space can be described by

$$T: \begin{cases} x = f(t) \\ y = g(t) \\ z = h(t) \end{cases}$$

where we have put $p = t$ and $q = (x, y, z)$. In this case, it often helps in studying T to regard these equations as a particular set of parametric

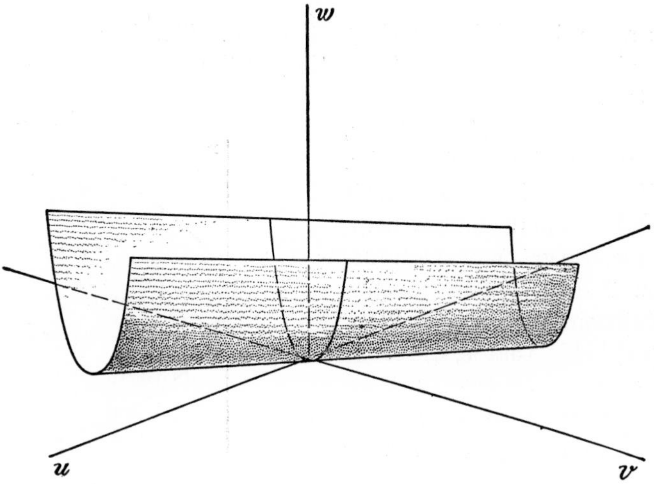

FIG. 5-3

equations for a curve in E^3. Similarly, when $n = 2$ and $m = 3$, we may write

$$\begin{cases} x = f(u, v) \\ y = g(u, v) \\ z = h(u, v) \end{cases}$$

and regard these as a set of parametric equations for a surface in E^3.

Transformations can be combined by substitution to yield new transformations, provided the dimensions of the domains and ranges are compatible. If T is a transformation from E^n to E^m, and S is a transformation from E^m to E^r, the transformation R defined by $R(p) = S(T(p))$ is a mapping from E^n into E^r; R is often called the product or composite of S and T. For example, let T be the mapping which sends (x, y) into $(xy, 2x, -y)$ and S the mapping which sends (x, y, z) into $(x - y, yz)$. Then, the mapping $R = ST$ sends (x, y) into $(xy - 2x, -2xy)$. T is a mapping of E^2 into E^3, and S a mapping of E^3 into E^2, so that R is a mapping from E^2 into E^2. If we wish to obtain the same result, and adhere to the equational descriptions of transformations, it is convenient to use different coordinate labels in the middle space, and write

$$T: \begin{cases} r = xy \\ s = 2x \\ t = -y \end{cases} \qquad S: \begin{cases} u = r - s \\ v = st \end{cases}$$

so that T sends (x, y) into (r, s, t) and S sends (r, s, t) into (u, v). R therefore sends (x, y) into (u, v), and may be described by

$$\begin{cases} u = xy - 2x \\ v = (2x)(-y) = -2xy. \end{cases}$$

In this particular example, we may also form the product $H = TS$, which will be a mapping of E^3 into E^3. Since S sends (x, y, z) into $(x - y, yz)$, and T sends (x, y) into $(xy, 2x, -y)$, H will send (x, y, z) into $([x - y]yz, 2[x - y], -yz)$. Note that $ST \neq TS$.

The notion of continuity applies to transformations, as it did to functions.

Definition. *A transformation T defined in a set D is said to be continuous at a point $p_0 \in D$ if and only if for any $\epsilon > 0$ there is a $\delta > 0$ such that $|T(p) - T(p_0)| < \epsilon$ whenever $|p - p_0| < \delta$ and $p \in D$.*

Because of the fact that the range of a transformation is a set of points, many of the consequences of continuity take a slightly different form.

Theorem 1. *Let T be a transformation from n-space into m-space, which is continuous on an open set $D \subset E^n$. Let S be any open set in E^m. Then, the set of all points p in D for which $T(p) \in S$ is also an open set.*

Let $V = \{\text{all } p \in D \text{ with } T(p) \in S\}$. This is the set of all points of D which map into S, and is also called the **inverse image** of S under T. Thus, the theorem asserts that the inverse image of any open set is open. To prove that V is open, take any point $p_0 \in V$, and let $q_0 = T(p_0)$. Since $q_0 \in S$ and S is open, we may choose ϵ so that the ϵ neighborhood N about q_0 lies in S. Since T is continuous at p_0, we can choose δ so that $|T(p) - T(p_0)| < \epsilon$ whenever $|p - p_0| < \delta$. But, this states that $T(p)$ lies in N and therefore in S, whenever p lies in the δ neighborhood about p_0. Thus, every point of D in a neighborhood of p_0 maps into a point of S, so that p_0 is an interior point of V. Since p_0 was any point of V, every point of V is interior, and V is open. ▌

The next result is a generalization of the intermediate value theorem.

Theorem 2. *Let T be a transformation from n-space to m-space which is continuous on a set D. Then, T carries any connected subset of D into a connected set.*

Let E be a connected set lying in D. If $T(E)$, the image of E, is not connected, then there are two nonempty open sets U_1 and U_2 which together (but not singly) cover $T(E)$ and which have no common points. Their inverse images are, by Theorem 1, open sets V_1 and V_2. Since the image of any point of E is in either U_1 or U_2, every point of E lies in either V_1 or V_2. Moreover, no point could belong to both V_1 and V_2, since its image would then have to belong to both U_1 and U_2. By assumption, E is connected; accordingly, one of the sets V_1 and V_2 is redundant, and E is covered completely by one of the sets. Assuming that it is V_1, we see that $T(E)$ is completely covered by U_1, contradicting the initial property of the pair U_1 and U_2. Thus, $T(E)$ must be connected. ▮

Finally, we prove the generalized form of the theorem which asserts that a continuous function takes a maximum value on any closed and bounded set.

Theorem 3. *Let T be a transformation from n-space into m-space which is continuous on a set D. Then, if D is closed and bounded, so is its image $T(D)$.*

We must show that for some number M, $|T(p)| \leq M$ whenever $p \in D$. Let U_n be the open sphere in m-space consisting of all points q with $|q| < n$. As n increases, the sets U_n expand. Let V_n be the inverse image of U_n, under T. By Theorem 1, these again form an expanding sequence of open sets. If p is any point of D, then $T(p)$ is eventually contained in the spheres U_n, so that the sets V_n eventually expand to take in p. Thus, the collection of sets $\{V_n\}$ covers D. By the Heine-Borel theorem (page 82) there must be an index k such that $D \subset V_k$. $T(D)$ is then contained in the sphere U_k, and is therefore a bounded set. To show that $T(D)$ is also closed, let q_0 be a boundary point of $T(D)$ which we assume does not belong to $T(D)$. Choose a sequence of points $\{q_n\}$ in $T(D)$ converging to q_0. These arise as images of a sequence of points $\{p_n\}$ in D. The sequence $\{p_n\}$ need not converge, but since D is closed and bounded, it has a convergent subsequence $\{p_{k_n}\}$ and a limit point p_0 in D, with $\lim_{n\to\infty} p_{k_n} = p_0$. Since T is continuous at p_0,

$$T(p_0) = \lim_{n\to\infty} T(p_{k_n}).$$

But, $T(p_{k_n}) = q_{k_n}$, and $\{q_{k_n}\}$, being a subsequence of $\{q_n\}$, converges to q_0. Thus, $q_0 = T(p_0)$ so that q_0 is the image of a point of D, and is therefore a member of $T(D)$. This contradiction proves that $T(D)$ is closed. ▮ (For another method of proof which avoids the use of the Heine-Borel theorem, see Exercise 8.)

EXERCISES

1. Verify the fact that every (u, v) inside the parabola $v^2 = 2u$ is an image under the transformation T described by (5-1) of a point (x, y).

2. What is the image of the line $x = 0$ under the transformation S described by (5-2)?

3. Discuss the nature of the transformation T of E^2 into E^2 which:

(*a*) Sends (x, y) into $(x + 3, y - 1)$.
(*b*) Sends (x, y) into (y, x).
(*c*) Sends (x, y) into $(x + y, x - y)$.
(*d*) Sends (x, y) into (x^2, y^2).

4. Discuss the nature of the transformation T which sends (x, y) into $(x^2 - y^2, 2xy)$.

5. Construct a transformation of E^2 into E^2 which maps the curve $y = x^2$ onto the horizontal axis, and the line $y = 3$ onto the vertical axis.

6. Find the products in each order of each pair of transformations given in Exercise 3.

7. When a transformation T of E^n into E^m is described by means of coordinate functions, as in (5-3), show that T is continuous in a set D if and only if each coordinate function f_j is continuous in D.

8. Using properties of continuous functions, and the result of Exercise 7, show that the image of a closed and bounded set under a continuous transformation is bounded.

9. (*a*) Formulate a definition of uniform continuity for transformations. cf p 404

(*b*) Show that a transformation T which is continuous in a closed and bounded set D is uniformly continuous there, by representing T in coordinate form.

10. A transformation T is said to be distance preserving if $|T(p) - T(q)| = |p - q|$ for all points p and q in the domain of T. Show that the transformation of the plane into itself which sends (x, y) into $\left(\dfrac{x + y}{\sqrt{2}}, \dfrac{x - y}{\sqrt{2}}\right)$ is distance preserving.

***11.** A transformation T of E^n into itself is called a translation if there is a point Q such that for every $p \in E^n$, $T(p) = p + Q$; it is called a radial expansion if there is a real number λ such that for every p, $T(p) = \lambda p$. What is the product of a general translation and a general radial expansion? What is the most general transformation that can be obtained from products of these?

5.2. Linear Functions and Transformations

The special class of **linear** transformations is of considerable importance.

Definition. *A transformation T from E^n to E^m is said to be linear if and only if it has the following two properties:*

(i) $\quad T(p + q) = T(p) + T(q)$ *for all p and q.*

(ii) $\quad T(\lambda p) = \lambda T(p)$ *for any real number λ.*

These defining properties immediately prescribe the form of T.

Theorem 4. *The general linear transformation from E^n to E^m has the coordinate form:*

$$(5\text{-}4) \qquad \begin{cases} y_1 = a_{11}x_1 + a_{12}x_2 + \cdots + a_{1n}x_n \\ y_2 = a_{21}x_1 + a_{22}x_2 + \cdots + a_{2n}x_n \\ \cdots\cdots\cdots\cdots\cdots\cdots \\ y_m = a_{m1}x_1 + a_{m2}x_2 + \cdots + a_{mn}x_n \end{cases}$$

where the coefficients a_{ij} are (real) constants.

We first prove a special case of this result. Let $m = 1$; then, the transformation T is merely a numerical-valued function L which obeys conditions (i) and (ii) above. For simplicity, let us suppose that $n = 3$. Determine three numbers A, B, and C, by $A = L(1, 0, 0)$, $B = L(0, 1, 0)$, $C = L(0, 0, 1)$. The general point in E^3 can be expressed as

$$(x, y, z) = x(1, 0, 0) + y(0, 1, 0) + z(0, 0, 1)$$

so that

$$\begin{aligned} L(x, y, z) &= xL(1, 0, 0) + yL(0, 1, 0) + zL(0, 0, 1) \\ &= Ax + By + Cz. \end{aligned}$$

To prove the general representation formula, we first write T in coordinate form: $T(x_1, x_2, \ldots, x_n) = (y_1, y_2, \ldots, y_m)$ where

$$\begin{aligned} y_1 &= f_1(p) = f_1(x_1, x_2, \ldots, x_n) \\ y_2 &= f_2(p) = f_2(x_1, x_2, \ldots, x_n) \\ &\cdots\cdots\cdots\cdots\cdots \\ y_m &= f_m(p) = f_m(x_1, x_2, \ldots, x_n). \end{aligned}$$

The assumption that T is linear immediately implies that each of the coordinate functions f_i is linear, so that f_i has the form

$$f_i(p) = a_{i1}x_1 + a_{i2}x_2 + \cdots + a_{in}x_n. \quad \blacksquare$$

A linear transformation may thus be completely specified by giving the rectangular array or **matrix** of its coefficients

$$A = [a_{ij}] = \begin{bmatrix} a_{11} & a_{12} & \cdots & a_{1n} \\ a_{21} & a_{22} & \cdots & a_{2n} \\ \cdots & \cdots & \cdots & \cdots \\ a_{m1} & a_{m2} & \cdots & a_{mn} \end{bmatrix}.$$

For example, the matrix

$$\begin{bmatrix} 1 & 2 & 4 \\ -1 & 0 & 3 \end{bmatrix}$$

describes the transformation from E^3 to E^2 sending (x, y, z) into (u, v) where

$$\begin{aligned} u &= x + 2y + 4z \\ v &= -x + 3z. \end{aligned}$$

Again,† the single-rowed matrix $[2, -4, 5]$ represents the linear function L for which $L(x, y, z) = 2x - 4y + 5z$.

† Other notations for matrices are current, for example,

$$\begin{pmatrix} 2 & 1 \\ 0 & -3 \end{pmatrix} \text{ or } \begin{Vmatrix} 2 & 1 \\ 0 & -3 \end{Vmatrix}.$$

The present choice is likely to be ambiguous only in the case of a single-rowed matrix with two columns such as $[3, 7]$ where it might be confused with the notation for a closed interval. This will always be made clear by the context.

A linear transformation has many special properties, and types of behavior. Most of these can be seen by studying the special case of linear transformations of 3-space into itself. These will be represented by 3-by-3 square matrices $A = [a_{ij}]$, and described by equations

$$(5\text{-}5)\qquad T: \begin{cases} u = a_{11}x + a_{12}y + a_{13}z \\ v = a_{21}x + a_{22}y + a_{23}z \\ w = a_{31}x + a_{32}y + a_{33}z. \end{cases}$$

The domain of T is all of XYZ space, and it is continuous everywhere. Two important questions may be asked: (1) What is the exact range of values of T in UVW space? (2) Is the mapping one-to-one, or many-to-one? Both may be answered by viewing Eqs. (5-5) as a set of simultaneous linear equations in the variables x, y, z. A point $q = (u, v, w)$ is the image of a point $p = (x, y, z)$ if and only if the numbers u, v, w are such that Eqs. (5-5) may be solved for x, y, and z; moreover, T is one-to-one if and only if there is a unique solution for x, y, and z. Having framed the original questions in an algebraic form, the familiar facts dealing with the solution of linear equations can now be applied.† If $\det(A)$, the determinant of A, is not zero, then Eqs. (5-5) can be solved for x, y, and z by Cramer's rule, regardless of the values of u, v, and w, and the solution is unique. This shows that when $\det(A) \neq 0$, the transformation T maps all of E^3 onto all of E^3 in a one-to-one fashion. In this case, we call T a nonsingular linear transformation. The solution of (5-5) takes the form

$$\begin{cases} x = b_{11}u + b_{12}v + b_{13}w \\ y = b_{21}u + b_{22}v + b_{23}w \\ z = b_{31}u + b_{32}v + b_{33}w \end{cases}$$

where the coefficients b_{ij} may be computed by determinants involving the numbers a_{ij}. These equations define a linear transformation of UVW space into XYZ space; since this transformation reverses the action of T, we may call it the inverse of T, denoted by T^{-1}. The determinant of the coefficient matrix $[b_{ij}]$ of T^{-1} can be shown to have the value $1/\det(A)$.

Suppose now that $\det(A) = 0$. We compute the rank of the matrix A. Since A is a 3-by-3 matrix, the rank is 2, 1 or 0. It may be computed by first examining all of the nine 2-by-2 submatrices which may be obtained from A by erasing a row and a column. A has rank 2 if at

† See, for example, G. Birkhoff and S. MacLane, "Survey of Modern Algebra," Chaps. VII, VIII, and X, The Macmillan Company, New York, 1953, or L. E. Dickson, "First Course in the Theory of Equations," Chap. VIII, John Wiley & Son, Inc., New York, 1922.

least one of these has a nonzero determinant; if all nine have zero determinant, we go on to the 1-by-1 submatrices, i.e., the entries a_{ij} themselves; if at least one of these is nonzero, A has rank 1; finally, A has rank 0 when all the entries a_{ij} are zero. In general, the **rank** of any matrix, square or not, is the size of the largest square submatrix which can be obtained by erasing rows and columns, and which has a nonzero determinant. The rank can also be defined as the largest number of rows (or columns) of the matrix which form an independent set.

Returning to our transformation T, described by Eqs. (5-5), let us suppose that A has rank 2. For example, we might have

$$A = \begin{bmatrix} 1 & 3 & 7 \\ -1 & 2 & -3 \\ 1 & 8 & 11 \end{bmatrix}.$$

This has rank 2 since $\det(A) = 0$, but

$$\det \begin{bmatrix} 1 & 3 \\ -1 & 2 \end{bmatrix} \neq 0.$$

The corresponding equations for T will be

$$\text{(5-6)} \qquad \begin{cases} u = x + 3y + 7z \\ v = -x + 2y - 3z \\ w = x + 8y + 11z. \end{cases}$$

From the first two equations, we obtain

$$2u + v = x + 8y + 11z.$$

The equations do not have a solution for all possible choices of u, v, and w; it is necessary that $w = 2u + v$. Conversely, if u, v, and w are so related, then Eqs. (5-6) have solutions for x, y, z, and in fact, there is an infinite one-parameter family of solutions for each choice of (u, v, w). Translating these statements into corresponding statements about the transformation T, we see that T maps all of XYZ space onto the plane $2u + v - w = 0$ in UVW space, and that the mapping is many-to-one; the inverse image of any point in this plane is a line through the origin in XYZ space.

In general, when the rank of A is 2, two of the defining equations will be independent, while the third is a linear combination of these; thus, the image of all XYZ space will be a plane $Au + Bv + Cw = 0$ passing through the origin.

Suppose now that A has rank 1. For example, we might have

$$A = \begin{bmatrix} 4 & -8 & 12 \\ 2 & -4 & 6 \\ 3 & -6 & 9 \end{bmatrix}$$

in which every 2-by-2 submatrix has a zero determinant. The defining equations for T are

$$\begin{cases} u = 4x - 8y + 12z \\ v = 2x - 4y + 6z \\ w = 3x - 6y + 9z. \end{cases} \tag{5-7}$$

Since $3u = 6v = 4w = 12x - 24y + 36z$, a necessary and sufficient condition that Eqs. (5-7) have a solution is that (u, v, w) obey the two restrictions:

$$w = \tfrac{3}{4}u \qquad v = \tfrac{1}{2}u.$$

Thus, T maps all of XYZ space onto a line through the origin in UVW space, in a many-to-one fashion.

Finally, when A has rank 0, all the entries a_{ij} are zero, and T maps XYZ space onto the origin (0, 0, 0).

Bringing these separate cases together, we have proved the following result.

Theorem 5. *Let T be a linear transformation of E^3 into E^3 with representation matrix A. If A has rank 3, T maps E^3 onto all of E^3, one-to-one; if A has rank 2, T maps E^3 onto a plane through the origin; if A has rank 1, T maps E^3 onto a line through the origin; if A has rank 0, T maps E^3 onto the origin. In all cases but the first, T is many-to-one.*

The general case may be treated in the same manner. Since we shall have little occasion to use it, we merely state it without proof, referring the reader to other books for the details (see footnote, page 173).

Theorem 6. *Let T be a linear transformation of E^n into E^m with representation matrix A. Let the rank of A be r. Then, if $r \geq m$, the image of E^n is all of E^m, while if $r < m$, the image of E^n is a "plane" of dimension r lying in E^m and passing through the origin.*† *The mapping is one-to-one only if $r = n$.*

Representation of linear transformations by rectangular matrices affords a simple procedure for computing the product of one or more linear transformations. The matrix which represents the product of two linear transformations S and T can be obtained by multiplying the matrices for S and T. Multiplication of 2-by-2 matrices is defined by

$$\begin{bmatrix} a & b \\ c & d \end{bmatrix} \begin{bmatrix} a' & b' \\ c' & d' \end{bmatrix} = \begin{bmatrix} aa' + bc' & ab' + bd' \\ ca' + dc' & cb' + dd' \end{bmatrix}$$

and for general matrices by

$$[a_{ij}][b_{ij}] = [c_{ij}]$$

† The word "plane" is used here to cover simultaneously the cases of a line (dimension 1), a plane (dimension 2), etc. It is synonymous with the term "linear subspace," since we are here concerned with generalized planes through the origin.

where $c_{ij} = \sum_{k=1}^{k=r} a_{ik}b_{kj}$ for $i = 1, 2, \ldots, m$, $j = 1, 2, \ldots, n$.

It is to be noticed that we cannot form the product AB unless the number of columns of A is the same as the number of rows of B (see Fig. 5-4). The algorithm for computing the entries of C is often described as multiplication of the rows of A by the columns of B.

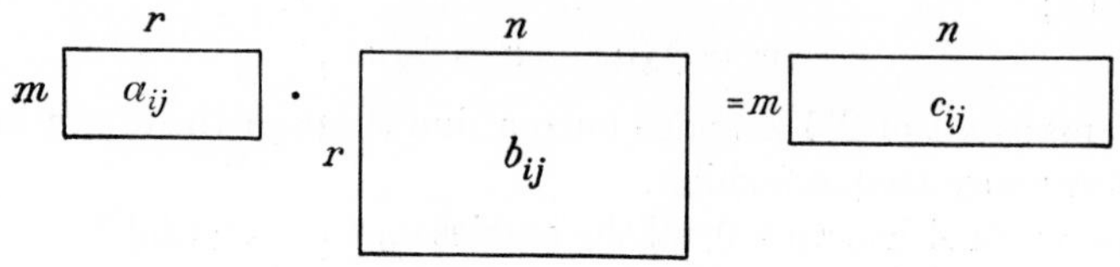

FIG. 5-4. Size restrictions for multiplication of matrices.

To see the connection between the product of linear transformations, and of their associated matrices, let T be a transformation of E^n into E^r with matrix B, and let S be a transformation of E^r into E^m with matrix A. Their product ST is then a transformation of E^n into E^m. Let T map $(x_1, x_2, \ldots, x_n)$ into $(y_1, y_2, \ldots, y_r)$, and let S map $(y_1, y_2, \ldots, y_r)$ into $(z_1, z_2, \ldots, z_m)$. Then,

(5-8) $$y_k = \sum_{j=1}^{n} b_{kj}x_j \qquad k = 1, 2, \ldots, r$$

and $$z_i = \sum_{k=1}^{k=r} a_{ik}y_k \qquad i = 1, 2, \ldots, m$$

so that $$z_i = \sum_{k=1}^{k=r} a_{ik} \sum_{j=1}^{j=n} b_{kj}x_j$$

Reversing the order of summation, we obtain

$$z_i = \sum_{j=1}^{j=n} x_j \left(\sum_{k=1}^{k=r} a_{ik}b_{kj} \right)$$
$$= \sum_{j=1}^{j=r} c_{ij}x_j$$

where $c_{ij} = \sum_{k=1}^{k=r} a_{ik}b_{kj}$. Since ST carries $(x_1, x_2, \ldots, x_n)$ into $(z_1, z_2, \ldots, z_m)$, the matrix $C = [c_{ij}]$ (which is the product AB) is the matrix representing ST.

We give several sample calculations. Let T and S be transformations of E^2 into E^2 described by:

$$S: \begin{cases} u = 2x - 3y \\ v = x + y \end{cases} \qquad A = \begin{bmatrix} 2 & -3 \\ 1 & 1 \end{bmatrix}$$

$$T: \begin{cases} u = x + y \\ v = 3x + y \end{cases} \qquad B = \begin{bmatrix} 1 & 1 \\ 3 & 1 \end{bmatrix}$$

Since

$$AB = \begin{bmatrix} 2 & -3 \\ 1 & 1 \end{bmatrix} \begin{bmatrix} 1 & 1 \\ 3 & 1 \end{bmatrix} = \begin{bmatrix} -7 & -1 \\ 4 & 2 \end{bmatrix}$$

the product ST is the linear transformation given by

$$ST: \begin{cases} u = -7x - y \\ v = 4x + 2y. \end{cases}$$

Since

$$BA = \begin{bmatrix} 1 & 1 \\ 3 & 1 \end{bmatrix} \begin{bmatrix} 2 & -3 \\ 1 & 1 \end{bmatrix} = \begin{bmatrix} 3 & -2 \\ 7 & -8 \end{bmatrix}$$

the transformation TS is given by

$$TS: \begin{cases} u = 3x - 2y \\ v = 7x - 8y. \end{cases}$$

Again, let T be the transformation of E^2 into E^4 given by

$$T: \begin{cases} u = x + 2y \\ v = -x \\ w = 2x \\ z = - y \end{cases}$$

and let S be the transformation of E^4 into E^3 given by

$$S: \begin{cases} r = u - w + 3z \\ s = -u + 2v + z \\ t = v + w + 2z \end{cases}$$

To compute the transformation ST, we form the product

$$\begin{bmatrix} 1 & 0 & -1 & 3 \\ -1 & 2 & 0 & 1 \\ 0 & 1 & 1 & 2 \end{bmatrix} \begin{bmatrix} 1 & 2 \\ -1 & 0 \\ 2 & 0 \\ 0 & -1 \end{bmatrix} = \begin{bmatrix} -1 & -1 \\ -3 & -3 \\ 1 & -2 \end{bmatrix}$$

Accordingly, ST is the transformation of E^2 into E^3 given by

$$ST: \begin{cases} r = -x - y \\ s = -3x - 3y \\ t = x - 2y \end{cases}$$

Matrix multiplication may also be used to compute the image of a point under a transformation. To see this, let T be the transformation with matrix $B = [b_{ij}]$ and let $T(x_1, x_2, \ldots, x_n) = (y_1, y_2, \ldots, y_r)$. Equation (5-8) is

$$y_k = \sum_{j=1}^{n} b_{kj}x_j, \qquad k = 1, 2, \ldots, r.$$

However, we recognise that this is the same relation as

$$\begin{bmatrix} y_1 \\ y_2 \\ y_3 \\ \cdot \\ \cdot \\ y_r \end{bmatrix} = \begin{bmatrix} b_{11} & b_{12} & \cdots & b_{1n} \\ b_{21} & b_{22} & \cdots & b_{2n} \\ b_{31} & b_{32} & \cdots & b_{3n} \\ \cdot & \cdot & \cdots & \cdot \\ \cdot & \cdot & \cdots & \cdot \\ b_{r1} & b_{r2} & \cdots & b_{rn} \end{bmatrix} \begin{bmatrix} x_1 \\ x_2 \\ x_3 \\ \cdot \\ \cdot \\ x_n \end{bmatrix}$$

For example, if T is represented by

$$\begin{bmatrix} 1 & -3 & 4 & 7 \\ 2 & 0 & -1 & 2 \end{bmatrix}$$

then the image of $(1, 2, 0, -1)$ is found by writing

$$\begin{bmatrix} 1 & -3 & 4 & 7 \\ 2 & 0 & -1 & 2 \end{bmatrix} \begin{bmatrix} 1 \\ 2 \\ 0 \\ -1 \end{bmatrix} = \begin{bmatrix} -12 \\ 0 \end{bmatrix};$$

that is, $T(1, 2, 0, -1) = (-12, 0)$.

A linear transformation is continuous everywhere, since this is clearly true for a linear function. More than this is true; any linear transformation from E^n into E^m is everywhere uniformly continuous. This is equivalent to the next theorem.

Theorem 7. *Let T be a linear transformation from E^n into E^m represented by the matrix $[a_{ij}]$. Then, there is a constant B such that $|T(p)| \le B|p|$ for all points p.*

We shall find that the number $\{\Sigma\Sigma|a_{ij}|^2\}^{1/2}$ will serve for B. Put $p = (x_1, x_2, \ldots, x_n)$ and $q = T(p) = (y_1, y_2, \ldots, y_m)$, so that

$$y_i = \sum_{j=1}^{n} a_{ij}x_j \qquad i = 1, 2, \ldots, m.$$

We have $|p|^2 = \sum_{j=1}^{n} |x_j|^2$ and $|q|^2 = \sum_{i=1}^{m} |y_i|^2$;

accordingly,

$$|y_i|^2 \leq \left\{ \sum_{j=1}^{n} |a_{ij}|\, |x_j| \right\}^2 \leq \sum_{j=1}^{n} |a_{ij}|^2 \sum_{j=1}^{n} |x_j|^2 \leq |p|^2 \sum_{j=1}^{n} |a_{ij}|^2$$

where we have used the Schwarz inequality (Sec. 1.1):

$$(\Sigma a_k b_k)^2 \leq \Sigma |a_k|^2 \Sigma |b_k|^2.$$

Adding these for $i = 1, 2, \ldots, m$, we obtain

$$|q|^2 = \sum_{i=1}^{m} |y_i|^2 \leq |p|^2 \sum_{i=1}^{m} \sum_{j=1}^{n} |a_{ij}|^2$$

and $|T(p)| = |q| \leq B|p|$ where $B = \left\{ \sum_{i=1}^{m} \sum_{j=1}^{n} |a_{ij}|^2 \right\}^{1/2}$. ∎

It should be remarked that the number B which we have found is not the smallest number with this property. For example, the transformation T specified by the simple matrix

$$\begin{bmatrix} 1 & 0 \\ 0 & 1 \end{bmatrix}$$

is such that $|T(p)| = |p|$, while the theorem provides the number

$$B = \sqrt{2} > 1.$$

However, this is not the case for linear *functions*. Let L be specified by the row matrix $[c_1, c_2, \ldots, c_n]$. Then, according to the theorem,

$$|L(p)| \leq \left(\sum_{i}^{n} |c_j|^2 \right)^{1/2} |p|.$$

This is best possible, for taking $p = (c_1, c_2, \ldots, c_n)$, we have

$$\begin{aligned} L(p) &= c_1 c_1 + \cdots + c_n c_n \\ &= \sum_{1}^{n} |c_j|^2 = \left(\sum_{1}^{n} |c_j|^2 \right)^{1/2} |p|. \end{aligned}$$

EXERCISES

1. Let L be the linear function specified by the coefficient matrix $[2, 0, -1, 3]$. What is $L(1, 1, -1, -1)$? What is $L(2, 0, 0, 1)$?

2. Find the linear function L such that $L(1, 0, 0) = 2$, $L(0, 1, 0) = -1$,

$$L(0, 0, 1) = 3.$$

3. Find the linear function L such that $L(1, 0, -1) = 3$, $L(2, -1, 0) = 0$,

$$L(0, 1, 0) = 2.$$

4. Let T be the linear transformation of E^2 into E^2 specified by the matrix

$$\begin{bmatrix} 2 & -1 \\ -3 & 0 \end{bmatrix}.$$

Find the images of the points $(1, 2)$, $(-2, 1)$, $(1, 0)$, $(0, 1)$.

5. Let T be the linear transformation specified by

$$\begin{bmatrix} 2 & 0 & -1 \\ -1 & 3 & 1 \end{bmatrix}.$$

Find the images of $(1, 2, 1)$, $(1, 0, 0)$, $(0, 1, 0)$.

6. Find the matrix representation for the linear transformation T which

(*a*) Maps $(1, 0, 0)$ into $(0, 1, 1)$, $(0, 1, 0)$ into $(1, 4, 0)$ and $(0, 0, 1)$ into $(2, 3, 1)$.

(*b*) Maps $(1, 1, 0)$ into $(0, 0, 1)$, $(0, 1, 1)$ into $(1, 0, 0)$, and $(1, 0, 1)$ into $(1, 0, 0)$.

7. Compute the ranks of the following matrices:

$$(a)\ \begin{bmatrix} 1 & 2 & -3 \\ 2 & -1 & 4 \\ 3 & 1 & 1 \end{bmatrix} \qquad (b)\ \begin{bmatrix} 0 & 1 & -1 \\ 2 & -1 & 3 \\ 1 & 0 & 1 \end{bmatrix}$$

$$(c)\ \begin{bmatrix} 3 & -6 & 9 \\ 2 & -4 & 6 \\ -2 & 4 & -12 \end{bmatrix} \qquad (d)\ \begin{bmatrix} 1 & -1 & 0 & 1 \\ 2 & 3 & 1 & 0 \\ 4 & 1 & 1 & -1 \end{bmatrix}$$

8. By computing ranks, discuss the nature of the image in UVW space of all of XYZ space. If either transformation is nonsingular, find the equations for its inverse.

$$(a)\ \begin{cases} u = x + 2y - 3z \\ v = 2x - y + 4z \\ w = 3x + y + z \end{cases} \qquad (b)\ \begin{cases} u = y - z \\ v = 3x - y + 3z \\ w = x + z \end{cases}$$

9. Compute the indicated matrix products:

$$(a)\ \begin{bmatrix} 2 & -3 \\ 0 & 1 \end{bmatrix}\begin{bmatrix} -1 & 4 \\ 1 & 3 \end{bmatrix} \qquad (b)\ \begin{bmatrix} 2 & -7 & 1 \\ -1 & 0 & 2 \end{bmatrix}\begin{bmatrix} 2 & -1 \\ 0 & 2 \\ 4 & 1 \end{bmatrix}$$

$$(c)\ \begin{bmatrix} 1 & -1 \\ -1 & 0 \\ 0 & 1 \end{bmatrix}\begin{bmatrix} 2 & 3 \\ -1 & 2 \end{bmatrix} \qquad (d)\ \begin{bmatrix} -1 & -1 & 0 \\ 2 & 0 & 1 \\ -1 & 1 & 1 \end{bmatrix}\begin{bmatrix} -1 & 1 \\ 3 & 2 \\ -2 & 0 \end{bmatrix}$$

10. Find the product ST of the transformations given by

$$S{:}\ (x, y, z) \to (6x - y + 2z,\ 2x + 4z)$$
$$T{:}\ (x, y) \to (x - y,\ 2x,\ -x + 2y)$$

Can you form the product TS?

5.3. The Differential of a Function

A simple approach to the notion of the differential of a function of several variables starts with that of the general **directional derivative.** A direction in the plane or in space may be regarded as determined by any point β with $|\beta| = 1$; such a point lies on the boundary of the unit circle or sphere, and can alternatively be described as a unit vector. If we wish to move away from a point p_0 in the direction β, we move from p_0 toward $p_0 + \beta$; the general point on this **ray** is given by $p = p_0 + \lambda\beta$, where $0 \leq \lambda < \infty$.

Suppose now that f is a real-valued function, defined and continuous in an open set D containing p_0. The directional derivative, or "rate of change," of f at p_0 in the direction β is

$$\mathbf{D}_\beta f(p_0) = \lim_{\lambda \downarrow 0} \frac{f(p_0 + \lambda\beta) - f(p_0)}{\lambda}$$

There are a variety of notations for directional derivative. Two others are: $\nabla_\beta f\Big|_{p_0}$ or $\dfrac{\partial f}{\partial \xi_\beta}\Big|_{p_0}$.

As an illustration, let $f(x, y) = x^2 + 3xy$, $p_0 = (1, 0)$ and

$$\beta = \left(\frac{1}{\sqrt{2}}, \frac{-1}{\sqrt{2}}\right),$$

which is the downward direction with slope -1. Since

$$p_0 + \lambda\beta = \left(1 + \frac{\lambda}{\sqrt{2}}, \frac{-\lambda}{\sqrt{2}}\right),$$

$$f(p_0 + \lambda\beta) = \left(1 + \frac{\lambda}{\sqrt{2}}\right)^2 + 3\left(1 + \frac{\lambda}{\sqrt{2}}\right)\left(\frac{-\lambda}{\sqrt{2}}\right)$$

$$= 1 - \frac{\lambda}{\sqrt{2}} - \lambda^2,$$

and

$$\mathbf{D}_\beta f(p_0) = \lim_{\lambda \downarrow 0} \frac{f(p_0 + \lambda\beta) - f(p_0)}{\lambda}$$

$$= \lim_{\lambda \downarrow 0} \frac{(1 - \lambda/\sqrt{2} - \lambda^2) - 1}{\lambda}$$

$$= \frac{-1}{\sqrt{2}}.$$

When β is chosen in turn as the coordinate axes directions, the corresponding special directional derivatives are called the **partial derivatives** of f. Again, a variety of notations are in use; depending upon the circumstances, one may be more convenient than another, and the table below gives most of the more common ones. The case of three variables is typical, and we write $w = f(x, y, z)$.†

† This usage of variables is common, but must be used carefully; one is apt to confuse w with the function f, especially if the notation $\partial w/\partial x$ is used. For an extremely lucid and painstaking discussion of this, I highly recommend Chap. VII, in Karl Menger, "Calculus, a Modern Approach," Ginn & Company, Boston, 1955.

$\beta =$	$(1, 0, 0)$	$(0, 1, 0)$	$(0, 0, 1)$
$\mathbf{D}_\beta f =$	f_1	f_2	f_3
	$D_1 f$	$D_2 f$	$D_3 f$
	$\dfrac{\partial f}{\partial x}$	$\dfrac{\partial f}{\partial y}$	$\dfrac{\partial f}{\partial z}$
	f_x	f_y	f_z
	$\dfrac{\partial w}{\partial x}$	$\dfrac{\partial w}{\partial y}$	$\dfrac{\partial w}{\partial z}$
	w_x	w_y	w_z

The numerical subscripts in the first two rows refer to the coordinate variables in order (e.g., *first* coordinate) and are especially useful when dealing with a complex set of interrelations. To illustrate the use of some of these notations, let $f(x, y, z) = x^2y + y^3 \sin(z^2) = w$. In computing f_1, $\beta = (1, 0, 0)$ so that $p + \lambda\beta$ is the point $(x + \lambda, y, z)$, and we have

$$f_1(x, y, z) = \lim_{\lambda \downarrow 0} \frac{f(x + \lambda, y, z) - f(x, y, z)}{\lambda}.$$

From this, we see that f_1 can be found by regarding x as the only free variable, holding y and z constant, and differentiating the resulting function of one real variable in the usual fashion. Following this method, we have

$$f_1(x, y, z) = \frac{\partial w}{\partial x} = 2xy$$
$$f_2(x, y, z) = \frac{\partial w}{\partial y} = x^2 + 3y^2 \sin(z^2)$$
$$f_3(x, y, z) = \frac{\partial w}{\partial z} = 2y^3 z \cos(z^2).$$

Since the partial derivative of a function of several variables is again a function, the operation may be repeated.

$$f_{11}(x, y, z) = \frac{\partial^2 w}{\partial x^2} = \frac{\partial}{\partial x}\left(\frac{\partial w}{\partial x}\right) = 2y$$
$$f_{12}(x, y, z) = \frac{\partial^2 w}{\partial y\,\partial x} = \frac{\partial}{\partial y}\left(\frac{\partial w}{\partial x}\right) = 2x$$
$$f_{22}(x, y, z) = \frac{\partial^2 w}{\partial y^2} = \frac{\partial}{\partial y}\left(\frac{\partial w}{\partial y}\right) = 6y \sin(z^2)$$
$$f_{21}(x, y, z) = \frac{\partial^2 w}{\partial x\,\partial y} = \frac{\partial}{\partial x}\left(\frac{\partial w}{\partial y}\right) = 2x.$$

Definition. *A function f which is continuous in a region D of the plane is said to be of class C' in D if the first-order derivatives f_1 and f_2 are defined* *and continuous in D. It is said to be of class C'' if it is of class C' and the second-order partial derivatives f_{11}, f_{12}, f_{21}, f_{22} are defined and continuous in D.*

It will be seen later that (as in the example worked out above) f_{12} and f_{21} are equal wherever they are continuous. For this reason, we may equivalently say that $w = f(x, y)$ is of class C'' in D whenever $\frac{\partial^2 w}{\partial x^2}$, $\frac{\partial^2 w}{\partial y^2}$, and $\frac{\partial^2 w}{\partial x \partial y}$ are continuous in D. In general, a function $w = f(x, y)$ of class C^{n-1} is of class C^n in D whenever all the functions $\frac{\partial^n w}{\partial x^n}$, $\frac{\partial^n w}{\partial y \partial x^{n-1}}$, $\dots$ $\frac{\partial^n w}{\partial y^{n-1} \partial x}$ and $\frac{\partial^n w}{\partial y^n}$ are defined and continuous in D. The corresponding definitions for functions of more than two variables are easily formulated.

It is natural to ask if a function of several variables has a nondirectional derivative. The answer to this lies in the concept of the **differential** of a function. Let us start by examining a special case. Let $f(x, y, z) = xy - z^2$, and consider $f(p + \Delta p)$, where $\Delta p = (\Delta x, \Delta y, \Delta z)$.

$$\begin{aligned} f(p + \Delta p) &= (x + \Delta x)(y + \Delta y) - (z + \Delta z)^2 \\ &= xy + x(\Delta y) + y(\Delta x) + (\Delta x)(\Delta y) - z^2 - 2z(\Delta z) - (\Delta z)^2 \\ &= \{xy - z^2\} + \{y(\Delta x) + x(\Delta y) - 2z(\Delta z)\} \\ &\qquad + \{(\Delta x)(\Delta y) - (\Delta z)^2\}. \end{aligned}$$

Of the terms on the right, the first is $f(p)$. The second term can be written as

$$\frac{\partial f}{\partial x} \Delta x + \frac{\partial f}{\partial y} \Delta y + \frac{\partial f}{\partial z} \Delta z$$

and is linear in the three variables Δx, Δy, Δz; accordingly, we may set

$$L = [y, x, -2z] = \left[\frac{\partial f}{\partial x}, \frac{\partial f}{\partial y}, \frac{\partial f}{\partial z}\right]$$

and write the second term as $L(\Delta p)$. The third term is quadratic in the variables Δx, Δy, Δz; when these are small, so that Δp is near $\mathbf{0}$, it is therefore considerably smaller than $|\Delta p|$. As a fair approximation, we therefore have

$$f(p + \Delta p) \sim f(p) + L(\Delta p)$$

where the accuracy improves as Δp approaches $\mathbf{0}$.

Such observations can be used to motivate the following definition.

Definition. *Let f be any function of class C' in a region D of n-space. Then, the differential of f at a point $p \in D$ is the linear function L of n variables specified by the matrix*

$$[f_1(p), f_2(p), \ldots, f_n(p)].$$

When we write $w = f(x, y)$, for example, the differential of f is given by $\left[\frac{\partial w}{\partial x}, \frac{\partial w}{\partial y}\right]$ and its value at a point $(\Delta x, \Delta y)$ is $\frac{\partial w}{\partial x} \Delta x + \frac{\partial w}{\partial y} \Delta y$. In the degenerate case of a function of one variable,† $w = f(x)$, the differential

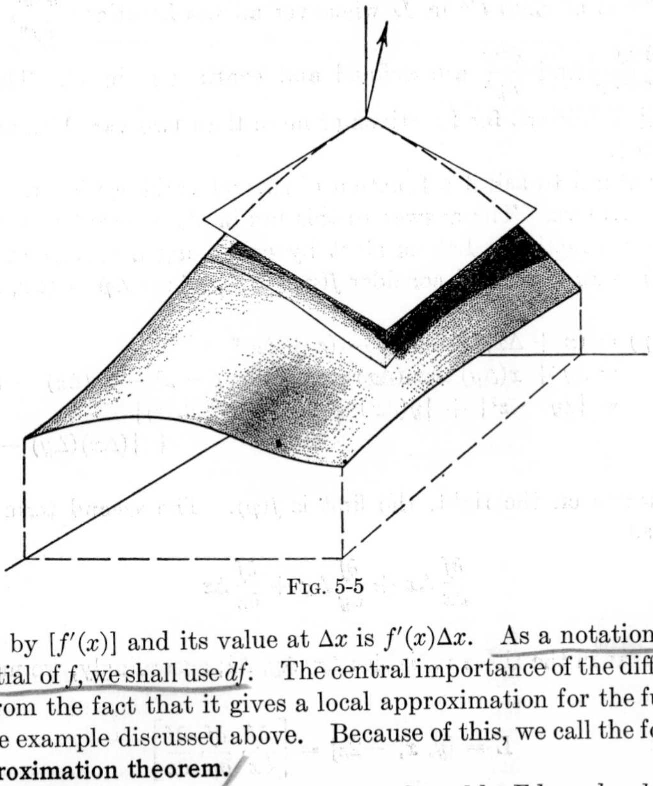

FIG. 5-5

is given by $[f'(x)]$ and its value at Δx is $f'(x)\Delta x$. As a notation for the differential of f, we shall use df. The central importance of the differential stems from the fact that it gives a local approximation for the function, as in the example discussed above. Because of this, we call the following the **approximation theorem.**

Theorem 8. *Let $f \in C'$ in an open region D and let E be a closed bounded subset of D. Let df be the differential of f at the point $p_0 \in E$. Then,*

$$f(p_0 + \Delta p) = f(p_0) + df(\Delta p) + R(\Delta p)$$

† The notion of the differential of a function does not appear in its true light in the theory of functions of one variable; one must draw the subtle distinction between a number c and the 1-by-1 matrix $[c]$. Thus, the derivative of f at a point x_0 is the *number* $f'(x_0)$, whereas the differential of f at x_0 is the *linear function* which multiplies every number by $f'(x_0)$.

where

$$\lim_{\Delta p \to 0} \frac{R(\Delta p)}{|\Delta p|} = 0$$

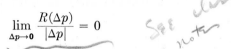

uniformly for $p_0 \in E$.

If this is written out with variables for a function $z = f(x, y)$, it becomes

$$f(x + \Delta x, y + \Delta y) = f(x, y) + \frac{\partial z}{\partial x} \Delta x + \frac{\partial z}{\partial y} \Delta y + R(\Delta x, \Delta y)$$

where the remainder term $R(\Delta x, \Delta y)$ is "of smaller order of magnitude" than $|\Delta p| = [(\Delta x)^2 + (\Delta y)^2]^{1/2}$. In this case, it is also possible to give the approximation property a geometric flavor by considering the plane through (x, y, z) with normal $(\partial z/\partial x, \partial z/\partial y, -1)$ (see Fig. 5-5). This plane is defined to be the tangent plane to the surface described by the equation $z = f(x, y)$, and Theorem 8 asserts that this plane is a good approximation to the surface in a neighborhood of (x, y, z). (These notions will be discussed further in Chap. 6.)

In proving the theorem, a preliminary step is needed which is in the nature of a **mean value theorem**; for simplicity, we consider only the two-variable case.

Lemma. *Let* $f \in C'$ *in an open disk* N *of radius* ρ *centered at* $p_0 = (x_0, y_0)$, *and let* $\Delta p = (\Delta x, \Delta y)$ *with* $|\Delta p| < \rho$. *Then, there are two points* p' *and* p'' *in* N *such that*

$$f(p_0 + \Delta p) - f(p_0) = f_1(p')\,\Delta x + f_2(p'')\,\Delta y.$$

Take $q = (x_0 + \Delta x, y_0)$. Using the one-variable mean value theorem, we can write

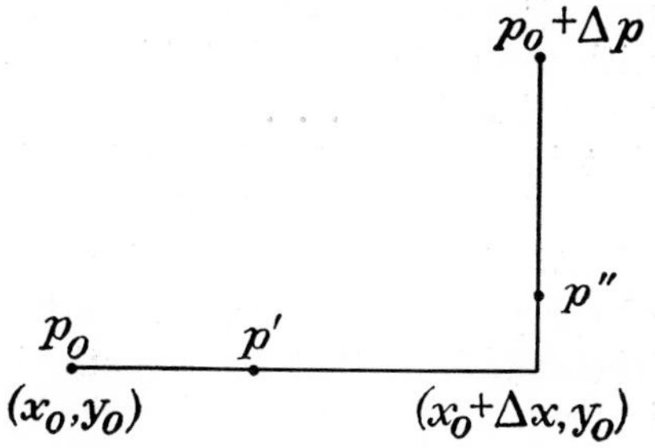

FIG. 5-6

$$\begin{aligned} f(q) - f(p_0) &= f(x_0 + \Delta x, y_0) - f(x_0, y_0) \\ &= f_1(x', y_0)\,\Delta x = f_1(p')\,\Delta x \end{aligned}$$

and
$$\begin{aligned} f(p_0 + \Delta p) - f(q) &= f(x_0 + \Delta x, y_0 + \Delta y) - f(x_0 + \Delta x, y_0) \\ &= f_2(x_0 + \Delta x, y')\,\Delta y = f_2(p'')\,\Delta y \end{aligned}$$

where $p' = (x', y_0)$ and $p'' = (x_0 + \Delta x, y')$ are points located somewhere on the segments joining p_0 to q and q to $p_0 + \Delta p$, respectively (see Fig. 5-6). Adding these, we have the desired result. ▌ (We shall obtain later a more symmetric form of this type of mean value theorem in which the points p' and p'' will be replaced by a single point p^* which lies somewhere on the line segment joining p_0 and $p_0 + \Delta p$.)

Returning to the proof of Theorem 8, we use the result of the lemma to write

$$\begin{aligned} f(p_0 + \Delta p) &= f(p_0) + f_1(p')\,\Delta x + f_2(p'')\,\Delta y \\ &= f(p_0) + \{f_1(p_0)\,\Delta x + f_2(p_0)\,\Delta y\} \\ &\qquad + \{[f_1(p') - f_1(p_0)]\,\Delta x + [f_2(p'') - f_2(p_0)]\,\Delta y\} \\ &= f(p_0) + df(\Delta p) + R(\Delta p) \end{aligned}$$

where

$$R(\Delta p) = [f_1(p') - f_1(p_0)]\,\Delta x + [f_2(p'') - f_2(p_0)]\,\Delta y.$$

Since $|\Delta x| \leq |\Delta p|$ and $|\Delta y| \leq |\Delta p|$, we have

$$\frac{|R(\Delta p)|}{|\Delta p|} \leq |f_1(p') - f_1(p_0)| + |f_2(p'') - f_2(p_0)|.$$

We assumed that f is of class C'; the functions f_1 and f_2 are therefore continuous at p_0, and uniformly continuous for p_0 in E. Since $|p' - p_0|$ and $|p'' - p_0|$ are smaller than $|\Delta p|$, we can choose a $\delta > 0$ for a given ϵ such that $|R(\Delta p)|/|\Delta p| < \epsilon$ whenever $|\Delta p| < \delta$ and $p_0 \in E$. This proves that $\lim_{\Delta p \to 0} \frac{|R(\Delta p)|}{|\Delta p|} = 0$ uniformly for p_0 in E, and completes the proof of the approximation theorem. ▮

In more advanced treatments, it is sometimes desirable to weaken the requirement that f be of class C'. This may be done by replacing this with the statement that f is **differentiable** on D, and is understood to mean that $f_1, f_2, \ldots$ are defined on D (but may be discontinuous), and that in addition the linear functions df have at each point of D the approximation property described in Theorem 8. Although we do not adopt this, the careful reader will see that in most of the remainder of the present chapter, we use the hypothesis "$f \in C'$" only to invoke Theorem 8, so that the hypothesis "f is differentiable" could be used instead. It should be remarked that, as Exercise 4 shows, it is not enough merely to have f_1 and f_2 defined.

With the differential as a tool, let us return to the general directional derivative.

Theorem 9. *If $f \in C'$ in D, then all the directional derivatives exist at any point of D; if df is the differential of f at a point $p \in D$, then $\mathbf{D}_\beta f(p) = df(\beta)$.*

Writing $w = f(x, y, z)$ and $\beta = (b_1, b_2, b_3)$, the final statement asserts that

$$\mathbf{D}_\beta f(p) = \frac{\partial w}{\partial x} b_1 + \frac{\partial w}{\partial y} b_2 + \frac{\partial w}{\partial z} b_3.$$

To prove this, we take $\Delta p = \lambda\beta$ and use the fact that df is linear to write

$$\begin{aligned}\frac{f(p+\lambda\beta)-f(p)}{\lambda} &= \frac{df(\lambda\beta)+R(\lambda\beta)}{\lambda}\\ &= \frac{\lambda df(\beta)+R(\lambda\beta)}{\lambda}\\ &= df(\beta)+\frac{R(\lambda\beta)}{|\Delta p|}\end{aligned}$$

so that $\mathbf{D}_\beta f(p) = df(\beta) + \lim\limits_{\lambda\downarrow 0} \dfrac{R(\Delta p)}{|\Delta p|} = df(\beta)$. ▌

To illustrate this, let us return to the example with which this section opened. With $f(x, y) = x^2 + 3xy$, $f_1(x, y) = 2x + 3y$ and $f_2(x, y) = 3x$ so that the differential of f at (x, y) is $[2x + 3y, 3x]$. To evaluate the directional derivative of f at $(1, 0)$ in the direction $\beta = (1/\sqrt{2}, -1/\sqrt{2})$, we find $df = [2, 3]$ and $df(\beta) = 2(1/\sqrt{2}) + 3(-1/\sqrt{2}) = -1/\sqrt{2}$.

Most of the results in Sec. 2.6 dealing with functions of one variable have their analogues in theorems dealing with partial differentiation.

Theorem 10. *Let f be of class C' in a region D and take a maximal value at an interior point p_0. Then, all the first-order partial derivatives of f are zero at p_0.*

Since p_0 is a maximum point for f, $f(p_0 + \Delta p) \le f(p_0)$ for all Δp, and

$$df(\Delta p) + R(\Delta p) \le 0$$

for all Δp. Putting $\Delta p = \lambda\beta$, where $|\beta| = 1$, and dividing by $\lambda = |\Delta p|$, we have

$$df(\beta) + \frac{R(\Delta p)}{|\Delta p|} \le 0.$$

Letting $\Delta p \to \mathbf{0}$, we see that $df(\beta) \le 0$ for all directions β. Since

$$df(-\beta) = -df(\beta),$$

it follows that $df(\beta) = 0$ for all β, and the linear function df must have only zero coefficients. ▌

Theorem 11. *Let f be of class C' in an open connected set D, and suppose that df is identically zero at each point of D. Then, f is constant in D.*

From the lemma (page 185) it follows at once that if p_0 is any point of D and N is a neighborhood of p_0 which lies in D, then $f(p) = f(p_0)$ for all $p \in N$. Set $C = f(p_0)$. To prove that f takes the value C everywhere in D, we use a special argument, based on the connectedness of D. Let $S_1 = \{\text{all } p \in D \text{ with } f(p) = C\}$, $S_2 = \{\text{all } p \in D \text{ with } f(p) \ne C\}$. The set S_2 is an open set. So also is the set S_1, for if p_1 is any point of

S_1, our first argument shows that $f(p) = f(p_1)$ for all points p in some neighborhood of p_1, and p_1 is surrounded by a neighborhood of points at which f has the value C. The sets S_1 and S_2 together cover D, and have no points in common; since D is connected, one of these is empty. This cannot be S_1, so that $S_1 = D$ and $f(p) = C$ for all points $p \in D$.† ▌

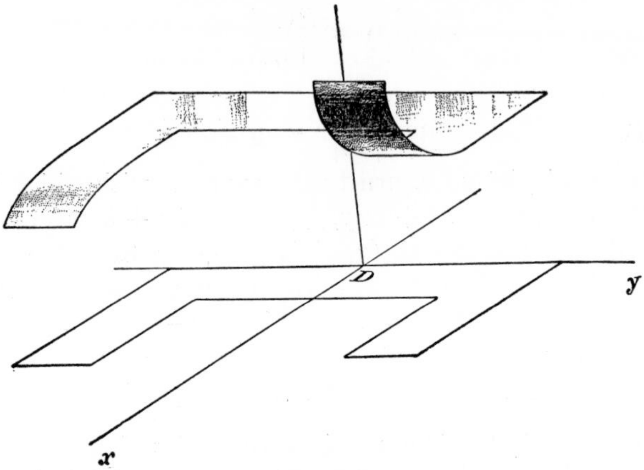

FIG. 5-7

It is natural to ask what happens if just one of the partial derivatives is identically zero. Such is the case, for example, in the function f

$$f(x, y, z) = x^2 + y^2,$$

where z is missing, and $\dfrac{\partial f}{\partial z} = 0$ at all points.

Theorem 12. *Let $w = f(x, y, z)$ where f is of class C' in a convex open set D, and let $\dfrac{\partial w}{\partial z} = 0$ throughout D. Then, z is missing, in the sense that*

$$f(x, y, z') = f(x, y, z'')$$

whenever (x, y, z') and (x, y, z'') are both in D.

The proof of this is again a simple consequence of the mean value lemma, and we omit it. Some restriction, such as convexity, is needed on D. This is shown by the function g whose graph $z = g(x, y)$ is shown in Fig. 5-7. The set D is a nonconvex horseshoe-shaped region and z is independent of y in a neighborhood of any point of D, but is not independent of y throughout D.

The inverse operation for partial differentiation is partial integration, that is, integration of $f(x, y)$ with respect to one variable while holding the other constant. This has already been discussed in Chap. 3. However, the following simple result was not given there.

† See also Exercise 22 and 23, Sec. 5.4.

Theorem 13. *Let f be of class C'' in a rectangle R with vertices $P_1 = (a_1, b_1)$, $Q_1 = (a_2, b_1)$, $P_2 = (a_2, b_2)$, $Q_2 = (a_1, b_2)$, where $a_1 \leq a_2$ and $b_1 \leq b_2$. Then,*

$$\iint_R f_{12} = \iint_R \frac{\partial^2 f}{\partial y \partial x}\, dx dy = f(P_1) - f(Q_1) + f(P_2) - f(Q_2).$$

Writing the double integral as an iterated integral, we have

$$\begin{aligned}
\iint_R f_{12} &= \int_{a_1}^{a_2} dx \int_{b_1}^{b_2} \frac{\partial}{\partial y}\left(\frac{\partial f}{\partial x}\right) dy \\
&= \int_{a_1}^{a_2} \left[\frac{\partial f}{\partial x}\right]_{y=b_1}^{y=b_2} dx \\
&= \int_{a_1}^{a_2} f_1(x, b_2)\, dx - \int_{a_1}^{a_2} f_1(x, b_1)\, dx \\
&= \Big[f(x, b_2)\Big]_{x=a_1}^{x=a_2} - \Big[f(x, b_1)\Big]_{x=a_1}^{x=a_2} \\
&= f(a_2, b_2) - f(a_1, b_2) - [f(a_2, b_1) - f(a_1, b_1)] \\
&= f(P_1) - f(Q_1) + f(P_2) - f(Q_2). \quad \blacksquare
\end{aligned}$$

Corollary. *If a function f is of class C'' in an open set D, then $f_{12} = f_{21}$ throughout D.*

If R is any rectangle lying in D, then the line of argument in the theorem shows that $\iint_R f_{12}$ and $\iint_R f_{21}$ are both equal to $f(P_1) - f(Q_1) + f(P_2) - f(Q_2)$, where P_1, Q_1, P_2, Q_2 are the vertices of R, in counterclockwise order. Thus, $\iint_R (f_{12} - f_{21}) = 0$ for every choice of R, and the integrand must be identically zero in D. $\blacksquare$

EXERCISES

1. Find $f_1(x, y)$, $f_2(x, y)$, $f_{12}(x, y)$ if (*a*) $f(x, y) = x^2 \log (x^2 + y^2)$; (*b*) $f(x, y) = x^y$.

2. With $f(x, y) = x^2y^3 - 2y$, find $f_1(x, y)$, $f_2(x, y)$, $f_2(2, 3)$, and $f_2(y, x)$.

3. Compute the differential of each of the following functions at the given point:

(*a*) $f(x, y) = 3x^2y - xy^3 + 2$ at $(1, 2)$

(*b*) $f(u, v) = u \sin (uv)$ at $(\pi/4, 2)$

(*c*) $f(x, y, z) = x^2yz + 3xz^2$ at $(1, 2, -1)$.

4. (*a*) Let $f(x, y) = xy/(x^2 + y^2)$, with $f(0, 0) = 0$. Show that f_1 and f_2 exist everywhere, but that f is not of class C'.

(*b*) Does f have directional derivatives at the origin?

(*c*) Is f continuous at the origin?

5. Let a function f be defined in an open set D of the plane, and suppose that f_1 and f_2 are defined and bounded everywhere in D. Show that f is continuous in D.

6. Can you formulate and prove an analogue for Rolle's theorem, for functions of two real variables?

7. Find the derivative of $f(x, y, z) = xy^2 + yz$ at the point (1, 1, 2) in the direction $(\frac{2}{3}, -\frac{1}{3}, \frac{2}{3})$.

8. The gradient of a function at a point is the maximum directional derivative at that point. Show that the value of the gradient of a function given by $z = f(x, y)$ is

$$\left\{\left(\frac{\partial z}{\partial x}\right)^2 + \left(\frac{\partial z}{\partial y}\right)^2\right\}^{1/2}.$$

9. Using the results dealing with linear functions which were discussed at the end of Sec. 5.2, generalize Exercise 8 to functions of n variables.

10. Let $f(x, y) = xy$. Show that the direction of the gradient of f is always perpendicular to the level lines of f.

11. Show that each of the following obey $\dfrac{\partial^2 u}{\partial x^2} + \dfrac{\partial^2 u}{\partial y^2} = 0$:

(a) $u = e^x \cos y$ (b) $u = \exp(x^2 - y^2) \sin(2xy)$

12. (a) Apply Theorem 13 to evaluate the double integral

$$\int_2^5 dx \int_{-1}^3 (x^2y + 5xy^2)\, dy.$$

(b) Formulate and prove a corresponding theorem for the evaluation of triple integrals.

13. Let $f(x, y) = xy(x^2 - y^2)/(x^2 + y^2)$ with $f(0, 0) = 0$. Show that f is continuous everywhere, that f_1, f_2, f_{12} and f_{21} exist everywhere, but $f_{12}(0, 0) \neq f_{21}(0, 0)$.

5.4. Differentiation of Composite Functions

A function may often be regarded as built up by composition from a number of other functions. If $f(x, y) = xy^2 + x^2$, $g(x, y) = y \sin x$, and $h(x) = e^x$, then a function F may be defined by

$$F(x, y) = f(g(x, y), h(x)) = ye^{2x} \sin x + y^2 \sin^2(x). \tag{5-9}$$

The introduction of additional variable symbols sometimes helps to clarify such relations. For example, an equivalent description of (5-9) is obtained by setting $w = F(x, y)$, and writing

$$\begin{aligned} w &= f(u, v) = uv^2 + u^2 \\ u &= g(x, y) = y \sin x \\ v &= h(x) = e^x \end{aligned} \tag{5-10}$$

These equations express w in terms of x and y indirectly through the intermediate variables u and v. The interdependence involved in this particular example may also be indicated schematically as in Fig. 5-8.

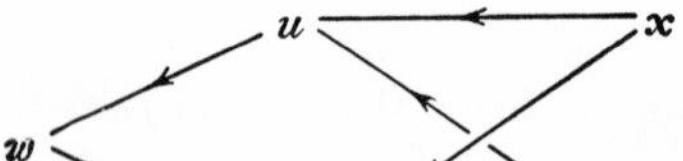

Fig. 5-8

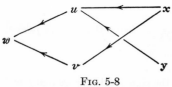

The main concern of this section is the theory and application of the rules for obtaining derivatives of such composite functions. Rather than state a theorem which would be inclusive enough to embrace all examples of the so-called "chain rules of differentiation," we shall merely prove a special case which illustrates the method of proof.

Theorem 14. *Let $w = f(u, v)$ where $u = g(x, y)$ and $v = h(x, y)$. Let g and h be of class C' in a neighborhood of $p_0 = (x_0, y_0)$ and f of class C' in a neighborhood of $q_0 = (g(p_0), h(p_0))$. Then, the function F with $w = F(x, y)$ is of class C' in a neighborhood of p_0, and there*

$$\frac{\partial w}{\partial x} = \frac{\partial w}{\partial u}\frac{\partial u}{\partial x} + \frac{\partial w}{\partial v}\frac{\partial v}{\partial x}$$
(5-11)
$$\frac{\partial w}{\partial y} = \frac{\partial w}{\partial u}\frac{\partial u}{\partial y} + \frac{\partial w}{\partial v}\frac{\partial v}{\partial y}.$$

We have $w = F(x, y) = f(g(x, y), h(x, y))$, and the differentiation rule (5-11) may be stated in the form

$$F_1(p_0) = f_1(q_0)g_1(p_0) + f_2(q_0)h_1(p_0)$$
$$F_2(p_0) = f_1(q_0)g_2(p_0) + f_2(q_0)h_2(p_0).$$

Let $p = p_0 + \Delta p$, where $\Delta p = (\Delta x, \Delta y)$, and set $q = (g(p), h(p))$ and $\Delta q = q - q_0$. Then, $\Delta q = (\Delta u, \Delta v)$ where $\Delta u = g(p) - g(p_0)$ and $\Delta v = h(p) - h(p_0)$. Using the approximation property of differentials, we may write

$$\Delta u = dg(\Delta p) + R_1(\Delta p)$$
$$\Delta v = dh(\Delta p) + R_2(\Delta p)$$

and

$$F(p) - F(p_0) = f(q) - f(q_0) = df(\Delta q) + R_3(\Delta q)$$

where the three remainder functions obey the conditions

$$\lim_{\Delta p \to 0} \frac{R_1(\Delta p)}{|\Delta p|} = \lim_{\Delta p \to 0} \frac{R_2(\Delta p)}{|\Delta p|} = \lim_{\Delta q \to 0} \frac{R_3(\Delta q)}{|\Delta q|} = 0.$$

Substituting for Δu and Δv, we have

$$\Delta q = (\, dg(\Delta p), dh(\Delta p)\,) + (\, R_1(\Delta p), R_2(\Delta p)\,)$$

so that

$$df(\Delta q) = df(\, dg(\Delta p), dh(\Delta p)\,) + df(\, R_1(\Delta p), R_2(\Delta p)\,)$$

Accordingly, we have

$$F(p) - F(p_0) = df(\, dg(\Delta p), dh(\Delta p)\,) + R(\Delta p)$$

where

$$R(\Delta p) = df(\, R_1(\Delta p), R_2(\Delta p)\,) + R_3(\Delta q)$$

If we expand the differentials into their coordinate form, we have

$$\begin{aligned} df(dg(\Delta p), dh(\Delta p)) &= f_1(q_0)\, dg(\Delta p) + f_2(q_0)\, dh(\Delta p) \\ &= f_1(q_0)\{g_1(p_0)\,\Delta x + g_2(p_0)\,\Delta y\} \\ &\qquad + f_2(q_0)\{h_1(p_0)\,\Delta x + h_2(p_0)\,\Delta y\} \\ &= \frac{\partial w}{\partial u}\left\{\frac{\partial u}{\partial x}\,\Delta x + \frac{\partial u}{\partial y}\,\Delta y\right\} + \frac{\partial w}{\partial v}\left\{\frac{\partial v}{\partial x}\,\Delta x + \frac{\partial v}{\partial y}\,\Delta y\right\} \\ &= \left\{\frac{\partial w}{\partial u}\frac{\partial u}{\partial x} + \frac{\partial w}{\partial v}\frac{\partial v}{\partial x}\right\}\Delta x + \left\{\frac{\partial w}{\partial u}\frac{\partial u}{\partial y} + \frac{\partial w}{\partial v}\frac{\partial v}{\partial y}\right\}\Delta y. \end{aligned}$$

To complete the proof of the theorem, all that is necessary is to show that

$\lim_{|\Delta p|\to 0} \frac{R(\Delta p)}{|\Delta p|} = 0$. In $\frac{R(\Delta p)}{|\Delta p|} = df\left(\frac{R_1(\Delta p)}{|\Delta p|}, \frac{R_2(\Delta p)}{|\Delta p|}\right) + \frac{R_3(\Delta q)}{|\Delta p|}$

the first term on the right approaches 0 since

$$\lim_{\Delta p \to \mathbf{0}} \left(\frac{R_1(\Delta p)}{|\Delta p|}, \frac{R_2(\Delta p)}{|\Delta p|}\right) = (0, 0)$$

and df is continuous. For the second term, we first observe that since dg and dh are linear functions, a number M can be found such that $|\Delta q| \le M|\Delta p|$ for all Δp near $\mathbf{0}$, so that

$$\frac{|R_3(\Delta q)|}{|\Delta p|} \le M \frac{|R_3(\Delta q)|}{|\Delta q|}$$

which approaches zero as Δp, and therefore Δq, approaches $\mathbf{0}$. ▌

To illustrate the use of this chain rule, let us reconsider the example given earlier by Eqs. (5-10):

$$w = uv^2 + u^2 \qquad u = y \sin x \qquad v = e^x.$$

Applying (5-11), we have

$$\frac{\partial w}{\partial x} = (v^2 + 2u)(y \cos x) + (2uv)(e^x)$$

and

$$\frac{\partial w}{\partial y} = (v^2 + 2u)(\sin x) + (2uv)(0).$$

The next illustration is somewhat more complicated; it also shows how the quotient notation for partial derivatives is sometimes ambiguous. Let w be related to x and y by the following equations:

(5-12) $$w = f(x, u, v) \qquad u = g(x, v, y), \qquad v = h(x, y).$$

The corresponding diagram is shown in Fig. 5-9. We see that the dependence of w upon x is complicated by the fact that x enters in directly, and also through u and v. Each path in the diagram joining x to w corresponds to a term in the formula for $\frac{\partial w}{\partial x}$, so that we obtain

$$\frac{\partial w}{\partial x} = \frac{\partial w}{\partial x} + \frac{\partial w}{\partial u}\frac{\partial u}{\partial x} + \frac{\partial w}{\partial v}\frac{\partial v}{\partial x} + \frac{\partial w}{\partial u}\frac{\partial u}{\partial v}\frac{\partial v}{\partial x}; \tag{5-13}$$

y enters in through v and u, so that

$$\frac{\partial w}{\partial y} = \frac{\partial w}{\partial u}\frac{\partial u}{\partial y} + \frac{\partial w}{\partial v}\frac{\partial v}{\partial y} + \frac{\partial w}{\partial u}\frac{\partial u}{\partial v}\frac{\partial v}{\partial y}. \tag{5-14}$$

In both of these formulas, the partial derivatives must be understood in the correct context of Eqs. (5-12) above. In (5-13), for example, the

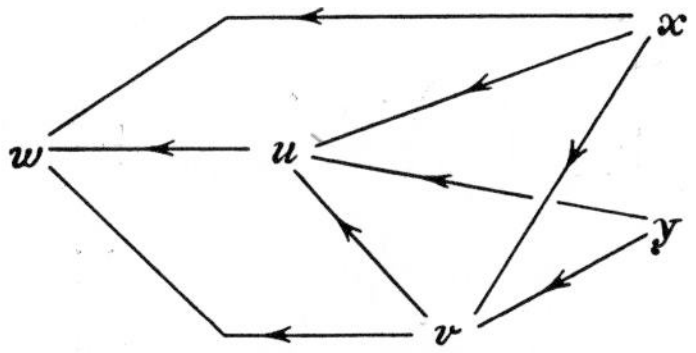

FIG. 5-9

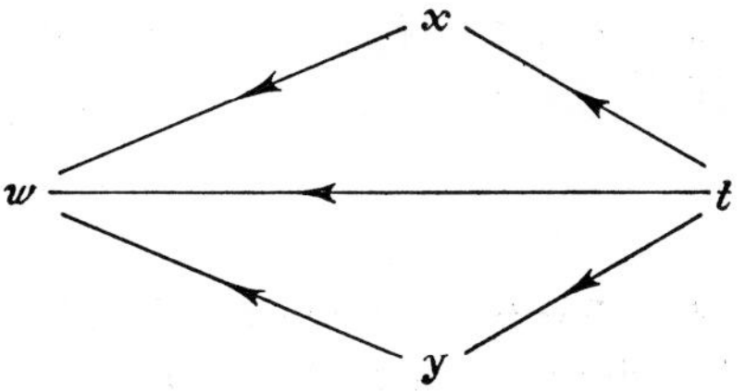

FIG. 5-10

first occurrence of "$\partial w/\partial x$" refers to the partial derivative of w, regarding it as "a function of the independent variables x and y." (This is often indicated by writing $\left.\frac{\partial w}{\partial x}\right|_y$ to show that y is being held constant.) The second occurrence of "$\partial w/\partial x$", however, refers to the partial derivative of w regarded as a function of the independent variables x, u, v. The use of numerical subscripts helps to remove such ambiguity. We may write (5-13) and (5-14) in the alternate forms

$$\frac{\partial w}{\partial x} = f_1 + f_2g_1 + f_3h_1 + f_2g_2h_1$$

$$\frac{\partial w}{\partial y} = f_2g_3 + f_3h_2 + f_2g_2h_2.$$

As another illustration of the use of chain rules, consider the following relationship

$$w = F(x, y, t), \qquad x = \phi(t), \qquad y = \psi(t);$$

these express w in the form $w = f(t)$, as shown by the diagram in Fig. 5-10, and

$$\frac{dw}{dt} = \frac{\partial w}{\partial t} + \frac{\partial w}{\partial x}\frac{dx}{dt} + \frac{\partial w}{\partial y}\frac{dy}{dt}. \tag{5-15}$$

This procedure can also be used to compute higher derivatives too. For example, to find d^2w/dt^2, we rewrite (5-15) in the form

$$\frac{dw}{dt} = F_3(x, y, t) + F_1(x, y, t)\frac{dx}{dt} + F_2(x, y, t)\frac{dy}{dt}$$

and then differentiate a second time, getting

$$\frac{d^2w}{dt^2} = F_{33} + F_{31}\frac{dx}{dt} + F_{32}\frac{dy}{dt} + F_{11}\left(\frac{dx}{dt}\right)^2 + F_{12}\frac{dx}{dt}\frac{dy}{dt} + F_{13}\frac{dx}{dt}$$
$$+ F_{22}\left(\frac{dy}{dt}\right)^2 + F_{21}\frac{dx}{dt}\frac{dy}{dt} + F_{23}\frac{dy}{dt} + F_1\frac{d^2x}{dt^2} + F_2\frac{d^2y}{dt^2}.$$

Assuming that F is of class C'', this may also be expressed in the form

$$\frac{d^2w}{dt^2} = \frac{\partial^2 w}{\partial t^2} + 2\left\{\frac{\partial^2 w}{\partial x\partial t}\frac{dx}{dt} + \frac{\partial^2 w}{\partial y\partial t}\frac{dy}{dt}\right\} + \frac{\partial^2 w}{\partial x^2}\left(\frac{dx}{dt}\right)^2$$
$$+ 2\frac{\partial^2 w}{\partial x\partial y}\frac{dx}{dt}\frac{dy}{dt} + \frac{\partial^2 w}{\partial y^2}\left(\frac{dy}{dt}\right)^2 + \frac{\partial w}{\partial x}\frac{d^2x}{dt^2} + \frac{\partial w}{\partial y}\frac{d^2y}{dt^2}$$

Another type of problem in which the chain rules prove useful is that of finding formulas for the derivatives of functions which are defined "implicitly." Consider the pair of equations

$$\text{(5-16)} \qquad \begin{cases} x^2 + ux + y^2 + v = 0 \\ x + yu + v^2 + x^2v = 0. \end{cases}$$

If we give x and y numerical values, we obtain a pair of algebraic equations which have one or more solutions for u and v; for some choices of x and y, these solutions will be real, so that Eqs. (5-16) serve to define one or more functions f and g such that

$$\text{(5-17)} \qquad \begin{cases} u = f(x, y) \\ v = g(x, y). \end{cases}$$

For example, if $x = 1$, $y = 1$, then (5-16) becomes

$$\begin{cases} u + v + 2 = 0 \\ u + v^2 + v + 1 = 0 \end{cases}$$

which has the solutions $(u, v) = (-1, -1)$ and $(u, v) = (-3, 1)$. General theorems, which we shall discuss later in Sec. 5.8, show that there are functions f and g defined in a neighborhood N of $(1, 1)$ such that $f(1, 1) = -3$, $g(1, 1) = 1$, and such that (5-16) holds with the substitutions (5-17) for all (x, y) in N. Knowing the function f, it would then be possible to compute $\partial u/\partial x = f_1$ and find $f_1(1, 1) = \partial u/\partial x\big|_{(1,1)}$.

By the use of the chain rules, it is possible to compute such partial derivatives without carrying out the often difficult task of solving explicitly for the functions f and g. To achieve this for the specific example above, differentiate each of the equations in (5-16) with respect to x while holding y constant.

$$2x + u + x\frac{\partial u}{\partial x} + 0 + \frac{\partial v}{\partial x} = 0$$

$$1 + y\frac{\partial u}{\partial x} + 2v\frac{\partial v}{\partial x} + 2xv + x^2\frac{\partial v}{\partial x} = 0.$$

Solving these for $\partial u/\partial x$, we find

$$\frac{\partial u}{\partial x} = \frac{1 - 2xv - 2uv - 2x^3 - ux^2}{2xv + x^3 - y}.$$

If we set $x = 1$, $y = 1$, $u = -3$, $v = 1$, we find the desired value

$$\left.\frac{\partial u}{\partial x}\right|_{(1,1)} = f_1(1, 1) = 3.$$

We can obtain a formula for the solution of a general class of such problems. Suppose that one is given two equations

$$\text{(5-18)} \qquad \begin{cases} F(x, y, u, v) = 0 \\ G(x, y, u, v) = 0 \end{cases}$$

which we may regard as solvable for u and v in terms of x and y. We wish to find $\partial u/\partial x$ and $\partial v/\partial x$. Holding y constant, differentiate (5-18) with respect to x.

$$F_1 + F_3\frac{\partial u}{\partial x} + F_4\frac{\partial v}{\partial x} = 0$$

$$G_1 + G_3\frac{\partial u}{\partial x} + G_4\frac{\partial v}{\partial x} = 0.$$

Solving these, we obtain the desired formulas

$$\frac{\partial u}{\partial x} = -\frac{\begin{vmatrix} F_1 & F_4 \\ G_1 & G_4 \end{vmatrix}}{\begin{vmatrix} F_3 & F_4 \\ G_3 & G_4 \end{vmatrix}} = -\frac{F_1G_4 - F_4G_1}{F_3G_4 - F_4G_3}$$

$$\frac{\partial v}{\partial x} = -\frac{\begin{vmatrix} F_3 & F_1 \\ G_3 & G_1 \end{vmatrix}}{\begin{vmatrix} F_3 & F_4 \\ G_3 & G_4 \end{vmatrix}} = -\frac{F_3G_1 - F_1G_3}{F_3G_4 - F_4G_3}$$

Determinants of this special form are common enough to have acquired a special name and notation; they are called **Jacobians,** and the notation is illustrated by

$$\frac{\partial(A, B)}{\partial(s, t)} = \begin{vmatrix} \dfrac{\partial A}{\partial s} & \dfrac{\partial A}{\partial t} \\[2ex] \dfrac{\partial B}{\partial s} & \dfrac{\partial B}{\partial t} \end{vmatrix}.$$

Using this, we can write the formulas above in simpler form as

$$\frac{\partial u}{\partial x} = -\frac{\partial(F, G)}{\partial(x, v)} \Big/ \frac{\partial(F, G)}{\partial(u, v)} \tag{5-19}$$
$$\frac{\partial v}{\partial x} = -\frac{\partial(F, G)}{\partial(u, x)} \Big/ \frac{\partial(F, G)}{\partial(u, v)}$$

To apply these to the pair of equations given in (5-16), we take

$$F(x, y, u, v) = x^2 + ux + y^2 + v$$

and

$$G(x, y, u, v) = x + yu + v^2 + x^2v.$$

Then,

$$\frac{\partial F}{\partial x} = 2x + u \qquad \frac{\partial F}{\partial u} = x \qquad \frac{\partial F}{\partial v} = 1$$
$$\frac{\partial G}{\partial x} = 1 + 2xv \qquad \frac{\partial G}{\partial u} = y \qquad \frac{\partial G}{\partial v} = 2v + x^2$$

so that

$$\frac{\partial u}{\partial x} = -\begin{vmatrix} 2x + u & 1 \\ 1 + 2xv & 2v + x^2 \end{vmatrix} \div \begin{vmatrix} x & 1 \\ y & 2v + x^2 \end{vmatrix}$$
$$= -\frac{2xv + 2uv + 2x^3 + ux^2 - 1}{2xv + x^3 - y}$$

and

$$\frac{\partial v}{\partial x} = -\begin{vmatrix} x & 2x + u \\ y & 1 + 2xv \end{vmatrix} \div \begin{vmatrix} x & 1 \\ y & 2v + x^2 \end{vmatrix}$$
$$= -\frac{x + 2x^2v - 2xy - uy}{2xv + x^3 - y}.$$

Further formulas of this nature will be found in the exercises. It should be pointed out that the Jacobian which occurs in the denominator of both fractions in (5-19) is one whose nonvanishing will be sufficient to ensure that Eqs. (5-18) really do have a solution in the form

$$u = f(x, y), v = g(x, y)$$

(see Sec. 5.8).

A somewhat more difficult problem is the following, which is patterned after a type of situation which occurs in physical applications. A physical law or hypothesis is often formulated as a partial differential equation. If a change of variables is made, what is the corresponding form for the differential equation? We first examine a simple case. Suppose the differential equation is $\partial^2u/\partial x^2 - \partial^2u/\partial y^2 = 0$, and suppose we wish to make the substitution

$$\begin{cases} x = s + t \\ y = s - t. \end{cases} \tag{5-20}$$

By the appropriate chain rule,

$$\frac{\partial u}{\partial x} = \frac{\partial u}{\partial s}\frac{\partial s}{\partial x} + \frac{\partial u}{\partial t}\frac{\partial t}{\partial x}$$
$$\frac{\partial u}{\partial y} = \frac{\partial u}{\partial s}\frac{\partial s}{\partial y} + \frac{\partial u}{\partial t}\frac{\partial t}{\partial y}.$$

Solving (5-20), we have $s = (x + y)/2$ and $t = (x - y)/2$ so that

$$\frac{\partial u}{\partial x} = \frac{\partial u}{\partial s}\left(\frac{1}{2}\right) + \frac{\partial u}{\partial t}\left(\frac{1}{2}\right) = \frac{1}{2}\left(\frac{\partial}{\partial s} + \frac{\partial}{\partial t}\right)(u)$$

and
$$\frac{\partial u}{\partial y} = \frac{\partial u}{\partial s}\left(\frac{1}{2}\right) + \frac{\partial u}{\partial t}\left(-\frac{1}{2}\right) = \frac{1}{2}\left(\frac{\partial}{\partial s} - \frac{\partial}{\partial t}\right)(u).$$

Repeating this, and assuming that $u = F(x, y)$ with F of class C'',

$$\frac{\partial^2 u}{\partial x^2} = \frac{\partial}{\partial x}\left(\frac{\partial u}{\partial x}\right) = \frac{1}{2}\left(\frac{\partial}{\partial s} + \frac{\partial}{\partial t}\right)\left(\frac{\partial u}{\partial s}\frac{1}{2} + \frac{\partial u}{\partial t}\frac{1}{2}\right)$$
$$= \frac{1}{4}\left(\frac{\partial^2 u}{\partial s^2} + 2\frac{\partial^2 u}{\partial s \partial t} + \frac{\partial^2 u}{\partial t^2}\right)$$

and
$$\frac{\partial^2 u}{\partial y^2} = \frac{1}{2}\left(\frac{\partial}{\partial s} - \frac{\partial}{\partial t}\right)\left(\frac{\partial u}{\partial s}\frac{1}{2} - \frac{\partial u}{\partial t}\frac{1}{2}\right)$$
$$= \frac{1}{4}\left(\frac{\partial^2 u}{\partial s^2} - 2\frac{\partial^2 u}{\partial s \partial t} + \frac{\partial^2 u}{\partial t^2}\right).$$

Subtracting these, we find that

$$\frac{\partial^2 u}{\partial x^2} - \frac{\partial^2 u}{\partial y^2} = \frac{\partial^2 u}{\partial s \partial t}$$

so that the transformed differential equation is $\partial^2 u/\partial s \partial t = 0$.† A more complicated problem of the same type is that of transforming the Laplace equation $\partial^2 u/\partial x^2 + \partial^2 u/\partial y^2 = 0$ into polar coordinates by the substitution

$$\begin{cases} x = r \cos \theta \\ y = r \sin \theta. \end{cases}$$

Differentiate the first of these with respect to y, and the second with respect to x, regarding x and y as independent.

(5-21)
$$0 = \frac{\partial r}{\partial y}\cos\theta - \frac{\partial \theta}{\partial y} r \sin\theta$$
$$0 = \frac{\partial r}{\partial x}\sin\theta + \frac{\partial \theta}{\partial x} r \cos\theta.$$

† The general solution of this equation is easily seen to be $u = A(s) + B(t)$, so that the general solution of the original equation is $u = f(x + y) + g(x - y)$.

Also, $x^2 + y^2 = r^2$ so that $2r(\partial r/\partial x) = 2x$ and $2r(\partial r/\partial y) = 2y$, and therefore

(5-22) $$\frac{\partial r}{\partial x} = \frac{x}{r} = \cos\theta \qquad \frac{\partial r}{\partial y} = \frac{y}{r} = \sin\theta$$

Putting these into (5-21), we obtain

(5-23) $$\frac{\partial\theta}{\partial x} = -\frac{\sin\theta}{r} \qquad \frac{\partial\theta}{\partial y} = \frac{\cos\theta}{r}$$

Then $$\frac{\partial u}{\partial x} = \frac{\partial u}{\partial r}\frac{\partial r}{\partial x} + \frac{\partial u}{\partial\theta}\frac{\partial\theta}{\partial x} = \cos\theta\frac{\partial u}{\partial r} - \frac{\sin\theta}{r}\frac{\partial u}{\partial\theta}$$
$$= \left(\cos\theta\frac{\partial}{\partial r} - \frac{\sin\theta}{r}\frac{\partial}{\partial\theta}\right)u$$

and $$\frac{\partial u}{\partial y} = \frac{\partial u}{\partial r}\frac{\partial r}{\partial y} + \frac{\partial u}{\partial\theta}\frac{\partial\theta}{\partial y} = \sin\theta\frac{\partial u}{\partial r} + \frac{\cos\theta}{r}\frac{\partial u}{\partial\theta}$$
$$= \left(\sin\theta\frac{\partial}{\partial r} + \frac{\cos\theta}{r}\frac{\partial}{\partial\theta}\right)u.$$

Iterating these,

$$\frac{\partial^2 u}{\partial x^2} = \left(\cos\theta\frac{\partial}{\partial r} - \frac{\sin\theta}{r}\frac{\partial}{\partial\theta}\right)\left(\cos\theta\frac{\partial u}{\partial r} - \frac{\sin\theta}{r}\frac{\partial u}{\partial\theta}\right)$$
$$= \cos^2\theta\frac{\partial^2 u}{\partial r^2} + \frac{\sin^2\theta}{r^2}\frac{\partial^2 u}{\partial\theta^2} - \frac{2\sin\theta\cos\theta}{r}\frac{\partial^2 u}{\partial r\partial\theta} + \frac{2\sin\theta\cos\theta}{r^2}\frac{\partial u}{\partial\theta} + \frac{\sin^2\theta}{r}\frac{\partial u}{\partial r}$$

$$\frac{\partial^2 u}{\partial y^2} = \left(\sin\theta\frac{\partial}{\partial r} + \frac{\cos\theta}{r}\frac{\partial}{\partial\theta}\right)\left(\sin\theta\frac{\partial u}{\partial r} + \frac{\cos\theta}{r}\frac{\partial u}{\partial\theta}\right)$$
$$= \sin^2\theta\frac{\partial^2 u}{\partial r^2} + \frac{\cos^2\theta}{r^2}\frac{\partial^2 u}{\partial\theta^2} + \frac{2\sin\theta\cos\theta}{r}\frac{\partial^2 u}{\partial r\partial\theta} - \frac{2\sin\theta\cos\theta}{r^2}\frac{\partial u}{\partial\theta} + \frac{\cos^2\theta}{r}\frac{\partial u}{\partial r}$$

and adding, we find that

$$\frac{\partial^2 u}{\partial x^2} + \frac{\partial^2 u}{\partial y^2} = \frac{\partial^2 u}{\partial r^2} + \frac{1}{r^2}\frac{\partial^2 u}{\partial\theta^2} + \frac{1}{r}\frac{\partial u}{\partial r}.$$

Thus, the equation $\partial^2u/\partial x^2 + \partial^2u/\partial y^2 = 0$ which governs the distribution of heat becomes

$$\frac{\partial^2 u}{\partial r^2} + \frac{1}{r^2}\frac{\partial^2 u}{\partial\theta^2} + \frac{1}{r}\frac{\partial u}{\partial r} = 0$$

in polar coordinates.

Finally, let us consider a special type of change-of-variable problem. Suppose that E, T, V, and p are four physical variables which are connected by two relations, of the form

$$(5\text{-}24)\qquad \begin{cases} F(E, T, V, p) = 0 \\ G(E, T, V, p) = 0. \end{cases}$$

We suppose also that these may be solved for any pair of the variables in terms of the remaining two, i.e., any pair may be selected as independent. When V and T are independent, the physical theory supplies the following differential relation between the variables

$$(5\text{-}25)\qquad \frac{\partial E}{\partial V} - T\frac{\partial p}{\partial T} + p = 0.$$

Suppose we wish to shift our point of view, and regard p and T as the independent variables; what form does Eq. (5-25) take? To find out, we assume that we have solved (5-24) in the form

$$(5\text{-}26)\qquad \begin{cases} E = f(p, T) \\ V = g(p, T). \end{cases}$$

Since (5-25) involves $\left.\dfrac{\partial E}{\partial V}\right|_T$ and $\left.\dfrac{\partial p}{\partial T}\right|_V$, we must obtain these from (5-26). Differentiating these with respect to T and V, we have

$$\frac{\partial E}{\partial V} = f_1\frac{\partial p}{\partial V} + 0 \qquad 1 = g_1\frac{\partial p}{\partial V} + 0$$

$$\frac{\partial E}{\partial T} = f_1\frac{\partial p}{\partial T} + f_2 \qquad 0 = g_1\frac{\partial p}{\partial T} + g_2$$

Solving these for the derivatives which are present in (5-25), we have $\partial E/\partial V = f_1/g_1$, $\partial p/\partial T = -g_2/g_1$, and substituting these into the differential equation,

$$0 = \frac{\partial E}{\partial V} - T\frac{\partial p}{\partial T} + p = \left(\frac{f_1}{g_1}\right) - T\left(\frac{-g_2}{g_1}\right) + p$$

or

$$f_1 + Tg_2 + pg_1 = 0.$$

Reverting to the more familiar notation, we see that the correct form for the transformed equation is

$$\frac{\partial E}{\partial p} + T\frac{\partial V}{\partial T} + p\frac{\partial V}{\partial p} = 0.$$

The next result is the symmetric form of the **mean value theorem** which was promised in Sec. 5.3.

Theorem 15. *Let f be of class C' in an open set which contains the points p_1, p_2, and the line segment joining them. There is then a point p^* on this line segment such that*

$$f(p_2) - f(p_1) = L(p_2 - p_1)$$

where L is the differential of f at p^*.

We give a proof for the case in which f is a function of two variables. If we have $p_1 = (x, y)$ and $p_2 = (x + \Delta y, y + \Delta y)$, then this theorem asserts that there is a number λ, $0 < \lambda < 1$, such that

$$f(p_2) - f(p_1) = f_1(p^*)\,\Delta x + f_2(p^*)\,\Delta y$$

where $p^* = (x + \lambda\,\Delta x,\ y + \lambda\,\Delta y)$. To prove this, we construct a special function F of one variable

$$\begin{aligned} F(t) &= f(p_1 + t(p_2 - p_1)) \\ &= f(x + t\,\Delta x,\ y + t\,\Delta y). \end{aligned}$$

Applying the one-variable mean value theorem,

$$F(1) - F(0) = (1 - 0)F'(\lambda)$$

where λ is some point between 0 and 1. By the chain rules,

$$F'(t) = f_1\,\Delta x + f_2\,\Delta y$$

so that $F'(\lambda) = L(\Delta x, \Delta y)$, where L is the differential of f at the point $p^* = (x + \lambda\,\Delta x,\ y + \lambda\,\Delta y)$. Since $F(1) - F(0) = f(p_2) - f(p_1)$, we have proved the theorem. ▌

If we apply Taylor's theorem to F, instead of merely the mean value theorem, we obtain the corresponding form of **Taylor's theorem** for functions of several variables.

Theorem 16. *Let f be of class C^{n+1} in a neighborhood of $p_0 = (x_0, y_0)$. Then, with $p = (x, y)$,*

$$\begin{aligned} f(p) = f(p_0) &+ \frac{(x - x_0)}{1}\frac{\partial f}{\partial x}\bigg|_{p_0} + \frac{(y - y_0)}{1}\frac{\partial f}{\partial y}\bigg|_{p_0} \\ &+ \frac{(x - x_0)^2}{2!}\frac{\partial^2 f}{\partial x^2}\bigg|_{p_0} + \frac{(x - x_0)}{1!}\frac{(y - y_0)}{1!}\frac{\partial^2 f}{\partial x \partial y}\bigg|_{p_0} + \frac{(y - y_0)^2}{2!}\frac{\partial^2 f}{\partial y^2}\bigg|_{p_0} \\ &+ \cdots + \frac{(x - x_0)^n}{n!}\frac{\partial^n f}{\partial x^n}\bigg|_{p_0} + \frac{(x - x_0)^{n-1}}{(n-1)!}\frac{(y - y_0)}{1!}\frac{\partial^n f}{\partial x^{n-1}\partial y}\bigg|_{p_0} \\ &+ \cdots + \frac{(y - y_0)^n}{n!}\frac{\partial^n f}{\partial y^n}\bigg|_{p_0} + R_n(x, y) \end{aligned}$$

where

$$R_n(x, y) = \frac{(x - x_0)^{n+1}}{(n+1)!}\frac{\partial^{n+1} f}{\partial x^{n+1}}\bigg|_{p^*} + \cdots + \frac{(y - y_0)^{n+1}}{(n+1)!}\frac{\partial^{n+1} f}{\partial y^{n+1}}\bigg|_{p^*}$$

and p^* is a point on the line segment joining p_0 and p.

By adopting a special notation, this can be thrown into a simpler appearing form. Let $\Delta x = x - x_0$ and $\Delta y = y - y_0$, so that

$$\Delta p = (\Delta x, \Delta y) = p - p_0.$$

Define a differential operator U by

$$U = \Delta x\frac{\partial}{\partial x} + \Delta y\frac{\partial}{\partial y}$$

so that, for instance, $Uf = \Delta x\, f_1 + \Delta y\, f_2$. Then, the Taylor expansion formula may be written as

$$f(p_0 + \Delta p) = f(p_0) + \frac{1}{1!}\, Uf(p_0) + \frac{1}{2!}\, U^2f(p_0) + \cdots + \frac{1}{n!}\, U^nf(p_0) + \frac{1}{(n+1)!}\, U^{n+1}f(p^*).$$

For example,

$$U^2f(p_0) = \left[(\Delta x)^2 \frac{\partial^2}{\partial x^2} + 2(\Delta x)(\Delta y)\frac{\partial^2}{\partial x \partial y} + (\Delta y)^2 \frac{\partial^2}{\partial y^2}\right](f)(p_0) = (\Delta x)^2 \left.\frac{\partial^2 f}{\partial x^2}\right|_{p_0} + 2(\Delta x)(\Delta y)\left.\frac{\partial^2 f}{\partial x \partial y}\right|_{p_0} + (\Delta y)^2 \left.\frac{\partial^2 f}{\partial y^2}\right|_{p_0}.$$

When the remainder $\frac{1}{(n+1)!}\, U^{n+1}f(p^*)$ approaches zero as n increases, f is said to be an analytic function of the two real variables x and y, and we obtain a convergent double power series expansion for f in a neighborhood of p_0. In many cases, however, it is possible to obtain this by a direct argument with series. For example, if $f(x, y) = ye^{x-y}$, then near (0, 0) we have

$$f(x, y) = y\left\{1 + \frac{(x-y)}{1!} + \frac{(x-y)^2}{2!} + \frac{(x-y)^3}{3!} + \cdots\right\} = y + xy - y^2 + \tfrac{1}{2}x^2y - xy^2 + \tfrac{1}{2}y^3 + \cdots.$$

EXERCISES

1. Construct schematic diagrams to show the following functional relationships, and find the indicated derivatives:

(*a*) $w = f(x, y, z)$, $x = \phi(t)$, $y = \psi(t)$, $z = \theta(t)$
Find dw/dt.

(*b*) $w = F(x, u, t)$, $u = f(x, t)$, $x = \phi(t)$,
Find dw/dt.

(*c*) $w = F(x, u, v)$, $u = f(x, y)$, $v = g(x, z)$,
Find $\partial w/\partial x$, $\partial w/\partial y$, and $\partial w/\partial z$.

2. Prove the version of the chain rule which was used in part (*a*) of Exercise 1.

3. If $w = f(x, y)$ and $y = F(x)$, find dw/dx and d^2w/dx^2.

4. When x, y, and z are related by the equation $x^2 + yz^2 + y^2x + 1 = 0$, find $\partial y/\partial x$ and $\partial y/\partial z$ when $x = -1$ and $z = 1$.

5. Let x, y, u, v be related by the equations $xy + x^2u = vy^2$, $3x - 4uy = x^2v$. Find $\partial u/\partial x$, $\partial u/\partial y$, $\partial v/\partial x$, $\partial v/\partial y$ first by implicit differentiation, and then by solving the equations explicitly for u and v.

6. Let $F(x, y, z) = 0$. Assuming that this can be solved for z in terms of (x, y), find $\partial z/\partial x$ and $\partial z/\partial y$.

7. Under the same assumptions as Exercise 6, find expressions for $\partial^2 z/\partial x^2$ and $\partial^2 z/\partial x \partial y$ in terms of F and its derivatives.

8. Let $F(x, y, z) = 0$. Prove that

$$\left.\frac{\partial z}{\partial y}\right|_x \left.\frac{\partial y}{\partial x}\right|_z \left.\frac{\partial x}{\partial z}\right|_y = -1.$$

9. Let $F(x, y, t) = 0$ and $G(x, y, t) = 0$ be used to express x and y in terms of t. Find general formulas for dx/dt and dy/dt.

10. Let $z = f(xy)$. Show that this obeys the differential relation

$$x\left(\frac{\partial z}{\partial x}\right) - y\left(\frac{\partial z}{\partial y}\right) = 0.$$

11. Let $w = F(x, yz)$. Show that

$$x\frac{\partial w}{\partial x} + y\frac{\partial w}{\partial y} = z\frac{\partial w}{\partial z}.$$

***12.** A function f is said to be homogeneous of degree k in a neighborhood N of the origin if $f(tx, ty) = t^k f(x, y)$ for all points $(x, y) \varepsilon N$ and all t, $0 \le t \le 1$. Assuming appropriate continuity conditions, prove that f satisfies in N the differential equation

$$xf_1(x, y) + yf_2(x, y) = kf(x, y).$$

13. Setting $z = f(x, y)$, Exercise 12 shows that $x(\partial z/\partial x) + y(\partial z/\partial y) = 0$ whenever f is homogeneous of degree $r = 0$. Show that in polar coordinates this differential equation becomes simply $r(\partial z/\partial r) = 0$, and from this deduce that the general homogeneous function of degree 0 is of the form $f(x, y) = F(y/x)$.

14. If $z = F(ax + by)$, then $b(\partial z/\partial x) - a(\partial z/\partial y) = 0$.

15. If $u = F(x - ct) + G(x + ct)$, then

$$c^2\frac{\partial^2 u}{\partial x^2} = \frac{\partial^2 u}{\partial t^2}.$$

16. If $z = \phi(x, y)$ is a solution of $F(x + y + z, Ax + By) = 0$, show that $A(\partial z/\partial y) - B(\partial z/\partial x)$ is constant.

17. Find a differential equation which is satisfied by all functions F of the form $F(x, y) = f(x^2 + y^2)$.

18. Show that the substitution $x = e^s$, $y = e^t$ converts the equation

$$x^2\left(\frac{\partial^2 u}{\partial x^2}\right) + y^2\left(\frac{\partial^2 u}{\partial y^2}\right) + x\left(\frac{\partial u}{\partial x}\right) + y\left(\frac{\partial u}{\partial y}\right) = 0$$

into the equation $\partial^2 u/\partial s^2 + \partial^2 u/\partial t^2 = 0$.

19. Show that the substitution $u = x^2 - y^2$, $v = 2xy$ converts the equation $\partial^2 W/\partial x^2 + \partial^2 W/\partial y^2 = 0$ into $\partial^2 W/\partial u^2 + \partial^2 W/\partial v^2 = 0$.

***20.** Let $u = f(x, y)$ and $v = g(x, y)$, where f and g are of class C'' and obey $f_1 = g_2$, $f_2 = -g_1$. Show that $\partial^2 W/\partial x^2 + \partial^2 W/\partial y^2 = 0$ becomes $\partial^2 W/\partial u^2 + \partial^2 W/\partial v^2 = 0$.

21. Show that if p and E are regarded as independent, the differential equation (5-25) takes the form

$$\frac{\partial T}{\partial p} - T\frac{\partial V}{\partial E} + p\frac{\partial(V, T)}{\partial(E, p)} = 0.$$

22. Let f be of class C'' in the plane, and let S be a closed and bounded set such that $f_1(p) = 0$ and $f_2(p) = 0$ for all $p \varepsilon S$. Show that there is a constant M such that $|f(p) - f(q)| \le M|p - q|^2$ for all points p and q lying in S.

***23.** (*Continuation of Exercise* 22.) Show that if S is the set of points on an arc given by the equations $x = \phi(t)$, $y = \psi(t)$, where ϕ and ψ are of class C', then the function f is constant-valued on S.

24. Let f be a function of class C' with $f(1, 1) = 1$, $f_1(1, 1) = a$ and $f_2(1, 1) = b$. Let $\phi(x) = f(x, f(x, f(x, x)))$. Find $\phi(1)$ and $\phi'(1)$.

5.5. Differentials of Transformations

Let us start by considering a transformation T of E^3 into itself which is given by a set of equations such as

$$T: \begin{cases} u = f(x, y, z) \\ v = g(x, y, z) \\ w = h(x, y, z) \end{cases} \tag{5-27}$$

We shall say that T is of class $C^{(n)}$ in a region D whenever each of the coordinate functions f, g, and h is of this class in D. In particular, T is of class C' in D if all the partial derivatives $\partial u/\partial x$, $\partial u/\partial y$, . . . , $\partial w/\partial y$, $\partial w/\partial z$ exist and are continuous in D. Following the line of previous discussions, we define the **differential** dT of such a transformation by

$$dT = \begin{bmatrix} f_1 & f_2 & f_3 \\ g_1 & g_2 & g_3 \\ h_1 & h_2 & h_3 \end{bmatrix} = \begin{bmatrix} \frac{\partial u}{\partial x} & \frac{\partial u}{\partial y} & \frac{\partial u}{\partial z} \\ \frac{\partial v}{\partial x} & \frac{\partial v}{\partial y} & \frac{\partial v}{\partial z} \\ \frac{\partial w}{\partial x} & \frac{\partial w}{\partial y} & \frac{\partial w}{\partial z} \end{bmatrix}$$

If this is evaluated at a point $p \in D$, the resulting matrix of numbers specifies a linear transformation of E^3 into itself which is called the differential of T at p. (This can be denoted by $dT|_p$; we shall occasionally use merely dT when the context makes clear at which point we are computing the differential of T.)

To illustrate this, let T be given by

$$\begin{cases} u = x^2 + y - z \\ v = xyz^2 \\ w = 2xy - y^2z \end{cases} \tag{5-28}$$

The differential of T at (x, y, z) is

$$dT = \begin{bmatrix} 2x & 1 & -1 \\ yz^2 & xz^2 & 2xyz \\ 2y & 2x - 2yz & -y^2 \end{bmatrix} \tag{5-29}$$

so that the differential of T at $p_0 = (1, 1, 1)$ is

$$dT\Big|_{p_0} = \begin{bmatrix} 2 & 1 & -1 \\ 1 & 1 & 2 \\ 2 & 0 & -1 \end{bmatrix}. \tag{5-30}$$

The differential of a general transformation is obtained in the same fashion. If T is a transformation from E^n into E^m and

$$T(x_1, x_2, \ldots, x_n) = (y_1, y_2, \ldots, y_m),$$

then

$$dT = \begin{bmatrix} \frac{\partial y_1}{\partial x_1} & \frac{\partial y_1}{\partial x_2} & \cdots & \frac{\partial y_1}{\partial x_n} \\ \cdot & \cdot & \cdots & \cdot \\ \frac{\partial y_m}{\partial x_1} & \frac{\partial y_m}{\partial x_2} & \cdots & \frac{\partial y_m}{\partial x_n} \end{bmatrix} \tag{5-31}$$

If T is of class C' in a region D, we have thus associated with each point of D a linear transformation. The significance of the differential lies in the next result which shows that these linear transformations provide local approximations for T.

Theorem 17. *Let T be of class C' in an open region D, and let E be a closed bounded subset of D. Let $dT\big|_{p_0}$ be the differential of T at a point $p_0 \in E$. Then,*

$$T(p_0 + \Delta p) = T(p_0) + dT\big|_{p_0}(\Delta p) + R(\Delta p)$$

where

$$\lim_{\Delta p \to 0} \frac{|R(\Delta p)|}{|\Delta p|} = 0$$

uniformly for $p_0 \in E$.

Let T be given by $T(x_1, x_2, \ldots, x_n) = (y_1, y_2, \ldots, y_m)$ where $y_i = \phi_i(p) = \phi_i(x_1, x_2, \ldots, x_n)$. (The subscript on ϕ_i does not indicate differentiation.) Then

$$T(p_0 + \Delta p) - T(p_0) = (\Delta y_1, \Delta y_2, \ldots, \Delta y_m)$$

where

$$\Delta y_i = \phi_i(p_0 + p) - \phi_i(p_0).$$

To each of these, we apply the approximation theorem for functions (Theorem 8, page 184) to write

$$\Delta y_i = d\phi_i(\Delta p) + R_i(\Delta p).$$

Combining these, we have

$$T(p_0 + \Delta p) = T(p_0) + L(\Delta p) + R(\Delta p)$$

where

$$L(\Delta p) = (d\phi_1(\Delta p), d\phi_2(\Delta p), \ldots, d\phi_m(\Delta p))$$

and

$$R(\Delta p) = (R_1(\Delta p), R_2(\Delta p), \ldots, R_m(\Delta p)).$$

If we now set $\Delta p = (\Delta x_1, \Delta x_2, \ldots, \Delta x_n)$, then

$$d\phi_i(\Delta p) = \frac{\partial y_i}{\partial x_1} \Delta x_1 + \frac{\partial y_i}{\partial x_2} \Delta x_2 + \cdots + \frac{\partial y_i}{\partial x_n} \Delta x_n$$

where the partial derivatives are evaluated at p_0. Thus,

$$L(\Delta p) = dT\Big|_{p_0}(\Delta p),$$

where $dT\Big|_{p_0}$ is the linear transformation with matrix (5-31). Again resorting to Theorem 8, we know that for each i, $i = 1, 2, \ldots, m$, $\lim_{\Delta p \to 0} \frac{|R_i(\Delta p)|}{|\Delta p|} = 0$, uniformly for all $p_0 \in E$. Since

$$|R(\Delta p)| \le |R_1(\Delta p)| + \cdots + |R_m(\Delta p)|,$$

it follows at once that

$$\lim_{\Delta p \to 0} \frac{|R(\Delta p)|}{|\Delta p|} = 0$$

uniformly for $p_0 \in E$. ▌

From a more sophisticated point of view, the notion of a differential may be introduced without reference to either coordinate representations, or matrices. One says that a transformation T is **differentiable** at a point p_0 if there is a linear transformation L such that for all Δp near **0**,

$$T(p_0 + \Delta p) = T(p_0) + L(\Delta p) + R(\Delta p)$$

where $\lim_{\Delta p \to 0} \frac{|R(\Delta p)|}{|\Delta p|} = 0$. L is then called the **differential** of T at p_0. When such a transformation L exists and T is given in coordinate form, then L has the matrix representation (5-31) (Exercise 5). In particular, the partial derivatives $\partial y_i/\partial x_j$ exist, although they may be discontinuous. As in the case of functions, many of the theorems which we prove will hold if "$T \in C'$ in D" is replaced by "T is differentiable in D."

Let T be a transformation from E^n into E^k and S a transformation from E^k into E^m. The product ST is a transformation from E^n into E^m. It is natural to seek a relation between the differentials of S and T and the differential of ST.

Theorem 18. *Let T be of class C' in an open set D, and let S be of class C' in an open set containing $T(D)$. Then, ST is of class C' in D, and if $p \in D$ and $q = T(p)$,*

$$d(ST)\Big|_p = dS\Big|_q \, dT\Big|_p.$$

We shall prove this in the special case $n = 2$, $k = m = 3$. Since the proof uses only the chain rules for differentiation and the rule for multiplying matrices, there is no difficulty in extending it to the general case; the notation becomes somewhat unwieldy (see also Exercise 6).

Let S and T be given by

$$S: \begin{cases} u = f(x, y, z) \\ v = g(x, y, z) \\ w = h(x, y, z) \end{cases} \qquad T: \begin{cases} x = F(s, t) \\ y = G(s, t) \\ z = H(s, t) \end{cases}$$

Their differentials are

$$dS = \begin{bmatrix} \frac{\partial u}{\partial x} & \frac{\partial u}{\partial y} & \frac{\partial u}{\partial z} \\ \frac{\partial v}{\partial x} & \frac{\partial v}{\partial y} & \frac{\partial v}{\partial z} \\ \frac{\partial w}{\partial x} & \frac{\partial w}{\partial y} & \frac{\partial w}{\partial z} \end{bmatrix} \qquad dT = \begin{bmatrix} \frac{\partial x}{\partial s} & \frac{\partial x}{\partial t} \\ \frac{\partial y}{\partial s} & \frac{\partial y}{\partial t} \\ \frac{\partial z}{\partial s} & \frac{\partial z}{\partial t} \end{bmatrix}$$

The transformation ST is given by

$$ST: \begin{cases} u = f(F(s, t), G(s, t), H(s, t)) \\ v = g(F(s, t), G(s, t), H(s, t)) \\ w = h(F(s, t), G(s, t), H(s, t)) \end{cases}$$

and its differential is

$$d(ST) = \begin{bmatrix} \frac{\partial u}{\partial s} & \frac{\partial u}{\partial t} \\ \frac{\partial v}{\partial s} & \frac{\partial v}{\partial t} \\ \frac{\partial w}{\partial s} & \frac{\partial w}{\partial t} \end{bmatrix}$$

Computing the partial derivatives by the chain rule, we obtain

$$d(ST) = \begin{bmatrix} \frac{\partial u}{\partial x}\frac{\partial x}{\partial s} + \frac{\partial u}{\partial y}\frac{\partial y}{\partial s} + \frac{\partial u}{\partial z}\frac{\partial z}{\partial s} & \frac{\partial u}{\partial x}\frac{\partial x}{\partial t} + \frac{\partial u}{\partial y}\frac{\partial y}{\partial t} + \frac{\partial u}{\partial z}\frac{\partial z}{\partial t} \\ \frac{\partial v}{\partial x}\frac{\partial x}{\partial s} + \frac{\partial v}{\partial y}\frac{\partial y}{\partial s} + \frac{\partial v}{\partial z}\frac{\partial z}{\partial s} & \frac{\partial v}{\partial x}\frac{\partial x}{\partial t} + \frac{\partial v}{\partial y}\frac{\partial y}{\partial t} + \frac{\partial v}{\partial z}\frac{\partial z}{\partial t} \\ \frac{\partial w}{\partial x}\frac{\partial x}{\partial s} + \frac{\partial w}{\partial y}\frac{\partial y}{\partial s} + \frac{\partial w}{\partial z}\frac{\partial z}{\partial s} & \frac{\partial w}{\partial x}\frac{\partial x}{\partial t} + \frac{\partial w}{\partial y}\frac{\partial y}{\partial t} + \frac{\partial w}{\partial z}\frac{\partial z}{\partial t} \end{bmatrix}$$

However, this is exactly the matrix which results from multiplying the matrices for dS and dT, so that $d(ST) = dS\,dT$. ▌

Other instances of this general formula for computing the differential of a composite transformation will be found in the exercises. The more complicated examples of Sec. 5.4 can also be obtained in this fashion. Consider, for example, the following set of equations:

$$u = f(x, y, z) \qquad \begin{aligned} z &= g(x, y, t) \\ y &= h(x, t) \end{aligned}$$

These may be used to express u in terms of x and t, and the corresponding diagram is Fig. 5-11. We introduce three transformations, R, S, and T, such that $u = (STR)(x, t)$. R is the mapping of E^2 into E^3 given by

$$R: \begin{cases} x = x \\ y = h(x, t) \\ t = t \end{cases}$$

T is the mapping of E^3 into E^3 given by

$$T: \begin{cases} x = x \\ y = y \\ z = g(x, y, t) \end{cases}$$

S is the mapping of E^3 into E^1 given by

$$S: \quad u = f(x, y, z).$$

In order to find the partial derivatives $\partial u/\partial x$ and $\partial u/\partial t$, we shall find the differential

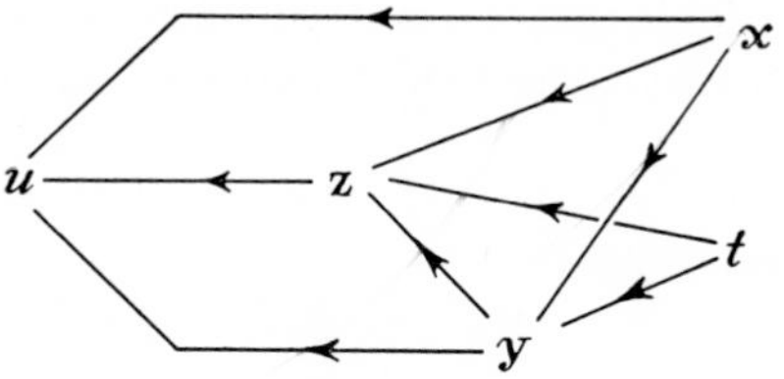

FIG. 5-11

$$d(STR) = \left[\frac{\partial u}{\partial x}, \frac{\partial u}{\partial t}\right]$$

By Theorem 18, $d(STR) = dS\,dT\,dR$, where we have

$$dS = [f_1, f_2, f_3] \qquad dT = \begin{bmatrix} 1 & 0 & 0 \\ 0 & 1 & 0 \\ g_1 & g_2 & g_3 \end{bmatrix} \qquad dR = \begin{bmatrix} 1 & 0 \\ h_1 & h_2 \\ 0 & 1 \end{bmatrix}$$

Computing these products, we have

$$dS\,dT = [f_1 + f_3g_1,\ f_2 + f_3g_2,\ f_3g_3]$$

and $\quad dS\,dT\,dR = [f_1 + f_3g_1 + (f_2 + f_3g_2)h_1,\ (f_2 + f_3g_2)h_2 + f_3g_3]$

so that we may read off the correct expressions for the desired partial derivatives

$$\frac{\partial u}{\partial x} = f_1 + f_3g_1 + f_2h_1 + f_3g_2h_1$$

$$\frac{\partial u}{\partial t} = f_2h_2 + f_3g_2h_2 + f_3g_3$$

We conclude this section with a useful **mean value theorem** for transformations. We state it for transformations of E^3 into itself, although a similar result is true in general.

Theorem 19. *Let T be a transformation of class C' defined for all points $p = (x, y, z)$ in an open set D by*

$$T: \begin{cases} u = f(x, y, z) \\ v = g(x, y, z) \\ w = h(x, y, z). \end{cases}$$

Let D contain the points p' and p'' and the line segment which joins them. Then, there are three points p_1^*, p_2^*, and p_3^* lying on this line segment such that

$$T(p'') - T(p') = L(p'' - p')$$

where L is the linear transformation represented by the matrix

$$\begin{bmatrix} f_1(p_1^*) & f_2(p_1^*) & f_3(p_1^*) \\ g_1(p_2^*) & g_2(p_2^*) & g_3(p_2^*) \\ h_1(p_3^*) & h_2(p_3^*) & h_3(p_3^*) \end{bmatrix} \tag{5-32}$$

This may be proved by applying the mean value theorem (Theorem 15) to each of the functions f, g, and h. Setting

$$p'' - p' = \Delta p = (\Delta x, \Delta y, \Delta z),$$

we have

$$f(p'') - f(p') = f_1(p_1^*)\,\Delta x + f_2(p_1^*)\,\Delta y + f_3(p_1^*)\,\Delta z$$

where p_1^* is some point on the line segment joining p' and p''. Similarly,

$$g(p'') - g(p') = g_1(p_2^*)\,\Delta x + g_2(p_2^*)\,\Delta y + g_3(p_2^*)\,\Delta z$$

$$h(p'') - h(p') = h_1(p_3^*)\,\Delta x + h_2(p_3^*)\,\Delta y + h_3(p_3^*)\,\Delta z$$

and the result follows. ▌

We note that the linear transformation L may possibly not coincide with dT at any point since the three points p_1^*, p_2^*, p_3^* may be distinct.

EXERCISES

1. Compute the differentials of the following transformations at the indicated points.

(a) $\begin{cases} u = xy^2 - 3x^3 \\ v = 3x - 5y^2 \end{cases}$ at (1, −1) and (1, 3).

(b) $\begin{cases} u = xyz^2 - 4y^2 \\ v = 3xy^2 - y^2z \end{cases}$ at (1, −2, 3)

(c) $\begin{cases} u = x + 6y \\ v = 3xy \\ w = x^2 - 3\,y^2 \end{cases}$ at (1, 1)

2. If L is a linear transformation, show that $dL = L$.

3. Verify Theorem 18 when S and T are the following transformations:

(a) $S\colon u = F(x, y)$ $\quad T\colon \begin{cases} x = \phi(t) \\ y = \psi(t) \end{cases}$

(b) $S\colon \begin{cases} u = F(x, y) \\ v = G(x, y) \end{cases}$ $\quad T\colon \begin{cases} x = \phi(t) \\ y = \psi(t) \end{cases}$

4. Let $w = F(x, y, t)$, $x = \phi(t)$, $y = \psi(t)$. Show that Theorem 18 can be applied to yield Eq. (5-15) for dw/dt.

5. Let T be a transformation from E^2 into E^2 given by $u = f(x, y)$, $v = g(x, y)$. Let

L be a linear transformation

$$L = \begin{bmatrix} A & B \\ C & D \end{bmatrix}$$

such that $T(p_0 + \Delta p) - T(p_0) = L(\Delta p) + R(\Delta p)$, where $\lim_{\Delta p \to 0} \frac{R(\Delta p)}{|\Delta p|} = \mathbf{0}$. Prove that $L = dT\Big|_{p_0}$.

**6. Prove Theorem 18 in the special case when S and T are transformations of E^2 into E^2 under the weaker assumption that S and T are differentiable but not necessarily of class C'.

7. Let T be a transformation from E^3 into E^3 which is of class C' in an open set D, and let $J(p) = \det\left(dT\Big|_p\right)$. Show that J is continuous throughout D. Is the rank of dT a continuous function of p?

8. Prove: If T is of class C' in an open connected set D, and $dT = 0$ at each point of D, then T is constant in D.

*9. Let $u = f(x, y)$, $v = g(x, y)$ define a transformation T of E^2 into E^2. Give a geometrical interpretation for dT, connected with the graph of T.

5.6. Inverses of Functions of One Variable

The topic of the inverse of a function is one for which the geometrical point of view is particularly well suited. Let f be a function of one variable. Considered as a transformation from E^1 into E^1, f sends the point a into the point $b = f(a)$. A function g is called an inverse for f if g reverses the effect of f, sending b back into a, so that $g(f(x)) = x$. In most cases, it is not possible to find such a function g which has this property for all points x in the domain of f. As an illustration, let $f(x) = x^2$, $-\infty < x < \infty$. If f had an inverse g such that $g(f(x)) = x$ for all real numbers x, then $g(x^2) = x$ and it would be necessary to have both $g(4) = g(2^2) = 2$ and $g(4) = g((-2)^2) = -2$. Such ambiguity is impossible for a function, since the point 4 must have a unique image. However, the function f has an inverse g on the interval $0 < x < \infty$ and a second inverse h on the interval $-\infty < x < 0$, namely, the functions defined on the interval $0 < x < \infty$ by $g(x) = \sqrt{x}$, and $h(x) = -\sqrt{x}$.

Let us examine the problem from the geometrical point of view. The graph of f is the set of points $(x, f(x))$, so that (a, b) is on the graph of f if and only if $b = f(a)$. If $g(b) = a$, then the point (b, a) must be on the graph of g. Let us introduce a special transformation R from E^2 into itself which sends (x, y) into (y, x). It is easily seen that this can be regarded as a rotation of the plane about the line $y = x$, in E^3. Let C be the image under R of the graph of f. If (a, b) is on the graph of f, $(b, a) \in C$. Thus, the graph of any function g which is an inverse for f must be part of the set C. Turning this around, any subset of C which is the graph of a function (i.e., any subset which is met no more than once by each vertical line) yields a particular inverse function for f.

Applying this to the example $f(x) = x^2$, we have given in Fig. 5-12 the graph of f, and its image C under the reflection R. The set C falls into two pieces each of which is the graph of a function; the upper half is the function g, $g(x) = \sqrt{x}$, and the lower half the function h,

$$h(x) = -\sqrt{x}.$$

Turning to a less trivial example, consider the function F given by $F(x) = \frac{3}{2}x - \frac{1}{2}x^3$. The graph of F and its reflection C are shown in Fig. 5-13. As indicated there, C can be split into three connected pieces, each of which is the graph of a function, and each of which therefore defines a function which is an inverse for F. The function g_1 is defined on the interval $-\infty < x < 1$, the function g_2 on $[-1, 1]$, and the function g_3 on the interval $-1 < x < \infty$. An accurate graph of F would enable us to read off the values of these functions, and thus tabulate them. (In this example, it is also possible to give analytical formulas for g_1, g_2, and g_3; see Exercise 1.)

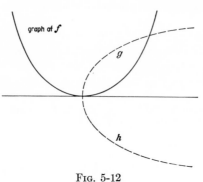

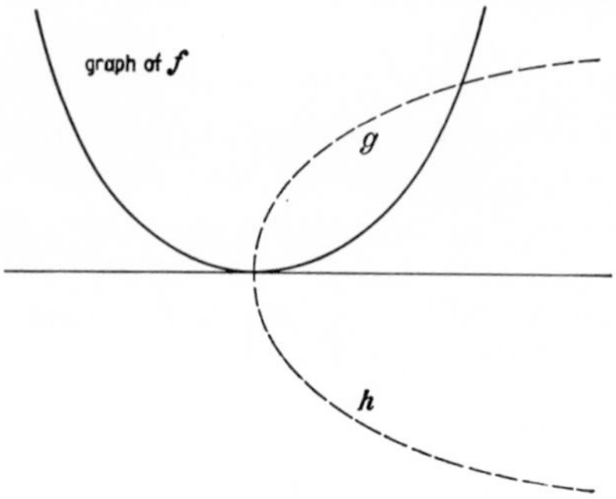

FIG. 5-12

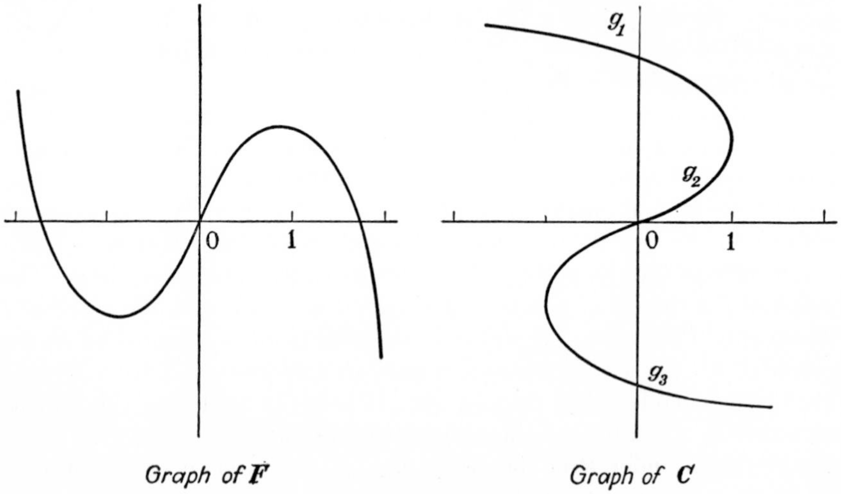

FIG. 5-13

Again, if $f(x) = \sin x$, then (see Fig. 5-14) the graph of the reflection C falls into an infinite number of connected pieces, each of which provides an inverse for f. Among these, one is usually singled out as shown, and is called the principal inverse for the sine function, $g(x) = \arcsin(x)$.

Theorem 20 is the main theorem dealing with inverses for functions of one variable.

Theorem 20. *Let f be of class C' on an interval $[a, b]$ with f' nonzero there. Then, f maps $[a, b]$ onto an interval $[\alpha, \beta]$ in a one-to-one fashion, and it has a unique inverse function g, which is of class C' on $[\alpha, \beta]$.*

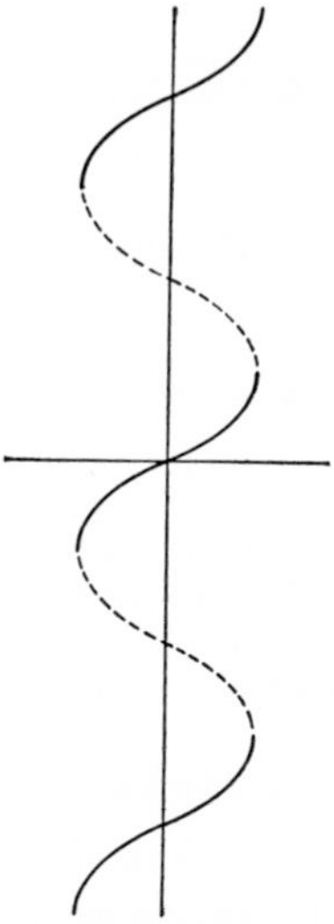

FIG. 5-14

Let $a \le x_1 \le x_2 \le b$; applying the mean value theorem,

$$f(x_2) - f(x_1) = (x_2 - x_1)f'(x^*)$$

for some choice of x^* between x_1 and x_2. Since $f'(x) \neq 0$ for all x, $a < x < b$, we cannot have $f(x_2) = f(x_1)$ unless $x_2 = x_1$. Thus, f is a one-to-one mapping of the interval $[a, b]$. Moreover, either $f'(x) > 0$ for all x in $[a, b]$ or $f'(x) < 0$ for all x in $[a, b]$, so that f is either monotone increasing on $[a, b]$ or monotone decreasing on $[a, b]$. Let us assume that we are dealing with the first case. If $\alpha = f(a)$ and $\beta = f(b)$, then $\alpha < \beta$ and by the intermediate value theorem (Theorem 12, Sec. 2.5) f maps $[a, b]$ exactly onto the interval $[\alpha, \beta]$. To any point y of $[\alpha, \beta]$ there corresponds a unique point x of $[a, b]$ such that $f(x) = y$. This defines a function g, inverse to f, such that $g(y) = x$ whenever $y = f(x)$. We shall next show that g is continuous on $[\alpha, \beta]$ and that in fact g is of class C' there. Let y_1 and y_2 be any points of $[\alpha, \beta]$, and let $x_j = g(y_j)$. The mean value theorem, applied to f, asserted that

$$f(x_2) - f(x_1) = (x_2 - x_1)f'(x^*).$$

Let $y^* = f(x^*)$. Then, an equivalent statement is that for some point y^* between y_1 and y_2,

$$\frac{g(y_2) - g(y_1)}{y_2 - y_1} = \frac{1}{f'(g(y^*))}. \tag{5-33}$$

The continuous function f' has a strictly positive minimum value m on $[a, b]$. Using this as an estimate for the right side of (5-33), we have $|g(y_2) - g(y_1)| \le |y_2 - y_1|/m$ which shows that g is (uniformly) continuous on $[\alpha, \beta]$. Returning to (5-33), let y_2 approach y_1; since y^* always lies between these, and since f' and g are both continuous, we have

$$\lim_{y_2 \to y_1} \frac{g(y_2) - g(y_1)}{y_2 - y_1} = \lim_{y^* \to y_1} \frac{1}{f'(g(y^*))} = \frac{1}{f'(g(y_1))}$$

showing both that g' exists and that it is continuous on $[\alpha, \beta]$. ∎

EXERCISES

1. Show that a formula for the function g_1 of Fig. 5-13 is

$$g_1(x) = \begin{cases} [\sqrt{x^2 - 1} - x]^{1/3} - [\sqrt{x^2 - 1} + x]^{1/3}, & -\infty < x < -1 \\ 2 \cos (1/3 \arccos (-x)), & -1 \leq x \leq 1 \end{cases}$$

2. Find inverses for the function f given by

$$f(x) = x^2 - 2x - 3.$$

3. How many continuous inverses are there for the function described by

$$F(x) = x^3 + 3x?$$

1 (no extrema)

4. Is there any interval on which the function f described by

$$f(x) = 2x + |x| - |x + 1|$$

fails to have an inverse?

5. Let f be continuous on the interval $[a, b]$ and map this onto the interval $[\alpha, \beta]$ one-to-one. Assuming nothing about differentiability of f, show that f has an inverse g which is continuous on $[\alpha, \beta]$.

5.7. Inverses of Transformations

Much of the discussion of Sec. 5.6 applies also to general transformations from E^n into E^n. If T is a transformation of the plane into itself, and maps a set D one-to-one onto a set D', then this defines a transformation T^{-1} which maps D' onto D, reversing the action of T. If $p \in D$, then $T^{-1}T(p) = p$, and if $q \in D'$, $TT^{-1}(q) = q$. A transformation which is not one-to-one may have a number of partial inverses. For example, the transformation

$$T: \begin{cases} u = 2xy \\ v = x^2 - y^2 \end{cases} \tag{5-34}$$

maps the whole XY plane onto the UV plane. It is not one-to-one in the whole plane, since T sends both $(1, 1)$ and $(-1, -1)$ into $(2, 0)$. More generally, $T(p) = T(-p)$ for any point p. However, if we take D to be the open half plane $\{$all (x, y) with $x > 0\}$, then T is one-to-one in D. To see this, let $T(x, y) = T(a, b)$. Then, $2xy = 2ab$ and

$$x^2 - y^2 = a^2 - b^2,$$

so that

$$\begin{aligned} 0 &= x^2(x^2 - y^2 - a^2 + b^2) \\ &= x^4 - x^2y^2 - a^2x^2 + b^2x^2 \\ &= x^4 - a^2b^2 - a^2x^2 + b^2x^2 \\ &= (x^2 + b^2)(x^2 - a^2). \end{aligned}$$

Hence, $x^2 = a^2$, and since $x > 0$ and $a > 0$, $x = a$ and $y = b$. T thus maps D onto a set D' in the UV plane in a one-to-one fashion. This mapping has an inverse which maps D' onto D. Solving Eqs. (5-34), we obtain

$$S_1: \begin{cases} x = \left[\dfrac{v + \sqrt{u^2 + v^2}}{2}\right]^{1/2} \\ y = u[2v + 2\sqrt{u^2 + v^2}]^{-1/2} \end{cases}$$

The set D' is the set of points (u, v) for which $v + \sqrt{u^2 + v^2} > 0$, that is, all points (u, v) except those of the form $(0, c)$ with $c \leq 0$.

The graphical approach which was used in Sec. 5.6 could also be used here; however, the graph of T and that of its reflection C are both two-dimensional surfaces in 4-space, and the geometrical treatment is difficult to visualize. This difficulty increases as the number of variables increases, so that an analytical treatment is preferable.

Let us first seek a condition which will play the role of the requirement "$f'(x) \neq 0$" in the hypotheses of Theorem 20. We first recall that for a linear transformation, the rank of the coefficient matrix was a determining factor in the geometrical properties of the transformation. In particular, if T is a linear transformation from E^n to E^n and the determinant of its coefficient matrix is nonzero, then T is one-to-one and has an everywhere defined inverse. Such linear transformations are called nonsingular. What is the analogous condition for a general transformation? If T is a transformation from E^3 into E^3 which is of class C' in an open set D, then associated with each point $p \in D$ there is a particular linear transformation, namely, $dT\Big|_p$, the differential of T at p. It is natural to conjecture that the desired condition is that each of these be a nonsingular linear transformation. This can be stated more neatly by introducing a special function associated with a transformation T.

Definition. *If T is a transformation from E^n into E^n which is of class C' in a set D, then the Jacobian of T is the function J defined in D by*

$$J(p) = \det\left(dT\Big|_p\right).$$

For example, if T is given by

$$\begin{cases} u = f(x, y, z) \\ v = g(x, y, z) \\ w = h(x, y, z) \end{cases}$$

then

$$J(p) = \begin{vmatrix} f_1(p) & f_2(p) & f_3(p) \\ g_1(p) & g_2(p) & g_3(p) \\ h_1(p) & h_2(p) & h_3(p) \end{vmatrix} = \frac{\partial(u, v, w)}{\partial(x, y, z)}\Bigg|_p.$$

The Jacobian of the transformation given in (5-34) is

$$\begin{vmatrix} 2y & 2x \\ 2x & -2y \end{vmatrix} = -4(x^2 + y^2).$$

One is thus led to the conjecture that if $J(p) \neq 0$ throughout a region D, then T is one-to-one in D. This conjecture is false. A simple counterexample is supplied by the transformation

$$T: \begin{cases} u = x \cos y \\ v = x \sin y \end{cases} \tag{5-35}$$

whose Jacobian is

$$J(x, y) = \begin{vmatrix} \cos y & -x \sin y \\ \sin y & x \cos y \end{vmatrix} = x.$$

In the right half plane $D = \{\text{all } (x, y) \text{ with } x > 0\}$, J is never zero. However, T is not one-to-one in D, for (a, b) and $(a, b + 2\pi)$ always have the same image. The effect of the transformation may be seen

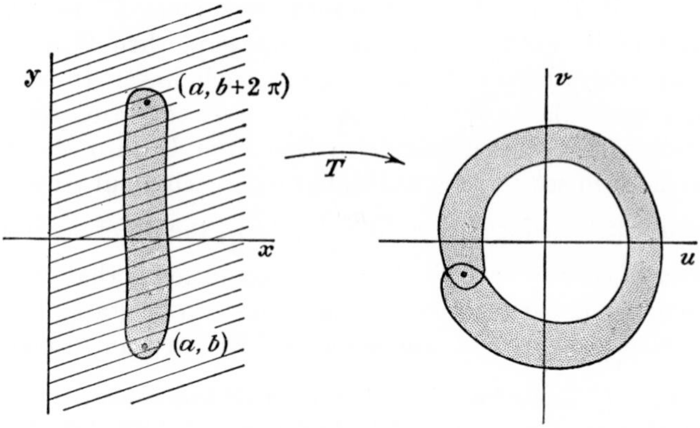

FIG. 5-15

from Fig. (5-15) where a set $S \subset D$ is shown, together with its image $T(S)$. We notice that although T is not one-to-one in S, two distinct points of S which have the same image must be widely separated; thus, in S (and in fact in D), T has the property of being **locally** one-to-one. We give this a formal definition.

Definition. *A transformation which is defined in an open set D is said to be locally one-to-one (or locally univalent) in D if about any point $p \in D$ there is a neighborhood in which T is one-to-one.*

We are now ready to state the fundamental theorem on the existence of inverses for transformations.

Theorem 21. *Let T be a transformation from E^n into E^n which is of class C' in an open set D, and suppose that $J(p) \neq 0$ for each $p \in D$. Then, T is locally one-to-one in D.*

The proof of this depends upon the mean value theorem for transformations (Theorem 19, Sec. 5.5). Again, although our present result is true regardless of the value of n, we shall write out a proof only for the case $n = 3$; the general case requires no change in method. Let us suppose that T is described by

$$\begin{cases} u = f(x, y, z) \\ v = g(x, y, z) \\ w = h(x, y, z). \end{cases}$$

Given a point $p \in D$, we shall produce a neighborhood of p in which T is one-to-one. Let p' and p'' be two points near p such that the line segment joining p' and p'' lies in D. By Theorem 19, we may then choose three points p_1^*, p_2^*, and p_3^* on this line segment such that

$$T(p'') - T(p') = L(p'' - p') \tag{5-36}$$

where L is the linear transformation represented by

$$L = \begin{bmatrix} f_1(p_1^*) & f_2(p_1^*) & f_3(p_1^*) \\ g_1(p_2^*) & g_2(p_2^*) & g_3(p_2^*) \\ h_1(p_3^*) & h_2(p_3^*) & h_3(p_3^*) \end{bmatrix}$$

Introduce a special function F defined for any triple of points of D by

$$F(p_1, p_2, p_3) = \det \begin{bmatrix} f_1(p_1) & f_2(p_1) & f_3(p_1) \\ g_1(p_2) & g_2(p_2) & g_3(p_2) \\ h_1(p_3) & h_2(p_3) & h_3(p_3) \end{bmatrix}.$$

Thus, $F(p_1^*, p_2^*, p_3^*) = \det(L)$, and $F(p, p, p) = J(p)$. Moreover, since $T \in C'$, F is continuous, so that, since $J(p) \neq 0$, there is a spherical neighborhood N about p and lying in D such that $F(p_1, p_2, p_3) \neq 0$ for all choices of the points p_1, p_2, and p_3 in N. We shall show that T is one-to-one in N. We must therefore show that if p' and p'' are points of N for which $T(p') = T(p'')$, then $p' = p''$. Since p' and p'' lie in N and N is convex, the entire line segment joining p' to p'' also lies in N; in particular, each of the points p_1^*, p_2^*, and p_3^* is a point of N. Using the characteristic property of N, we have $F(p_1^*, p_2^*, p_3^*) = \det(L) \neq 0$. The linear transformation L is therefore nonsingular. Returning to Eq. (5-36) and using the assumption that $T(p') = T(p'')$, we have $L(p'' - p') = 0$ or $L(p') = L(p'')$. But, since L is nonsingular, L is one-to-one, and $p' = p''$. ▮

Corollary. *If T is a transformation from E^n into E^n which is of class C' in a neighborhood of a point p_0, and $J(p_0) \neq 0$, then T is one-to-one on a (usually smaller) neighborhood of p_0, and has there an inverse T^{-1}.*

Our next results deal with the properties of any of these local inverses for the transformation T.

Theorem 22. *Let T be a continuous transformation which is one-to-one in a closed bounded set S. Then, the corresponding inverse transformation T^{-1} is continuous, and maps $T(S)$ back onto S.*

By Theorem 3 (Sec. 5.1), $T(S)$ is closed and bounded. Let $q_n \in T(S)$ with $\lim_{n\to\infty} q_n = q$. We shall prove that $\lim_{n\to\infty} T^{-1}(q_n) = T^{-1}(q)$. Set $p_n = T^{-1}(q_n)$ and $p = T^{-1}(q)$. Let p^* be any limit point of the sequence $\{p_n\}$, and let $\{p_{r_n}\}$ be a subsequence which converges to p^*. Since T is continuous, $\lim_{n\to\infty} T(p_{r_n}) = T(p^*)$. But, since $T(p_k) = q_k$,

$$T(p^*) = \lim_{n\to\infty} q_{r_n},$$

and $T(p^*) = q$. However, T is one-to-one in S so that $p^* = T^{-1}(q) = p$. The sequence $\{p_n\}$ therefore has exactly one limit point, p; since it is a bounded sequence (because the set S is bounded) we see that $\{p_n\}$ converges to p. ▌

Theorem 23. *Let T be of class C' in a set D with $J(p) \neq 0$ for each $p \in D$, and let T map D one-to-one onto a set $T(D)$. Then, the inverse T^{-1} of T is of class C' on $T(D)$ and the differential of T^{-1} is $(dT)^{-1}$, the inverse of the differential of T.*

Let q_0 and $q_0 + \Delta q$ be nearby points of $T(D)$. We shall show that T^{-1} is of class C' by exhibiting a linear transformation which has the characteristic approximating property of the differential, and whose entries are continuous functions. By Exercise 5, Sec. 5.5, this transformation must be the differential of T^{-1} and the entries are the required partial derivatives.

Let $p_0 = T^{-1}(q_0)$ and $p = T^{-1}(q_0 + \Delta q)$, and set $\Delta p = p - p_0$. Thus,

(5-37) $$\Delta q = T(p) - T(p_0) = T(p_0 + \Delta p) - T(p_0)$$

(5-38) $$\Delta p = T^{-1}(q_0 + \Delta q) - T^{-1}(q_0).$$

Let dT be the differential of T at p_0. By the approximation property (Theorem 17), applied to (5-37) we have

(5-39) $$\Delta q = dT(\Delta p) + R(\Delta p)$$

where

(5-40) $$\lim_{\Delta p\to 0} \frac{|R(\Delta p)|}{|\Delta p|} = 0.$$

Since $J(p_0) \neq 0$, dT is a nonsingular linear transformation and has an inverse $(dT)^{-1}$. Applying this linear transformation to both sides of (5-39),

$$(5\text{-}41) \qquad \begin{aligned}(dT)^{-1}(\Delta q) &= (dT)^{-1}dT(\Delta p) + (dT)^{-1}(R(\Delta p)) \\ &= \Delta p + (dT)^{-1}(R(\Delta p))\end{aligned}$$

so that, starting from (5-38),

$$\begin{aligned}T^{-1}(q_0 + \Delta q) - T^{-1}(q_0) &= \Delta p \\ &= (dT)^{-1}(\Delta q) - (dT)^{-1}(R(\Delta p)). \\ &= (dT)^{-1}(\Delta q) + R^*(\Delta q)\end{aligned}$$

where
$$R^*(\Delta q) = -(dT)^{-1}(R(\Delta p)).$$
If we can show that

$$(5\text{-}42) \qquad \lim_{\Delta q \to 0} \frac{|R^*(\Delta q)|}{|\Delta q|} = 0$$

then we shall have shown that $(dT)^{-1}$ is the differential of T^{-1} at q_0. Since the entries of $(dT)^{-1}$ are rational functions of the entries of dT and since $J(p) \neq 0$ for all $p \in D$, it follows that T^{-1} has continuous partial derivatives throughout $T(D)$ (see also Example 5, Sec. 5.5). To obtain (5-42), we recall that since $(dT)^{-1}$ is a linear transformation, a number B can be found such that $|(dT)^{-1}(r)| \leq B|r|$ for all points r. Using this with $r = \Delta q$ and with $r = R(\Delta p)$, we have

$$|(dT)^{-1}(\Delta q)| \leq B|\Delta q|$$

and

$$(5\text{-}43) \qquad |R^*(\Delta q)| = |(dT)^{-1}(R(\Delta p))| \leq B|R(\Delta p)|$$

so that from (5-41), we have

$$|\Delta p| \leq B|\Delta q| + B|R(\Delta p)|.$$

By (5-40), the fact that T^{-1} is continuous, and (5-38) we can choose δ for a given $\epsilon > 0$ so that $|R(\Delta p)| < (\epsilon/B)|\Delta p|$ whenever $|\Delta q| < \delta$. Since we are interested only in small numbers ϵ, we may assume $\epsilon < \frac{1}{2}$. Then,

$$\begin{aligned}|\Delta p| &\leq B|\Delta q| + B\left(\frac{\epsilon}{B}\right)|\Delta p| \\ &< B|\Delta q| + (\tfrac{1}{2})|\Delta p|\end{aligned}$$

and
$$|\Delta p| < 2B|\Delta q|$$

whenever $|\Delta q| < \delta$. Using this estimate in (5-43) we have

$$\begin{aligned}|R^*(\Delta q)| &\leq B|R(\Delta p)| \\ &\leq B\left(\frac{\epsilon}{B}\right)|\Delta p| = \epsilon|\Delta p| \\ &< 2B\epsilon|\Delta q|.\end{aligned}$$

Since ϵ may be arbitrarily small, $\lim_{\Delta q \to 0} \dfrac{|R^*(\Delta q)|}{|\Delta q|} = 0.$ ▮

We conclude with a result which clarifies the geometrical nature of a transformation with nonvanishing Jacobian, and shows that any such transformation shares a special property with the general nonsingular linear transformations.

Theorem 24. *Let T be a transformation from E^n into E^n which is of class C' in an open set D, and suppose that $J(p) \neq 0$ for each $p \in D$. Then, $T(D)$, the image of D under T, is also an open set.*

Take any point $q_0 \in T(D)$. We must show that q_0 is surrounded by a neighborhood which is composed entirely of image points of D. Let p_0 be any point in D with $T(p_0) = q_0$. Since D is open and $J(p_0) \neq 0$, we can choose a closed neighborhood N about p_0 (a closed disk if $n = 2$, a closed ball if $n = 3$) which lies in D and on which T is a one-to-one

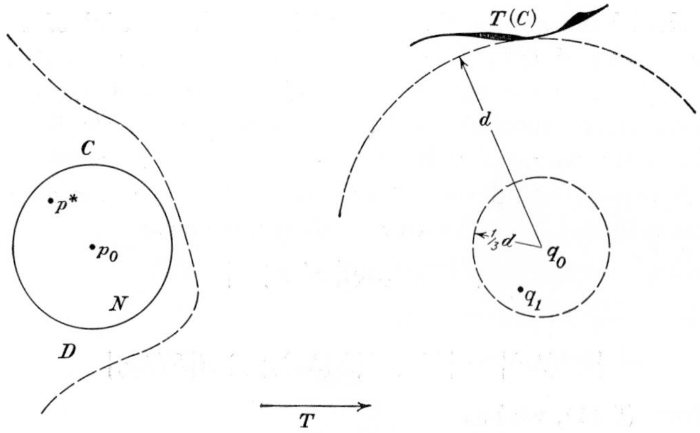

FIG. 5-16

transformation. Let C be the closed set which is the boundary of N (a circle for $n = 2$, a spherical surface for $n = 3$). Since T is continuous and one-to-one in N, Theorem 3 shows that the image $T(C)$ of this set is a closed and bounded set which does not contain q_0, the image of p_0. Let d be the distance from q_0 to the nearest point of $T(C)$ (see Fig. (5-16)). We shall show that any point within $d/3$ of q_0 is in $T(D)$. Let q_1 be any such point, so that $|q_1 - q_0| < d/3$. As p wanders throughout N, how close does $T(p)$ come to q_1? The square of the distance from $T(p)$ to q_1 is

$$\phi(p) = |T(p) - q_1|^2$$

which is continuous for $p \in N$. Let p^* be a point in N for which $\phi(p)$ is minimum; this is then a point whose image $T(p^*)$ is as close as possible to the point q_1. Can p^* lie on C, the boundary of N? When p is on C,

$|T(p) - q_0| \geq d$ so that $|T(p) - q_1| \geq d - \frac{1}{3}d = \frac{2}{3}d$. Thus, the closest that $T(p)$ can get to q_1 for p on C is $\frac{2}{3}d$. However, the point p_0 itself has image q_0 which is only $\frac{1}{3}d$ away from q_1. Thus, the point p^* will not lie on C, and is therefore an interior point of N. Since p^* minimizes $\phi(p)$, the partial derivatives of ϕ must all vanish at p^*. To see what this implies, we return to a coordinate description of T, and obtain a formula for ϕ. Let us suppose that $n = 2$ so that T may be given by

$$\begin{cases} u = f(x, y) \\ v = g(x, y). \end{cases}$$

Let $q_1 = (a, b)$. Then, the formula for the distance between q_1 and $(u, v) = T(p)$ gives

$$\phi(p) = (u - a)^2 + (v - b)^2.$$

The partial derivatives of ϕ are given by

$$\phi_1(p) = 2(u - a)\frac{\partial u}{\partial x} + 2(v - b)\frac{\partial v}{\partial x}$$

$$\phi_2(p) = 2(u - a)\frac{\partial u}{\partial y} + 2(v - b)\frac{\partial v}{\partial y}$$

At the extremal point p^*, both are zero, so that

$$\begin{aligned} 0 &= (u - a)f_1(p^*) + (v - b)g_1(p^*) \\ 0 &= (u - a)f_2(p^*) + (v - b)g_2(p^*). \end{aligned} \tag{5-44}$$

The determinant of the coefficient matrix of these equations, regarded as linear equations in $u - a$ and $v - b$, is

$$\begin{vmatrix} f_1(p^*) & g_1(p^*) \\ f_2(p^*) & g_2(p^*) \end{vmatrix} = J(p^*) \neq 0.$$

The only solutions of (5-44) are then the null solutions, $u - a = 0$, $v - b = 0$. Thus, $T(p^*) = (u, v) = (a, b)$, and $T(p^*) = q_1$. This shows that the minimum value of ϕ is actually zero, and the point q_1 is always the image point of some point in N. This holds for any point q_1 lying in the neighborhood of radius $d/3$ about q_0, so that q_0 is an interior point of the image set $T(D)$. Since q_0 was any point of $T(D)$, $T(D)$ is an open set.† ▌

We may combine the last several theorems to obtain a general statement concerning inverses of transformations.

† It should be pointed out that a result of this nature can also be proved without assuming any differentiability properties of T. If T is continuous and one-to-one on an open set D, and has a continuous inverse, then $T(D)$ is open. A proof of this result, known as the Brouwer theorem on invariance of domain, may be found in Hurewicz and Wallman, "Dimension Theory," Princeton University Press, Princeton, New Jersey.

Theorem 25. *Let T be a transformation from E^n to E^n which is of class C' in an open set D. Suppose also that the Jacobian, $J(p)$, of T at p is never zero for any $p \in D$. Let $p_0 \in D$ and $q_0 = T(p_0)$. Then, a neighborhood N about p_0 exists which is mapped by T in a one-to-one fashion onto an open set $T(N)$ about q_0, and there is defined in $T(N)$ a transformation S which is of class C' in $T(N)$ and which is a local inverse for T. Moreover, if dT is the differential of T at p_0 and dS is the differential of S at q_0, then $(dS)(dT) = I$, the identity transformation of E^n onto itself.*

This is an example of what is termed an **existence** theorem. It is a theorem asserting that something exists (in this case, a collection of local inverses for a transformation T), but which does not detail a method by which it is to be found or constructed. The chief value of Theorem 25 is then in the fact that by its use we may be assured that a transformation *has* an inverse, or that a set of equations *has* a solution; with this knowledge, we are then justified in proceeding with additional steps (such as implicit differentiation) which are predicated upon this.

We may illustrate Theorem 25 with the transformation given in (5-35):

$$(5\text{-}45) \qquad T: \begin{cases} u = x \cos y \\ v = x \sin y \end{cases}$$

whose Jacobian is $J(x, y) = x$. Since this is zero only on the vertical axis, T has local inverses about any point $p_0 = (x_0, y_0)$ with $x_0 \neq 0$. To find these explicitly, we must solve (5-45). We have $u^2 + v^2 = x^2$, and $2uv = 2x^2 \sin y \cos y = x^2 \sin (2y)$, so that $\sin (2y) = 2uv/(u^2 + v^2)$. If p_0 is a point in the right half plane, so that $x_0 > 0$, then the desired solution for x is $x = \sqrt{u^2 + v^2}$. If $x_0 < 0$, then $x = -\sqrt{u^2 + v^2}$. If $\sin (2y_0) \neq \pm 1$, then one of the inverses for the sine function may be chosen so that in an interval about y_0, $y = \frac{1}{2} \arcsin (2uv/(u^2 + v^2))$. If $\sin (2y_0) = 1$ or -1, then we proceed differently; we have

$$u^2 - v^2 = x^2(\cos^2 y - \sin^2 y) = x^2 \cos (2y)$$

so that $\cos (2y) = (u^2 - v^2)/(u^2 + v^2)$. Choosing an appropriate inverse for the cosine function, we obtain $y = \frac{1}{2} \arccos ([u^2 - v^2]/[u^2 + v^2])$ in an interval about y_0. For example, with $p_0 = (1, 0)$ we have as equations for the desired inverse,

$$S: \begin{cases} x = \sqrt{u^2 + v^2} \\ y = \frac{1}{2} \arcsin \left[\dfrac{2uv}{u^2 + v^2} \right] \end{cases}$$

This transformation is defined and of class C' at all points $(u, v) \neq (0, 0)$. If we also rule out $u = 0$, the simpler equivalent formula $y = \arctan (v/u)$

may also be used. Computing the differential of S, one finds

$$dS = \begin{bmatrix} \dfrac{u}{(u^2 + v^2)^{1/2}} & \dfrac{v}{(u^2 + v^2)^{1/2}} \\ \dfrac{-v}{u^2 + v^2} & \dfrac{u}{u^2 + v^2} \end{bmatrix}$$

so that the Jacobian of S at (u, v) is $(u^2 + v^2)^{-1/2}$. It will be noticed that this is x^{-1}, in agreement with Theorem 25 and the fact that the Jacobian of T is x. Also, changing back to x and y, the differential of S may be written as

$$dS = \begin{bmatrix} \cos y & \sin y \\ -x^{-1} \sin y & x^{-1} \cos y \end{bmatrix}$$

so that

$$dS\,dT = \begin{bmatrix} \cos y & \sin y \\ -x^{-1} \sin y & x^{-1} \cos y \end{bmatrix} \begin{bmatrix} \cos y & -x \sin y \\ \sin y & x \cos y \end{bmatrix} = \begin{bmatrix} 1 & 0 \\ 0 & 1 \end{bmatrix} = I.$$

When a transformation T maps a closed bounded region D onto a region D^* and is locally one-to-one in D, then when certain conditions are satisfied by D and D^*, it is possible to infer the T is one-to-one in all of D. One such condition is that D^* shall be a **simply connected** set. (See Sec. 7.5, for a discussion of this important concept.) A proof of this theorem may be found in de la Vallée Poussin, "Cours d'analyse," vol. 1, pp. 355ff., Paris, 1923.

EXERCISES

1. Compute the Jacobians of the following transformations:

(a) $\begin{cases} u = x + y \\ v = 2xy^2 \end{cases}$ (b) $\begin{cases} u = x^2 + 2xy + y^2 \\ v = 2x + 2y \end{cases}$

(c) $\begin{cases} u = e^x \cos y \\ v = e^x \sin y \end{cases}$ (d) $\begin{cases} u = x^2 \\ v = y/x \end{cases}$

2. Discuss the local behavior of the transformations in Exercise 1.

3. Where it is possible, find formulas for the local inverses of the transformations in Exercise 1.

4. Find the image under each of the transformations of Exercise 1 of the open set $D = \{\text{all } (x, y),\ 0 < x < 1,\ 0 < y < 1\}$. For which is the image an open set?

5. The second half of the proof of Theorem 24 assumed that T was a transformation from 2-space into 2-space. Carry out the corresponding discussion with $n = 3$.

6. Let T be the transformation sending (x, y) into $(2x + 4y, x - 3y)$. Find T^{-1} and verify directly that the differential of T^{-1} is $(dT)^{-1}$.

7. Let $T(x, y) = (u, v)$. Show that $\dfrac{\partial(u, v)}{\partial(x, y)} \dfrac{\partial(x, y)}{\partial(u, v)} = 1$.

5.8. The Implicit Function Theorems

The theorems of the present section have to do with the solution of one or more equations in several unknowns. They are existence theorems in that they give assurance that there are solutions, but do not give directions for obtaining them. In the simplest of these situations, suppose we are concerned with the solution of an equation $F(x, y, z) = 0$ for one of the variables as a function of the others. To "solve for z," for example, means to find a function ϕ such that $F(x, y, \phi(x, y)) = 0$ for all x and y in some open set. This is not always possible. In general, there are two reasons for this. One reason is illustrated by the equation

$$x^2 - z^2 + (z - y)(z + y) = 0.$$

This cannot be solved for z, for z is not really present. The second reason is illustrated by the equation

$$x^2 + y^2 + z^2 + 10 = 0.$$

This cannot be solved for z, and in fact, there is no real triple (x, y, z) which satisfies the equation. Our first result is a theorem which gives sufficient conditions for such an equation to be solvable for z.

Theorem 26. *Let F be a function of three variables which is of class C' in an open set D, and let $p_0 = (x_0, y_0, z_0)$ be a point of D for which $F(p_0) = 0$. Suppose that $F_3(p_0) \neq 0$. Then, there is a function ϕ of class C' in a neighborhood N of (x_0, y_0) such that $z = \phi(x, y)$ is a solution of $F(x, y, z) = 0$ for (x, y) in N, and such that $\phi(x_0, y_0) = z_0$.*

Consider the following special transformation from E^3 into E^3:

$$T: \begin{cases} u = x \\ v = y \\ w = F(x, y, z). \end{cases}$$

This is of class C' in D and its Jacobian is

$$J(p) = \det \begin{bmatrix} 1 & 0 & 0 \\ 0 & 1 & 0 \\ F_1(p) & F_2(p) & F_3(p) \end{bmatrix} = F_3(p)$$

Since $J(p_0) = F_3(p_0) \neq 0$, we may apply the principal result of Sec. 5.7 (Theorem 25) and conclude that there is a transformation T^{-1} which is of class C' in a neighborhood of $q_0 = T(p_0) = (x_0, y_0, 0)$, and which is an inverse for T. Moreover, from the nature of the equations which describe T, we have for T^{-1}

$$T^{-1}: \begin{cases} x = u \\ y = v \\ z = f(u, v, w) \end{cases}$$

where f is of class C' in a neighborhood of q_0. Since T and T^{-1} are inverses, we must have

$$w = F(x, y, z) = F(u, v, f(u, v, w)) \tag{5-46}$$

holding identically for all (u, v, w) near $(x_0, y_0, 0) = q_0$. Set $w = 0$, replace u by x and v by y, and define ϕ by $\phi(x, y) = f(x, y, 0)$. Then, (5-46) becomes

$$0 = F(x, y, \phi(x, y))$$

holding for all points (x, y) in a neighborhood of (x_0, y_0). This shows that $z = \phi(x, y)$ is a solution of $F(x, y, z) = 0$. Since f is of class C', so is ϕ. ▮

By the same device, we can find sufficient conditions for the solution of an equation $F(x, y, z, u, v, \ldots) = 0$ for any one of the variables as a function of the remaining. In addition to the differentiability conditions, the two requirements are: (1) there is a point p_0 that satisfies the equation, and (2) the partial of F with respect to the sought-for variable does not vanish at p_0.

Turning to the more complicated cases in which more than one equation is involved, the following will amply illustrate the general procedure.

Theorem 27. *Let F and G be of class C' in an open set $D \subset E^5$. Let $p_0 = (x_0, y_0, z_0, u_0, v_0)$ be a point of D at which both of the equations*

$$\begin{aligned} F(x, y, z, u, v) &= 0 \\ G(x, y, z, u, v) &= 0 \end{aligned} \tag{5-47}$$

are satisfied. Suppose also that $\dfrac{\partial(F, G)}{\partial(u, v)} \neq 0$ *at p_0. Then, there are two functions ϕ and ψ of class C' in a neighborhood N of (x_0, y_0, z_0) such that*

$$\begin{cases} u = \phi(x, y, z) \\ v = \psi(x, y, z) \end{cases}$$

is a solution of (5-47) in N giving u_0 and v_0 at (x_0, y_0, z_0).

To prove this, we construct a special transformation from E^5 into E^5:

$$T: \begin{cases} t_1 = x \\ t_2 = y \\ t_3 = z \\ t_4 = F(x, y, z, u, v) \\ t_5 = G(x, y, z, u, v) \end{cases}$$

The Jacobian of T is

$$J = \det \begin{bmatrix} 1 & 0 & 0 & 0 & 0 \\ 0 & 1 & 0 & 0 & 0 \\ 0 & 0 & 1 & 0 & 0 \\ F_1 & F_2 & F_3 & F_4 & F_5 \\ G_1 & G_2 & G_3 & G_4 & G_5 \end{bmatrix} = \begin{vmatrix} F_4 & F_5 \\ G_4 & G_5 \end{vmatrix}$$
$$= \frac{\partial(F, G)}{\partial(u, v)}$$

By our hypotheses, $J(p_0) \neq 0$ so that T has a local inverse there. The form of this must be

$$\begin{cases} x = t_1 \\ y = t_2 \\ z = t_3 \\ u = f(t_1, t_2, t_3, t_4, t_5) \\ v = g(t_1, t_2, t_3, t_4, t_5) \end{cases}$$

where f and g are of class C'. Setting $t_4 = 0$ and $t_5 = 0$ to correspond to the original equations $F(x, y, z, u, v) = 0$ and $G(x, y, z, u, v) = 0$, and replacing t_1, t_2, t_3 by x, y, and z, and defining

$$\phi(x, y, z) = f(x, y, z, 0, 0)$$
$$\psi(x, y, z) = g(x, y, z, 0, 0)$$

we have

$$0 = F(x, y, z, \phi(x, y, z), \psi(x, y, z))$$
$$0 = G(x, y, z, \phi(x, y, z), \psi(x, y, z))$$

holding for all (x, y, z) in a neighborhood of (x_0, y_0, z_0). Thus, $u = \phi(x, y, z)$ and $v = \psi(x, y, z)$ are the desired solutions. ▌

To give a simple illustration of this theorem, let us discuss the solution of the following equations for u and v.

(5-48)
$$\begin{cases} x^2 - yu = 0 \\ xy + uv = 0. \end{cases}$$

Put $F(x, y, u, v) = x^2 - yu$ and $G(x, y, u, v) = xy + uv$. We find

$$\frac{\partial(F, G)}{\partial(u, v)} = \begin{vmatrix} -y & 0 \\ v & u \end{vmatrix} = -yu.$$

Thus, if x_0, y_0, u_0, v_0 satisfy Eqs. (5-48) and $y_0u_0 \neq 0$, then there are continuous solutions for u and v around the point (x_0, y_0). The limitation $u_0 \neq 0$, $y_0 \neq 0$ is needed, and both imply $x_0 \neq 0$. In this example, it is possible to solve explicitly and obtain

$$u = \frac{x^2}{y}$$
$$v = \frac{-y^2}{x}$$

which is valid at all points (x, y) except those on the axes.

EXERCISES

1. Can the curve whose equation is $x^2 + y + \sin(xy) = 0$ be described by an equation of the form $y = f(x)$ in a neighborhood of the point $(0, 0)$? Can it be described by an equation of the form $x = g(y)$?

2. Can the surface whose equation is $xy - z \log y + e^{xz} = 1$ be represented in the form $z = f(x, y)$ in a neighborhood of $(0, 1, 1)$? In the form $y = g(x, z)$?

3. The point $(1, -1, 2)$ lies on both of the surfaces described by the equations $x^2(y^2 + z^2) = 5$ and $(x - z)^2 + y^2 = 2$. Show that in a neighborhood of this point, the curve of intersection of the surfaces can be described by a pair of equations of the form $z = f(x)$, $y = g(x)$.

4. Study the corresponding question for the surfaces with equations $x^2 + y^2 = 4$ and $2x^2 + y^2 - 8z^2 = 8$ and the point $(2, 0, 0)$ which lies on both.

5. (*a*) Let f be a function of one variable for which $f(1) = 0$. What additional conditions on f will allow the equation

$$2f(xy) = f(x) + f(y)$$

to be solved for y in a neighborhood of $(1, 1)$?

(*b*) Obtain the explicit solution for the choice $f(t) = t^2 - 1$.

***6.** With f again a function of one variable obeying $f(1) = 0$, discuss the problem of solving the equation $f(xy) = f(x) + f(y)$ for y near the point $(1, 1)$.

7. Using the method of Theorem 27, state and prove a theorem which gives sufficient conditions for the equations

$$F(x, y, z, t) = 0$$
$$G(x, y, z, t) = 0$$
$$H(x, y, z, t) = 0$$

to be solvable for x, y, and z as functions of t.

5.9. Functional Dependence

In Sec. 5.7, we studied at some length the properties of a transformation from E^3 into E^3 which was of class C' and had a nonvanishing Jacobian in an open set D. In this section, we shall examine the effect produced by a transformation whose Jacobian is zero throughout D. We illustrate this first with a simple example. Consider the transformation described by

$$T: \begin{cases} u = \cos(x + y^2) \\ v = \sin(x + y^2) \end{cases}$$

At (x, y), the Jacobian of T is

$$\begin{aligned} J(x, y) &= \det \begin{bmatrix} -\sin(x + y^2) & -2y \sin(x + y^2) \\ \cos(x + y^2) & 2y \cos(x + y^2) \end{bmatrix} \\ &= -2y \sin(x + y^2) \cos(x + y^2) + 2y \sin(x + y^2) \cos(x + y^2) \\ &= 0. \end{aligned}$$

This transformation fails to have many of the properties which were shown to hold for those with nonvanishing Jacobian. For example, although it is continuous and in fact of class C^∞, it does not map open sets in the XY plane into open sets in the UV plane. Since $u^2 + v^2 = 1$ for any choice of (x, y), T maps the entire XY plane onto the set of points on this circle of radius 1. Furthermore, it is not locally one-to-one. All the points on the parabola $x + y^2 = c$ map into the same point $(\cos c, \sin c)$, and as c changes, these parabolas cover the entire XY plane. Thus, any disk, no matter how small, contains points having the same image. Speaking on the intuitive level for the moment, T might be called a dimension-reducing transformation; if we regard open sets in the plane as two-dimensional, and curves as one-dimensional, then T takes a two-dimensional set into a one-dimensional set.

All this degenerate behavior of T stems from the fact that the functions which we chose for the coordinates u and v were not independent, but were functionally related. There was a function F such that

$$F(u, v) = 0$$

for all x and y.

Definition. *Two functions, f and g, are said to be functionally dependent in a set D if there is a function F of two variables, which itself is not identically zero in any open set, such that $F(f(p), g(p)) = 0$ for all $p \in D$.*

A similar definition may be formulated to describe functional dependence for any finite set of functions. As a special case of this, we say that a function g is **functionally dependent** in D upon the functions $f_1, f_2, \ldots, f_m$ if there is a function F of m variables such that

$$g(p) = F(f_1(p), f_2(p), \ldots, f_m(p))$$

for all $p \in D$. When the function F is a *linear* function, g is said to be **linearly dependent** upon $f_1, f_2, \ldots, f_m$. In this case, there are m numbers $C_1, C_2, \ldots, C_m$ such that g can be expressed in D as a linear combination of the functions f_j:

$$g = C_1 f_1 + C_2 f_2 + \cdots + C_m f_m.$$

Linear dependence is thus a special case of the general notion of functional dependence. The sine and cosine functions are linearly independent, since neither is a constant multiple of the other; however, they are functionally dependent, since

$$\cos x = \sqrt{1 - (\sin x)^2}$$

for x in the interval $[0, \frac{1}{2}\pi]$.

Returning to the study of a general transformation from E^3 into E^3, let us recall the effect on a linear transformation T of the vanishing of its Jacobian. If T is represented by a matrix $A = [a_{ij}]$, then the Jacobian of T is $\det(A)$; if this is zero, then T maps all of E^3 onto a (two-dimensional) plane, or onto a (one-dimensional) line, or onto a single point. Which it does is determined by the rank of A. If $\text{rank}(A) = 2$, the image is a plane, and if $\text{rank}(A) = 1$, it is a line. Using this as a guide, one is led to guess the correct generalization of this for transformations T which are not linear. When the Jacobian of T vanishes throughout the open domain D, we expect T to be a dimension-reducing transformation. It will map D onto something like a surface, or a curve, or a single point; which it is will depend upon the rank of dT, the differential of T. In the statements of the next two theorems, we shall use the terms "surface" and "curve" in their intuitive meanings; we postpone formal discussion of these notions until Chap. 6.

Theorem 28. *Let T be a transformation from E^3 into E^3 described by*

$$\begin{aligned} u &= f(x, y, z) \\ v &= g(x, y, z) \\ w &= h(x, y, z) \end{aligned} \tag{5-49}$$

which is of class C' in an open set D, and suppose that at each point $p \in D$ the differential dT has rank 2. Then, T maps D onto a surface in UVW space, that is, the functions f, g, and h are functionally dependent in D.

Theorem 29. *If T is given by (5-49), and dT has rank 1 at each point of D, then T maps D onto a curve in UVW space, that is, f, g, and h satisfy two independent functional relations in D. In particular, about any point of D there is a neighborhood in which one of the functions can be used to express each of the others.*

The conclusion of the first theorem says that near any point of D, one may write either $u = \phi(v, w)$ or $v = \psi(w, u)$ or $w = \gamma(u, v)$. As p moves about in D, one may be forced to change from one type of relation to another. Thus, all the points (u, v, w) which arise as image points $T(p)$ lie on the graph of a surface. Similarly, the conclusion of the second theorem says that near any point of D, one may write either $u = \phi(v)$ and $w = \psi(v)$, or $v = \alpha(w)$ and $u = \beta(w)$, or $w = \gamma(u)$ and $v = \eta(u)$; again, it may not be possible to adhere to one of these relationships throughout D. Thus, in this case, the points (u, v, w) lie on the graph of a curve in

UVW space. Stated in terms of Jacobians, we have the following simple condition for functional dependence.

Corollary. *If u, v, and w are C' functions of x, y, and z in D, and if $\dfrac{\partial(u, v, w)}{\partial(x, y, z)} = 0$ at all points of D, then u, v, and w are functionally related in D.*

We prove both theorems together. The differential of T is given by

$$dT = \begin{bmatrix} f_1 & f_2 & f_3 \\ g_1 & g_2 & g_3 \\ h_1 & h_2 & h_3 \end{bmatrix}.$$

Let us first suppose that dT has rank 1 at all points of D. This means that every 2-by-2 submatrix of dT has zero determinant but at least one entry of dT is not zero. Let us suppose that at a point $p_0 \in D$, $f_1(p_0) \neq 0$. Writing the first line of (5-49) as $f(x, y, z) - u = 0$ and regarding the left side as $F(x, y, z, u)$, we may apply the implicit function theorem (see Theorem 26); since $F_1 = f_1$, which does not vanish at p_0, we can solve the equation $f(x, y, z) - u = 0$ for x, getting

$$x = K(y, z, u).$$

Making this substitution in the remaining equations of (5-49), we obtain

$$\begin{aligned} v &= g(K(y, z, u), y, z) = G(y, z, u) \\ w &= h(K(y, z, u), y, z) = H(y, z, u). \end{aligned} \tag{5-50}$$

We shall next show that the variables y and z are not really present, that is, that G and H do not depend upon y and z. To show that y is absent, let us return to Eqs. (5-49), and differentiate the first and second with respect to y while holding z and u constant. (This may be done since Eqs. (5-50) allow us to regard y, z, and u as the independent variables.) Doing so, we obtain

$$0 = f_1 \frac{\partial x}{\partial y} + f_2$$

$$\frac{\partial v}{\partial y} = g_1 \frac{\partial x}{\partial y} + g_2.$$

Solving the first, we have $\partial x/\partial y = -f_2/f_1$ and

$$\frac{\partial v}{\partial y} = G_1(y, z, u) = \frac{f_1 g_2 - g_1 f_2}{f_1}.$$

However

$$f_1 g_2 - g_1 f_2 = \begin{vmatrix} f_1 & f_2 \\ g_1 & g_2 \end{vmatrix}$$

is the determinant of one of the 2-by-2 submatrices in dT, and by assumption, it has the value 0. Thus, in a neighborhood of p_0, we find that $G_1(y, z, u) = 0$. By a previous result (Theorem 12, Sec. 5.3), this shows that G does not depend upon y. Similar computations show that G and H are both independent of y and of z. We may therefore write Eqs. (5-50) in the simpler form

$$\begin{aligned} v &= \phi(u) \\ w &= \psi(u). \end{aligned}$$

This proves Theorem 29. ▌

To prove Theorem 28, let us assume that dT has rank 2 throughout D. This means that the Jacobian of T is zero at each point of D, but that about any point $p_0 \in D$ is a neighborhood in which one of the 2-by-2 submatrices is nonsingular. We may suppose that it is the upper left-hand submatrix. Thus, $\partial(f, g)/\partial(x, y) \neq 0$. By the implicit function theorem, we can solve the equations

$$\begin{aligned} f(x, y, z) - u &= 0 \\ g(x, y, z) - v &= 0 \end{aligned}$$

for x and y as functions of u, v, and z, obtaining

$$\begin{aligned} x &= F(u, v, z) \\ y &= G(u, v, z). \end{aligned} \tag{5-51}$$

Substituting these into the last equation in (5-49), we have

$$\begin{aligned} w &= h(F(u, v, z), G(u, v, z), z) \\ &= H(u, v, z). \end{aligned} \tag{5-52}$$

We shall show that, due to the fact that $J = 0$, the variable z is not really present, so that H does not depend upon its third variable. To see this, return to Eqs. (5-49), and differentiate each with respect to z, holding u and v constant. (This may be done since Eqs. (5-51) and (5-52) allow us to regard u, v, and z as the independent variables.) Doing this, we obtain

$$\begin{aligned} 0 &= f_1 \frac{\partial x}{\partial z} + f_2 \frac{\partial y}{\partial z} + f_3 \\ 0 &= g_1 \frac{\partial x}{\partial z} + g_2 \frac{\partial y}{\partial z} + g_3 \\ \frac{\partial w}{\partial z} &= h_1 \frac{\partial x}{\partial z} + h_2 \frac{\partial y}{\partial z} + h_3 \end{aligned}$$

Solving for $\partial w/\partial z$, we obtain

$$\frac{\partial w}{\partial z} = \frac{\begin{vmatrix} f_1 & f_2 & -f_3 \\ g_1 & g_2 & -g_3 \\ h_1 & h_2 & -h_3 \end{vmatrix}}{\begin{vmatrix} f_1 & f_2 & 0 \\ g_1 & g_2 & 0 \\ h_1 & h_2 & -1 \end{vmatrix}} = \frac{J}{\begin{vmatrix} f_1 & f_2 \\ g_1 & g_2 \end{vmatrix}}$$

Since $J = 0$, we have $\partial w/\partial z = H_3(u, v, z) = 0$ in a neighborhood, and w may be expressed in the form $w = \phi(u, v)$. This proves the functional dependence, and thus Theorem 28. ▮

So far, we have discussed only transformations whose domain and whose range lay in spaces of the same dimension, e.g., transformations from E^2 into E^2, from E^3 into E^3, etc. The techniques that have been developed will also apply to other types of transformations. Several samples will be sufficient to illustrate the manner in which this is done.

Theorem 30. *Let T be a transformation which is of class C' in an open set D in E^3 and mapping this into E^2. Let T be described by*

$$u = f(x, y, z)$$
$$v = g(x, y, z).$$

Then, if the differential dT has rank 2 throughout D, f and g are functionally independent in D and T maps D onto an open set in the UV plane; while if dT has rank 1 throughout D, then f and g are functionally dependent in D, and the image of D under T is a curve in the UV plane.

Corollary. *If* $\dfrac{\partial(u, v)}{\partial(x, y)} = \dfrac{\partial(u, v)}{\partial(y, z)} = \dfrac{\partial(u, v)}{\partial(z, x)} = 0$ *throughout D then about every point of D is a neighborhood in which $u = \phi(v)$ or $v = \psi(u)$.*

Theorem 31. *Let T be a transformation from E^2 into E^3 which is of class C' in an open set D, and is given there by the equations*

$$x = f(u, v)$$
$$y = g(u, v) \qquad (5\text{-}53)$$
$$z = h(u, v).$$

If the rank of dT is 2 throughout D, then T maps D onto a surface in XYZ space, while if the rank of dT is 1 throughout D, T maps D onto a curve.

Both of these may be reduced to special cases of Theorems 28 and 29. To prove Theorem 30, we adjoin an equation

$$w = 0$$

to make T a transformation from E^3 into E^3. Its differential is now

$$\begin{bmatrix} f_1 & f_2 & f_3 \\ g_1 & g_2 & g_3 \\ 0 & 0 & 0 \end{bmatrix}$$

whose rank is always the same as that of dT. ▮

To prove Theorem 31, we introduce a dummy variable w into the equations (5-53) which describe T to again make T a transformation from E^3 into E^3. (For instance, one might write $x = f(u, v) + w - w$.) The differential of the resulting transformation is

$$\begin{bmatrix} f_1 & f_2 & 0 \\ g_1 & g_2 & 0 \\ h_1 & h_2 & 0 \end{bmatrix}$$

whose rank is again the same as that of dT. ▌

For future use, we note that the condition that the rank of this matrix be 2 may also be expressed in the equivalent form

$$\left[\frac{\partial(x, y)}{\partial(u, v)}\right]^2 + \left[\frac{\partial(y, z)}{\partial(u, v)}\right]^2 + \left[\frac{\partial(z, x)}{\partial(u, v)}\right]^2 > 0. \tag{5-54}$$

The reader will have noticed that the hypotheses of the theorem of this section, and the previous one, were of two types. Either it was assumed that a Jacobian was nonzero throughout a region D, or it was assumed that it was identically zero throughout D; either it was assumed that a matrix had rank 2 throughout D, or that it had rank 1 throughout D. For a general transformation, however, the following behavior would be more typical. The Jacobian would be nonzero everywhere in space, except on one or more surfaces. On these surfaces, the rank of dT would be 2 except on certain curves. On these curves, the rank of dT would be 1, except at certain points where the rank would be 0. What sort of general behavior should one expect for such a transformation in a neighborhood of a point on one of the singular surfaces where $J = 0$? In the simplest cases, one is led into the field of algebraic geometry; the behavior can be quite complicated, and we shall not attempt to go into this. One simple example may serve to illustrate the possibilities. Consider the transformation T from the plane into the plane which is given by

$$\begin{cases} u = x^2 \\ v = y^2. \end{cases}$$

The differential is

$$dT = \begin{bmatrix} 2x & 0 \\ 0 & 2y \end{bmatrix}$$

and $J(x, y) = 4xy$. The rank of dT is 2 everywhere except on the lines $x = 0$ and $y = 0$. On these, it has rank 1, except for the origin where the rank is 0. The effect of T may be indicated crudely by Fig. (5-17). We see that the lines $x = 0$ and $y = 0$ are the creases along which T folds the XY plane, and where T is locally two-to-one, while the origin corresponds to the point of the final fold, and at which T is locally four-to-one.

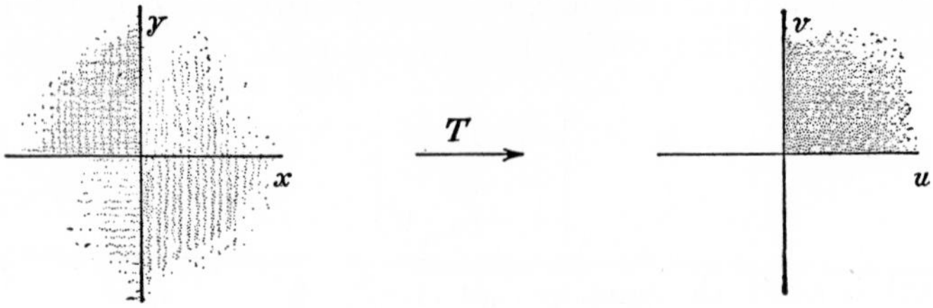

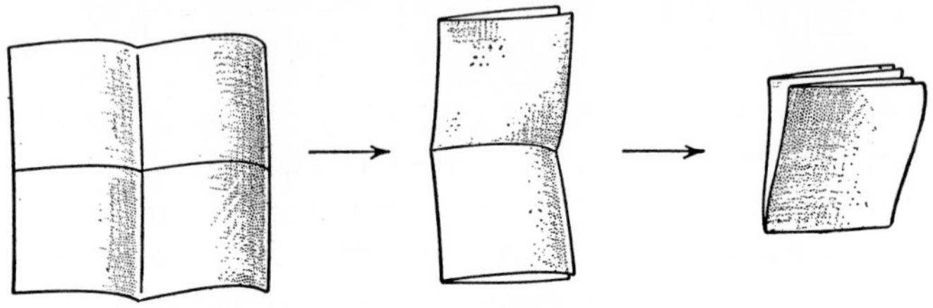

FIG. 5-17

EXERCISES

1. Determine whether or not the following pairs of functions are functionally dependent:

(a) $u = \log(x + y)$, $v = x^2 + y^2 + 2xy + 1$
(b) $u = (x + y)/x$, $v = (x + y)/y$
(c) $u = x + y$, $v = x^2 + y^2$
(d) $u = (1 - xy)/(x + y)$, $v = (x + y)^2/(1 + x^2)(1 + y^2)$

2. By consideration of their differentials, discuss the nature of the following transformations:

(a) $\begin{cases} u = x^2 \\ v = y \end{cases}$ (b) $\begin{cases} u = x^2y^2 \\ v = 2xy \end{cases}$

(c) $\begin{cases} u = x - y \\ v = x^2 + y^2 - 2xy \end{cases}$ (d) $\begin{cases} u = x + y \\ v = x + z \\ w = y^2 + z^2 - 2yz \end{cases}$

3. In the proof of Theorem 29, complete the argument to show that the function G in Eqs. (5-50) is independent of z.

4. Discuss the nature of a transformation T whose differential is of rank 0 throughout an open set D.

5. Let $u = F(x, y)$ and $v = G(x, y)$, and suppose that F and G are functionally dependent in a set D. Show that $\partial(u, v)/\partial(x, y) = 0$ in D.

6. Show that $x - y$, xy, and xe^y are functionally dependent.

7. Are any three functions of two variables functionally dependent? Are they linearly dependent?

8. Let $E = \left(\frac{\partial x}{\partial u}\right)^2 + \left(\frac{\partial y}{\partial u}\right)^2 + \left(\frac{\partial z}{\partial u}\right)^2$

$$F = \frac{\partial x}{\partial u}\frac{\partial x}{\partial v} + \frac{\partial y}{\partial u}\frac{\partial y}{\partial v} + \frac{\partial z}{\partial u}\frac{\partial z}{\partial v}$$

$$G = \left(\frac{\partial x}{\partial v}\right)^2 + \left(\frac{\partial y}{\partial v}\right)^2 + \left(\frac{\partial z}{\partial v}\right)^2$$

Show that the inequality (5-54) can also be expressed as $EG - F^2 > 0$.

9. Let $u = f(x, y, z)$ and $v = g(x, y, x)$, and suppose that f and g are functionally dependent in an open set D, with $F(u, v) = 0$, where $F_1(u, v)$ and $F_2(u, v)$ are never both zero. Show that

$$\frac{\partial(u, v)}{\partial(x, y)} = \frac{\partial(u, v)}{\partial(y, z)} = \frac{\partial(u, v)}{\partial(z, x)} = 0$$

in D.

CHAPTER 6

APPLICATIONS TO GEOMETRY AND ANALYSIS

6.1. Transformations of Multiple Integrals

In this chapter, we shall discuss certain additional properties of transformations; in particular, the present section is devoted to their effect on volume and area. This is a subject of considerable technical complexity, and one that is still near the frontier of research.†

To gain some insight into what may be expected, let us start with a linear transformation L from E^n into E^n. If D is a bounded set in E^n whose n-dimensional volume is $\mathrm{v}(D)$, what can be said about the n-dimensional volume of the image $L(D)$?

Theorem 1. *The volume of $L(D)$ is $k\mathrm{v}(D)$, where $k = |\det (L)|$.*

This asserts that the effect of L on volumes is simply to multiply by a fixed numerical factor k, which is independent of the set D. Moreover, if L is singular, this factor is 0, so that the image of any set D is a set of zero volume; this agrees with the fact that in this case, the image of all n-space will be a set of lower dimension. To make the geometry easier, let us take $n = 3$ so that L may be represented by a matrix of the form

$$A = \begin{bmatrix} a_{11} & a_{12} & a_{13} \\ a_{21} & a_{22} & a_{23} \\ a_{31} & a_{32} & a_{33} \end{bmatrix}$$

A general set D in 3-space which has volume can be approximated from inside and outside by finite unions of cubes; thus, the general result will follow if it can be shown to hold when D is restricted to be a cube. In this case, the theorem can be interpreted as the equivalent of a familiar statement about determinants, and the fact that the general 3-by-3 matrix A can be factored as a product of simpler matrices.‡ Rather

† The interested student may consult, for example, the recent monograph by Radó and Reichelderfer, "Continuous Transformations in Analysis, with an Introduction to Algebraic Topology," Springer-Verlag, Berlin, 1955.

‡ A proof for the n-dimensional case along these lines is to be found in G. Birkhoff and S. MacLane, "Survey of Modern Algebra," pp. 307–310, The Macmillan Company, New York, 1953.

than digress to supply the proof, we shall merely give an indication of the validity of the theorem by showing that the formula $\mathrm{v}(L(D)) = k\mathrm{v}(D)$ holds whenever D is a tetrahedron with one of its vertices at the origin. Let the other vertices be $P_j = (x_j, y_j, z_j)$, for $j = 1, 2, 3$. The volume of such a tetrahedron can be expressed by the formula

$$\mathrm{v}(D) = (1/6)|\det(U)|,$$

where U is the matrix

$$U = \begin{bmatrix} x_1 & x_2 & x_3 \\ y_1 & y_2 & y_3 \\ z_1 & z_2 & z_3 \end{bmatrix}$$

The transformation L carries D into another tetrahedron D' with vertices $(0, 0, 0)$ and $P'_j = (x'_j, y'_j, z'_j)$, for $j = 1, 2, 3$. Form the corresponding matrix U' from these points. The fact that $P'_j = L(P_j)$ can also be expressed by the matrix equation $U' = AU$. Since the determinant of the product of two square matrices is the product of their determinants, we also have the equation $\det(U') = \det(A)\det(U)$. Since the volume of the tetrahedron D' is $(1/6)|\det(U')|$, this shows that

$$\mathrm{v}(L(D)) = k\mathrm{v}(D),$$

where $k = |\det(A)|$. ▌

L carries the triangular faces of the tetrahedron D into the corresponding faces of D'. It is natural to ask if there is an equally simple relation holding between the areas of these triangles. However, such is not the case; the area of the image of a triangle under a linear transformation of 3-space into itself will depend not only upon the area of the original triangle, but also upon its position. Congruent triangles might have images of different area. This is not the case, of course, if the transformation is one from 2-space into itself; by Theorem 1, the area of any set D in the plane, and that of its image $L(D)$, are connected by the formula $A(L(D)) = kA(D)$, where k depends only upon L and not upon D.

If, however, we consider linear transformations from 2-space into 3-space (or more generally, into n-space), then we can obtain a result of comparable simplicity. Let L be the transformation represented by the matrix

$$\begin{bmatrix} a_{11} & a_{12} \\ a_{21} & a_{22} \\ a_{31} & a_{32} \end{bmatrix}$$

If R is a rectangle with vertices $(0, 0)$, $(a, 0)$, $(0, b)$, and (a, b), then L carries R into a parallelogram $L(R)$ with vertices $(0, 0, 0)$, aP_1, bP_2, and

$aP_1 + bP_2$ where

$$P_1 = (a_{11}, a_{21}, a_{31}), \qquad P_2 = (a_{12}, a_{22}, a_{32}).$$

The area of R is $|ab|$; the area of $L(R)$ is

$$|aP_1|\,|bP_2| \sin\theta = |ab|\,|P_1|\,|P_2| \sin\theta,$$

where θ is the angle between the lines OP_1 and OP_2 (see Fig. 6-1). Thus, we again have a relation of the form $A(L(D)) = kA(D)$, where

$$k = |P_1|\,|P_2| \sin\theta$$

is a constant which is determined solely by the matrix of L. To obtain an explicit formula for k, we recall that the cosine of the angle between

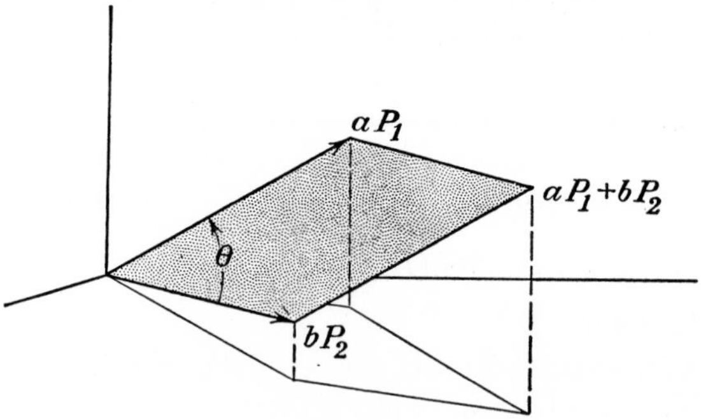

FIG. 6-1

two vectors (points) may be found by means of their inner product (see Sec. 1.1).

$$\cos\theta = \frac{(P_1 \cdot P_2)}{|P_1|\,|P_2|}$$

Using this, we find that

$$\begin{aligned} k &= |P_1|\,|P_2| \sin\theta \\ &= |P_1|\,|P_2| \left\{1 - \left(\frac{P_1 \cdot P_2}{|P_1|\,|P_2|}\right)^2\right\}^{1/2} \\ &= \{|P_1|^2|P_2|^2 - (P_1 \cdot P_2)^2\}^{1/2} \\ &= \left\{\sum_{i=1}^{3} (a_{i1})^2 \sum_{i=1}^{3} (a_{i2})^2 - \left(\sum_{i=1}^{3} a_{i1}a_{i2}\right)^2\right\}^{1/2} \end{aligned}$$

In the general case where L is a linear transformation from 2-space into n-space, the result is the same with

$$k = \left\{\sum_{i=1}^{n} (a_{i1})^2 \sum_{i=1}^{n} (a_{i2})^2 - \left(\sum_{i=1}^{n} a_{i1}a_{i2}\right)^2\right\}^{1/2}$$

For example, if L is the transformation

$$\begin{bmatrix} 1 & -1 \\ 2 & 0 \\ -1 & 1 \\ 0 & 3 \end{bmatrix}$$

then $k^2 = (1 + 4 + 1 + 0)(1 + 0 + 1 + 9) - (-1 + 0 - 1 - 0)^2 = 62$ and $k = \sqrt{62}$.

There is a special identity involving determinants which gives an alternate expression for k. For example, direct computation shows that for $n = 3$,

$$\begin{aligned} k^2 &= (a_{11}^2 + a_{21}^2 + a_{31}^2)(a_{12}^2 + a_{22}^2 + a_{32}^2) - (a_{11}a_{12} + a_{21}a_{22} + a_{31}a_{32})^2 \\ &= \begin{vmatrix} a_{11} & a_{12} \\ a_{21} & a_{22} \end{vmatrix}^2 + \begin{vmatrix} a_{21} & a_{22} \\ a_{31} & a_{32} \end{vmatrix}^2 + \begin{vmatrix} a_{31} & a_{32} \\ a_{11} & a_{12} \end{vmatrix}^2 \end{aligned}$$

In the general case, k^2 is equal to the sum of the squares of the determinants of all the 2-by-2 submatrices of the matrix for L. Thus, in the numerical example given above, we would have

$$\begin{aligned} k^2 = \begin{vmatrix} 1 & -1 \\ 2 & 0 \end{vmatrix}^2 + \begin{vmatrix} 1 & -1 \\ -1 & 1 \end{vmatrix}^2 + \begin{vmatrix} 1 & -1 \\ 0 & 3 \end{vmatrix}^2 + \begin{vmatrix} 2 & 0 \\ -1 & 1 \end{vmatrix}^2 \\ + \begin{vmatrix} 2 & 0 \\ 0 & 3 \end{vmatrix}^2 + \begin{vmatrix} -1 & 1 \\ 0 & 3 \end{vmatrix}^2 \\ = 4 + 0 + 9 + 4 + 36 + 9 \\ = 62. \end{aligned}$$

Let us turn now to the study of a general (nonlinear) transformation T. If T is of class C' in an open set Ω, then the approximation theorem allows us to write as in Theorem 17, Sec. 5.5,

$$T(p + \Delta p) = T(p) + dT\Big|_p(\Delta p) + R(\Delta p) \tag{6-1}$$

(6-2) where

$$\lim_{\Delta p \to 0} \frac{|R(\Delta p)|}{|\Delta p|} = 0$$

uniformly for all points p in any closed bounded subset of Ω. If T is a transformation from E^n into E^n, then $dT\Big|_p$ is a linear transformation from E^n into E^n. As such, it alters volumes by the factor

$$k = \left|\det\left(dT\Big|_p\right)\right| = |J(p)|$$

the absolute value of the Jacobian of T at p. If it is true that the local behavior of T is the same as the behavior of dT, then we would expect the volume of $T(D)$ to be about $J(p)\mathrm{v}(D)$ if D is a sufficiently small set surrounding p. As a first step in proving this, we have Theorem 2.

Theorem 2. *If E is a closed bounded subset of Ω of zero volume, then $T(E)$ has zero volume.*

Since T is of class C' in Ω, the entries in the matrix representation of dT are continuous. Thus, by Theorem 7, Sec. 5.2, a constant B can be chosen such that $\left| dT|_p(\Delta p) \right| \le B|\Delta p|$ for all $p \in E$ and from Eqs. (6-1) and (6-2), we see that for some M,

$$|T(p + \Delta p) - T(p)| \le M|\Delta p|$$

holding for all $|\Delta p| < \delta$. Suppose now that S is a spherical region with center p_0 and radius $r < \delta$. We have

$$|T(p) - T(p_0)| \le M|p - p_0| \le Mr,$$

for all $p \in S$, so that $T(S)$ is a set contained in the sphere of radius Mr with center at $T(p_0)$. Thus, $T(S)$ is part of a set whose n-dimensional volume is $M^n \mathrm{v}(S)$. If E is a set with zero volume, then for any $\epsilon > 0$ there can be chosen a finite number of spheres $S_1, S_2, \ldots, S_N$ which together cover E and such that $\sum_1^N \mathrm{v}(S_j) < \epsilon$. The sets $T(S_1), T(S_2), \ldots$ will together cover $T(E)$, and are in turn covered by spheres whose total volume is at most $\sum_1^N M^n \mathrm{v}(S_j) < M^n \epsilon$. Thus, $T(E)$ can be covered by a finite collection of spherical regions of arbitrarily small total volume, and $T(E)$ must have zero volume. ▌

As an application of this, we see that one-to-one C' transformations preserve the property of possessing an area or volume.

Corollary. *Let T be a transformation from E^3 into E^3 which is of class C' in an open set Ω. Furthermore, suppose that $J(p) \ne 0$ for all $p \in \Omega$. Then, if D is a closed bounded subset of Ω which has volume, $T(D)$ is also a set having volume.*

By Theorem 24, Sec. 5.7, the boundary of $T(D)$ is the image under T of the boundary of D. Since D is a set having volume, the boundary of D is a set of zero volume. By the present theorem, the image of this is also of zero volume, and as was shown in Chap. 3, this shows that the set $T(D)$ is one having volume.† ▌

What can be said about the value of $\mathrm{v}(T(D))$ in comparison with $\mathrm{v}(D)$? Expressing these in terms of integrals, the result is a special case of the formula for change of variable in multiple integrals.

† This result, among many others in the present chapter, is one which assumes its most elegant and natural form when use is made of the theory of measure, rather than that of area or volume. (See again the monograph by Radó and Reichelderfer.)

Theorem 3. *Let T be a transformation from 3-space into 3-space, with $T(u, v, w) = (x, y, z)$, which is of class C' and one-to-one in an open set Ω, with $J(p) \neq 0$ throughout Ω. If D is a closed bounded subset of Ω in UVW space, then the volume of its image is given by*

$$\mathrm{v}(T(D)) = \iiint\limits_{T(D)} dxdydz = \iiint\limits_{D} \left| \frac{\partial(x, y, z)}{\partial(u, v, w)} \right| dudvdw = \iiint\limits_{D} |J|.$$

In proving this, we shall use the theory of differentiation of set functions, as developed in Sec. 3.6. Define a set function F on the class of sets D possessing volume by the equation

$$F(D) = \mathrm{v}(T(D)).$$

Since T is one-to-one, disjoint sets have disjoint images, and F is an additive set function. If F has a derivative f, that is, if the limit

$$\lim_{D \downarrow p} \frac{F(D)}{\mathrm{v}(D)} = f(p)$$

exists, then by Theorem 19, Sec. 3.5,

$$F(D) = \mathrm{v}(T(D)) = \iiint\limits_{D} f.$$

In the light of the remarks made earlier about the local behavior of T, it is easy to conjecture that this will hold, and that $f(p) = J(p)$. Since this result is important in itself, we single it out.

Lemma. *Let E be a closed bounded subset of Ω and T as above. Then,*

$$\lim_{C \downarrow p} \frac{\mathrm{v}(T(C))}{\mathrm{v}(C)} = J(p)$$

where C ranges over the family of cubes lying in Ω and having center p, and the limit is uniform for all $p \in E$.

We start from the more precise statement of the approximation property of the differential of a transformation, as given in Theorem 17, Sec. 5.5. Given ϵ there is a $\delta > 0$ such that for any point $p_0 \in E$ and $|\Delta p| < \delta$,

$$T(p_0 + \Delta p) = T(p_0) + dT\Big|_{p_0}(\Delta p) + R(\Delta p) \tag{6-3}$$

where $|R(\Delta p)| < \epsilon|\Delta p|$.

In applying this, we first consider the case in which $dT\Big|_{p_0} = I$, the identity transformation. Since $I(\Delta p) = \Delta p$, (6-3) becomes

$$T(p_0 + \Delta p) = T(p_0) + \Delta p + R(\Delta p). \tag{6-4}$$

If the remainder term $R(\Delta p)$ were absent, then this equation would assert that the transformation T is nothing more than a translation; it would shift a cube with center at p_0 so that its center would become $T(p_0)$, without altering lengths or direction. The term $R(\Delta p)$ causes a slight alteration of this picture. To estimate its effect, we see from (6-4) that whenever $|\Delta p| < \delta$

$$(6\text{-}5) \qquad |T(p_0 + \Delta p) - T(p_0)| < |\Delta p| + \epsilon|\Delta p| = (1 + \epsilon)|\Delta p|$$

and that

$$(6\text{-}6) \qquad |T(p_0 + \Delta p) - T(p_0)| > |\Delta p| - \epsilon|\Delta p| = (1 - \epsilon)|\Delta p|$$

We wish to estimate the volume of the image under T of a cube C whose center is at p_0; to illustrate the method, let us do this first for a sphere. If $p = p_0 + \Delta p$ and p lies in the sphere S with center p_0 and radius $r < \delta$, then, by (6-5), $T(p)$ lies in the sphere whose center is $T(p_0)$ and whose radius is $(1 + \epsilon)r$. Moreover, when p lies on the boundary of S so that $|\Delta p| = r$, we see by (6-6) that $T(p)$ lies outside the sphere whose center is again $T(p_0)$, and whose radius is $(1 - \epsilon)r$. Since T is one-to-one and takes open sets into open sets, we see that $T(S)$ must contain this smaller sphere. Thus the set $T(S)$ lies in a sphere of radius $(1 + \epsilon)r$ and contains a sphere of radius $(1-\epsilon)r$, and the volume of $T(S)$ satisfies the inequality

$$\tfrac{4}{3}\pi[(1 - \epsilon)r]^3 < \mathrm{v}(T(S)) < \tfrac{4}{3}\pi[(1 + \epsilon)r]^3$$

or

$$(1 - \epsilon)^3 < \frac{\mathrm{v}(T(S))}{\mathrm{v}(S)} < (1 + \epsilon)^3.$$

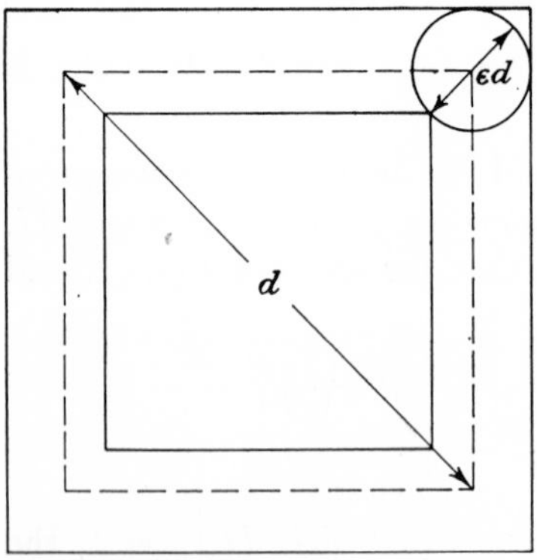

FIG. 6-2. The diameter of the outer square is $(1 + \sqrt{2}\epsilon)d$ and that of the inner is $(1 - \epsilon)d$.

The same type of argument applies to a cubical set. If C is a cube with center at p_0 and diameter (diagonal) $d < \delta$, then, by (6-4) and (6-5), the image $T(C)$ lies in the cube with center $T(p_0)$ and diameter $(1 + \sqrt{3}\,\epsilon)d$. Moreover, the image of the boundary of C lies outside a similar cube of diameter $(1 - \epsilon)d$. [Figure 6-2 illustrates the situation in the case when T is a transformation of 2-space into 2-space. By (6-4), the true position of the image $T(p)$ is somewhere within a disk of radius $\epsilon|\Delta p|$ whose center is the point $T(p_0) + \Delta p$.] The volume of $T(C)$ lies between the volumes of these two cubes, so that we again have an estimate from above and below:

$$(1 - \epsilon)^3 < \frac{v(T(C))}{v(C)} < (1 + \sqrt{3}\,\epsilon)^3$$

Suppose now that $dT\Big|_{p_0} = L$. Since $J(p_0) = \det(L) \neq 0$, L is a nonsingular linear transformation, and thus has an inverse L^{-1} with the property that $L^{-1}L = I$. Moreover, since T is of class C' and the entries of L^{-1} are therefore continuous functions of p_0, we can choose a number B depending only upon the bounded set E such that $|L^{-1}(q)| \leq B|q|$ for all q, and all $p_0 \in E$. (Here, we once again use Theorem 7, Sec. 5.2.) According to Eq. (6-3) with $p = p_0 + \Delta p$,

$$T(p) - T(p_0) = L(\Delta p) + R(\Delta p)$$

Apply to this the linear transformation L^{-1}, obtaining

$$L^{-1}\{T(p) - T(p_0)\} = L^{-1}\{L(\Delta p) + R(\Delta p)\}$$

or

$$\text{(6-7)} \qquad \begin{aligned} L^{-1}(T(p)) - L^{-1}(T(p_0)) &= L^{-1}L(\Delta p) + L^{-1}(R(\Delta p)) \\ &= \Delta p + L^{-1}(R(\Delta p)). \end{aligned}$$

In this, $|L^{-1}(R(\Delta p))| \leq B|R(\Delta p)| < B\epsilon|\Delta p|$. Using (6-7) in place of (6-4), we find that

$$\text{(6-8)} \qquad (1 - B\epsilon)^3 < \frac{v(L^{-1}T(C))}{v(C)} < (1 + B\sqrt{3}\,\epsilon)^3$$

holding for any cube C centered at a point p_0 in E with diameter $d < \delta$. The linear transformation L^{-1}, by Theorem 1, multiplies volumes by the factor $k = |\det(L^{-1})|$. Accordingly, $v(L^{-1}T(C)) = kv(T(C))$. Since L^{-1} is the inverse of $L = dT\Big|_{p_0}$ and $J(p_0)$ is the determinant of $dT\Big|_{p_0}$,

$$k = \frac{1}{|J(p_0)|}.$$

Thus, (6-8) becomes

$$(1 - B\epsilon)^3|J(p_0)| < \frac{v(T(C))}{v(C)} < (1 + B\sqrt{3}\,\epsilon)^3|J(p_0)|$$

and the lemma is proved. ▌

The proof of Theorem 3 itself is immediate. Since the set function F is defined on cubes by $F(C) = v(T(C))$, the lemma shows that F is uniformly differentiable on E, with derivative at p the point function $|J(p)|$. By theorem 19, Sec. 3.5, F can be obtained by integrating its derivative, and for any set D having volume,

$$F(D) = \mathrm{v}(T(D)) = \iiint\limits_D |J| = \iiint\limits_D \left| \frac{\partial(x, y, z)}{\partial(u, v, w)} \right| dudvdw. \quad \blacksquare$$

With a slight modification of the argument, we also obtain a general theorem dealing with transformation of multiple integrals.

Theorem 4. *Let T be a transformation from 3-space into 3-space, with $T(u, v, w) = (x, y, z)$, which is of class C' and one-to-one in an open set Ω with $J(p) \neq 0$ throughout Ω. Let D^* be a closed bounded set in XYZ space which is the image under T of a set $D \subset \Omega$ in UVW space. Let f be a continuous function defined on D^*. Then,*

$$\text{(6-9)} \qquad \iiint\limits_{D^*} f(x, y, z)\, dxdydz = \iiint\limits_D f(T(u, v, w))|J(u, v, w)|\, dudvdw$$

The sets D and D^* are assumed to possess volume. If f is a constant function, the result is covered by Theorem 3. We may suppose that f is everywhere positive by adding, if necessary, a suitable constant. We may also suppose that f is continuous throughout Ω. (This is a typical application of the Tietze extension theorem which was proved at the end of Sec. 4.2.) Define a set function F on subsets of Ω having volume by

$$F(S) = \iiint\limits_{T(S)} f.$$

Let E be a closed bounded subset of Ω which contains D in its interior. Let C be a cube lying in E. Applying the mean value theorem for integrals, we can write $F(C) = f(q^*)\mathrm{v}(T(C))$, where $q^* \in T(C)$. As the cube C closes down on a point p_0, $T(C)$ closes down on $T(p_0)$, and q^* approaches $T(p_0)$. Thus,

$$\begin{aligned}
\lim_{C \downarrow p_0} \frac{F(C)}{\mathrm{v}(C)} &= \lim_{C \downarrow p_0} f(q^*) \frac{\mathrm{v}(T(C))}{\mathrm{v}(C)} \\
&= f(T(p_0)) \lim_{C \downarrow p_0} \frac{\mathrm{v}(T(C))}{\mathrm{v}(C)} \\
&= f(T(p_0))|J(p_0)|
\end{aligned}$$

using the lemma for the last step. Moreover, since f is uniformly continuous on $T(E)$, we have uniform convergence of this limit for all $p_0 \in E$. Having thus computed the derivative of the set function F, application of Theorem 19, Sec. 3.5, yields

$$
\begin{aligned}
F(D) &= \iiint\limits_{T(D)} f = \iiint\limits_{D^*} f(x, y, z)\, dxdydz \\
&= \iiint\limits_{D} f(T(u, v, w))|J(u, v, w)|\, dudvdw \\
&= \iiint\limits_{D} f(T(u, v, w)) \left| \frac{\partial(x, y, z)}{\partial(u, v, w)} \right| dudvdw. \quad \blacksquare
\end{aligned}
$$

It is enlightening to compare this result with the corresponding theorem dealing with transformation of (substitution into) integrals of functions of one variable. As stated in the corollary to Theorem 7, Sec. 3.2, the substitution $x = \phi(u)$ in the integral $\int_a^b f(x)\,dx$ results in the integral $\int_\alpha^\beta f(\phi(u))\phi'(u)\,du$, where $\phi(\alpha) = a$ and $\phi(\beta) = b$. Comparing these, we see that the factor $\phi'(u) = dx/du$ corresponds to the Jacobian $\partial(u, v, w)/\partial(x, y, z)$ and the new limits of integration $[\alpha, \beta]$ to the set D. However, the one-variable theorem was considerably stronger than the present form of the several-variable theorem. For example, there is no need to have $\phi'(u) \neq 0$, nor must ϕ be a one-to-one mapping from the interval $[\alpha, \beta]$ onto the interval $[a, b]$. Another contrast is that $\phi'(u)$ rather than $|\phi'(u)|$ appears; however, the explanation for this lies in the fact that the simple one-variable integral is a directed or oriented integral,† while we have so far not oriented the multiple integral. This suggests, correctly, that similar improvements can be made in Theorem 4. In Chap. 7, we shall obtain such a result for double integrals, using a different approach which assumes that T is of class C''. A more general treatment of the whole subject is to be found in the monograph by Radó and Reichelderfer, which we have mentioned earlier.

Returning to the result given in Theorem 4, we recall that the symbols "$dxdydz$" or "$dudvdw$" serve to show what integration is to be performed, but have no meaning out of context. Following a device used in Sec. 3.2, (6-9) might also be written, for emphasis of this point of view, in the form

$$
\iiint\limits_{D^*} f(x, y, z)\, \boxed{x\ y\ z} = \iiint\limits_{D} f(T(u, v, w))|J(u, v, w)|\, \boxed{u\ v\ w}
$$

The rule for change of variable in a triple integral can be given thus: to make the substitution $x = \phi(u, v, w)$, $y = \psi(u, v, w)$, $z = \theta(u, v, w)$ in

† $\int_1^2 f$ and $\int_2^1 f$ have opposite signs.

the triple integral $\iiint_{D^*} f(x, y, z)\, dxdydz$, replace the region D^* by the region D in the UVW plane which corresponds to D^* under the transformation, replace the integrand $f(x, y, z)$ by

$$f(\phi(u, v, w), \psi(u, v, w), \theta(u, v, w)),$$

and replace $dxdydz$ by $|\partial(x, y, z)/\partial(u, v, w)|\, dudvdw$. In the one-variable case, the notation assisted the application of the rule. When the substitution was $x = \phi(u)$, the formula $dx/du = \phi'(u)$ made the replacement of dx by $\phi'(u)\, du$ a routine operation. It is natural to ask if a similar formalism can be used for multiple integrals. In Chap. 7, we shall explain how one may write

$$dx = (\partial x/\partial u)\, du + (\partial x/\partial v)\, dv + (\partial x/\partial w)\, dw, \qquad dy = \ldots,$$

and then "evaluate" $dxdydz$ by multiplying together these differential forms; the result obtained will be $J(u, v, w)\, dudvdw$, as required.

We conclude this section by giving a number of illustrations of the use of these formulas.

Consider first the transformation described by

$$T: \begin{cases} x = u + v \\ y = v - u^2 \end{cases}$$

and let D be the set in the UV plane bounded by the lines $u = 0$, $v = 0$, and $u + v = 2$. The image of D is the set D^* bounded by $x = 2$, $y = x$, and $y = -x^2$ (see Fig. 6-3). Computing the Jacobian of T,

$$J(u, v) = \frac{\partial(x, y)}{\partial(u, v)} = \det \begin{bmatrix} 1 & 1 \\ -2u & 1 \end{bmatrix} = 1 + 2u.$$

By Theorem 3, the area of D^* is

$$\iint_D J = \iint_D (1 + 2u)\, dudv = \int_0^2 dv \int_0^{2-v} (1 + 2u)\, du$$
$$= \int_0^2 (v^2 - 5v + 6)\, dv = 14/3.$$

For comparison, we may calculate the area of D^* directly:

$$A(D^*) = \int_0^2 dx \int_{-x^2}^{x} dy = \int_0^2 (x + x^2)\, dx = 14/3.$$

With the same set D^*, let us evaluate the integral $\displaystyle\iint_{D^*} \frac{dxdy}{(x - y + 1)^2}$.

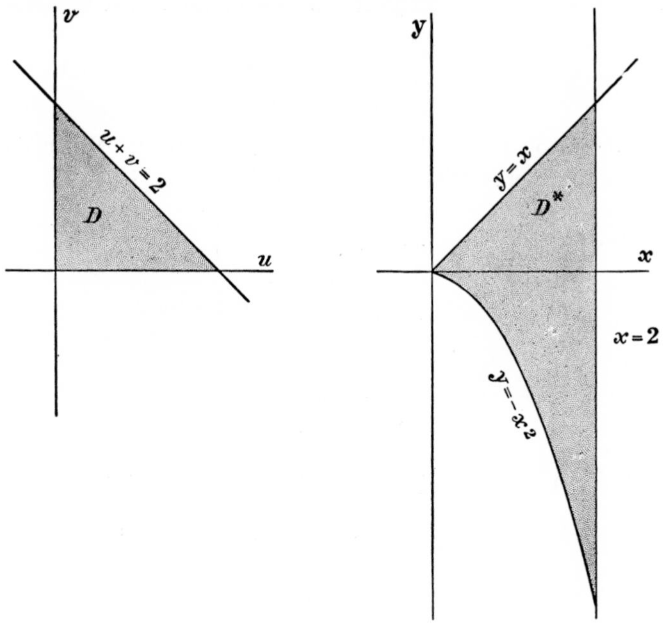

FIG. 6-3

Using the same transformation, this becomes

$$\iint\limits_D \frac{(1 + 2u)\,dudv}{(u^2 + u + 1)^2} = \int_0^2 dv \int_0^{2-v} \frac{(1 + 2u)\,du}{(u^2 + u + 1)^2}$$
$$= \int_0^2 dv \Big[-(u^2 + u + 1)^{-1}\Big]_{u=0}^{u=2-v}$$
$$= \int_0^2 \{1 - (v^2 - 5v + 7)^{-1}\}\,dv$$
$$= 2 - \frac{2}{\sqrt{3}}\left[\arctan\left(\frac{5}{\sqrt{3}}\right) - \arctan\left(\frac{1}{\sqrt{3}}\right)\right]$$
$$= 2 - \frac{2}{\sqrt{3}} \arctan\left(\frac{\sqrt{3}}{2}\right)$$

For another example, consider the integral

$$\iint\limits_{D^*} \exp\left(\frac{x - y}{x + y}\right) dxdy$$

where D^* is the region bounded by the lines $x = 0$, $y = 0$, $x + y = 1$.

The form of the integrand suggests the use of the linear transformation

$$T: \begin{cases} u = x - y \\ v = x + y \end{cases}$$

This maps D^* onto a triangular region D (see Fig. 6-4). Since T is linear, it is sufficient to observe that T sends (0, 1) into (−1, 1), (1, 0) into (1, 1),

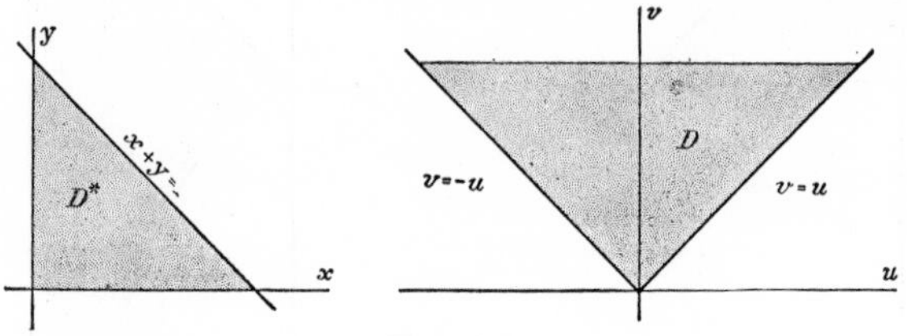

FIG. 6-4

and (0, 0) into (0, 0). The inverse of T is the (linear) transformation

$$T^{-1}: \begin{cases} x = \tfrac{1}{2}u + \tfrac{1}{2}v \\ y = -\tfrac{1}{2}u + \tfrac{1}{2}v \end{cases}$$

so that

$$\frac{\partial(x, y)}{\partial(u, v)} = \det \begin{bmatrix} \tfrac{1}{2} & \tfrac{1}{2} \\ -\tfrac{1}{2} & \tfrac{1}{2} \end{bmatrix} = \frac{1}{2}.$$

Accordingly,

$$\iint_{D^*} \exp\left(\frac{x - y}{x + y}\right) dxdy = \iint_{D} \tfrac{1}{2}(e^{u/v})\, dudv$$

$$= \tfrac{1}{2} \int_0^1 dv \int_{-v}^{v} e^{u/v}\, du = \tfrac{1}{2} \int_0^1 dv \left[ve^{u/v}\right]_{-v}^{v}$$

$$= \tfrac{1}{2} \int_0^1 (e - e^{-1})v\, dv = \frac{e - e^{-1}}{4}$$

Another very familiar transformation is $x = r \cos \theta$, $y = r \sin \theta$, which we regard as a mapping from the (r, θ) plane into the (x, y) plane.† The Jacobian of this transformation is

$$\frac{\partial(x, y)}{\partial(r, \theta)} = \det \begin{bmatrix} \cos \theta & -r \sin \theta \\ \sin \theta & r \cos \theta \end{bmatrix} = r$$

so that $dxdy$ is to be replaced by $r\, dr\, d\theta$ when transforming a double integral. The condition $J(p) \neq 0$ requires that we avoid the line $r = 0$

† In the conventional use of polar coordinates, a point in the (x, y) plane is also given a second labeling, namely, that of a point in the (r, θ) plane which maps into it under this transformation. The "radius-vector, angle" interpretation of polar coordinates is a device which makes it easier to locate points of one plane which correspond to points of the other (see Fig. 6-5).

in the (r, θ) plane; this corresponds to the origin in the (x, y) plane. If D^* is a region in the XY plane which does not contain the origin, then the inverse transformation $r = (x^2 + y^2)^{1/2}$, $\theta = \arctan (y/x)$ determines a region D in the (r, θ) plane which is mapped onto D^* one-to-one, and

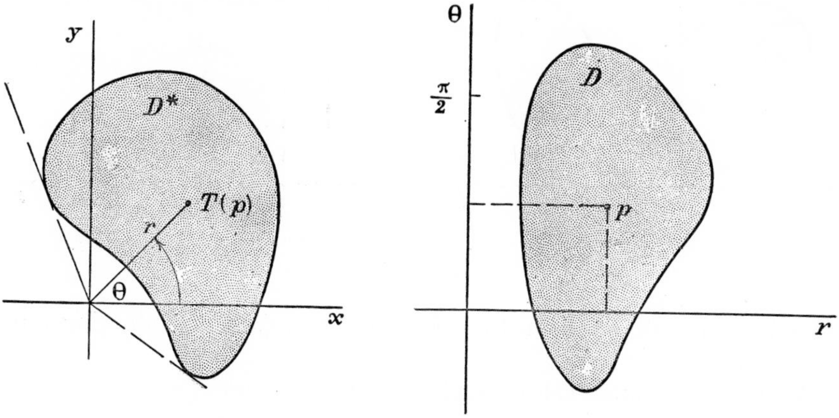

FIG. 6-5

in which $J(p) \neq 0$ (see Fig. 6-5). Theorem 4 then gives the familiar formula

$$\iint_{D^*} f(x, y)\, dxdy = \iint_{D} f(r \cos \theta, r \sin \theta) r\, drd\theta \tag{6-10}$$

If D^* is a region containing the origin, then the corresponding set D will contain points on the line $r = 0$ where $J(p) = 0$. Theorem 4, as stated, does not apply. However, for this familiar transformation, it is not difficult to extend it. If D^* has the origin for an interior point, we can divide it into two pieces by the horizontal axis; each of these will have the origin as a boundary point, and if we can prove formula (6-10) for such a set, addition will give it for a general set D^*. Assuming therefore that D^* lies in the half plane $y \geq 0$, we choose a region D in the (r, θ) plane which is mapped onto D^*, one-to-one, except for the points of D on $r = 0$, all of which map into $(0, 0)$ (see Fig. 6-6). Let D_ρ^* be the set which is obtained from D^* by removing the points within the open disk of radius ρ, and center $\mathbf{0}$. The corresponding set D_ρ is obtained by removing all the points (r, θ) in D with $0 \leq r < \rho$. In D_ρ, $J(p) = r \neq 0$ so that Theorem 4 applies, and

$$\iint_{D_\rho^*} f(x, y)\, dxdy = \iint_{D_\rho} f(r \cos \theta, r \sin \theta) r\, drd\theta$$

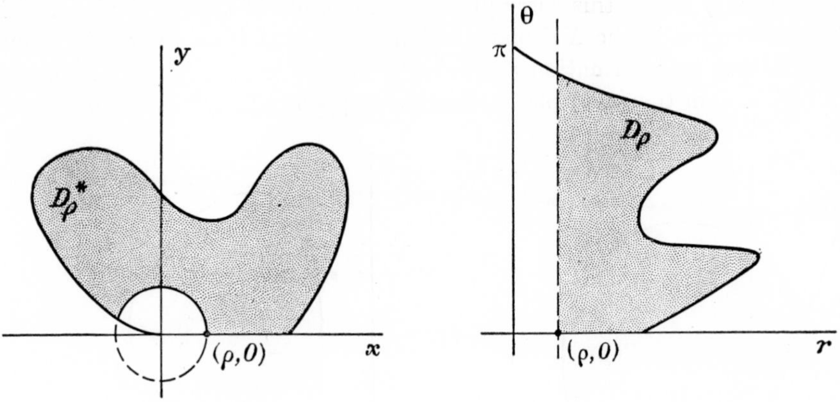

FIG. 6-6

This holds for all $\rho > 0$, so that we can obtain (6-10) by allowing ρ to approach zero.

A similar treatment can be applied to the equations

$$\text{(6-11)} \qquad \begin{cases} x = \rho \sin \phi \cos \theta \\ y = \rho \sin \phi \sin \theta \\ z = \rho \cos \phi \end{cases}$$

which serve to define the system of spherical coordinates (see Fig. 6-7). If we regard (6-11) as describing a transformation T mapping (ρ, ϕ, θ)

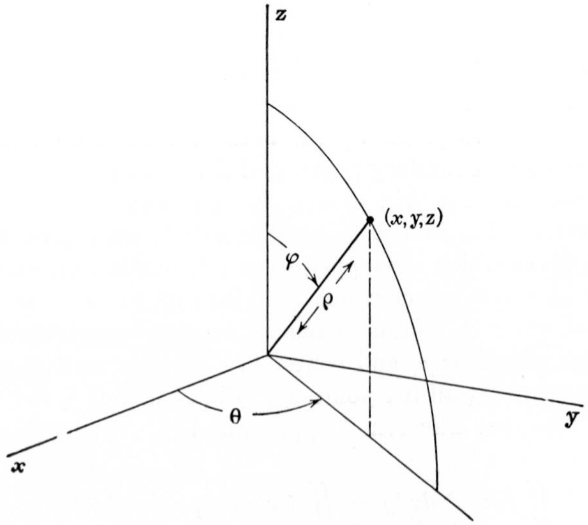

FIG. 6-7. Spherical coordinates.

into (x, y, z), then T has for its Jacobian

$$\frac{\partial(x, y, z)}{\partial(\rho, \phi, \theta)} = \begin{vmatrix} \sin \phi \cos \theta & \rho \cos \phi \cos \theta & -\rho \sin \phi \sin \theta \\ \sin \phi \sin \theta & \rho \cos \phi \sin \theta & \rho \sin \phi \cos \theta \\ \cos \phi & -\rho \sin \phi & 0 \end{vmatrix}$$
$$= \rho^2 \sin \phi.$$

Thus, $dxdydz$ is to be replaced by $\rho^2 \sin \phi \, d\rho d\phi d\theta$ in transforming a

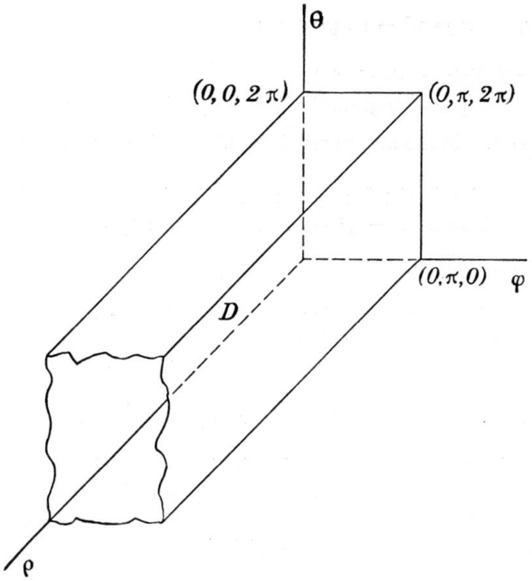

FIG. 6-8

triple integral with this substitution. It will be observed that T maps the region (Fig. 6-8)

$$D = \{\text{all } (\rho, \phi, \theta) \text{ with } 0 \le \rho,\ 0 \le \phi \le \pi,\ 0 \le \theta \le 2\pi\}$$

onto all of XYZ in a fashion which is one-to-one at all interior points of D. It is not one-to-one on the boundary of D; for example, the entire face $\rho = 0$ maps onto the single point $(0, 0, 0)$. Moreover, the Jacobian is also zero at points on portions of the boundary. However, by a limiting argument similar to that used above, the transformation formula can also be shown to hold for bounded subsets of D.

EXERCISES

1. Show that the linear transformation which sends $(1, 1)$ into $(2, 5)$ and $(1, -1)$ into $(0, -1)$ is an area-preserving transformation.

2. Let $A = [a_{ij}]$ be a matrix with two columns and four rows. Show that the number $k^2 = \sum_{i=1}^{4} (a_{i1})^2 \sum_{i=1}^{4} (a_{i2})^2 - \left(\sum_{i=1}^{4} a_{i1}a_{i2}\right)^2$ is in fact the same as the sum of the squares of the determinants of all of the 2-by-2 submatrices.

3. Make the indicated change of variables in the following integrals, and evaluate the result.

(a) $\int_0^1 dx \int_0^x xy\, dy, \quad x = u + v,\ y = u - v$

(b) $\int_0^1 dx \int_{1-x}^{1+x} xy\, dy, \quad x = u,\ y = u + v$

(c) $\iint_D xy\, dxdy, \quad x = u^2 - v^2,\ y = 2uv$

where D is the unit disk, $x^2 + y^2 \leq 1$.

4. Let D^* be the parallelogram bounded by the lines $y = \frac{1}{2}x$, $y = \frac{1}{2}x + 2$, $y = 3x$, $y = 3x - 4$. Make an appropriate substitution, and evaluate $\iint_{D^*} xy\, dxdy$.

5. Let D be the region in the first quadrant which is bounded by the curves $xy = 1$, $xy = 3$, $x^2 - y^2 = 1$ and $x^2 - y^2 = 4$. Make an appropriate substitution, and evaluate $\iint_D (x^2 + y^2)\, dxdy$.

6. The equation of a curve in polar coordinates is $r = \sin(\theta/2)$ for $0 \leq \theta \leq 2\pi$. Find the area of the region which is bounded by this curve.

7. In 4-space, "double" polar coordinates are defined by the equations

$$x = r\cos\theta, \qquad y = r\sin\theta, \qquad z = \rho\cos\phi, \qquad w = \rho\sin\phi$$

Obtain the correct formula for making this substitution in a fourfold multiple integral, and use this to show that the volume of the spherical region $x^2 + y^2 + z^2 + w^2 \leq R^2$ is $\frac{1}{2}\pi^2 R^4$.

8. The linear transformation L whose matrix is

$$\begin{bmatrix} 1 & 0 & -1 \\ 2 & 1 & 1 \\ 0 & -1 & 2 \end{bmatrix}$$

maps the unit cube with vertices (0, 0, 0), (1, 0, 0), (0, 1, 0), (0, 0, 1), (1, 1, 0), (0, 1, 1), (1, 0, 1), (1, 1, 1) into a parallelepiped R. Find the area of each of the faces of R, and find its volume.

9. Let $P = (-1, 0)$ and $Q = (1, 0)$ and let $p = (x, y)$ be any point with $y \geq 0$. Set $s = |P - p|^2$ and $t = |Q - p|^2$. Show that the correspondence $p \to (s, t)$ provides a coordinate system for the upper half plane, and discuss this as a transformation between (x, y) and (s, t). What is the image in the (x, y) plane of lines in the (s, t) plane? Where is $\partial(s, t)/\partial(x, y)$ zero?

10. (Alternate approach to Theorem 4.) Let T be the transformation described by $x = u$, $y = \psi(u, v)$. Let D be the region bounded by the lines $u = a$, $u = b$, and the smooth curves $v = \beta(u)$ and $v = \alpha(u)$ [with $\beta(u) > \alpha(u)$ for all $u \in [a, b]$. Let D^* be the image of D under T, and suppose that $\psi_2(u, v) > 0$ for all $(u, v) \in D$. Show that for any function f which is continuous in D^*,

$$\iint_{D^*} f(x, y)\, dxdy = \iint_D f(T(u, v))\psi_2(u, v)\, dudv.$$

(*Hint:* Write each side as an iterated integral, and use the substitution formula for single integrals.)

***11.** (*Continuation*) Let T be a transformation of class C' in an open set Ω which is described by

$$x = \phi(u, v)$$
$$y = \psi(u, v).$$

Assume also that $\partial(x, y)/\partial(u, v) > 0$ throughout Ω. Show that in a sufficiently small neighborhood of any point $p \in \Omega$, the transformation T can be factored in one of the following two ways:

$$\begin{cases} x = s \\ y = G(s, t) \end{cases} \qquad \begin{cases} s = \phi(u, v) \\ t = v \end{cases}$$

or

$$\begin{cases} x = s \\ y = G(s, t) \end{cases} \qquad \begin{cases} s = \phi(u, v) \\ t = u \end{cases}$$

where G is a function of class C' which is determined by the functions ϕ and ψ.

12. (*Continuation*) When such a factoring is made, show that Exercise 10 can be applied to each successively to obtain the result stated in the lemma to Theorem 3.

6-2. Curves and Arc Length

In our treatment of these topics, we shall deviate from the more traditional approach and adopt one which is of more significance in analysis. The terms "curve" and "surface" have several meanings in mathematics. For example, in one usage, "curve" means a set of points which has certain topological properties associated with the intuitive notion of "thinness." The word is also used to refer to a set of equations. We adopt the following formal definition.

Definition. *A curve γ in n-space is a mapping or transformation from E^1 into E^n.*

For example, the general continuous curve in 3-space is a continuous transformation of the form

$$\begin{cases} x = \phi(t) \\ y = \psi(t) \\ z = \theta(t) \end{cases} \tag{6-12}$$

defined for t in one or more intervals $[a, b]$. In more familiar terminology, we have identified the notion of curve with what is often called a parametric representation. A point p in E^3 is said to **lie on** the curve when there is a t for which $p = \gamma(t)$. The set of all points which lie on γ is called the **trace** or graph of γ. It is important to keep in mind the fact that the curve is the transformation (6-12) and not the set of points lying on γ. Many different curves can have the same trace. For example, each of the following curves has for its trace the unit circle† $C = \{\text{all } (x, y) \text{ with } x^2 + y^2 = 1\}$.

$$\begin{cases} x = \cos t \\ y = \sin t \end{cases} \quad \begin{cases} x = \cos (2t) \\ y = \sin (2t) \end{cases} \quad \begin{cases} x = \sin t \\ y = \cos t \end{cases}$$
$$0 \le t \le 2\pi \qquad 0 \le t \le 2\pi \qquad 0 \le t \le 2\pi$$

However, the three curves are quite different. The first and third have length 2π, while the second (which goes around C twice) has length 4π. Again, the first curve starts and ends at (1, 0) and goes around C in the counterclockwise direction, while the third begins and ends at (0, 1), and goes in the opposite direction. Such distinctions are of great importance in the analytical theory of curves. In this section, we shall take up some of the simpler portions of this theory.

We begin with some convenient terminology. If a curve γ is defined for the interval $a \le t \le b$, then the **end points** of γ are $\gamma(a)$ and $\gamma(b)$; the former is called the first point on γ, and the latter the last point on γ. A curve γ is **closed** if its end points coincide so that $\gamma(a) = \gamma(b)$. The three curves given above are examples of closed curves. A point p which lies on a curve γ is said to be a multiple point if there is more than one value of t for which $\gamma(t) = p$. A curve is said to be **simple** if it has no multiple points; the mapping γ is then one-to-one. A continuous closed curve is said to be simple if the only multiple points are the coincident end points. (The terms "Jordan arc" and "Jordan curve" are also used.) In the examples given above, the first and third are simple closed curves, but the second is not.

It is also convenient to impose certain differentiability requirements.

Definition. *A curve γ is said to be smooth on an interval I if γ is of class C' and the differential $d\gamma$ is always of rank* 1 *on I.*

When γ is given in the form (6-12), this asserts that ϕ', ψ', and θ' exist and are continuous on $[a, b]$ and that at no point of this interval do all of them become zero. This latter condition can also be written as

$$\left(\frac{dx}{dt}\right)^2 + \left(\frac{dy}{dt}\right)^2 + \left(\frac{dz}{dt}\right)^2 > 0. \tag{6-13}$$

The word "smooth" is used to suggest that the motion of a point which traces the curve has no abrupt changes of direction. The need for a condition such as (6-13) to ensure this is shown by the following example of a curve of class C' which violates condition (6-13) when $t = 0$:

$$\gamma: \begin{cases} x = t^3 \\ y = |t^3| \end{cases} \qquad -\infty < t < \infty$$

† Here and elsewhere, geometrical terms like "circle," "parabola," etc., will usually refer to the set of points which satisfy the conventional equations.

We note that $dx/dt = 3t^2$, and that $dy/dt = 3t^2$ for $t \geq 0$ and $-3t^2$ for $t \leq 0$; both are continuous, and both become zero for $t = 0$. However, the trace of γ is the set of points (x, y) with $y = |x|$ (Fig. 6-9).

By the term "straight line" we shall mean a curve of the form

$$\gamma(t) = p_0 + \mathbf{v}t \qquad -\infty < t < \infty \tag{6-14}$$

where the point (vector) $\mathbf{v}$ obeys the restriction $|\mathbf{v}| \neq 0$. For example, in 3-space, the general straight line is

$$\begin{cases} x = x_0 + at \\ y = y_0 + bt \\ z = z_0 + ct \end{cases} \tag{6-15}$$

where $a^2 + b^2 + c^2 > 0$. Since $\gamma(0) = p_0$ and $\gamma(1) = p_0 + \mathbf{v}$, the line (6-14) may be graphed as the line which goes through p_0 toward $p_0 + \mathbf{v}$, in a direction which is specified by $\mathbf{v}$. Since we have defined the notion of direction in n-space by means of the points on the unit sphere, we form the unit vector $\beta = \mathbf{v}/|\mathbf{v}|$ which has length 1, and specifies the same direction. In the customary language of analytical geometry, $\mathbf{v}$ is a set of direction components for the line, while β is a set of direction cosines; either may be used. A line through $(1, 2, -1)$ toward $(3, 1, 1)$ has the equation

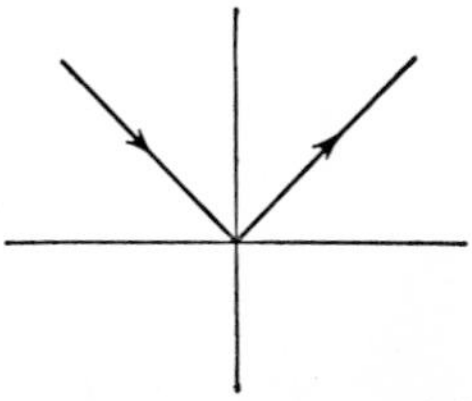

FIG. 6-9. $x = t^3$, $y = |t^3|$.

$$\begin{aligned}\gamma(t) &= (1, 2, -1) + \{(3, 1, 1) - (1, 2, -1)\}t \\ &= (1, 2, -1) + (2, -1, 2)t\end{aligned}$$

or $x = 1 + 2t$, $y = 2 - t$, $z = -1 + 2t$. The direction of this line is $\beta = (2/3, -1/3, 2/3)$.

We observe that the coordinates of $\mathbf{v}$ can be obtained from (6-15) by differentiation; $a = dx/dt$, $b = dy/dt$, and $c = dz/dt$. This suggests a similar procedure for the general smooth curve.

Definition. *If γ is a smooth curve, then the direction of γ at a point p corresponding to the value t is $\beta = \mathbf{v}/|\mathbf{v}|$, where*

$$\mathbf{v} = \gamma'(t) = \left(\frac{dx}{dt}, \frac{dy}{dt}, \frac{dz}{dt}\right)$$

When the parameter t is interpreted as time, $\mathbf{v}$ is interpreted as the velocity vector of the point whose position at time t is $\gamma(t)$, and the speed† of the point along its path is

$$|\mathbf{v}| = \left\{\left(\frac{dx}{dt}\right)^2 + \left(\frac{dy}{dt}\right)^2 + \left(\frac{dz}{dt}\right)^2\right\}^{1/2}.$$

† The requirement that γ be a smooth curve implies that the speed be never zero.

If the point p is a multiple point for the curve γ, then γ may have several directions at p. Two curves which have the same direction at a common point p are said to be **tangent** there. The straight line α:

$$\alpha(t) = p_0 + \mathbf{v}t \qquad -\infty < t < \infty$$

where $p_0 = \gamma(t_0)$ and $\mathbf{v} = \gamma'(t_0)$, is tangent to γ at p_0.

In discussing a particular curve, it is helpful to plot the trace of the curve, being sure to record points in the order assigned by t. Consider, for example, the plane curve

$$\text{(6-16)} \qquad \gamma: \begin{cases} x = t - t^3 \\ y = t^2 - t \end{cases} \qquad -\infty < t < \infty$$

which has the trace shown in Fig. (6-10). The origin is a double point corresponding to both $t = 0$ and $t = 1$. Differentiating, we have $\gamma'(t) = (1 - 3t^2,\ 2t - 1)$ so that

$$\gamma'(0) = (1, -1)$$

and $\qquad \gamma'(1) = (-2, 1).$

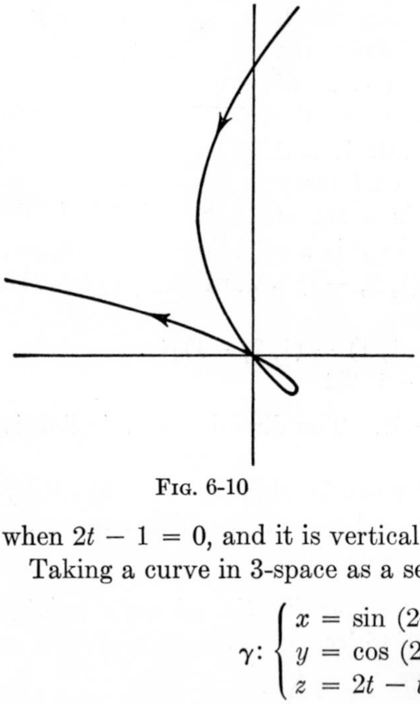

FIG. 6-10

At the origin, γ has two tangent lines. The first is $x = t$, $y = -t$ with slope -1, and the second is $x = -2t$, $y = t$ with slope $-\frac{1}{2}$. The direction of γ for a general value of t is

$$\beta = \frac{\gamma'(t)}{|\gamma'(t)|} = \frac{(1 - 3t^2,\ 2t - 1)}{(9t^4 - 2t^2 - 4t + 2)^{1/2}}$$

Thus, γ is horizontal $[\beta = (1, 0)]$ when $2t - 1 = 0$, and it is vertical $[\beta = (0, 1)]$ when $1 - 3t^2 = 0$.

Taking a curve in 3-space as a second illustration, consider

$$\gamma: \begin{cases} x = \sin(2\pi t) \\ y = \cos(2\pi t) \\ z = 2t - t^2 \end{cases} \qquad 0 \le t \le 2$$

In graphing the trace of this curve, it is helpful to observe that

$$x^2 + y^2 = 1,$$

for all t (see Fig. 6-11). It is a closed curve, but is not simple since $t = \frac{1}{2}$ and $t = \frac{3}{2}$ both correspond to the point $(0, -1, \frac{3}{4})$. We have $\gamma'(t) = (2\pi\cos(2\pi t),\ -2\pi\sin(2\pi t),\ 2 - 2t)$. At $t = 0$, this becomes $(2\pi, 0, 2)$ and at $t = 2$, $(2\pi, 0, -2)$, so that the curve has two tangent lines at the point $(0, 1, 0)$ which is at once the first and last point on γ.

As with general transformations, a curve γ is said to be of **class C^m** if the coordinate functions which describe the curve are of class C^m, and to be **analytic** if the coordinate functions are analytic, that is, representable by power series. All the examples that we have discussed are analytic curves, and may be represented in the form

$$\gamma(t) = \gamma(c) + \gamma'(c)(t-c) + \frac{\gamma''(c)(t-c)^2}{2!} + \cdots$$

convergent for all t in a neighborhood of c. In this Taylor series repre-

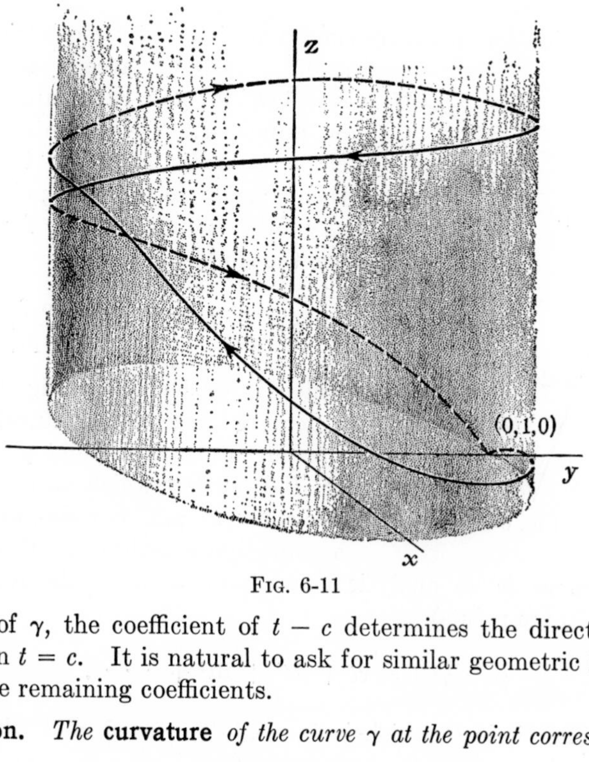

FIG. 6-11

sentation of γ, the coefficient of $t - c$ determines the direction of the curve when $t = c$. It is natural to ask for similar geometric interpretations of the remaining coefficients.

Definition. *The* **curvature** *of the curve γ at the point corresponding to $t = c$ is*

(6-17) $$k = \frac{\sqrt{|\gamma'(c)|^2|\gamma''(c)|^2 - (\gamma'(c)\cdot\gamma''(c))^2}}{|\gamma'(c)|^3}.$$

If γ is the circle $\gamma(t) = (R\cos t, R\sin t)$, then

$$\gamma'(t) = (-R\sin t, R\cos t),$$

and $\gamma''(t) = (-R\cos t, -R\sin t)$ so that for any point on γ,

$$k = \frac{\sqrt{R^2R^2 - 0}}{R^3} = \frac{1}{R}$$

Thus, the curvature of a circle is constant, and is the reciprocal of the radius. For a straight line, $\gamma''(t) = 0$ for all t, so that $k = 0$. With the curve given in (6-16), $\gamma'(t) = (1 - 3t^2, 2t - 1)$ and $\gamma''(t) = (-6t, 2)$ so that the curvatures at the multiple point (0, 0) are

$$k_1 = \frac{\sqrt{(2)(4) - (-2)^2}}{(\sqrt{2})^3} = \frac{1}{\sqrt{2}}$$

and

$$k_2 = \frac{\sqrt{(5)(40) - (14)^2}}{(\sqrt{5})^3} = \frac{2}{5\sqrt{5}}.$$

? same pt, two values! how? t = ( ) not (x, y) = !!!

This definition for curvature can be motivated by geometric considerations. Let us accept the formula $k = 1/R$ for the curvature of a circle of radius R. To compute this for a circle C, it is sufficient to be given the tangent to C at a point p_0, and any other point p on C, for one may use the simple relation

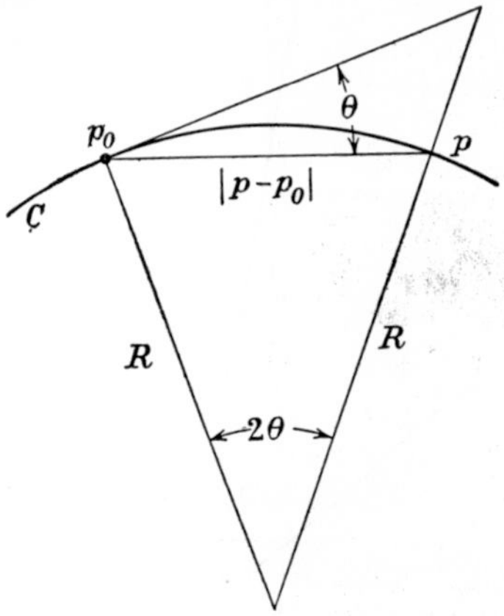

FIG. 6-12

$$k = \frac{1}{R} = \frac{2 \sin \theta}{|p - p_0|} \tag{6-18}$$

which is evident from Fig. 6-12. For a general curve, it is natural to define the curvature at a point p_0 by means of the circles which are tangent to the curve at p_0. For simplicity, let us assume that p_0 is the origin $\mathbf{0}$, and assume that the curve is an analytic curve expressible in the form (where $\mathbf{v}, \mathbf{A}, \mathbf{B}, \ldots$ are points)

$$p = \gamma(t) = \mathbf{v}t + \mathbf{A}t^2 + \mathbf{B}t^3 + \cdots. \tag{6-19}$$

Construct the circle C which is tangent to γ at $\mathbf{0}$, and which passes through p. Let this have curvature $k(t)$. Then, we may define the curvature of γ at $\mathbf{0}$ to be $k = \lim_{t \to 0} k(t)$. We shall show that for a curve such as the one above, this limit exists, and is given by the formula (6-17) which was first given above. Using the relation (6-18) and the fact that $p_0 = \mathbf{0}$, we have

$$k(t) = \frac{2 \sin \theta}{|p|}$$

where θ is the angle between the tangent to γ at $\mathbf{0}$ and the line from

0 to p. We recall that the tangent has the direction of **v**, so that

$$\cos\theta = \frac{(p \cdot \mathbf{v})}{|p|\,|\mathbf{v}|}.$$

This leads to

$$[k(t)]^2 = 4\left\{\frac{|p|^2|\mathbf{v}|^2(\sin\theta)^2}{|p|^4|\mathbf{v}|^2}\right\} = 4\left\{\frac{|p|^2|\mathbf{v}|^2 - (p\cdot\mathbf{v})^2}{|p|^4|\mathbf{v}|^2}\right\}.$$

From (6-19) we have

$$\begin{aligned} |p|^2 = p \cdot p &= (\mathbf{v}t + \mathbf{A}t^2 + \mathbf{B}t^3 + \cdots)\cdot(\mathbf{v}t + \mathbf{A}t^2 + \mathbf{B}t^3 + \cdots) \\ &= |\mathbf{v}|^2t^2 + 2(\mathbf{v}\cdot\mathbf{A})t^3 + \{2(\mathbf{v}\cdot\mathbf{B}) + |\mathbf{A}|^2\}t^4 + \cdots \\ |p|^2|\mathbf{v}|^2 &= |\mathbf{v}|^4t^2 + 2|\mathbf{v}|^2(\mathbf{v}\cdot\mathbf{A})t^3 + \{2|\mathbf{v}|^2(\mathbf{v}\cdot\mathbf{B}) + |\mathbf{v}|^2|\mathbf{A}|^2\}t^4 + \cdots \\ (p\cdot\mathbf{v})^2 &= \{|\mathbf{v}|^2t + (\mathbf{v}\cdot\mathbf{A})t^2 + (\mathbf{v}\cdot\mathbf{B})t^3 + \cdots\}^2 \\ &= |\mathbf{v}|^4t^2 + 2|\mathbf{v}|^2(\mathbf{v}\cdot\mathbf{A})t^3 + \{2|\mathbf{v}|^2(\mathbf{v}\cdot\mathbf{B}) + (\mathbf{v}\cdot\mathbf{A})^2\}t^4 + \cdots \end{aligned}$$

Thus, the numerator of the fraction whose value is $[k(t)]^2$ is

$$|p|^2|\mathbf{v}|^2 - (p\cdot\mathbf{v})^2 = \{|\mathbf{v}|^2|\mathbf{A}|^2 - (\mathbf{v}\cdot\mathbf{A})^2\}t^4 + \cdots.$$

The denominator is

$$\begin{aligned} |p|^4|\mathbf{v}|^2 &= |\mathbf{v}|^2\{|\mathbf{v}|^4t^4 + 4|\mathbf{v}|^2(\mathbf{v}\cdot\mathbf{A})t^5 + \cdots\} \\ &= |\mathbf{v}|^6t^4 + \cdots. \end{aligned}$$

Hence
$$[k(t)]^2 = 4\,\frac{|\mathbf{v}|^2|\mathbf{A}|^2 - (\mathbf{v}\cdot\mathbf{A})^2 + t\{\cdots\}}{|\mathbf{v}|^6 + t\{\cdots\}}$$

so that
$$k = \lim_{t\to 0} k(t) = \frac{2\{|\mathbf{v}|^2|\mathbf{A}|^2 - (\mathbf{v}\cdot\mathbf{A})^2\}^{1/2}}{|\mathbf{v}|^3}$$

Since $\mathbf{v} = \gamma'(0)$ and $2\mathbf{A} = \gamma''(0)$, this can be also given as

$$k = \frac{\{|\gamma'(0)|^2|\gamma''(0)|^2 - (\gamma'(0)\cdot\gamma''(0))^2\}^{1/2}}{|\gamma'(0)|^3}$$

in agreement with the previous definition, (6-17).†

We next take up the important subject of **arc length.** If γ is a smooth curve defined for $a \le t \le b$, then we could define the length of γ by the formula

(6-20) $$L(\gamma) = \int_a^b |\gamma'(t)|\,dt.$$

† Further discussion of the geometrical nature of a curve and the significance of the higher-order coefficients in (6-19) is omitted. The interested reader is urged to consult any text on classical differential geometry, for example, W. C. Graustein, "Differential Geometry," The Macmillan Company, New York, 1935; E. P. Lane, "Metric Differential Geometry of Curves and Surfaces," University of Chicago Press, Chicago, 1940; D. J. Struik, "Lectures on Classical Differential Geometry," Addison-Wesley Publishing Company, Cambridge, Mass., 1950.

In 3-space, this takes the form

$$L(\gamma) = \int_a^b \left\{\left(\frac{dx}{dt}\right)^2 + \left(\frac{dy}{dt}\right)^2 + \left(\frac{dz}{dt}\right)^2\right\}^{1/2} dt.$$

Alternatively, this formula can be obtained by starting with a geometrical definition for the length of a curve. Given γ let us choose a subdivision of the interval $[a, b]$ by points t_j, $a = t_0 < t_1 \cdots < t_n = b$, and set $P_j = \gamma(t_j)$. The consecutive line segments joining P_0 to P_1, P_1 to P_2, . . . , form a polygonal path C. Since each point P_j lies on γ, we speak of C as inscribed in γ. For such a polygon, we define length by

$$\begin{aligned} L(C) &= |P_0 - P_1| + |P_1 - P_2| + \cdots \\ &= \sum_{j=0}^{n-1} |\gamma(t_{j+1}) - \gamma(t_j)|. \end{aligned}$$

Intuitively, the length of γ itself will exceed that of any of these inscribed polygons. This suggests that we adopt the following definition.

Definition. *The length of a continuous curve γ is defined to be the least upper bound of the numbers $L(C)$, where C ranges over all polygons inscribed in γ.*

When the set of numbers $L(C)$ has no finite upper bound, then we write $L(\gamma) = \infty$, and say that γ has infinite length. If $L(\gamma) < \infty$, then γ is said to be **rectifiable.**

Theorem 5. *If γ is a smooth curve whose domain is the interval $[a, b]$ then γ is rectifiable, and $L(\gamma)$ is given by formula* (6-20).

We shall prove this for curves in the plane; the proof of the general case follows the same method. Consider a general inscribed polygon C. The length of the jth segment is

$$|\gamma(t_{j+1}) - \gamma(t_j)| = \{[X(t_{j+1}) - X(t_j)]^2 + [Y(t_{j+1}) - Y(t_j)]^2\}^{1/2}$$

where we have written the curve as $x = X(t)$, $y = Y(t)$, $a \le t \le b$. Since X and Y are differentiable functions, we may use the mean value theorem and write the right side as

$$\{[X'(\tau_j')(t_{j+1} - t_j)]^2 + [Y'(\tau_j'')(t_{j+1} - t_j)]^2\}^{1/2} = \{[X'(\tau_j')]^2 + [Y'(\tau_j'')]^2\}^{1/2} \Delta t_j$$

where $\Delta t_j = t_{j+1} - t_j$ and τ_j' and τ_j'' are two points in the interval $[t_j, t_{j+1}]$. Thus,

$$L(C) = \sum_{j=0}^{n-1} \{[X'(\tau_j')]^2 + [Y'(\tau_j'')]^2\}^{1/2} \Delta t_j.$$

This closely resembles a Riemann sum for the definite integral $\int_a^b f(t)\, dt$, where $f(t) = \{[X'(t)]^2 + [Y'(t)]^2\}^{1/2}$. In fact, it would be one if the points in each pair τ_j', τ_j'' were to coincide. Introduce a special function F by

$$F(t', t'') = \{[X'(t')]^2 + [Y'(t'')]^2\}^{1/2},$$

and observe that $F(t, t) = f(t)$ while

$$L(C) = \sum_{j=0}^{n-1} F(\tau_j', \tau_j'') \, \Delta t_j.$$

Since γ is smooth, F is continuous in the closed rectangle R consisting of the points (t', t'') with $a \leq t' \leq b$, $a \leq t'' \leq b$. Accordingly, F is uniformly continuous in R; given ϵ, we may choose δ so that $|F(p) - F(q)| < \epsilon$ whenever p and q lie in R and $|p - q| < \delta$. In particular, we shall have

$$|F(\tau_j', \tau_j'') - F(t_j, t_j)| < \epsilon$$

or equivalently,

$$|F(\tau_j', \tau_j'') - f(t_j)| < \epsilon$$

whenever τ_j' and τ_j'' lie in an interval $[t_j, t_{j+1}]$ with $\Delta t_j < \delta$. Assuming that the subdivision of $[a, b]$ has mesh less than δ, we obtain

$$\left| \sum_{j=0}^{n-1} F(\tau_j', \tau_j'') \, \Delta t_j - \sum_{=0}^{n-1} f(t_j) \, \Delta t_j \right| \leq \sum_{0}^{n-1} |F(\tau_j', \tau_j'') - f(t_j)| \, \Delta t_j$$

$$\leq \epsilon \sum_{0}^{n-1} \Delta t_j = \epsilon(b - a).$$

However, $\sum_{0}^{n-1} F(\tau_j', \tau_j'') \, \Delta t_j = L(C)$, while $\sum_{0}^{n-1} f(t_j) \, \Delta t_j$ is a Riemann sum for the integral $\int_a^b f$, so that we find that $L(C)$ approaches this integral as the mesh size of the subdivision decreases. Since $L(\gamma)$ is the least upper bound of the numbers $L(C)$, and since $L(C)$ increases (or at worst, remains the same) when an additional subdivision point is introduced, we also have $L(\gamma) = \int_a^b f$, the desired formula. ▮

For example, let us find the length of the helical curve $x = \cos t$, $y = \sin t$, $z = t^{3/2}$ for $0 \leq t \leq 4$. The function f is

$$f(t) = |\gamma'(t)| = \{(-\sin t)^2 + (\cos t)^2 + ((3/2)t^{1/2})^2\}^{1/2}$$
$$= \sqrt{1 + (9/4)t}$$

so that its length is $\int_0^4 \sqrt{1 + (9/4)t} \, dt = \dfrac{80\sqrt{10} - 8}{27}$.

As we have seen, different curves may have the same trace. Some of these curves are closely related and have many properties in common.

Definition. *Two curves γ and γ^* are said to be parametrically* **equivalent** *when the following conditions hold:* (i) *γ is a continuous mapping from an interval $[a, b]$ into E^n;* (ii) *γ^* is a continuous mapping from an interval $[\alpha, \beta]$ into E^n;* (iii) *there is a continuous function f which maps $[\alpha, \beta]$ onto $[a, b]$ one-to-one with $f(\alpha) = a$, $f(\beta) = b$ and with $\gamma^*(t) = \gamma(f(t))$ for all t in $[\alpha, \beta]$.*

Briefly, this means that γ and γ^* are connected by a reversible change of parameter. For example, the following three curves are equivalent.

$$\begin{cases} x = t \\ y = t^2 \end{cases} \quad \begin{cases} x = t^2 \\ y = t^4 \end{cases} \quad \begin{cases} x = \tfrac{1}{2}(1 + t^{1/3}) \\ y = \tfrac{1}{4}(1 + 2t^{1/3} + t^{2/3}) \end{cases}$$
$$0 \le t \le 1 \qquad 0 \le t \le 1 \qquad -1 \le t \le 1$$

It should be noticed that the second of these is not smooth, due to the fact that $dx/dt = dy/dt = 0$ when $t = 0$, while the third is not even of class C' at $t = 0$.

In speaking of equivalence of smooth curves, more is required of the function f. When γ and γ^* are smooth, then they are parametrically equivalent (**smoothly** equivalent) if there is a function f of class C' such that $\gamma^*(t) = \gamma(f(t))$ and $f'(t) > 0$ for all t. The effect of the last condition is to ensure that the inverse of f is also of class C'.

The relation of equivalence separates the class of all smooth curves into classes of mutually equivalent curves. All the curves in any one equivalence class have the same trace, and also share other geometric properties. We cite the next two results as examples.

Theorem 6. *Let γ_1 and γ_2 be smoothly equivalent smooth curves, and let p be a simple point on their trace. Then, γ_1 and γ_2 have the same direction at p.*

Let $\gamma_2(t) = \gamma_1(f(t))$, where $f'(t) > 0$ for all t. If $p = \gamma_2(c)$, then $p = \gamma_1(c^*)$, where $c^* = f(c)$. To find the direction of γ_2 at p, we write

$$\gamma_2'(t) = \frac{d}{dt}\gamma_1(f(t)) = \gamma_1'(f(t))\, f'(t)$$

so that
$$\gamma_2'(c) = \gamma_1'(f(c))\, f'(c) = \gamma_1'(c^*)f'(c).$$

The direction of γ_2 at p is therefore

$$\frac{\gamma_2'(c)}{|\gamma_2'(c)|} = \frac{\gamma_1'(c^*)f'(c)}{|\gamma_1'(c^*)f'(c)|} = \frac{\gamma_1'(c^*)}{|\gamma_1'(c^*)|}$$

which is thus the same as the direction† of γ_1 at p. ▌

If the function f is assumed to be of class C'', then a similar computation shows that γ_1 and γ_2 have also the same curvature at p (see also Exercises 5, 13, and 9). Equivalent curves also have the same length.

† Note that the velocity vectors $\mathbf{v}$ of γ_1 and γ_2 may be different at p.

Theorem 7. *If* γ_1 *and* γ_2 *are smoothly equivalent curves, then* $L(\gamma_1) = L(\gamma_2)$.

Assume that $\gamma_2(t) = \gamma_1(f(t))$ for $a \le t \le b$. Then, as before,

$$\gamma_2'(t) = \gamma_1'(f(t))\, f'(t).$$

Since $f'(t)$ is never negative, $|\gamma_2'(t)| = |\gamma_1'(f(t))|f'(t)$

and $$L(\gamma_2) = \int_a^b |\gamma_2'(t)|\, dt = \int_a^b |\gamma_1'(f(t))|f'(t)\, dt.$$

Putting $s = f(t)$ and $\alpha = f(a)$, $\beta = f(b)$, this becomes

$$L(\gamma_2) = \int_\alpha^\beta |\gamma_1'(s)|\, ds = L(\gamma_1). \quad \blacksquare$$

In the equivalence class containing a smooth γ, one curve has a special role. This is obtained by using arc length as a parameter. If γ is defined on the interval $[a, b]$, define a function g by

$$g(t) = \int_a^t |\gamma'|$$

Then, $g'(t) = |\gamma'(t)|$ for all t, $a \le t \le b$ and $g(a) = 0$, $g(b) = L(\gamma) = l$, so that g is a C' one-to-one map of $[a, b]$ onto $[0, l]$. Its inverse, which we call f, maps $[0, l]$ onto $[a, b]$ and is also of class C'. Let $\gamma^*(t) = \gamma(f(t))$; γ^* is then a smooth curve which is equivalent to γ, and is distinguished among all the curves equivalent to γ by the fact that $\left|\dfrac{d}{dt}\gamma^*(t)\right| = 1$ for all t. Many of the formulas involving curves take on a simpler form for such curves (see Exercises 7, 8, and 9.)

Equivalence classes of curves have been introduced in topology and differential geometry to obtain alternative definitions for the notion of "curve." In this approach, a curve is no longer an individual mapping γ, but is, instead, an entire **equivalence class** of such mappings, under a prescribed collection of permissible parameter changes. Depending upon the nature of these, special designations are used such as "Frechet curve," "Lebesgue curve," etc., when one wishes to refer to the individual equivalence classes.† As an example, let us consider briefly the notion of an **algebraic curve.** One of the simplest ways in which a curve in the plane can be given is by an equation of the form $y = f(x)$; this can be thrown at once into a standard parametric form $x = t$, $y = f(t)$. One also says that an equation of the form $F(x, y) = 0$ specifies a curve. In a sense, one is again speaking of equivalence classes here, the class of all curves $x = \phi(t)$, $y = \psi(t)$ which satisfy the equation $F(\phi(t), \psi(t)) = 0$.

† For an amplification of this and a guide to the literature, the reader should read the brief article by J. W. T. Youngs, Curves and Surfaces, *Am. Math. Monthly*, vol. 51, pp. 1–11, 1944.

If F is a polynomial in x and y, then one may restrict ϕ and ψ to be rational functions of t, and thus discuss the class of curves which are equivalent to a given curve under one-to-one birational correspondences. For example the circle $x^2 + y^2 = 1$ has the rational parametrization $x = (1 - t^2)/(1 + t^2)$, $y = 2t/(1 + t^2)$. The situation becomes considerably more complicated when we turn to space curves. Here, one deals with pairs of algebraic equations, $F(x, y, z) = 0$, and $G(x, y, z) = 0$; again, with this one may associate a class of curves $x = \phi(t)$, $y = \psi(t)$, $z = \theta(t)$ which satisfy both equations for all t and whose coordinate functions ϕ, ψ, θ are of specified sort, for example, rational functions.†

We may also consider the effect on a curve of a transformation which is applied to the space containing its trace. If γ is a curve whose trace lies in a region D and T is a continuous transformation which maps D onto a region D^*, then T carries γ into a curve γ^* lying in D^* defined by $\gamma^*(t) = T(\gamma(t))$. If T is one-to-one in a neighborhood N of p_0 and γ is a simple closed curve lying in N, then γ^* is a simple closed curve lying in $T(N)$. Suppose that D and D^* are each sets in the plane. As p moves along the trace of γ, $T(p)$ will move along the trace of γ^*. They may move in the same direction—i.e., both clockwise, or both counterclockwise—or they may move in opposite directions. When the first holds for all simple closed curves γ in N, T is said to be **orientation preserving**; when the second holds, T is said to be **orientation reversing.**‡ When T is a nonsingular linear transformation, this may be determined by the sign of det (T); if det (T) is positive, T is orientation preserving, and if det (T) is negative, T is orientation reversing. For a general transformation of the plane, the same role is played by the sign of the Jacobian. For example, the transformation

$$T: \begin{cases} u = x^2 - y^2 \\ v = 2xy \end{cases} \tag{6-21}$$

has Jacobian $4(x^2 + y^2)$ which is never negative. T is therefore orientation preserving at all points of the plane, with the possible exception of the origin. Here, the Jacobian is zero; examining the image of a general curve γ which loops around the origin, one sees that T preserves the orientation of γ, but not its winding number. In Fig. 6-13, the curve

† An introduction to the modern theory of algebraic curves is to be found in the book by R. J. Walker, "Algebraic Curves," vol. 13, Princeton Mathematical Series, Princeton University Press, Princeton, New Jersey, 1950.

‡ This discussion is intended to be intuitive and nonrigorous. An adequate treatment would require the concept of the degree of a mapping at a point. For curves, this can be related to the **winding number** of a closed curve with respect to a point; this counts the number of times that a closed curve loops around a point, with a counterclockwise revolution counting as 1, and a clockwise revolution counting as -1.

γ_2 which loops the origin once has an image γ_2^* which loops the origin twice. There is a similar theory for transformations from E^n into E^n; again, T is orientation preserving in a region D if the Jacobian of T is everywhere positive in D, and orientation reversing in D if the Jacobian is everywhere negative. The behavior of T near points where $J(P) = 0$

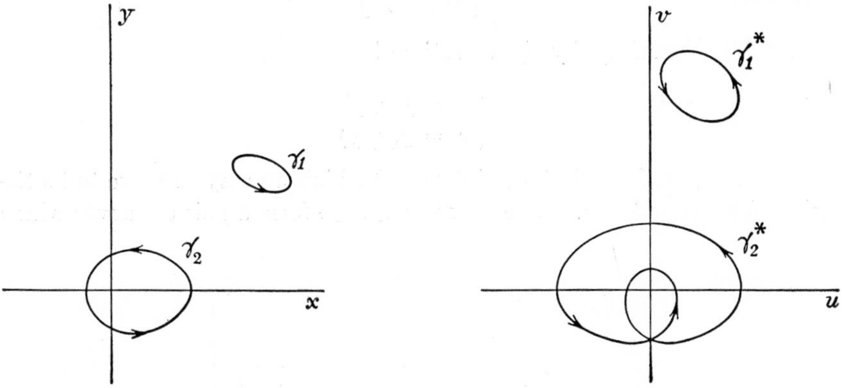

FIG. 6-13

is indeterminate. In 3-space, the notion of "orientation preserving" can be visualized in terms of a spherical surface enclosing a point p_0 and its image under T (see Fig. 6-14).

We may also examine the effect which a transformation has upon angles at a point. If two smooth curves, γ_1 and γ_2 pass through a point

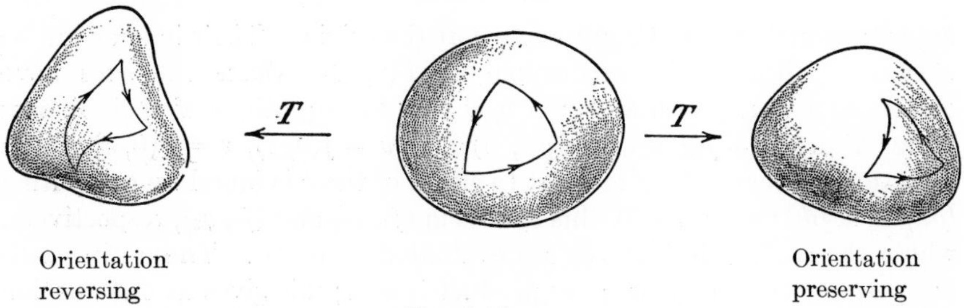

FIG. 6-14

p_0, their images under T will pass through $T(p_0)$. Let θ be the angle between γ_1 and γ_2 at p_0. (More precisely, θ is the angle between the tangent lines to γ_1 and γ_2 at p_0.) If T is of class C', then the image curves will be smooth, and we can speak of the angle θ^* which they form at $T(p_0)$ (see Fig. 6-15). T is said to be a **conformal** transformation if it is always true that $\theta^* = \theta$, and **directly conformal** if T is also orientation preserving.

Theorem 8. *Let p be a transformation from E^2 into E^2 which is of class C' in an open region D. Furthermore, let T be conformal and have a strictly positive Jacobian throughout D. Then, at each point of D, the differential of T has a matrix representation of the form*

$$\begin{bmatrix} A & B \\ -B & A \end{bmatrix}.$$

Let T be described by the equations†

$$\begin{cases} u = f(x, y) \\ v = g(x, y) \end{cases}$$

and let T be conformal at a point $p_0 \in D$ which we may suppose to be the origin for convenience. The coordinate axes form a pair of curves which

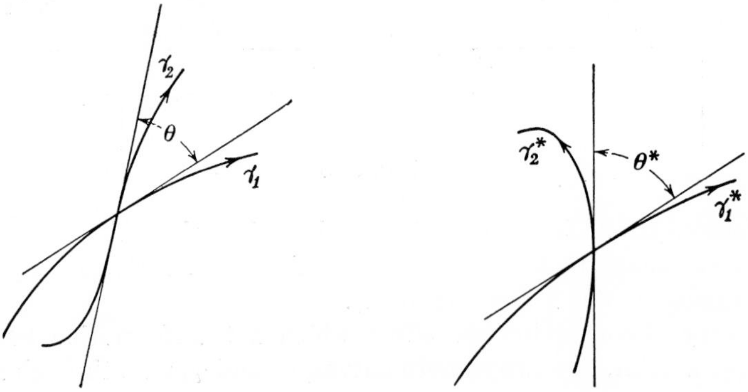

FIG. 6-15

are orthogonal (meet at right angles) at the origin. Their images will be curves which must be orthogonal at $T(0, 0)$. Since the axes have equations $x = t$, $y = 0$ and $x = 0$, $y = t$, the equations of their images under T are $u = f(t, 0)$, $v = g(t, 0)$ and $u = f(0, t)$, $v = g(0, t)$. The direction numbers of the tangent to either of these is found by computing $(du/dt, dv/dt)$; when $t = 0$, this results in (f_1, g_1) and (f_2, g_2), respectively, where the partial derivatives are evaluated at $(0, 0)$. These directions are perpendicular if their inner product is zero; this gives us one relation connecting the functions f and g, namely,

$$f_1 f_2 + g_1 g_2 = 0. \tag{6-22}$$

To obtain a second relation, we consider another pair of orthogonal lines

† Since

$$dT = \begin{bmatrix} u_x & u_y \\ v_x & v_y \end{bmatrix},$$

the conclusion of the theorem may be given as $u_x = v_y$, $u_y = -v_x$. These are called the **Cauchy-Riemann equations.**

through the origin; we choose the lines of slopes 1 and -1 with equations $x = t$, $y = t$ and $x = t$, $y = -t$. Their images are the curves $u = f(t, t)$, $v = g(t, t)$ and $u = f(t, -t)$, $v = g(t, -t)$. At $t = 0$, the tangents to these have direction numbers $(f_1 + f_2, g_1 + g_2)$ and $(f_1 - f_2, g_1 - g_2)$; since these must be perpendicular,

$$0 = (f_1^2 - f_2^2) + (g_1^2 - g_2^2). \tag{6-23}$$

Multiplying this by f_2^2 and making use of (6-22),

$$\begin{aligned} 0 &= f_1^2f_2^2 + g_1^2f_2^2 - (f_2^2 + g_2^2)f_2^2 \\ &= g_1^2g_2^2 + g_1^2f_2^2 - (f_2^2 + g_2^2)f_2^2 \\ &= (f_2^2 + g_2^2)(g_1^2 - f_2^2). \end{aligned}$$

If the first factor were zero, then $f_2 = g_2 = 0$ and the Jacobian

$$\frac{\partial(u, v)}{\partial(x, y)} = f_1g_2 - f_2g_1$$

would be zero. Thus, $g_1^2 = f_2^2$. Returning to (6-23), we must also have $f_1^2 = g_2^2$, so that $g_1 = \pm f_2$ and $g_2 = \pm f_1$. If the choice of signs were the same in each, then (6-22) would hold only if all the quantities were zero, and the Jacobian of T would again be zero; thus, we either have $f_2 = g_1$ and $f_1 = -g_2$ or we have $f_2 = -g_1$ and $f_1 = g_2$. In the first event, dT, which is

$$\begin{bmatrix} f_1 & f_2 \\ g_1 & g_2 \end{bmatrix}$$

would have the form

$$\begin{bmatrix} A & B \\ B & -A \end{bmatrix}.$$

This can be ruled out, since a matrix of this form always has a negative determinant, while T has a positive Jacobian. When the second possibility holds, dT has the form

$$\begin{bmatrix} A & B \\ -B & A \end{bmatrix}$$

as stated in the theorem. (The entries, of course, need not be constants; we are only describing the form of the matrix.) ▮

The converse of this theorem is also true; if T is a transformation of class C' whose differential is represented by a matrix of the form

$$\begin{bmatrix} A & B \\ -B & A \end{bmatrix}$$

at each point of a region D, then T is conformal at all points of D, except those where the Jacobian is zero (see Exercise 11). An example of a conformal transformation is supplied by that given in (6-21). The differential of T at (x, y) is

$$\begin{bmatrix} 2x & -2y \\ 2y & 2x \end{bmatrix}$$

which has the required form; T is therefore conformal everywhere in the plane, except at the origin. It fails to be conformal there; two lines through the origin which form the angle θ have as images two lines forming the angle 2θ (see Fig. 6-16).

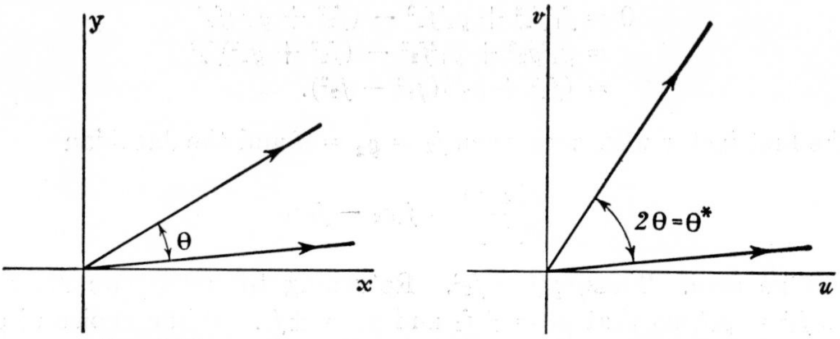

FIG. 6-16. $u = x^2 - y^2 = \rho^2 \cos 2\phi$, $v = 2xy = \rho^2 \sin 2\phi$.

It may be shown that there is no similar extensive class of transformations of E^n into itself, with $n > 2$. If such a transformation T is required to be conformal throughout an open set, then it may be shown that T is necessarily a linear transformation plus a translation, where the linear part is represented by an orthogonal matrix; thus, the only conformal transformations of 3-space into itself are the ordinary rigid motions.

EXERCISES

1. Plot the trace of the plane curve $x = t^2$, $y = t^3 - 4t$ for $-\infty < t < \infty$. Find the tangents at the double point.
2. Find the curvature of the helical curve of Fig. 6-11 at the double point.
3. Express the length of the loop of the curve (6-16) as a definite integral.
4. Prove Theorem 5 when γ is a curve in 3-space.
5. If γ_1 and γ_2 are smoothly equivalent curves of class C'' and if the parameter change is effected by a function f which is also of class C'', show that γ_1 and γ_2 have the same curvature at corresponding points.
6. Find the curvature of the curve $x = t^2 - 2t$, $y = 3t$, $z = -t^3$, $w = t - t^2$ at the origin.
7. Show that for a curve which has arc length as the parameter, the curvature is given by $k = |\gamma''(t)|$.
8. If γ is the curve given by $y = f(x)$, show that the curvature is given by

$$k = \frac{|f''(x)|}{(1 + f'(x)^2)^{3/2}}$$

and the length of γ between $x = a$ and $x = b$ by $\int_a^b \{1 + f'(x)^2\}^{1/2}\, dx$.

×9. If γ is a curve which satisfies the equation $F(x, y) = 0$, show that the curvature at a point on γ is given by

$$k = \frac{|F_{11}F_2^2 + F_{22}F_1^2 - 2F_1F_2F_{12}|}{|F_1^2 + F_2^2|^{3/2}}$$

10. Prove the converse of Theorem 8.

11. Apply Exercise 10 to show that the transformation

$$u = x^3 - 3xy^2, \qquad v = 3x^2y - y^3$$

is directly conformal everywhere in the plane, except at the origin.

12. Let γ be a curve in 3-space which satisfies both of the equations $f(x, y, z) = 0$, $g(x, y, z) = 0$. Show that the direction of γ at a point on it has direction components

$$\left(\begin{vmatrix} f_2 & f_3 \\ g_2 & g_3 \end{vmatrix}, \begin{vmatrix} f_3 & f_1 \\ g_3 & g_1 \end{vmatrix}, \begin{vmatrix} f_1 & f_2 \\ g_1 & g_2 \end{vmatrix} \right)$$

***13.** Let γ_1 and γ_2 be two simple curves which have the same trace, and which both start at (0, 0, 0) and end at (1, 1, 1). Show that γ_1 and γ_2 are parametrically equivalent.

14. Find a rational parametrization for the hyperbola $x^2 - y^2 = 4$.

15. What can be said about the nature of the curves of the form $x = a + bt + ct^2$, $y = A + Bt + Ct^2$?

— **16.** The graph of the equation $x^3 + y^3 = 3xy$ is known as the folium of Descartes. Show that a rational parametrization of this is $x = 3t/(1 + t^3)$, $y = 3t^2/(1 + t^3)$, and graph this curve.

— **17.** Find the length of one arch of the cycloid $x = a(t - \sin t)$, $y = a(1 - \cos t)$.

6.3. Surfaces and Surface Area

The theory of curves, as outlined in Sec. 6.2, can be presented in a manner which is relatively free of topological features. This is much more difficult to do for the theory of surfaces; for this reason, certain topics in the present section will be presented on the intuitive level. Many of the basic definitions are direct analogues of those for curves.

Definition. *A surface Σ in n-space is a transformation or mapping from E^2 into E^n.*

For example, the general continuous surface in 3-space can be expressed as a continuous transformation of the form

$$\Sigma: \begin{cases} x = \phi(u, v) \\ y = \psi(u, v) \\ z = \theta(u, v) \end{cases} \tag{6-24}$$

whose domain is a set D in the UV plane. A point p is said to **lie on** the surface Σ if $p = \Sigma(u, v)$ for some $(u, v) \in D$, and the set of all points that lie on Σ is called the **trace** or graph of the surface Σ. As with curves, many different surfaces can have the same trace. A point p lying on Σ is said to be a **multiple** point if it is the image of more than one point in the domain of Σ. A surface is **simple** if it has no multiple points; the mapping Σ is then one-to-one in D.

Any set D which lies on one of the coordinate XYZ planes is the trace of a simple surface which is obtained from the identity mapping; if D is contained in the XY plane, then the surface may be defined by $x = x$, $y = y$, $z = 0$, using x and y as parameters rather than u and v.

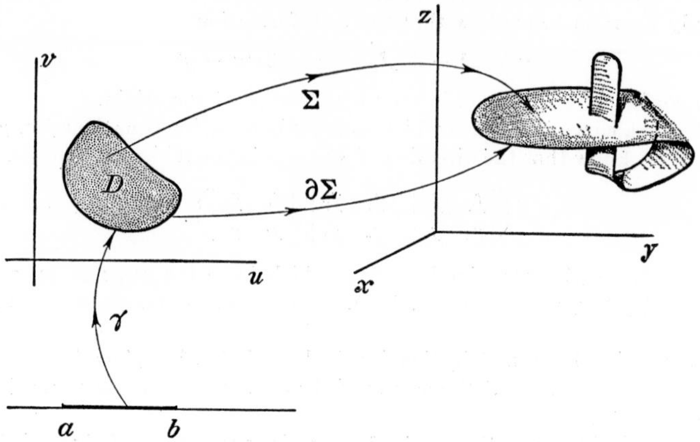

FIG. 6-17

Let Σ be a continuous surface whose domain D is such that its boundary is the trace of a simple closed curve γ defined for $a \leq t \leq b$. The image of γ under Σ is a closed curve Γ defined by $\Gamma(t) = \Sigma(\gamma(t))$ which is called the **boundary** or **edge** of Σ (see Fig. 6-17). We shall use $\partial\Sigma$ as a notation

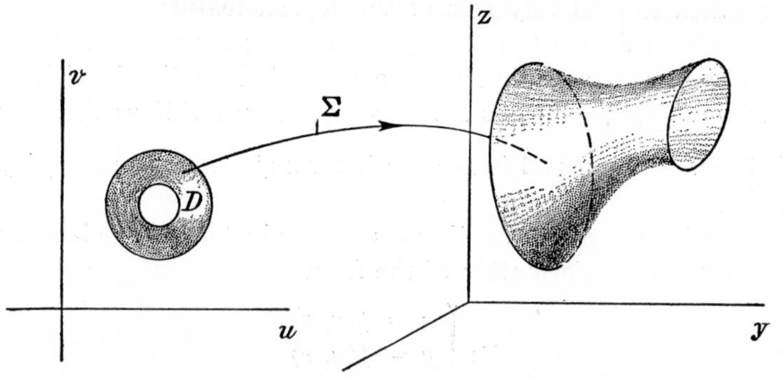

FIG. 6-18

for Γ. The trace of $\partial\Sigma$ is the image under Σ of the boundary of the set D. If the boundary of D is composed of several simple closed curves, $\partial\Sigma$ will be made up of several closed curves. If Σ is a simple surface, $\partial\Sigma$ will consist also of simple closed curves (see Fig. 6-18).

To obtain a nice theory, it is again convenient to impose certain differentiability requirements.

Definition. *A surface Σ is said to be smooth if Σ is of class C' and $d\Sigma$ is of rank 2 throughout D.*

When Σ is described by (6-24), then

$$d\Sigma \doteq \begin{bmatrix} \frac{\partial x}{\partial u} & \frac{\partial x}{\partial v} \\ \frac{\partial y}{\partial u} & \frac{\partial y}{\partial v} \\ \frac{\partial z}{\partial u} & \frac{\partial z}{\partial v} \end{bmatrix}$$

The requirement that this have rank 2 is equivalent to the assertion that the 2-by-2 determinants formed from this matrix do not all vanish at any point of D. This can also be given in the form [see (5-54)]:

$$\left|\frac{\partial(x, y)}{\partial(u, v)}\right|^2 + \left|\frac{\partial(y, z)}{\partial(u, v)}\right|^2 + \left|\frac{\partial(z, x)}{\partial(u, v)}\right|^2 > 0 \tag{6-25}$$

The significance of this condition is to be found in the fact that if (6-25)

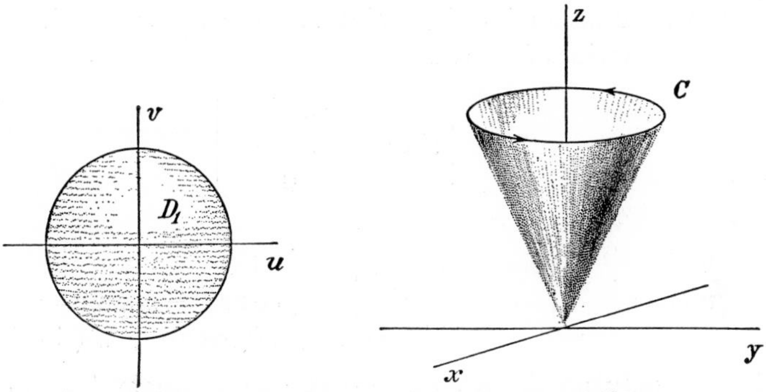

FIG. 6-19. Graph of Σ_1 and $\partial\Sigma_1$.

holds, Σ is locally one-to-one in D (see Theorem 30, Sec. 5.9.) It also corresponds to the intuitive notion of smoothness in the sense of "lack of sharp corners."

Consider, for example, the surfaces given by the following sets of equations

$$\Sigma_1: \begin{cases} x = u \\ y = v \\ z = \sqrt{u^2 + v^2} \end{cases} \qquad \Sigma_2: \begin{cases} x = u \cos v \\ y = u \sin v \\ z = u \end{cases}$$

$$D_1: u^2 + v^2 \leq 1 \qquad D_2: \begin{matrix} 0 \leq u \leq 1 \\ 0 \leq v \leq 2\pi \end{matrix}$$

The trace of each is a portion of the cone whose equation is $x^2 + y^2 = z^2$ (see Figs. 6-19 and 6-20). The edge of Σ_1 is the curve $\partial\Sigma_1$ whose trace is the circle C. The edge of Σ_2 is the curve $\partial\Sigma_2$ whose trace is the curve consisting of C and the line segment L taken twice, once in each direction. Σ_1 is not a smooth surface since $\partial z/\partial u = u/(u^2 + v^2)^{1/2}$ is not continuous at $u = 0$, $v = 0$; geometrically, this corresponds to the presence of the

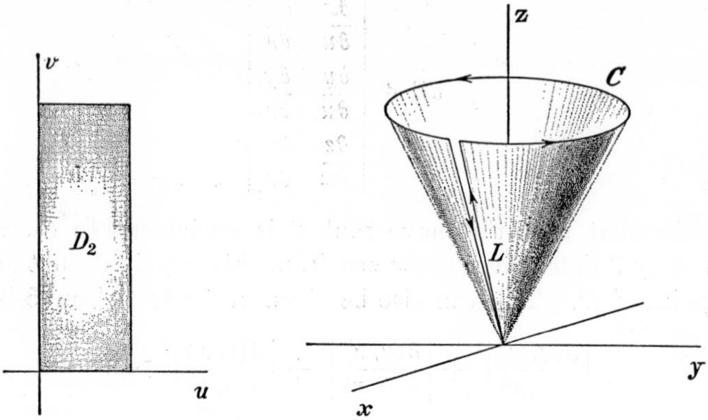

FIG. 6-20. Graph of Σ_2 and $\partial\Sigma_2$.

point of the cone as an interior point of the surface. Σ_2 is a smooth surface on the interior of D_2 since

$$d\Sigma_2 = \begin{bmatrix} \cos v & -u \sin v \\ \sin v & u \cos v \\ 1 & 0 \end{bmatrix}$$

and

$$\begin{vmatrix} \cos v & -u \sin v \\ \sin v & u \cos v \end{vmatrix}^2 + \begin{vmatrix} \sin v & u \cos v \\ 1 & 0 \end{vmatrix}^2 + \begin{vmatrix} 1 & 0 \\ \cos v & -u \sin v \end{vmatrix}^2$$
$$= u^2 + u^2(\cos v)^2 + u^2(\sin v)^2 = 2u^2$$

which is zero only on the edge $u = 0$ of the rectangle D_2. (The fact that the rank of dT is less than 2 when $u = 0$ is matched by the fact that the curve $\partial\Sigma_2$ sends this entire edge of D_2 into the point at the apex of the cone.)

Any equation of the form $z = f(x, y)$ will serve to define a surface, either by the equations $x = u$, $y = v$, $z = f(u, v)$, or simply $x = x$, $y = y$, $z = f(x, y)$. An equation of the form $F(x, y, z) = 0$ which can be solved locally for one of the variables leads similarly to one or more surfaces. Sometimes it is possible to obtain a single smooth surface whose trace is the entire set of points (x, y, z) satisfying the equation $F(x, y, z) = 0$. For example, a suitable choice for the unit sphere $x^2 + y^2 + z^2 = 1$ is

$$\text{(6-26)} \qquad \begin{cases} x = \cos u \sin v \\ y = \sin u \sin v \\ z = \cos v \end{cases}$$

where D is the set of (u, v) obeying $0 \leq u \leq 2\pi$, $0 \leq v \leq \pi$. The edge of this surface is the closed curve whose trace is the semicircular arc σ taken twice in opposite directions (see Fig. 6-21).

By the term "plane" we shall mean any surface of the form

$$p = \Sigma(u, v) = p_0 + \alpha u + \beta v \tag{6-27}$$

defined for all (u, v), where α and β are assumed nonparallel in order to satisfy condition (6-25). Since p_0, $p_0 + \alpha$, and $p_0 + \beta$ lie on Σ, the trace

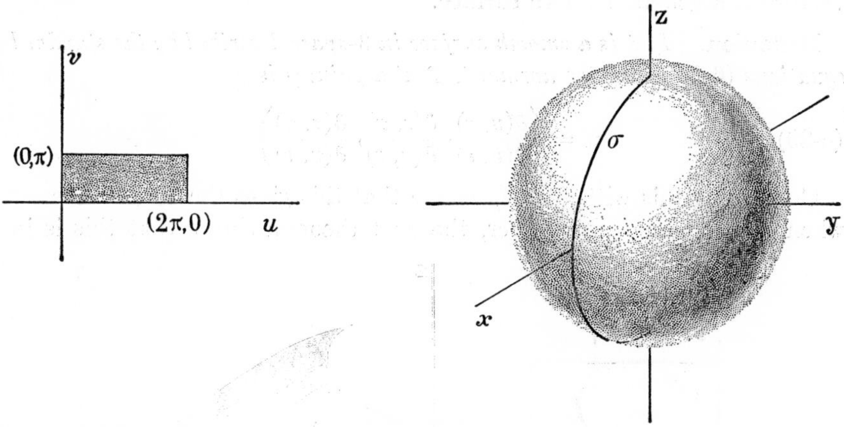

FIG. 6-21

of this surface contains these three noncollinear points. If the surface lies in 3-space and $\alpha = (a_1, a_2, a_3)$, $\beta = (b_1, b_2, b_3)$, $p_0 = (x_0, y_0, z_0)$, then (6-27) becomes

$$\Sigma: \begin{cases} x = x_0 + a_1 u + b_1 v \\ y = y_0 + a_2 u + b_2 v \\ z = z_0 + a_3 u + b_3 v. \end{cases} \tag{6-28}$$

Put $$A = \begin{vmatrix} a_2 & b_2 \\ a_3 & b_3 \end{vmatrix}, \quad B = \begin{vmatrix} a_3 & b_3 \\ a_1 & b_1 \end{vmatrix}, \quad C = \begin{vmatrix} a_1 & b_1 \\ a_2 & b_2 \end{vmatrix}$$

and $\mathbf{n} = (A, B, C)$. Then, from (6-28),

$$\begin{aligned} A(x - x_0) + B(y - y_0) + C(z - z_0) \\ &= A(a_1 u + b_1 v) + B(a_2 u + b_2 v) + C(a_3 u + b_3 v) \\ &= (Aa_1 + Ba_2 + Ca_3)u + (Ab_1 + Bb_2 + Cb_3)v \\ &= \begin{vmatrix} a_1 & a_1 & b_1 \\ a_2 & a_2 & b_2 \\ a_3 & a_3 & b_3 \end{vmatrix} u + \begin{vmatrix} b_1 & a_1 & b_1 \\ b_2 & a_2 & b_2 \\ b^3 & a_3 & b_3 \end{vmatrix} v \\ &= 0 + 0 = 0. \end{aligned}$$

Thus, every point (x, y, z) on the trace of Σ satisfies the equation

$$A(x - x_0) + B(y - y_0) + C(z - z_0) = 0,$$

which justifies our use of the word "plane" for the surface Σ. The requirement that Σ be smooth is equivalent to the condition $A^2 + B^2 + C^2 > 0$, and may thus be stated in the form $\mathbf{n} \neq \mathbf{0}$. In the analytical geometry of 3-space, the vector $\mathbf{n}$ is a set of direction numbers called the normal to the plane $A(x - x_0) + B(y - y_0) + C(z - z_0) = 0$. Since $(x - x_0, y - y_0, z - z_0) = \mathbf{v}$ is a vector from the point p_0 to the general point (x, y, z) on the plane, this equation asserts that $\mathbf{n} \cdot \mathbf{v} = 0$, and $\mathbf{n}$ and $\mathbf{v}$ are always orthogonal. By analogy, we may introduce a normal vector for a general smooth surface.

Definition. *If Σ is a smooth surface in 3-space described by the standard equations* (6-24), *then the normal to Σ at a point p is*

$$\mathbf{n} = \left(\frac{\partial(y, z)}{\partial(u, v)}, \frac{\partial(z, x)}{\partial(u, v)}, \frac{\partial(x, y)}{\partial(u, v)}\right) \tag{6-29}$$

Comparing this with (6-28), we see that this gives the correct answer when Σ is a plane. Moreover, the next theorem shows that this is in

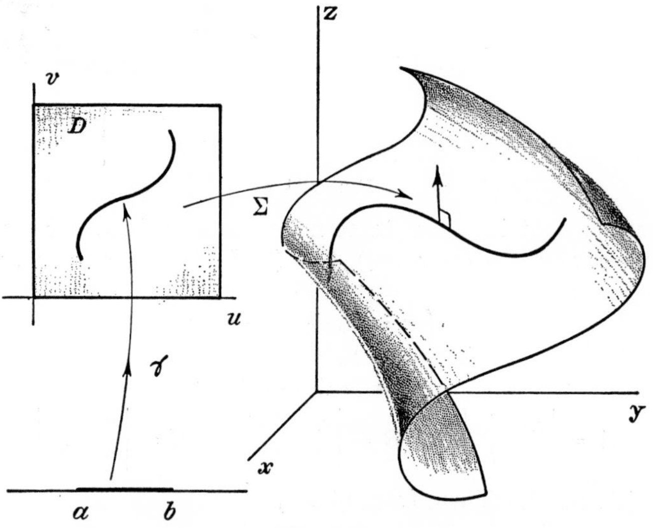

FIG. 6-22

agreement with the intuitive notion of the normal as a "direction which is orthogonal to the surface."

Theorem 9. *Let Σ be a smooth surface and p a point lying on Σ. Then, the normal to Σ at p is orthogonal to any smooth curve which lies on Σ and passes through p.*

Let Σ have domain D and let γ be any smooth curve whose trace lies in D. The mapping Σ carries γ into a curve Γ lying on the surface Σ (see Fig. 6-22). The equation of Γ is $\Gamma(t) = \Sigma(\gamma(t))$. Let us suppose that Γ passes through p when $t = 0$. The direction of Γ is determined by the vector $\mathbf{v} = \Gamma'(0)$. Since $\Gamma(t) = (x, y, z)$ where $(x, y, z) = \Sigma(u, v)$ and $(u, v) = \gamma(t)$, we apply the chain rule of differentiation to find that

$$\mathbf{v} = (d\Sigma)(d\gamma) = \left(\frac{\partial x}{\partial u}\frac{du}{dt} + \frac{\partial x}{\partial v}\frac{dv}{dt}, \quad \frac{\partial y}{\partial u}\frac{du}{dt} + \frac{\partial y}{\partial v}\frac{dv}{dt}, \quad \frac{\partial z}{\partial u}\frac{du}{dt} + \frac{dz}{\partial v}\frac{\partial v}{dt}\right)$$

The vectors $\mathbf{v}$ and $\mathbf{n}$ are orthogonal if $\mathbf{v} \cdot \mathbf{n} = 0$.

$$\begin{aligned}
\mathbf{v} \cdot \mathbf{n} &= \left(\frac{\partial x}{\partial u}\frac{du}{dt} + \frac{\partial x}{\partial v}\frac{dv}{dt}\right)\frac{\partial(y, z)}{\partial(u, v)} + \left(\frac{\partial y}{\partial u}\frac{du}{dt} + \frac{\partial y}{\partial v}\frac{dv}{dt}\right)\frac{\partial(z, x)}{\partial(u, v)} \\
&\qquad + \left(\frac{\partial z}{\partial u}\frac{du}{dt} + \frac{\partial z}{\partial v}\frac{dv}{dt}\right)\frac{\partial(x, y)}{\partial(u, v)} \\
&= \left(\frac{\partial x}{\partial u}\frac{\partial(y, z)}{\partial(u, v)} + \frac{\partial y}{\partial u}\frac{\partial(z, x)}{\partial(u, v)} + \frac{\partial z}{\partial u}\frac{\partial(x, y)}{\partial(u, v)}\right)\frac{du}{dt} \\
&\qquad + \left(\frac{\partial x}{\partial v}\frac{\partial(y, z)}{\partial(u, v)} + \frac{\partial y}{\partial v}\frac{\partial(z, x)}{\partial(u, v)} + \frac{\partial z}{\partial v}\frac{\partial(x, y)}{\partial(u, v)}\right)\frac{dv}{dt} \\
&= \begin{vmatrix} \frac{\partial x}{\partial u} & \frac{\partial x}{\partial u} & \frac{\partial x}{\partial v} \\ \frac{\partial y}{\partial u} & \frac{\partial y}{\partial u} & \frac{\partial y}{\partial v} \\ \frac{\partial z}{\partial u} & \frac{\partial z}{\partial u} & \frac{\partial z}{\partial v} \end{vmatrix}\frac{du}{dt} + \begin{vmatrix} \frac{\partial x}{\partial v} & \frac{\partial x}{\partial u} & \frac{\partial x}{\partial v} \\ \frac{\partial y}{\partial v} & \frac{\partial u}{\partial u} & \frac{\partial y}{\partial v} \\ \frac{\partial z}{\partial v} & \frac{\partial z}{\partial u} & \frac{\partial z}{\partial v} \end{vmatrix}\frac{dv}{dt} \\
&= 0\frac{du}{dt} + 0\frac{dv}{dt} = 0,
\end{aligned}$$

since a matrix with two columns alike has zero determinant. ▌

Two smooth surfaces in 3-space which pass through the same point p_0, and which have at p_0 normals pointing in the same or in opposite directions, are said to be **tangent** at p_0. The direction of the normal to the general plane (6-27) is specified by the vectors α and β; since

$$\Sigma(u, v) = p_0 + \alpha u + \beta v,$$

these may be obtained by partial differentiation, with

$$\alpha = \Sigma_u = \frac{\partial \Sigma}{\partial u} = \left(\frac{\partial x}{\partial u}, \frac{\partial y}{\partial u}, \frac{\partial z}{\partial u}\right)$$

and

$$\beta = \Sigma_v = \frac{\partial \Sigma}{\partial v} = \left(\frac{\partial x}{\partial v}, \frac{\partial y}{\partial v}, \frac{\partial z}{\partial v}\right).$$

The tangent plane to a smooth surface Σ at a point p_0 is therefore given by the equation

$$p = p_0 + \left(\frac{\partial \Sigma}{\partial u}\right)_{p_0} u + \left(\frac{\partial \Sigma}{\partial v}\right)_{p_0} v.$$

As with curves, a surface Σ is of **class C^m** if the coordinate functions are of class C^m, and is **analytic** if the coordinate functions are analytic, in the variables u and v. An analytic surface may be represented locally in the form of an absolutely convergent double series

$$\begin{aligned}\Sigma(u, v) &= \Sigma(u_0, v_0) + (u - u_0)\frac{\partial\Sigma}{\partial u} + (v - v_0)\frac{\partial\Sigma}{\partial v} \\ &\quad + \frac{1}{2}\left\{(u - u_0)^2\frac{\partial^2\Sigma}{\partial u^2} + 2(u - u_0)(v - v_0)\frac{\partial^2\Sigma}{\partial u\partial v}\right. \\ &\qquad\qquad \left. + (v - v_0)^2\frac{\partial^2\Sigma}{\partial v^2}\right\} + \cdots.\end{aligned}$$

The vectors Σ_u and Σ_v which are the coefficients of the first-degree terms, $u - u_0$ and $v - v_0$, determine the direction of the normal to Σ and thus the tangent plane.† The coefficients of the higher-degree terms serve to describe certain other geometrical data for the surfaces, such as curvature, etc. Again, we leave this, and refer an interested reader to any book on classical differential geometry.

We may also obtain a formula for the normal to a surface Σ when it is described by means of an equation $F(x, y, z) = 0$.

Theorem 10. *If Σ is a surface which satisfies the equation $F(x, y, z) = 0$, where F is of class C', then the normal to Σ at a simple point p_0 lying on Σ is a scalar multiple of $dF|_{p_0} = (F_1(p_0), F_2(p_0), F_3(p_0))$, unless this is $(0, 0, 0)$.*

Assume that Σ has the form $x = \phi(u, v)$, $y = \psi(u, v)$, $z = \theta(u, v)$ for $(u, v) \in D$. Then,

$$F(\phi(u, v), \psi(u, v), \theta(u, v)) = 0$$

for all $(u, v) \in D$. Differentiating, and setting $(u, v) = (u_0, v_0)$ so that $(x, y, z) = p_0$, we obtain

$$0 = F_1(p_0)\frac{\partial x}{\partial u} + F_2(p_0)\frac{\partial y}{\partial u} + F_3(p_0)\frac{\partial z}{\partial u}$$
$$0 = F_1(p_0)\frac{\partial x}{\partial v} + F_2(p_0)\frac{\partial y}{\partial v} + F_3(p_0)\frac{\partial z}{\partial v}$$

Setting $\beta = (F_1(p_0), F_2(p_0), F_3(p_0)) = dF\Big|_{p_0}$, these equations assert that β is orthogonal to both Σ_u and Σ_v at p_0; but, the normal vector $\mathbf{n}$ is also orthogonal to these, so that β is a multiple of $\mathbf{n}$. ▌

† In particular, the normal $\mathbf{n}$ is $\Sigma_u \times \Sigma_v$, the cross product (vector product) of Σ_u and Σ_v (see Exercise 9, Sec. 7.3). It may also be described as a vector orthogonal to both Σ_u and Σ_v (Exercise 9 of the present section).

We turn next to the topic of surface area.

Definition. *The area of a smooth surface* Σ *with domain* D *is defined to be*

$$A(\Sigma) = \iint_D |\mathbf{n}(u, v)|\, dudv$$

$$(6\text{-}30) \qquad = \iint_D \left\{\left|\frac{\partial(x, y)}{\partial(u, v)}\right|^2 + \left|\frac{\partial(y, z)}{\partial(u, v)}\right|^2 + \left|\frac{\partial(z, x)}{\partial(u, v)}\right|^2\right\}^{1/2} dudv$$

This rather arbitrary definition can be motivated by geometrical considerations. First, it agrees with our previous notion for area when Σ is merely a region embedded in one of the coordinate planes. For example, if Σ is the surface defined by $x = u$, $y = v$, $z = 0$ for $(u, v) \in D$, then $\Sigma_u = (1, 0, 0)$ and $\Sigma_v = (0, 1, 0)$ and the normal $\mathbf{n}$ is $(0, 0, 1)$. The integral for the area of Σ becomes $\iint_D 1\, dudv$ which is precisely $A(D)$, the area of the set D. Again, when Σ is the portion of a plane defined by

$$\Sigma: \begin{cases} x = a_1u + b_1v \\ y = a_2u + b_2v \\ z = a_3u + b_3v \end{cases} \qquad (u, v) \in D$$

then

$$d\Sigma = \begin{bmatrix} a_1 & b_1 \\ a_2 & b_2 \\ a_3 & b_3 \end{bmatrix}$$

and (6-30) yields

$$A(\Sigma) = \iint_D k\, dudv = kA(D)$$

where

$$k^2 = \begin{vmatrix} a_1 & b_1 \\ a_2 & b_2 \end{vmatrix}^2 + \begin{vmatrix} a_2 & b_2 \\ a_3 & b_3 \end{vmatrix}^2 + \begin{vmatrix} a_3 & b_3 \\ a_1 & b_1 \end{vmatrix}^2.$$

Since Σ, in this case, is a linear transformation, this result is in agreement with that obtained earlier (page 237). We may also use this to justify (not prove!) the general formula. Suppose that the domain of Σ is a rectangle R. If we subdivide R by a net into small rectangles R_j, then in any one of these, the transformation Σ might be expected to behave very much like its differential

$$d\Sigma = \begin{bmatrix} \dfrac{\partial x}{\partial u} & \dfrac{\partial x}{\partial v} \\ \dfrac{\partial y}{\partial u} & \dfrac{\partial y}{\partial v} \\ \dfrac{\partial z}{\partial u} & \dfrac{\partial z}{\partial v} \end{bmatrix}$$

As a linear transformation from E^2 into E^3, this multiplies area by the factor k where

$$k^2 = \begin{vmatrix} \dfrac{\partial x}{\partial u} & \dfrac{\partial x}{\partial v} \\ \dfrac{\partial y}{\partial u} & \dfrac{\partial y}{\partial v} \end{vmatrix}^2 + \begin{vmatrix} \dfrac{\partial y}{\partial u} & \dfrac{\partial y}{\partial v} \\ \dfrac{\partial z}{\partial u} & \dfrac{\partial z}{\partial v} \end{vmatrix}^2 + \begin{vmatrix} \dfrac{\partial z}{\partial u} & \dfrac{\partial z}{\partial v} \\ \dfrac{\partial x}{\partial u} & \dfrac{\partial x}{\partial v} \end{vmatrix}^2$$

$$= \left|\frac{\partial(x, y)}{\partial(u, v)}\right|^2 + \left|\frac{\partial(y, z)}{\partial(u, v)}\right|^2 + \left|\frac{\partial(z, x)}{\partial(u, v)}\right|^2$$

Referring to Fig. (6-23), we may expect that the area of the surface Σ should be approximately $\Sigma k(p_j)A(R_j)$ where p_j is an appropriate point

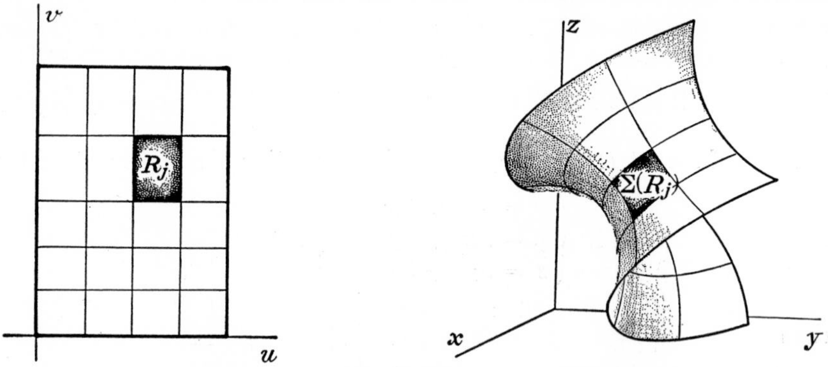

FIG. 6-23

in R_j at which the Jacobians are evaluated. Since this has the form of a Riemann sum for the integral $\iint_D k$, we are led to the formula (6-30) as a reasonable† definition for $A(\Sigma)$.

As an illustration, let us find the area of the torus (doughnut) of Fig. (6-24) whose equation is

$$(6\text{-}31) \qquad \Sigma: \begin{cases} x = (R - \cos v)\cos u & -\pi \le u \le \pi \\ y = (R - \cos v)\sin u & -\pi \le v \le \pi \\ z = \sin v & R > 1 \end{cases}$$

† The subject of general surface area is one which is still in the process of development, and the approach outlined here is not the only one used. It is possible to define the area of a surface in terms of the area of inscribed polyhedrons; however, there is no longer a simple inequality between the area of a surface and that of an inscribed polyhedron, such as there was between the length of a curve and that of an inscribed polygon. A radically different approach stems from the fact that the area of Σ can also be defined as the average of the area of the projections of Σ upon all possible planes. An elementary discussion of the theory of area may be found in the article by T. Radó, What Is the Area of a Surface? *Am. Math. Monthly*, vol. 50, pp. 139–141, 1943.

We have

$$d\Sigma = \begin{bmatrix} -(R - \cos v) \sin u & \sin v \cos u \\ (R - \cos v) \cos u & \sin v \sin u \\ 0 & \cos v \end{bmatrix}$$

so that

$$\begin{aligned} |\mathbf{n}(u, v)|^2 &= |-(R - \cos v)(\sin^2 u \sin v + \cos^2 u \sin v)|^2 \\ &\quad + |(R - \cos v) \cos u \cos v|^2 + |(R - \cos v) \sin u \cos v|^2 \\ &= (R - \cos v)^2(\sin^2 v + \cos^2 u \cos^2 v + \sin^2 u \cos^2 v) \\ &= (R - \cos v)^2. \end{aligned}$$

Accordingly,

$$A(\Sigma) = \int_{-\pi}^{\pi} du \int_{-\pi}^{\pi} (R - \cos v)\, dv = (2\pi)^2 R.$$

Again, consider the surface described by the equation $z = 2 - x^2 - y$,

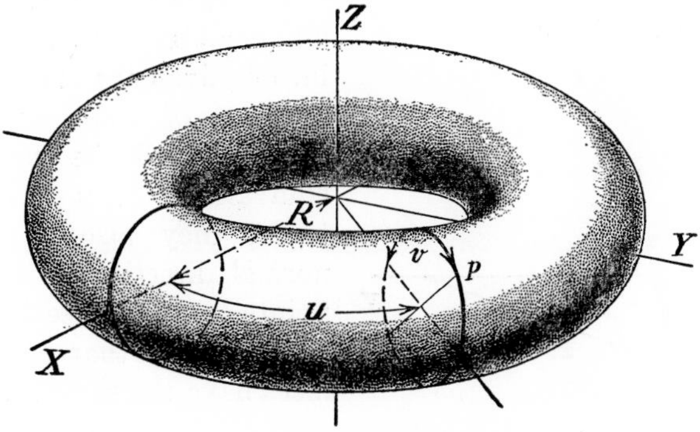

FIG. 6-24

with (x, y) restricted to lie in the triangle D bounded by the lines $x = 0$, $y = 1$, $y = x$ (see Fig. 6-25). Using x and y in place of u and v, we find that

$$\begin{aligned} |\mathbf{n}(x, y)|^2 &= \left|\frac{\partial(x, y)}{\partial(x, y)}\right|^2 + \left|\frac{\partial(y, z)}{\partial(x, y)}\right|^2 + \left|\frac{\partial(z, x)}{\partial(x, y)}\right|^2 \\ &= 1 + \left(\frac{\partial z}{\partial x}\right)^2 + \left(\frac{\partial z}{\partial y}\right)^2 \\ &= 1 + 4x^2 + 1 = 2 + 4x^2 \end{aligned}$$

so that the area of this surface is

$$\begin{aligned} A(\Sigma) &= \iint_D \sqrt{2 + 4x^2}\, dxdy \\ &= \int_0^1 dx \sqrt{2 + 4x^2} \int_x^1 dy \qquad (6\text{-}32) \\ &= \int_0^1 (1 - x) \sqrt{2 + 4x^2}\, dx. \end{aligned}$$

This can either be evaluated approximately, or may be transformed into an elementary form by the substitution $u = 2^{-1/2} \tan \theta$. The former, with a division of [0, 1] into 10 subintervals, gives $A(\Sigma) = .811$; the latter eventually gives $A(\Sigma) = \frac{1}{2} \log(\sqrt{2} + \sqrt{3}) + \sqrt{2}/6 = .809$.

The important notion of **parametric equivalence** applies to surfaces as it did to curves, with appropriate modifications.

Definition. *Two smooth surfaces, Σ and Σ^*, are said to be smoothly equivalent if there is a transformation T mapping D^*, the domain of Σ^*, onto D, the domain of Σ, which is one-to-one, is of class C', and has a strictly positive Jacobian in D^*, and such that $\Sigma^*(u, v) = \Sigma(T(u, v))$ for all $(u, v) \in D^*$.*

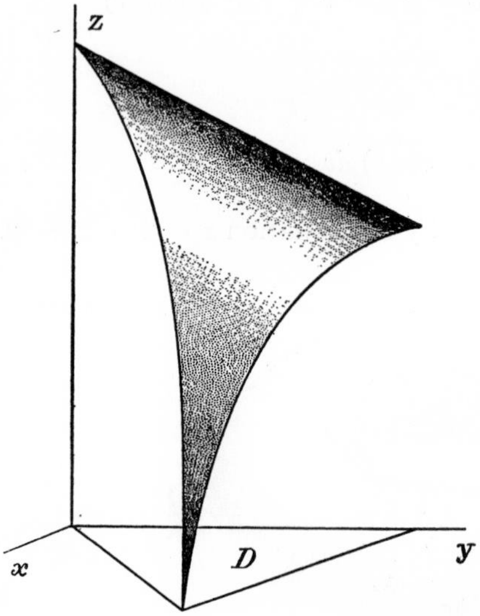

FIG. 6-25

By means of this, the class of all smooth surfaces falls apart into equivalence classes, with each a class of mutually equivalent surfaces. All the surfaces in one equivalence class have the same trace; they also have the same normal direction at corresponding points (see Exercise 5). The next result shows that equivalent surfaces have the same area.

Theorem 11. *If Σ and Σ^* are smoothly equivalent surfaces, then $A(\Sigma) = A(\Sigma^*)$.*

We may assume that $\Sigma^*(u, v) = \Sigma(r, s) = \Sigma(T(u, v))$, where T maps the set of points (u, v) forming the domain D^* of Σ^* onto the set of points (r, s) forming the domain D of Σ. The area of Σ is given by

$$A(\Sigma) = \iint_D \left\{ \left| \frac{\partial(x, y)}{\partial(r, s)} \right|^2 + \left| \frac{\partial(y, z)}{\partial(r, s)} \right|^2 + \left| \frac{\partial(z, x)}{\partial(r, s)} \right|^2 \right\}^{1/2} drds$$

To this double integral, apply Theorem 4, Sec. 6.1, and make the change of variable produced by the transformation T. D will be replaced by D^*, r and s will be replaced by their expressions in terms of u and v in the integrand, and $drds$ will be replaced by $|\partial(r, s)/\partial(u, v)|\, dudv$. This results in the formula

$$(6\text{-}32) \quad A(\Sigma) = \iint_{D^*} \left\{ \left| \frac{\partial(x, y)}{\partial(r, s)} \right|^2 + \left| \frac{\partial(y, z)}{\partial(r, s)} \right|^2 + \left| \frac{\partial(z, x)}{\partial(r, s)} \right|^2 \right\}^{1/2} \frac{\partial(r, s)}{\partial(u, v)}\, dudv$$

However, since $\Sigma^*(u, v) = \Sigma(T(u, v))$, the chain rule of differentiation (Theorem 18, Sec. 5.5) asserts that $d\Sigma^* = d\Sigma\, dT$ so that

$$\frac{\partial(x, y)}{\partial(u, v)} = \frac{\partial(x, y)}{\partial(r, s)} \frac{\partial(r, s)}{\partial(u, v)}$$
$$\frac{\partial(y, z)}{\partial(u, v)} = \frac{\partial(y, z)}{\partial(r, s)} \frac{\partial(r, s)}{\partial(u, v)}$$
$$\frac{\partial(z, x)}{\partial(u, v)} = \frac{\partial(z, x)}{\partial(r, s)} \frac{\partial(r, s)}{\partial(u, v)}.$$

If we use these relations in (6-32), we obtain

$$\begin{aligned} A(\Sigma) &= \iint_{D^*} \left\{ \left| \frac{\partial(x, y)}{\partial(u, v)} \right|^2 + \left| \frac{\partial(y, z)}{\partial(u, v)} \right|^2 + \left| \frac{\partial(z, x)}{\partial(u, v)} \right|^2 \right\}^{1/2} du dv \\ &= A(\Sigma^*) \end{aligned}$$

proving equality of the areas of the surfaces. ▮

From a more sophisticated point of view, it is now natural to alter the terminology so that the word "surface" no longer refers to an individual mapping Σ but rather to the entire equivalence class that contains Σ. Depending upon the notion of equivalence that is used, one speaks of Frechet surfaces, Lebesgue surfaces, etc. It is in the guise of equivalence classes, perhaps, that one is best able to speak of "the" surface defined by an equation $F(x, y, z) = 0$; this may be understood to be the equivalence class of smooth surfaces Σ which satisfy this equation.†

So far, we have been chiefly concerned with the theory of surfaces "in the small," that is, the behavior of a surface in the neighborhood of a point lying on it. Such considerations have to do with the existence and direction of a normal, with the curvature of the surface at the point, or with the relationship between the normal vector and curves which lie on the surface and pass through its base. Much of the modern theory of surfaces deals instead with properties "in the large," which require the consideration of the surface as a whole. For example, all smooth surfaces might be said to be approximately plane "in the small"; thus, the essential distinction between a sphere and a torus is a property "in the large." Similarly, the property of being orientable is one which cannot be settled by local considerations.

To discuss such aspects as these, it is necessary to deal with the more general notion of a two-dimensional **manifold.** This can be thought of as a generalization of our previous notion of surface, and is obtained by considering the union of a number of pieces of surfaces to form a larger object.

† See again the article by J. W. T. Youngs, Curves and Surfaces, *Am. Math. Monthly*, vol. 51, pp. 1–11, 1944.

Definition. *A 2-manifold M is a set of mappings Σ_1, Σ_2, . . . such that* (i) *the domain of each is an open disk D in the* (u, v) *plane and* (ii) *each Σ_j is a continuous one-to-one mapping having a continuous inverse.*

If we denote the trace of Σ_j by S_j, then the **trace** of M is defined to be the union of the sets S_j. It is usual to require that the trace of M be a connected set of points; a manifold that is not connected is therefore

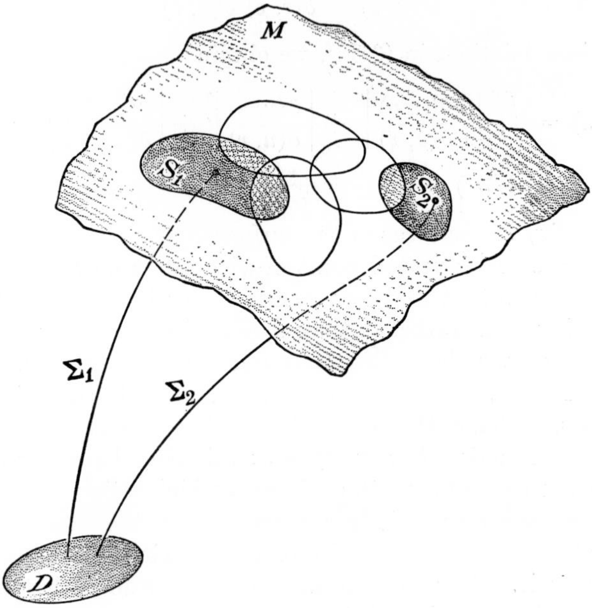

FIG. 6-26

the union of a number of connected manifolds. We may say that the manifold M is the union of the surface pieces (or surface elements) Σ_j. This may be visualized as shown in Fig. 6-26. It is not necessary that all of the mappings Σ_j have the same domain. Any smooth surface which is simple, is a manifold with just one surface element; any smooth surface Σ with multiple points is a manifold with a number of surface elements, for the mapping Σ is locally one-to-one, and its domain can be covered with open disks D_j in each of which Σ is one-to-one.

In order to speak of differentiability properties of a manifold, it is convenient to impose restrictions on the way the surface elements fit together. Let Σ_i and Σ_j be any two pieces of M, and let $S = S_i \cap S_j$, the intersection of their traces (see Fig. 6-27). Since Σ_i maps D onto S_i, it maps a part of it, D_i, onto S. In the same way, Σ_j maps a part, D_j, also onto S, one-to-one. (In Fig. 6-27, we have shown D_i and D_j disjoint, although this may not be the case in general.) Consider the transformation T_{ij} from D into D which is defined on D_j by

$$T_{ij}(p) = \Sigma_i^{-1}\Sigma_j(p).$$

This is a one-to-one mapping of D_j onto D_i. Such a mapping is defined for every pair of overlapping sets S_i and S_j. (Note that T_{ij} and T_{ji} are inverses, and that T_{ii} is the identity map of D onto itself.) The manifold M is said to be a **differentiable manifold** of class C' if each of the transformations T_{ij} is of class C' and has a nonvanishing Jacobian.

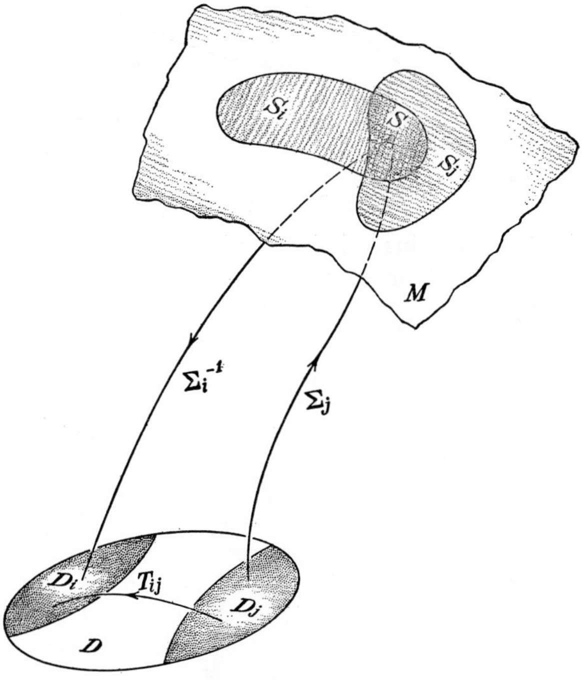

FIG. 6-27

We are now ready to say what is meant by an **orientable** manifold.

Definition. *A differentiable manifold M is orientable if each of the connection transformations T_{ij} has a positive Jacobian. Otherwise, M is said to be nonorientable.*

An orientable manifold can be given a consistent orientation by orienting D. Choose once and for all, a positive "side" for D. This may be done by choosing which way a normal to D shall point. This in turn determines a direction of positive rotation for simple closed curves lying in D, counterclockwise about the normal. The mappings Σ_i carry these over to the individual surface elements. Since the Jacobian of the transformation T_{ij} is positive, T_{ij} is an orientation preserving mapping of D_j onto D_i; this guarantees that the orientations produced by Σ_i and Σ_j are consistent in the overlapping set (see Fig. 6-28). Thus, we arrive at a consistent sense of "outward" normal on M, or equivalently, a consistent sense of positive rotation for neighborhoods of

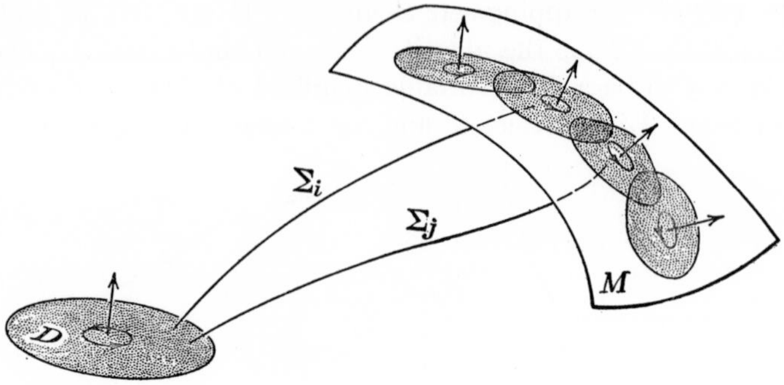

FIG. 6-28

points on M. The Möebius strip is a familiar example of a nonorientable manifold (Fig. 6-29). If one starts with an "outward" normal at one point of the strip, and attempts to carry this around the strip, one finds that it will have reversed direction when the starting point is again

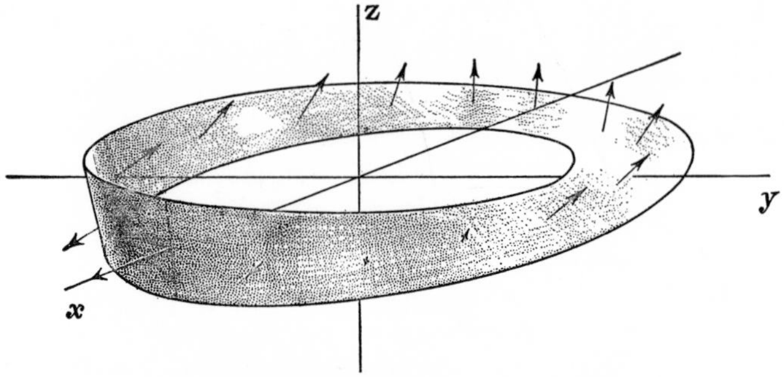

FIG. 6-29. Möbius strip (nonorientable).

reached. To verify that this manifold is nonorientable directly from the definition, we express M as the union of two surface elements, defined by the same mapping Σ, but with differing domains. Let

$$\Sigma:\begin{cases} x = \left(2 - v\sin\left(\dfrac{u}{2}\right)\right)\cos u \\ y = \left(2 - v\sin\left(\dfrac{u}{2}\right)\right)\sin u \\ z = v\cos\left(\dfrac{u}{2}\right) \end{cases} \tag{6-33}$$

and let Σ_1 be the surface obtained by restricting (u, v) to the rectangle $|v| < 1$, $0 < u < 2\pi$, and Σ_2 the surface obtained by restricting (u, v) to the rectangle $|v| < 1$, $|u| < \frac{\pi}{2}$. The traces of these overlap, and together cover the twisted strip completely. The sets D_1 and D_2 are not connected; examining the equations for Σ, and Fig. 6-27, we see that D_1 consists of the two rectangles

$$D_1' = \left\{\text{all } (u, v) \text{ with } |v| < 1 \text{ and } 0 < u < \frac{\pi}{2}\right\}$$
$$D_1'' = \{\text{all } (u, v) \text{ with } |v| < 1 \text{ and } \tfrac{3}{2}\pi < u < 2\pi\}$$

The transformation T_{21} is therefore given by

$$T_{21}(u, v) = \begin{cases} (u, v) \text{ in } D_1' \\ (u - 2\pi, -v) \text{ in } D_1'' \end{cases}$$

and has negative Jacobian in D_1''.

Another property "in the large" is the classification of manifolds as open and closed; this has little to do with the previous use of these words. A manifold is **closed** if it is compact, that is, if it has the property

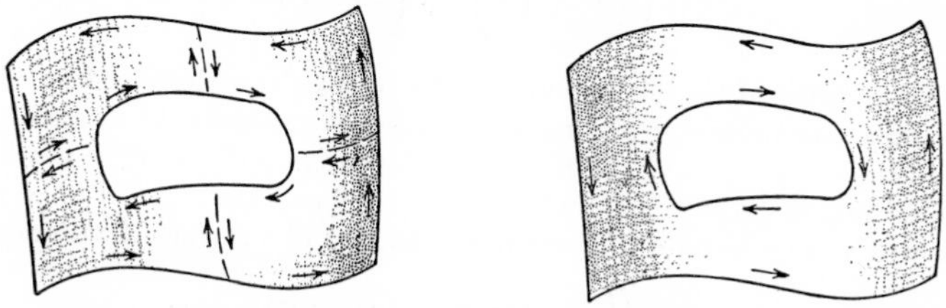

FIG. 6-30. "Open" manifold with two boundary curves, formed from simple elements.

that any sequence of points lying on it has a subsequence which converges to a point lying on it. A manifold that is not closed is called **open.** The surface of a sphere defines a closed manifold; if we punch out a closed disk, the resulting manifold is open, since a sequence of points which converges to a point on the deleted rim of the disk will have no subsequence converging to a point on the manifold. A closed manifold has no edge or boundary; to define a notion of boundary for an open manifold, it is convenient to modify the construction by contracting the open domains of the surface elements Σ_{ij} so that we have overlapping of the sets S_j only along their edges. If this is done, then the manifold can be regarded as obtained by gluing these surface elements together along specified edges. When there are only a finite number of such pieces, the edge of the manifold is defined to be the curve or set of curves which is made up of the unmatched edges. When a manifold is orientable, the surface elements can be oriented so that each matched edge occurs once in one direction and once in the other; these may be said to cancel out, and the remaining unmatched curves constitute the oriented boundary of the manifold (see Fig. 6-30). A detailed treatment of these subjects must be left to a course in algebraic topology.

EXERCISES

1. Plot the trace of the surface $x = u^2 - v^2$, $y = u + v$, $z = u^2 + 4v$, $|u| \leq 1$, $0 \leq v \leq 1$, and find the tangent plane at $(-\frac{1}{4}, \frac{1}{2}, 2)$.

2. Show that all of the normal lines to the sphere (6-26) pass through the origin.

3. Let Σ be the surface described by $z = f(x, y)$, $(x, y) \in D$, with $f \in C'$. Show that the normal to Σ at p_0 is $(-f_1(p_0), -f_2(p_0), 1)$, and that the area of Σ is

$$A(\Sigma) = \iint_D \sqrt{1 + f_1^2 + f_2^2}.$$

4. The curve γ given by $x = t$, $y = t^2$, $z = 2t^3$, $-\infty < t < \infty$, has a point in common with the surface Σ given by $z = x^2 + 3y^2 - 2xy$. What is the angle between γ and the normal to Σ at this point?

5. Show that two surfaces which are smoothly equivalent have the same normal directions at corresponding points.

6. Find the surface area of the sphere (6-26).

7. Set up a definite integral for the surface area of the ellipsoid

$$\left(\frac{x}{a}\right)^2 + \left(\frac{y}{b}\right)^2 + \left(\frac{z}{c}\right)^2 = 1$$

8. Set up an integral for the area of the Möebius strip as described by (6-33).

9. Show that the normal to a surface Σ is always orthogonal to Σ_u and Σ_v.

10. Find the surface area of the portion of the paraboloid $z = x^2 + y^2$ which is cut out by the region between the cylinder $x^2 + y^2 = 2$ and the cylinder $x^2 + y^2 = 6$.

11. Show that an alternate expression for the area of a surface Σ with domain D is

$$A(\Sigma) = \iint_D \{|\Sigma_u|^2|\Sigma_v|^2 - (\Sigma_u \cdot \Sigma_v)^2\}^{\frac{1}{2}}\, dudv.$$

[In the study of the differential geometry of surfaces the notation $E = |\Sigma_u|$, $F = \Sigma_u \cdot \Sigma_v$ and $G = |\Sigma_v|$ is customary.]

12. A two-dimensional surface in 4-space is a mapping from E^2 into E^4. If

$$\Sigma(u, v) = (x, y, z, w),$$

with domain D, then the area of Σ is defined by

$$A(\Sigma) = \iint_D \{|\Sigma_u|^2|\Sigma_v|^2 - (\Sigma_u \cdot \Sigma_v)^2\}^{\frac{1}{2}}\, dudv$$

Find the area of the surface whose equation is $x = 2uv$, $y = u^2 - v^2$, $z = u + v$, $w = u - v$, for $u^2 + v^2 \leq 1$.

*13. A three-dimensional surface in 4-space is a transformation χ from a domain D in E^3 into E^4. The three-dimensional volume (analogous to surface area) of χ is defined to be $V(\chi) = \iiint_D \sqrt{K}$, where K is the sum of the squares of determinants of the 3-by-3 submatrices of $d\chi$. Thus, if χ is given by $\chi(\theta, \phi, \psi) = (x, y, z, w)$, then

$$K = \left|\frac{\partial(x, y, z)}{\partial(\theta, \phi, \psi)}\right|^2 + \left|\frac{\partial(y, z, w)}{\partial(\theta, \phi, \psi)}\right|^2 + \left|\frac{\partial(z, w, x)}{\partial(\theta, \phi, \psi)}\right|^2 + \left|\frac{\partial(w, x, y)}{\partial(\theta, \phi, \psi)}\right|^2$$

The boundary of the four-dimensional ball of radius R is a three-dimensional manifold called the 3-sphere, given either by the equation $x^2 + y^2 + z^2 + w^2 = R^2$, or paramatrically by $x = \cos\psi \sin\phi \cos\theta$, $y = \cos\psi \sin\phi \sin\theta$, $z = \cos\psi \cos\phi$, $w = \sin\psi$, for $-(\pi/2) \le \psi \le \pi/2$, $0 \le \phi \le \pi$, $0 \le \theta \le 2\pi$. Show that the "area" of the 3-sphere is $2\pi^2 R^3$.

*14. Can a general formula be obtained for the area of a surface Σ which satisfies the equation $F(x, y, z) = 0$, which is given entirely in terms of the functions F_1, F_2, and F_3?

6.4. Extremal Properties of Functions of Several Variables

Any continuous function f defined on a closed bounded set D attains a maximum (and a minimum) value at some point of D. If f is of class C' in D, and p_0 is an interior point of D at which f attains such an extremal value, then Theorem 10, Sec. 5.3, showed that all the first-order partial derivatives of f are zero at p_0. This suggests that we single out the points in the domain of a function which have the last property.

Definition. *A* **critical point** *for a function f is a point p where*

$$f_1(p) = f_2(p) = \cdots = 0.$$

The discussion in the first paragraph can be rephrased as asserting that the extremal points for the function f, which lie in the set D but do not lie on the boundary of D, are among the critical points for f in D. A critical point need not yield a local maximum or minimum value of f. To see what the general behavior may be, let us examine the graph of f. If f is a function of two variables, then its graph, which is the set of all points (x, y, z) with $z = f(x, y)$ and $(x, y) \in D$, can also be regarded as the trace of the surface

$$\Sigma: \begin{cases} x = u \\ y = v \\ z = f(u, v) \end{cases} \qquad (u, v) \in D$$

Since f is of class C', Σ is smooth and

$$d\Sigma = \begin{bmatrix} 1 & 0 \\ 0 & 1 \\ f_1 & f_2 \end{bmatrix}.$$

The normal to Σ at (x_0, y_0, z_0) is $(-f_1(x_0, y_0), -f_2(x_0, y_0), 1)$ or $(-\partial z/\partial x, -\partial z/\partial y, 1)$. Thus, a critical point for f corresponds to a point on the surface where the normal is $(0, 0, 1)$ and where the tangent plane is horizontal. It is clear that we can have critical points at interior points of D where f does not attain an extreme value, but where the graph of f has the saddle-like shape shown in Fig. 6-31. Before proceeding further, it will be helpful to study the analogous behavior in a function of one variable. A critical point is now a solution of the equation $f'(x) = 0$, and corresponds to a point on the curve with equation $y = f(x)$ at which the tangent line is horizontal. The critical point may be an extremal point for f, or it may yield a point of inflection on the curve. As an illustration, suppose we wish to find the maximum value of

$$f(x) = 4x^3 - 15x^2 + 18x$$

for x in the interval $I = [0, 2]$. The critical points for f in I are found to be 1 and $\frac{3}{2}$. The maximum value of f on I must therefore be attained either at one of these, or on the boundary of I, that is, at one of the end

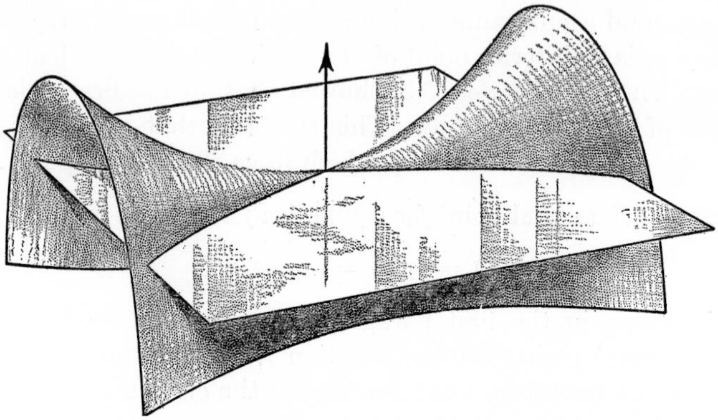

FIG. 6-31. Horizontal tangent plane at saddle point.

points 0 and 2. Computing the value of f at each, we find $f(0) = 0$, $f(2) = 8$, $f(1) = 7$, $f(\frac{3}{2}) = \frac{27}{4}$. Hence, the maximum value of f on I is 8, and it is attained on the boundary. (However, f has a local maximum value of 7 at 1, and a local minimum value of $\frac{27}{4}$ at $\frac{3}{2}$.)

The same technique may be used for functions of several variables. As an illustration, consider the function f given by $f(x, y) = 4xy - 2x^2 - y^4$ in the square $D = \{\text{all } (x, y) \text{ with } |x| \leq 2, |y| \leq 2\}$. The critical points for f are the simultaneous solutions of the equations

$$0 = f_1(x, y) = 4y - 4x$$
$$0 = f_2(x, y) = 4x - 4y^3$$

and are $(0, 0)$, $(1, 1)$, and $(-1, -1)$. The maximum value of f in D must be attained at one of these, or on the boundary of D. We do not have to compute the values of f on all the edges of this square; since we are looking for a maximum value, we may discard the parts of ∂D lying in the second and fourth quadrants where the term xy which occurs in $f(x, y)$ is negative. Moreover, $f(-x, -y) = f(x, y)$ so that f takes the same values at symmetric points in the first and third quadrants. This reduces our work to an examination of the values of f on the line $x = 2$, $0 \leq y \leq 2$, and the line $y = 2$, $0 \leq x \leq 2$. On the former,

$$f(2, y) = 8y - 8 - y^4.$$

Proceeding as in the previous illustration, we find that the largest value of this for y in [0, 2] is $6(2)^{1/3} - 8 \sim -.44$, attained when $y = 2^{1/3}$. On the second part of ∂D, $f(x, 2) = 8x - 2x^2 - 16$, whose greatest value for x in [0, 2] is -8. This shows that the maximum value of f on the boundary of D is approximately $-.44$. Comparing this with the values which f has at the three critical points, $f(0, 0) = 0$,

$$f(1, 1) = f(-1, -1) = 1,$$

we see that the (absolute) maximum value of f in D is 1, attained at the

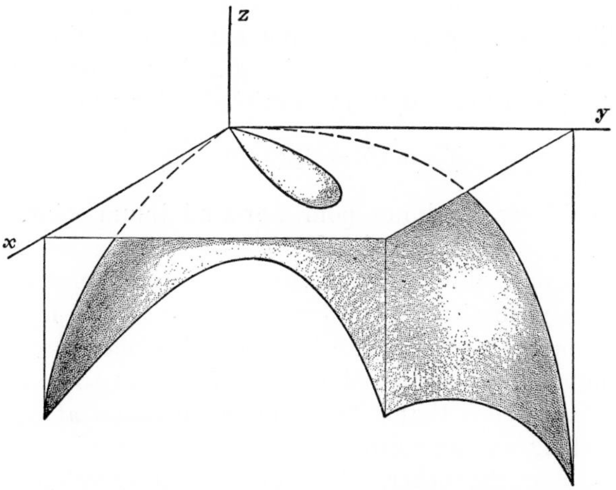

FIG. 6-32. Graph of $z = 4xy - 2x^2 - y^4$ for $0 \leq x \leq 2$, $0 \leq y \leq 2$.

two points (1, 1) and $(-1, -1)$. (A graph of f is given in Fig. 6-32.) In the same fashion, one may show that the minimum value of f in D is -40, attained at the two boundary points $(2, -2)$ and $(-2, 2)$.

In the more familiar case of a function of one variable, the second derivative may be used to test the nature of a critical point.

Theorem 12. *Let f be of class C'' in the interval $[a, b]$ and let c be an interior point of this interval with $f'(c) = 0$. Then, in order that c be a local maximum point for f, it is necessary that $f''(c) \leq 0$, and sufficient that $f''(c) < 0$; for c to be a minimum point, the conditions are the same with the inequality signs reversed.*

The proof is an immediate deduction from Taylor's theorem. Write

$$\begin{aligned} f(c + h) &= f(c) + f'(c)h + \frac{f''(\tau)h^2}{2} \\ &= f(c) + f''(\tau)h^2 \end{aligned}$$

where τ is a point between c and $c + h$. If $f''(c) < 0$, then $f''(\tau) < 0$

whenever $|h|$ is sufficiently small, so that $f(c + h) < f(c)$ and f has a local maximum value at c. Conversely, if f has a local maximum value at c, then $f''(\tau)h^2 \leq 0$ for all small h. Since $h^2 \geq 0$, and τ approaches c as $h \to 0$, we have $f''(c) \leq 0$. ▌

What is the corresponding statement for functions of two variables? Clearly, if p_0 is a critical point for f lying interior to a set D, and if f has an extremal value at p_0, then this must also be extremal if we examine the values of f on any curve passing through p_0. In particular, approaching p_0 along the vertical and the horizontal directions, a necessary condition that p_0 be a maximum point for f is that $f_{11}(p_0) \leq 0$ and $f_{22}(p_0) \leq 0$. These conditions are not sufficient, nor are the conditions obtained by removing the equal signs (see Exercise 3). For example, the function given by $f(x, y) = xy$ has $(0, 0)$ for a critical point and

$$f_{11}(0, 0) = f_{22}(0, 0) = 0,$$

but $(0, 0)$ is neither a maximum point nor a minimum point. The shape of the graph of f is again like the saddle shown in Fig. 6-31. The name "saddle point" or "minimax" is given to a critical point for a function which does not yield either a local maximum or a local minimum value for the function. A simple condition which is sufficient to ensure that a critical point p_0 be a saddle point is that $f_{11}(p_0)f_{22}(p_0)$ be strictly negative, since this implies that f has a local maximum at p_0 when p_0 is approached along one axis direction, and a local minimum when p_0 is approached along the other. A more general criterion can also be obtained.

Theorem 13. *Let f be of class C'' in a neighborhood of the critical point p_0, and let*

$$\Delta = (f_{12}(p_0))^2 - f_{11}(p_0)f_{22}(p_0).$$

Then,

(i) *If $\Delta > 0$, p_0 is a saddle point for f.*

(ii) *If $\Delta < 0$, p_0 is an extremal point for f, and is a maximum if $f_{11}(p_0) < 0$, and a minimum if $f_{11}(p_0) > 0$.*

(iii) *If $\Delta = 0$, the nature of p_0 is not determined by this test.*

In conclusion (ii), $f_{22}(p_0)$ may also be used to distinguish between maxima and minima. Let us apply the test to the function given by $f(x, y) = 4xy - 2x^2 - y^4$ which was used as an illustration on page 286, and whose critical points are $(0, 0)$, $(1, 1)$, and $(-1, -1)$. We find that $f_{11}(x, y) = -4$, $f_{12}(x, y) = 4$, $f_{22}(x, y) = -12y^2$ so that $\Delta = 16 - 48y^2$. At $(0, 0)$, $\Delta = 16 > 0$ so that $(0, 0)$ is a saddle point. At $(1, 1)$ and $(-1, -1)$, $\Delta = -32 < 0$, so that each is extremal. Since $f_{11} = -4 < 0$, both are local maxima.

The proof of the general test is based upon the following special case.

Lemma. *Let* $P(x, y) = Ax^2 + 2Bxy + Cy^2$, *and set*

$$\Delta = \frac{(P_{12})^2 - P_{11}P_{22}}{4} = B^2 - AC.$$

Then,

(i) *If* $\Delta > 0$, *then there are two lines through the origin such that* $P(x, y) > 0$ *for all* (x, y) *on one, and* $P(x, y) < 0$ *for all* (x, y) *on the other, with the point* $(0, 0)$ *omitted.*

(ii) *If* $\Delta < 0$, *then* $P(x, y)$ *never changes sign, and* $P(x, y) > 0$ *for all points except* $(0, 0)$ *if* $A > 0$, *and* $P(x, y) < 0$ *for all points except* $(0, 0)$ *if* $A < 0$.

We prove (ii) first. If $\Delta < 0$, then $AC \neq 0$ so that $A \neq 0$. Write

$$\begin{aligned} AP(x, y) &= A^2x^2 + 2ABxy + ACy^2 \\ &= (Ax + By)^2 - \Delta y^2. \end{aligned}$$

Since Δ is negative, $AP(x, y) \geq 0$ for all (x, y), with equality only at $(0, 0)$. Thus, $P(x, y)$ always has the same sign as the number A.

To prove (i), we assume that $\Delta > 0$ and compute

$$\begin{aligned} P(B, -A) &= AB^2 - 2B^2A + CA^2 = -A\Delta \\ P(C, -B) &= AC^2 - 2B^2C + CB^2 = -C\Delta \end{aligned}$$

Since P is homogeneous of degree 2, $P(\lambda x, \lambda y) = \lambda^2 P(x, y)$, it will be sufficient if we can find two points at which P has opposite signs, since the same will then hold on the entire line joining these to the origin. Let us suppose first that $A \neq 0$. Then, recalling that Δ is positive, $P(1, 0) = A$ and $P(B, -A) = -A\Delta$ have opposite signs. Similarly, if $C \neq 0$, then $P(0, 1)$ and $P(C, -B)$ have opposite signs. Finally, if $A = C = 0$, then $P(x, y) = 2Bxy$ and P takes opposite signs at $(1, 1)$ and $(-1, 1)$. ▌

To apply this lemma to the proof of Theorem 13, assume that p_0 is a critical point for f, and write the Taylor expansion of f near p_0

$$(6\text{-}34) \quad f(p_0 + \Delta p) = f(p_0) + \tfrac{1}{2}\{f_{11}(p^*)(\Delta x)^2 + 2f_{12}(p^*)(\Delta x)(\Delta y) + f_{22}(p^*)(\Delta y)^2\},$$

where p^* is a point lying on the line segment joining p_0 and $p_0 + \Delta p$. We shall again prove (ii) first. We note first that the expression in brackets in (6-34) has the form $P(\Delta x, \Delta y)$, where P is the quadratic polynomial with coefficients $A = f_{11}(p^*)$, $B = f_{12}(p^*)$, $C = f_{22}(p^*)$. If $\Delta < 0$, then $B^2 - AC < 0$ whenever $|\Delta p|$ is sufficiently small. Hence,

$P(\Delta x, \Delta y)$ has, by the lemma, the same sign as A. Thus, if $f_{11}(p_0) < 0$, then $P(\Delta x, \Delta y) < 0$ for $0 < |\Delta p| < \delta$, and $f(p_0 + \Delta p) = f(p) \leq f(p_0)$ for all p in a neighborhood of p_0, with equality holding only at p_0. The point p_0 is then an extremal point for f which yields a local maximum. If $f_{11}(p_0) > 0$, then $P(\Delta x, \Delta y) > 0$, and $f(p) \geq f(p_0)$ so that p_0 yields a local minimum. To prove part (i), we must show that f takes values which are bigger than $f(p_0)$ and smaller than $f(p_0)$, in any neighborhood of p_0. Write $\Delta p = (\rho \cos \theta, \rho \sin \theta)$. Since P is homogeneous,

$$P(\Delta x, \Delta y) = \rho^2 P(\cos \theta, \sin \theta).$$

Since f is of class C'', we have

$$(6\text{-}35) \quad \lim_{\Delta p \to 0} P(\cos \theta, \sin \theta) = f_{11}(p_0)(\cos \theta)^2 + 2f_{12}(p_0)(\cos \theta \sin \theta) + f_{22}(p_0)(\sin \theta)^2 = P_0(\cos \theta, \sin \theta).$$

Since $\Delta > 0$, the lemma implies that $P_0(\cos \theta, \sin \theta)$ takes both positive and negative values for $0 \leq \theta \leq 2\pi$. In particular, we may choose θ'

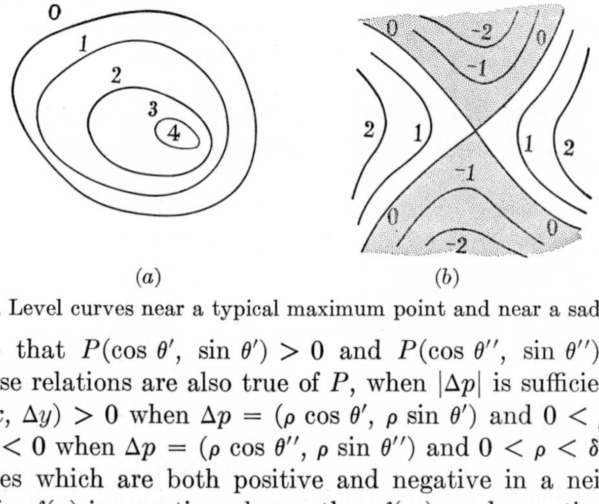

FIG. 6-33. Level curves near a typical maximum point and near a saddle point.

and θ'' so that $P(\cos \theta', \sin \theta') > 0$ and $P(\cos \theta'', \sin \theta'') < 0$. By (6-35), these relations are also true of P, when $|\Delta p|$ is sufficiently small. Thus $P(\Delta x, \Delta y) > 0$ when $\Delta p = (\rho \cos \theta', \rho \sin \theta')$ and $0 < \rho < \delta$, and $P(\Delta x, \Delta y) < 0$ when $\Delta p = (\rho \cos \theta'', \rho \sin \theta'')$ and $0 < \rho < \delta$. Since P takes values which are both positive and negative in a neighborhood of the origin, $f(p)$ is sometimes larger than $f(p_0)$, and sometimes smaller, and p_0 is indeed a saddle point for f. ▌

In the vicinity of a critical point for a function of class C'', the level curves form characteristic patterns which can also be used to determine the character of the critical point. For example, if p_0 is a simple maximum point for f so that $f(p) < f(p_0)$ for all $p \neq p_0$ near p_0, then the level lines of f have an appearance similar to those shown in Fig. 6-33a. On the other hand, the pattern in Fig. 6-33b is typical of a simple saddle point corresponding to the pass between two peaks. A more complicated type of saddle point is illustrated by the so-called "monkey saddle" or triple peak pass (Fig. 6-34).

To give another simple illustration, let us study the function F given

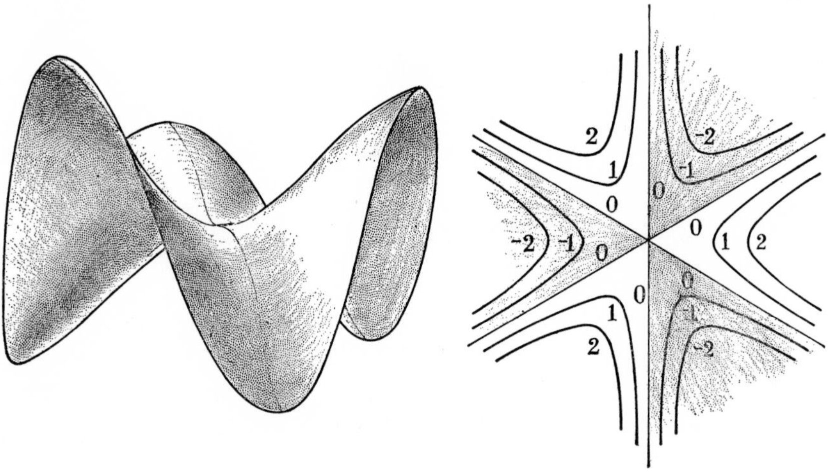

FIG. 6-34

by $F(x, y) = x^2 + y^3 - 3xy$. Differentiating, we find

$$F_1(x, y) = 2x - 3y \qquad F_2(x, y) = 3y^2 - 3x$$
$$F_{11}(x, y) = 2 \qquad F_{12}(x, y) = -3 \qquad F_{22}(x, y) = 6y.$$

The critical points of F are found to be $(0, 0)$ and $(9/4, 3/2)$. Computing $\Delta = 9 - 12y$ at each, the first gives $\Delta = 9$ and the second, $\Delta = -9$. Thus (0, 0) is a saddle point, and $(9/4, 3/2)$ is an extremal point; since $F_{11} = 2$, it is a local minimum for F. (The level curves for F are sketched in Fig. 6-35.)

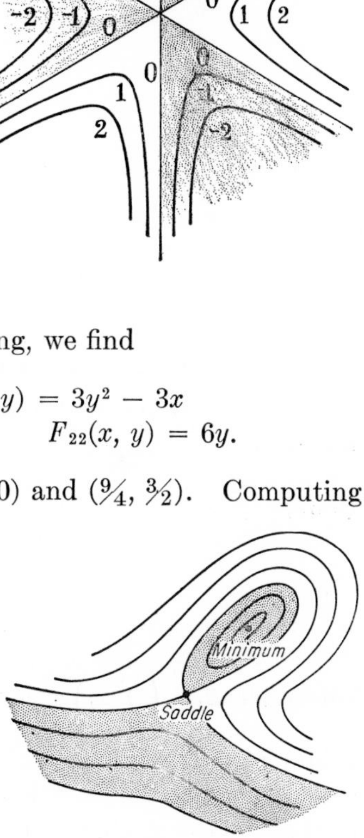

FIG. 6-35

The technique can also be applied to the standard problem of obtaining the linear function which best fits a set of data, in the sense of **least squares.** Given n points $(x_1, y_1), \ldots, (x_n, y_n)$, not all the same, we wish to find the function F of the form $F(x) = ax + b$ for which

$$f(a, b) = \sum_1^n (F(x_j) - y_j)^2 = \sum_1^n (ax_j + b - y_j)^2 \tag{6-36}$$

is a minimum. The function f is of class C'' in the whole (a, b) plane and has a minimum value which is attained at some point, or points, $(a_0, b_0) = p_0$. If we take the region D as a large disk, then we can rule out the boundary of D, for $f(a, b)$ becomes arbitrarily large as (a, b) recedes from the origin. We compute the derivatives of f.

$$\begin{aligned} f_1(a, b) &= \sum_1^n 2(ax_j + b - y_j)x_j \\ &= 2a \sum_1^n (x_j)^2 + 2b \sum_1^n x_j - 2 \sum_1^n x_j y_j \\ f_2(a, b) &= \sum_1^n 2(ax_j + b - y_j) \\ &= 2a \sum_1^n x_j + 2nb - 2 \sum_1^n y_j, \end{aligned}$$

$$\begin{aligned} f_{11}(a, b) &= 2 \sum_1^n (x_j)^2 \\ f_{12}(a, b) &= 2 \sum_1^n x_j \\ f_{22}(a, b) &= 2n \end{aligned}$$

The critical points for f are the solutions of the following equations for a and b:

(6-37)
$$\begin{aligned} a \sum_1^n (x_j)^2 + b \sum_1^n x_j &= \sum_1^n x_j y_j \\ a \sum_1^n x_j + nb \qquad &= \sum_1^n y_j \end{aligned}$$

Introduce $\bar{x} = \left(\sum_1^n x_j\right)\Big/ n$ and $\bar{y} = \left(\sum_1^n y_j\right)\Big/ n$ so that $(\bar{x}, \bar{y})$ is the **center of gravity** of the points (x_j, y_j). The second equation in (6-37) can now be written $a\bar{x} + b = \bar{y}$, and asserts that a and b must be chosen so that $F(\bar{x}) = \bar{y}$, that is, the graph of F is a line passing through $(\bar{x}, \bar{y})$. A solution of (6-37) can be written as

$$a = \frac{\dfrac{1}{n} \displaystyle\sum_1^n x_j y_j - \bar{x}\bar{y}}{\dfrac{1}{n} \displaystyle\sum_1^n (x_j)^2 - (\bar{x})^2}, \qquad b = \bar{y} - a\bar{x}$$

There is only one critical point. To check that it is a local minimum point for f, we compute

$$\Delta = (f_{12})^2 - f_{11}f_{22} = \left(2\sum_1^n x_j\right)^2 - (2n)\left(2\sum_1^n (x_j)^2\right)$$
$$= 4\left\{\left(\sum_1^n x_j\right)^2 - n\sum_1^n (x_j)^2\right\}.$$

By the Schwarz inequality (Sec. 1.1),

$$\left(\sum_1^n x_j\right)^2 = \left(\sum_1^n 1\cdot x_j\right)^2 \le \sum_1^n 1^2 \sum_1^n x_j^2 = n\sum_1^n x_j^2$$

and equality holds only if all of the x_j are the same. Hence, $\Delta < 0$ and our critical point (a, b) is extremal. Since $f_{11} = 2\Sigma x_j^2 > 0$, it is indeed a local (and therefore an absolute) minimum point for f. Other extremal problems will be found in the exercises.† (See especially Exercise 15 where a different notion of the best-fitting line for a set of points (x_j, y_j) is used.)

Some functions, from their nature, never possess interior extremal points. If f is such a function, and D is a region whose boundary is composed of one or more simple closed curves, then the largest value of $f(p)$ for p in D is attained on ∂D. In particular, if the inequality $f(p) \le M$ holds for p on ∂D, then it holds for p in D. One important class of functions having this maximum property is the class of **harmonic functions.** We give a simple proof of this for functions of two variables which can be extended immediately to the general case.

Theorem 14. *Let U be a function of class C'' in a bounded open set D which satisfies the differential equation $U_{xx} + U_{yy} = 0$ throughout D, and which is continuous on the closure of D. Let $U(p) \le M$ for all points p on ∂D, the boundary of D. Then, $U(p) \le M$ for all $p \in D$.*

We shall prove this for the more general class of subharmonic functions U which obey the differential inequality $U_{xx} + U_{yy} \ge 0$ in D. Take any $\epsilon > 0$ and set $V(x, y) = U(x, y) + \epsilon x^2$. The function V is continuous in the closure of D, and must take on a maximum value either on ∂D, or at an interior point p^* of D. If the latter holds, then it is necessary that $V_{xx}(p^*) \le 0$ and $V_{yy}(p^*) \le 0$ so that $V_{xx}(p^*) + V_{yy}(p^*) \le 0$. However, $V_{xx} = U_{xx} + 2\epsilon$ and $V_{yy} = U_{yy}$ so that this means that

† It would be misleading if the impression were given that one only looks for the extremal points for a function. In many applications, it is in fact the saddle points which are desired. This is particularly true in problems stemming from the theory of games, or statistical theory.

$U_{xx}(p^*) + U_{yy}(p^*) \leq -2\epsilon < 0$. This violates the hypothesis $U_{xx} + U_{yy} \geq 0$; thus, V must assume its maximum value on the boundary of D. Let A be the largest value of x for $(x, y) \in D$. If p is any point on ∂D, then

$$V(p) = U(p) + \epsilon x^2 \leq M + \epsilon A^2.$$

At any point $p_0 \in D$, we have

$$U(p_0) + \epsilon x_0{}^2 = V(p_0) \leq \max_{p \in \partial D} V(p) \leq M + \epsilon A^2$$

or

$$U(p_0) \leq M + \epsilon(A^2 - x_0{}^2).$$

This estimate of the value of U at p_0 holds for any choice of ϵ, so letting $\epsilon \to 0$, we obtain $U(p_0) \leq M$. ▮

Many problems arise in which it is known that the sought-for extremal point is not an interior point of the set D. A familiar example of this is the category of problems known as extremal problems with **constraints** or side conditions. As an illustration, we may be interested in the point $p = (x, y, z)$ at which $f(p)$ has a maximum value, where p is restricted to lie on a portion S of the surface described by $g(p) = 0$. As a subset of 3-space, S is a closed set which has no interior points; thus, the extremal point need not be among the critical points for f. The side condition $g(p) = 0$ which forces p to move on the surface piece S has the effect of decreasing the number of free variables from 3 to 2. This can be done explicitly if we can solve $g(x, y, z) = 0$ for one of the variables, in a neighborhood of the sought-for point. If $z = \phi(x, y)$, then

$$f(x, y, z) = f(x, y, \phi(x, y)) = F(x, y)$$

and we now look for the maximum value of F.

For example, let us find the point (x, y, z) obeying

$$g(x, y, z) = 2x + 3y + z - 12 = 0$$

for which $f(x, y, z) = 4x^2 + y^2 + z^2$ is minimum. We find that

$$z = 12 - 2x - 3y$$

so that

$$F(x, y) = 4x^2 + y^2 + (12 - 2x - 3y)^2.$$

The critical points of F are found from the equations

$$0 = F_1(x, y) = 8x + 2(12 - 2x - 3y)(-2)$$
$$0 = F_2(x, y) = 2y + 2(12 - 2x - 3y)(-3).$$

These have only one solution, $(6/11, 36/11)$. Checking, we find that $F_{11} = 16$, $F_{12} = 12$, and $F_{22} = 20$, so that $\Delta = (12)^2 - (16)(20) < 0$ and this point yields a local minimum for F. Using the side condition to find z, we find that the solution to the original problem is the point $(6/11, 36/11, 12/11)$.

In many cases, it is undesirable to carry out this direct approach. It may be inconvenient to solve the equation $g(x, y, z) = 0$. One therefore wishes an approach which may be used with the original set of equations. We recall that a critical point for a general transformation T is a point where the rank of dT is less than the largest value which is allowed by the dimensions of the matrix. (See the final paragraphs of Sec. 5.9.)

Theorem 15. *The points $p = (x, y, z)$ which lie in the set S described by $g(x, y, z) = 0$ and at which $f(x, y, z)$ is locally a maximum or a minimum, are among the critical points for the transformation*

$$T: \begin{cases} u = f(x, y, z) \\ v = g(x, y, z). \end{cases}$$

Since
$$dT = \begin{bmatrix} f_1 & f_2 & f_3 \\ g_1 & g_2 & g_3 \end{bmatrix},$$

an equivalent assertion is to say that p is among the simultaneous solutions of the equations

$$(6\text{-}38) \qquad 0 = \begin{vmatrix} f_1 & f_2 \\ g_1 & g_2 \end{vmatrix} \qquad 0 = \begin{vmatrix} f_2 & f_3 \\ g_2 & g_3 \end{vmatrix} \qquad 0 = \begin{vmatrix} f_1 & f_3 \\ g_1 & g_3 \end{vmatrix}$$

as well as $g(x, y, z) = 0$. (It should be noticed that any two of the determinant equations implies the third; the assertion that dT has rank less than 2 means that (f_1, f_2, f_3) and (g_1, g_2, g_3) are multiples of one another.) For example, let us apply this to the illustrative example of the previous page. Since $f(x, y, z) = 4x^2 + y^2 + z^2$ and

$$g(x, y, z) = 2x + 3y + z - 12,$$

we have

$$dT = \begin{bmatrix} 8x & 2y & 2z \\ 2 & 3 & 1 \end{bmatrix}$$

If the top row is a multiple of the bottom row, then $y = 6x$ and $z = 2x$. Substituting these into $g(x, y, z) = 0$, we again obtain the point $(6/11, 36/11, 12/11)$.

We sketch two proofs† of Theorem 15. For the first, we assume that $g_3 \neq 0$ and solve $g(x, y, z) = 0$ for z, obtaining $z = \phi(x, y)$. We then seek extremal values for $F(x, y) = f(x, y, \phi(x, y))$. The critical points for F are the solutions of

$$\begin{aligned} 0 &= F_1(x, y) = f_1 + f_3\phi_1 \\ 0 &= F_2(x, y) = f_2 + f_3\phi_2 \end{aligned}$$

† In this theorem, we have assumed that the extremal point p does not lie on the edge of the surface element S. As in previous examples, this possibility must be examined separately.

Since $g(x, y, \phi(x, y)) = 0$ for all x and y, we also have

$$\begin{aligned} 0 &= g_1 + g_3\phi_1 \\ 0 &= g_2 + g_3\phi_2 \end{aligned}$$

Eliminating ϕ_1 and ϕ_2, we have

$$\begin{vmatrix} f_1 & f_3 \\ g_1 & g_3 \end{vmatrix} = 0 \qquad \text{and} \qquad \begin{vmatrix} f_2 & f_3 \\ g_2 & g_3 \end{vmatrix} = 0$$

so that (f_1, f_2, f_3) and (g_1, g_2, g_3) are proportional, and dT has rank 1 or 0. ▮

For the second proof, let us assume that p^* is a point on a surface element S defined by $g(x, y, z) = 0$ at which $f(p)$ takes its maximum value. The transformation T maps a portion of 3-space containing S

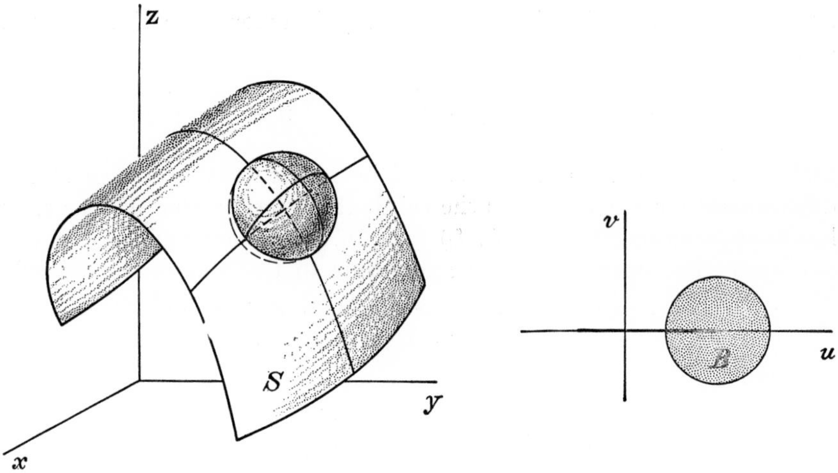

FIG. 6-36. $T(x, y, z) = (u, v)$.

into the (u, v) plane. Since $v = g(x, y, z)$, the points on S map into an interval of the u axis. Since $u = f(x, y, z)$, the point p^* at which f is greatest must map into the right-hand end point B of this interval (see Fig. 6-36). If the rank of dT at p^* were 2, then by Theorem 30, Sec. 5.9, T would carry a full neighborhood of p^* into a neighborhood of B. There would then be points p on S whose images are on the u axis and are to the right of B. Since this is impossible, the rank of dT at p^* must be less than 2. ▮

The method of this theorem can be given in another form, due to Lagrange. The key to this is the observation that if one forms the special function

$$H(x, y, z, \lambda) = f(x, y, z) + \lambda g(x, y, z)$$

then its critical points are the solutions of the equations

$$\begin{aligned} 0 &= H_1 = f_1 + \lambda g_1 \\ 0 &= H_2 = f_2 + \lambda g_2 \\ 0 &= H_3 = f_3 + \lambda g_3 \\ 0 &= H_4 = \qquad g \end{aligned}$$

The first three equations merely assert that (f_1, f_2, f_3) is a multiple of (g_1, g_2, g_3), so that we again obtain Eqs. (6-38). Thus, the extreme points for f, constrained to satisfy $g(p) = 0$, are among the critical points of the function H.

These results may be extended also to the case in which several constraints are imposed. If we wish to maximize $f(x, y, z)$ for points

$$p = (x, y, z)$$

which are required to obey $g(p) = h(p) = 0$, then the method of Lagrange multipliers would be to consider the special function

$$H(x, y, z, \lambda, \mu) = f(x, y, z) + \lambda g(x, y, z) + \mu h(x, y, z).$$

The critical points of H are the solutions of the equations

$$\begin{aligned} 0 &= f_1 + \lambda g_1 + \mu h_1 \\ 0 &= f_2 + \lambda g_2 + \mu h_2 \\ 0 &= f_3 + \lambda g_3 + \mu h_3 \\ 0 &= \qquad g \\ 0 &= \qquad\qquad h \end{aligned}$$

Alternatively, we may find the critical points for the transformation

$$T: \begin{cases} u = f(x, y, z) \\ v = g(x, y, z) \\ w = h(x, y, z) \end{cases}$$

which also satisfy the equations $g(p) = h(p) = 0$.

As an illustration, let us maximize $f(x, y, z) = z$ among the points satisfying $2x + 4y = 5$ and $x^2 + z^2 = 2y$. (In intuitive geometric language, we are asking for the highest point on the curve of intersection of a certain plane and a paraboloid of revolution.) Setting up T and dT, we have

$$dT = \begin{bmatrix} 0 & 0 & 1 \\ 2 & 4 & 0 \\ 2x & -2 & 2z \end{bmatrix}$$

This has rank less than 3 if its determinant vanishes. Expanding it, we obtain $x = -\frac{1}{2}$. Using the constraints to find y and z, the desired point is $(-\frac{1}{2}, \frac{3}{2}, \frac{11}{2})$.

EXERCISES

1. Find the maximum and minimum value of $2x^2 - 3y^2 - 2x$ for $x^2 + y^2 \leq 1$.

2. Find the maximum and minimum value of $2x^2 + y^2 + 2x$ for $x^2 + y^2 \leq 1$.

3. Discuss the nature of the critical points of each of the functions described by:

(a) $f(x, y) = x^2 - y^2$

(b) $f(x, y) = 3xy - x^2 - y^2$

(c) $f(x, y) = 2x^4 + y^4 - x^2 - 2y^2$

(d) $f(x, y) = 4x^2 - 12xy + 9y^2$

(e) $f(x, y) = x^4 + y^4$

(f) $f(x, y) = x^4 - y^4$

4. Sketch the level curves of f for the functions given in Exercise 3, parts (a), (b), (d), and (e).

5. Let $f(x, y) = (y - x^2)(y - 2x^2)$. Show that the origin is a critical point for f which is a saddle point, although on any line through the origin, f has a local minimum at (0, 0).

6. Given n points in space, $P_1, P_2, \ldots, P_n$, find the point P for which

$$f(P) = \sum_1^n |P - P_j|^2$$

is a minimum.

7. Find the point on the line through (1, 0, 0) and (0, 1, 0) which is closest to the line: $x = t$, $y = t$, $z = t$.

8. Find the maximum value of $x^2 + 12xy + 2y^2$, among the points (x, y) for which $4x^2 + y^2 = 25$.

9. What is the maximum value of $x - 2y + 2z$ among the points (x, y, z) with $x^2 + y^2 + z^2 = 9$?

10. Find the minimum of $xy + yz$ for points (x, y, z) which obey the relations $x^2 + y^2 = 2$, $yz = 2$.

11. What is the volume of the largest rectangular box with sides parallel to the coordinate planes which can be inscribed in the ellipsoid $(x/a)^2 + (y/b)^2 + (z/c)^2 = 1$?

12. In the solution of the **normalized two-person game** whose **pay-off matrix** is

$$\begin{bmatrix} 1 & 2 & -1 \\ -2 & 0 & 1 \\ 1 & -2 & 0 \end{bmatrix},$$

one is led to the problem of finding the saddle points of the function F described by

$$F(x_1, x_2, x_3, y_1, y_2, y_3) = (x_1 - 2x_2 + x_3)y_1 + (2x_1 - 2x_3)y_2 + (-x_1 + x_2)y_3$$

subject to the constraints $x_1 + x_2 + x_3 = 1$, $y_1 + y_2 + y_3 = 1$. Show that the saddle point is $x = (\frac{1}{3}, \frac{1}{3}, \frac{1}{3})$, $y = (\frac{2}{7}, \frac{1}{7}, \frac{4}{7})$.

***13.** Let $z = f(x, y)$ be the equation of a convex surface Σ lying above the unit disk $x^2 + y^2 \leq 1$, and let P be any point on Σ. Let S be the region which is bounded below by Σ, on the sides by the cylinder $x^2 + y^2 = 1$, and on top by the tangent plane to Σ at P (see Fig. 6-37). For what position of P will S have minimum volume?

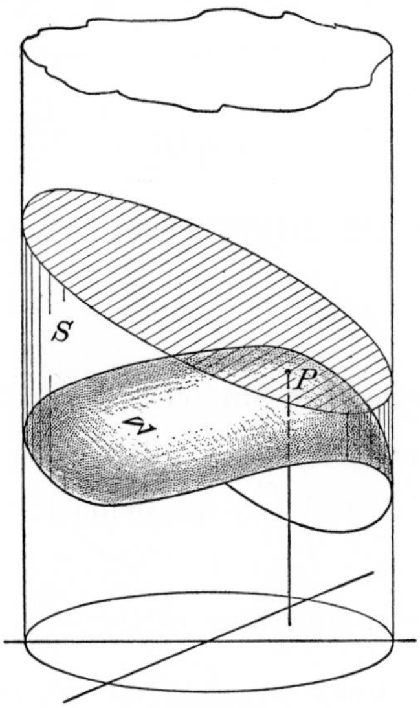

FIG. 6-37

**14. Let $C_1 \geq C_2 \geq \cdots \geq C_n$ be a fixed set of positive numbers. Maximize the linear function $L(x_1, x_2, \ldots, x_n) = \sum_1^n C_j x_j$, in the closed set described by the inequalities $0 \leq x_j \leq 1$, $\sum_1^n x_j \leq A$.

**15. Let $(x_1, y_1) = P_1$, $(x_2, y_2) = P_2, \ldots, P_n$ be a set of points, not all the same. Find the line L which "fits" these points best in the sense that it minimizes $\sum_1^n d_j^2$, where d_j is the distance from P_j to L. [Note that this is not the same as the function f given in (6-36).]

*16. Using Theorem 14, prove the following: if D is a closed bounded set, and if f and g are both harmonic in D, and if $f(p) = g(p)$ for all p on the boundary of D, then $f \equiv g$ in D. [*Hint:* Consider both $f - g$ and $g - f$.]

CHAPTER 7

ELEMENTS OF DIFFERENTIAL GEOMETRY

7.1. Integrals over Curves and Surfaces

In Chap. 3, we discussed in some detail the theory of integration. The value of a single integral $\int_a^b f$ was defined to be the limit of certain sums $\Sigma f(t_j^*)\,\Delta t_j$, where $\Delta t_j = t_{j+1} - t_j$, $a = t_0 < t_1 < \cdots < t_n = b$, and $t_j \le t_j^* \le t_{j+1}$. Similarly, the value of the double integral $\iint_D f$ can be defined as the limit of sums $\Sigma f(p_{ij}) A(D_{ij})$, where $p_{ij} \in D_{ij}$ and the sets D_{ij} form a subdivision of D into pieces of small diameter.

As a direct generalization of these, we may also define the integral of a continuous function along a smooth curve γ or over a smooth surface Σ. For example, let γ be a smooth curve defined on the interval $[a, b]$ and let f be a function which is defined on a set containing the trace of γ. A subdivision of the interval $[a, b]$ yields a subdivision of γ into curved segments $\gamma_1, \gamma_2, \ldots, \gamma_n$. Take a point p_j lying on γ_j and form the sum $\Sigma f(p_j)L(\gamma_j)$. Then, the limit of these sums, as the norm of the subdivision of $[a, b]$ tends to zero, is defined to be the integral of f along γ, written $\int_\gamma f$. Explicitly, if the subdivision of $[a, b]$ is

$$a = t_0 < t_1 < \cdots < t_n = b,$$

then γ_j has domain $[t_{j-1}, t_j]$ and

$$L(\gamma_j) = \int_{t_{j-1}}^{t_j} |\gamma'(t)|\,dt.$$

Using the mean value theorem, this can also be written as

$$L(\gamma_j) = |\gamma'(\tau_j)|(t_j - t_{j-1})$$

where τ_j is a point in the interval $[t_{j-1}, t_j]$. If p_j is a point on γ_j, then $p_j = \gamma(t_j^*)$, where t_j^* also is a point in the interval $[t_{j-1}, t_j]$. The approximating sum $\Sigma f(p_j)L(\gamma_j)$ is thus the same as $\Sigma f(\gamma(t_j^*))|\gamma'(\tau_j)|(t_j - t_{j-1})$. By the line of argument which we used in the discussion of arc length (Sec.

6.2) we arrive at the fundamental equation

$$\int_\gamma f = \int_a^b f(\gamma(t))\,|\gamma'(t)|\,dt. \tag{7-1}$$

This shows that evaluation of the integral of a continuous function along a smooth curve can be reduced to the evaluation of an ordinary definite integral. We notice that in the special case in which f is constantly 1, $\int_\gamma f$ becomes the expression for the length of γ. One immediate consequence of (7-1) is that if γ and γ^* are smoothly equivalent, then

$$\int_\gamma f = \int_{\gamma^*} f$$

(see Exercise 5). If we choose γ^* as the curve which is equivalent to γ and which has arc length as parameter, then $|\gamma^{*\prime}(s)| = 1$ for all $s \in [0, l]$, where l is the length of γ; by (7-1), we then have

$$\int_\gamma f = \int_0^l f(\gamma^*(s))\,ds \tag{7-2}$$

Since $\gamma^*(s)$ is also a point on the trace of γ, this is frequently written

$$\int_\gamma f = \int_\gamma f(x, y, z)\,ds$$

and for this reason, an integral along a curve γ is sometimes referred to as the result of "integrating with respect to arc length."

As an illustration, let us find the center of gravity of a uniform wire which is bent into the shape of a semicircle. To describe this shape, we shall use the curve γ whose equation is $x = \cos t$, $y = \sin t$, $0 \le t \le \pi$. By definition, the center of gravity will be the point $(\bar{x}, \bar{y})$ where

$$M\bar{x} = \int_\gamma x\rho\,ds \qquad M\bar{y} = \int_\gamma y\rho\,ds$$

and

$$M = \int_\gamma \rho\,ds.$$

The function ρ specifies the density of the wire (mass per unit length), M is the total mass of the wire, and the first two integrals are the moments of the wire about the lines $x = 0$ and $y = 0$, respectively. Since the wire is uniform, ρ is constant, and $M = \rho L(\gamma) = \rho\pi$. From the equation for γ,

$$|\gamma'(t)| = |(-\sin t)^2 + (\cos t)^2|^{1/2} = 1$$

and γ has arc length for its parameter. Substituting for x and y, and using (7-2),

$$\int_\gamma \rho x\,ds = \rho \int_0^\pi \cos t\,dt = 0 = M\bar{x}$$

$$\int_\gamma \rho y\,ds = \rho \int_0^\pi \sin t\,dt = 2\rho = M\bar{y}$$

so that the center of gravity is $(0, 2/\pi)$. Other examples involving integrals along curves will be found in the Exercises.

Turning to integrals over surfaces, let Σ be a smooth surface with domain D, and let f be a continuous function defined on the trace of Σ. A subdivision of D into sets D_{ij} produces a subdivision of Σ into small surface elements Σ_{ij}. Let p_{ij} be a point lying on Σ_{ij} and form the sum $\Sigma f(p_{ij})A(\Sigma_{ij})$. If these have a limit as the norm of the subdivision of D tends to zero, then this limit is called the value of the integral of f over the surface Σ, and is written as $\iint_{\Sigma} f$. By an argument which is analogous to that used for integrals along curves, we arrive at the equivalent expression

$$\iint_{\Sigma} f = \iint_{D} f(\Sigma(u, v))\,|\mathbf{n}(u, v)|\,dudv \tag{7-3}$$

where
$$|\mathbf{n}(u, v)| = \left\{\frac{\partial(x, y)}{\partial(u, v)}^2 + \frac{\partial(y, z)}{\partial(u, v)}^2 + \frac{\partial(z, x)}{\partial(u, v)}^2\right\}^{1/2}.$$

Thus, evaluation of the integral of a function over a surface is reduced to the evaluation of an ordinary double integral. If f is constantly 1, then $\iint_{\Sigma} f = A(\Sigma)$, the area of Σ. For this reason, the general integral $\iint_{\Sigma} f$ is often written $\iint_{\Sigma} f(x, y, z)\,dA$, and one speaks of integrating f with respect to the element of surface area, over the surface Σ.

To illustrate this, let us find the center of gravity of a thin uniform sheet of metal which is in the shape of the paraboloid $z = x^2 + y^2$, with $x^2 + y^2 \leq 1$. The center of gravity is the point $(0, 0, \bar{z})$, where

$$M\bar{z} = \iint_{\Sigma} \rho z\,dA$$

and $M = \iint_{\Sigma} \rho\,dA$. Since the sheet of metal is uniform, ρ is constant, and $M = \rho A(\Sigma)$. To compute this, we need the value of $|\mathbf{n}|$ on Σ. Using x and y as the parameters for Σ rather than introducing u and v, and Exercise 3, Sec. 6.3, we have $|\mathbf{n}(x, y)| = [1 + 4x^2 + 4y^2]^{1/2}$ so that

$$A(\Sigma) = \iint_{D} \sqrt{1 + 4(x^2 + y^2)}\,dxdy$$

where D is the unit disk, $x^2 + y^2 \leq 1$. The form of the integrand and of D suggest that we transform to polar coordinates. Accordingly, the integrand becomes $(1 + 4r^2)^{1/2}$, $dxdy$ is replaced by $r\,drd\theta$, and D is replaced by the rectangle $0 \leq \theta \leq 2\pi$, $0 \leq r \leq 1$. Thus,

$$A(\Sigma) = \int_0^{2\pi} d\theta \int_0^1 \sqrt{1 + 4r^2}\, r\, dr$$
$$= \frac{\pi}{6}(5\sqrt{5} - 1)$$

In the same fashion, we have

$$\iint_\Sigma z\, dA = \iint_D (x^2 + y^2)\sqrt{1 + 4(x^2 + y^2)}\, dxdy$$
$$= \int_0^{2\pi} d\theta \int_0^1 r^2 \sqrt{1 + 4r^2}\, r\, dr$$
$$= \frac{\pi}{12}(5\sqrt{5} + 1/5).$$

Hence

$$\bar{z} = \left(\frac{1}{2}\right)\frac{5\sqrt{5} + 1/5}{5\sqrt{5} - 1} = .56.$$

Both of these notions, the integral along a curve and the integral over a surface, are simple examples of the more general category of functions whose domain of definition need not be sets of points. For example, $\int_\gamma f$ is a number which is determined by the pair (γ, f) composed of the smooth curve γ and the continuous function f. Similarly, $\iint_\Sigma f$ is determined by the pair (Σ, f). If one member of the pair, say Σ, is held fixed, then $\iint_\Sigma f$ is determined by the function f. This might be indicated by writing

$$\sigma(f) = \iint_\Sigma f.$$

σ is then a numerical-valued function whose domain is the class of continuous functions f which are defined on the trace of Σ. The name "functional" is often used for such functions to distinguish them from the more familiar type of function. Returning to $\iint_\Sigma f$, we might also hold f fixed, and regard this as determined by the choice of Σ. This may be indicated by writing

$$F(\Sigma) = \iint_\Sigma f \tag{7-4}$$

The domain of F is the class of smooth surfaces Σ having their trace in the region of definition of f. The surface area function A is an example of such a functional, arising from the choice of f as the constant function 1.

In our discussion of line and surface integrals, it is convenient to introduce a special nomenclature for these functionals. We shall say that F is a **curve-functional** if its domain is a class of smooth curves; a curve-functional F assigns a numerical value $F(\gamma)$ to any curve γ in its domain. Likewise, a **surface-functional** F has for its domain a class of smooth surfaces, and assigns a numerical value $F(\Sigma)$ to any surface Σ in its domain. An extensive class of curve-functionals can be put into the form $F(\gamma) = \int_\gamma f$, and many surface-functionals are of the form (7-4). (However, some of the most important functionals that concern us are not of these forms.) The theory of arc length, outlined in Sec. 6.2, is the study of the particular curve-functional L; the theory of surface area is the study of the surface-functional A.

To complete the classification system, we shall use the term "point function" for an ordinary numerical-valued function whose domain is a set of points. At the other end of the scale, we shall want to use functions F whose domain is a class of regions in 3-space. An example is given by

$$F(\Omega) = \iiint_\Omega f$$

We shall call these "region-functionals." Since curve- and surface-functionals have domains which are classes of mappings (e.g., classes of curves or classes of surfaces), we shall preserve this by associating with each region Ω in 3-space the identity mapping which sends Ω into itself, one-to-one.†

In the theory of integration of functions of one variable, one writes $\int_a^b f$ rather than $\int_{[a,b]} f$ in order to effect the orientation of the integral. We speak of integrating "from a to b" rather than integrating "over the interval $[a, b]$." Moreover, we write $\int_b^a f = -\int_a^b f$. Similarly, we

† This is a somewhat crude description of the n-dimensional case, reduced to $n = 3$. In the general case, the domain of a functional F will be a class of mappings from k-space into n-space, for $k = 1, 2, \ldots, n$. Each choice of k gives a category of functionals F. When $k = 1$, we have the curve-functionals, and when $k = 2$, the surface-functionals. The mappings from k-space to n-space generate the class of *k-chains*. When $k = n$, an n-chain can be thought of as a mapping of a portion of n-space into itself. What we have done is to consider only those that are identity maps of a set onto itself. An adequate treatment of this may be found in the mimeographed lecture notes by B. Eckmann, "Differentiable Manifolds," University of Michigan, 1950.

can introduce orientation into the integral along a curve. Let us use $-\gamma$ for the curve which is obtained by reversing the direction of γ.† If $F(\gamma) = \int_\gamma f$, then $F(-\gamma) = -F(\gamma)$, for

$$\begin{aligned} F(-\gamma) &= \int_{-\gamma} f = \int_b^a f(\gamma(t))\,|\gamma'(t)|\,dt \\ &= -\int_a^b f(\gamma(t))\,|\gamma'(t)|\,dt = -F(\gamma). \end{aligned}$$

Likewise, we can introduce orientation into double integrals, or more generally, into integration over surfaces. If D is a region in the (u, v) plane, then D can be assigned one of two orientations, corresponding intuitively to the two "sides" of D. Stated another way, a normal vector can point forward, toward the viewer, or backward, away from the viewer. This, in turn, leads to an accepted sense of "positive" rotation. It is conventional to assign the term "positive" to a counterclockwise rotation, and "negative" to a clockwise rotation. Once a direction of positive rotation has been assigned to D, it, in turn, induces an orientation in the boundary curves of D, as indicated in Fig. 7-1; in the standard description, "trace each boundary curve in a direction which keeps the left hand in D." (Note that turning D over has the effect of reversing the orientation.) When D has been oriented, $-D$ will indicate the region endowed with the opposite orientation. When D is positively oriented, $\iint_D f$ has its usual meaning. When the orientation of D is reversed, it is natural to require that the integral change sign; thus, $\iint_{-D} f = -\iint_D f$.

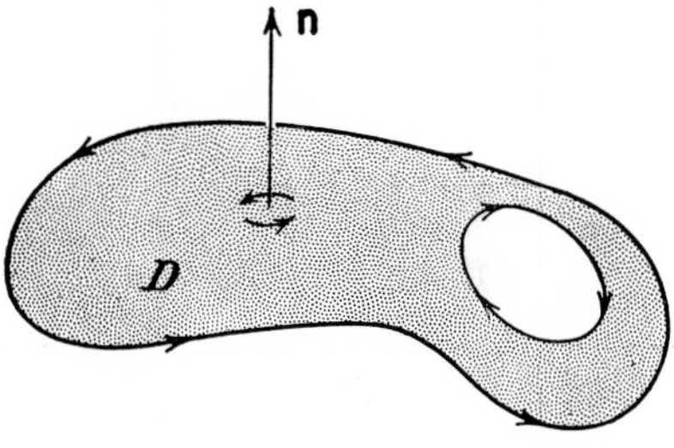

FIG. 7-1

Before proceeding further, let us give an illustration to show the usefulness of this notation. Let D be the region in the (x, y) plane bounded by $x = 0$, $x = 2$, $y = 0$, and $y = f(x)$. Assuming that $f(x) > 0$, the area of D is given by

$$\iint_D 1 = \int_0^2 dx \int_0^{f(x)} dy = \int_0^2 f \tag{7-5}$$

so that we say that the integral of a (positive) function is the area under

† If γ has domain $[0, 1]$ then $-\gamma$ is the mapping defined by $(-\gamma)(t) = \gamma(1 - t)$, $0 \leq t \leq 1$.

its graph. Suppose f is not positive; for example, let $f(x) = x^2 - 1$. Is (7-5) still valid? Examining the right half of Fig. 7-2, we see that the graph of f crosses the axis, and the region D is not connected, but falls into two pieces, D_1 and D_2. If the integral of f is expressed in terms of areas, we must write

$$\int_0^2 f = A(D_2) - A(D_1).$$

As oriented sets, however, D_2 has positive orientation and D_1 negative

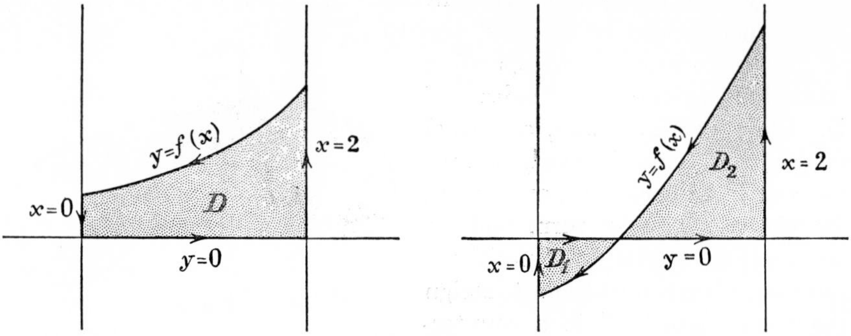

FIG. 7-2

orientation, if we orient the bounding graphs in the natural way. Thus,

$$\iint_{D_2} 1 = A(D_2) \quad \text{but} \quad \iint_{D_1} 1 = -A(D_1).$$

This gives

$$\int_0^2 f = \iint_{D_1} 1 + \iint_{D_2} 1 = \iint_D 1$$

and reestablishes Eq. (7-5).

For integrals over surfaces, an analogous treatment is possible. If the domain of a surface Σ is oriented, then the mapping Σ carries this over to the image set, as indicated in Fig. 6-27. The reduction of the integral of a function over Σ to the computation of an integral over the domain D, made possible by (7-3), shows that $\iint_\Sigma f$ changes sign when the orientation of Σ is reversed.

In 3-space, a region Ω may be assigned one of two orientations. The most familiar instance of this is in the choice of labels for the axes of a coordinate trihedral. There are only two essentially different systems. They are called "right-handed" or "left-handed"; as indicated in Fig. 7-3, they may be distinguished by viewing the origin from the first octant. If the trihedral is rotated so that the X axis moves to the position occupied by the Y, the Y to the Z, and the Z to the X, then the direction of rotation will be counterclockwise for a right-hand system, and clockwise for a left-hand system. We choose, by convention, to call the right-hand system **positive.** Any other labeling of the axes may be brought into one of the two that are shown, by a rotation. This has the

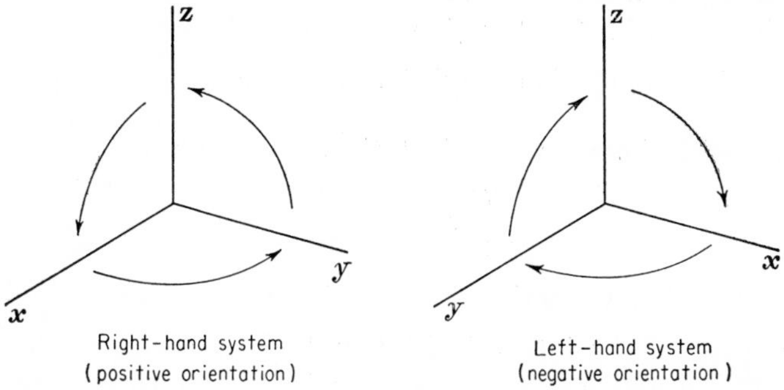

FIG. 7-3

effect of permuting the labels cyclically; thus the positive systems are XYZ, YZX, and ZXY, and the negative systems are YXZ, XZY, and ZYX. Just as the choice of orientation for a plane region whose boundary is a simple closed curve γ induces an orientation in γ, and vice versa,

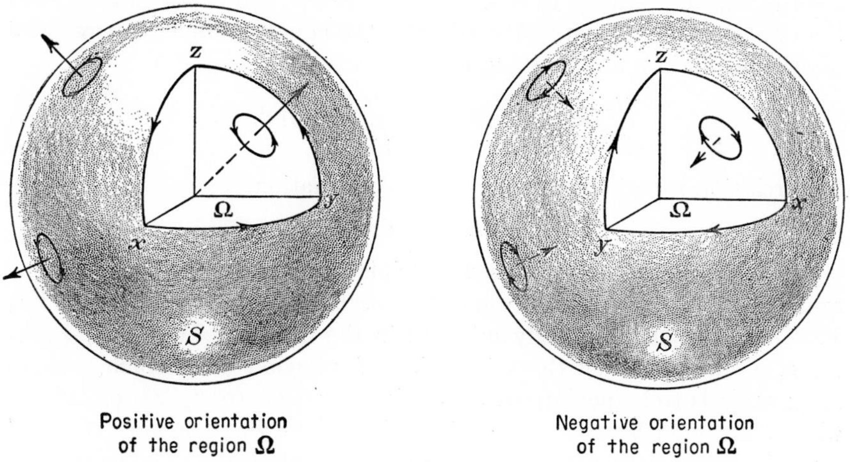

FIG. 7-4

so orientation of a three-dimensional region whose boundary is a simple closed surface S induces an orientation in S, and conversely. If Ω is a solid ball and S is the sphere which forms its boundary, then, viewing S from outside, positive orientation of Ω gives counterclockwise orientation of S, and negative orientation of Ω gives clockwise orientation of S (see Fig. 7-4). Moreover, if the direction of the normals to S are chosen to correspond to the local orientation of S, then it will be seen that positive orientation of Ω goes with the fact that the normals to S always point out of the region, while negative orientation of Ω makes the normals point inward.

When a region Ω has positive orientation, we define the value of the oriented integral of a function f over Ω to be the same as before; when Ω has negative orientation, we define the value to be $-\iiint_{\Omega} f$. If $-\Omega$ indicates Ω with the opposite orientation, then we have

$$\iiint_{-\Omega} f = -\iiint_{\Omega} f.$$

In the integral of a function of one variable, the notation $\int_a^b f$ conveys the orientation of the interval of integration by means of the position of the limits, a and b. In discussing oriented multiple integrals, this device is no longer possible. However, another device is available. In the expression $\iint_D f(x, y)\, dxdy$, the symbol "$dxdy$" has been used so far only to convey the names of the variables of integration. Let us use it now to convey the orientation of D as well, writing "$dxdy$" when D has the same orientation as that of the XY plane, and "$dydx$" when it has the opposite orientation. Accordingly, the equation governing reversal of orientation in a double integral becomes†

$$\iint_D f(x, y)\, dydx = -\iint_D f(x, y)\, dxdy.$$

This relation is embodied in the symbolic equation

$$dydx = -dxdy. \tag{7-6}$$

A similar device may be used in triple integrals. The X, Y, and Z axes are positively oriented when they occur in one of the orders XYZ, YZX, ZXY, and negatively oriented in the orders XZY, ZYX, YXZ. Thus, we may convey the orientation of a region over which a triple integration is to be performed by writing "$dxdydz$" (or $dydzdx$ or $dzdxdy$) when the region has the same orientation as XYZ space, and "$dxdzdy$" (or $dzdxdy$ or $dydxdz$) when it has the opposite orientation. For example, we would have

$$\iiint_{\Omega} f(x, y, z)\, dydxdz = -\iiint_{\Omega} f(x, y, z)\, dxdydz.$$

† This has nothing to do with the reversal of the order of integration in iterated integrals; the latter, being repeated singlefold integrals, are oriented by the use of upper and lower limits of integration.

We observe that this relation is also consistent with the symbolic equation (7-6). Since $dydx = -dxdy$, $dydxdz = -dxdydz$. Again,

$$\begin{aligned} dydzdx &= dy(dzdx) = dy(-dxdz) = -dydxdz \\ &= -(-dxdy)\,dz = dxdydz. \end{aligned}$$

EXERCISES

1. Find the center of gravity of a homogeneous wire which has the shape of the curve $y = (e^x + e^{-x})/2$, $-1 \le x \le 1$.

2. The moment of inertia of a particle of mass m about an axis of rotation whose distance is l is defined to be ml^2. Show that a reasonable definition for the moment of inertia of a wire in the shape of the plane curve γ about the Y axis is

$$I = \int_\gamma \rho x^2\, ds.$$

3. A wire has the shape of the curve $y = x^2$, $-1 \le x \le 1$. The density of the wire at (x, y) is $k\sqrt{y}$. What is the moment of inertia of the wire about the Y axis?

4. Formulate a definition for the moment of inertia of a wire in space about the Z axis.

5. Let γ_1 and γ_2 be smoothly equivalent curves, and let f be continuous on their trace. Show by (7-1) that $\int_{\gamma_1} f = \int_{\gamma_2} f$.

6. The force of attraction between two particles acts along the line joining them, and its magnitude is given by $km_1m_2r^{-2}$, where m_1 and m_2 are their masses, and r is the distance between them. Find the attraction on a unit mass located at the origin which is due to a homogeneous straight wire of infinite length, whose distance from the origin is l.

***7.** Let Σ_1 and Σ_2 be smoothly equivalent surfaces, and let f be continuous on their trace. Show by (7-3) that

$$\iint_{\Sigma_1} f = \iint_{\Sigma_2} f.$$

8. Find the moment of inertia of a homogeneous spherical shell about a diameter.

9. A sheet of metal has the shape of the surface $z = x^2 + y^2$, $0 \le x^2 + y^2 \le 2$. The density at (x, y, z) is kz. Find the moment of inertia about the Z axis.

10. What is the force of attraction upon a unit mass located at $(0, 0, l)$ which is due to a homogeneous circular disk of radius R, center $(0, 0, 0)$, and lying in the XY plane? What happens if R is allowed to become infinite?

***11.** Show that the force of attraction within a spherical shell of constant density is everywhere zero.

7.2. Differential Forms

It is not possible to put all curve-functionals into the form $F(\gamma) = \int_\gamma f$, where the function f is independent of γ. As we shall see, an example is furnished by the class of functionals that are known as line integrals. These form a special division of the more general category known as differential forms. In n-space, there are $n + 1$ classes of differential forms, called in turn **0-forms, 1-forms, . . . , n-forms.** In 3-space we shall deal with 0-forms, 1-forms, 2-forms, and 3-forms, while in the plane, we shall meet only 0-forms, 1-forms, and 2-forms. For simplicity, we begin with the theory of differential forms in the plane ($n = 2$), starting with the class of 1-forms. These are also called **line integrals.**

Definition. *The general continuous 1-form in the XY plane is a curve-functional ω denoted by*

$$\omega = A(x, y)\, dx + B(x, y)\, dy$$

where A and B are continuous functions defined in a region Ω. If γ is a smooth curve, with equation $x = \phi(t)$, $y = \psi(t)$, $a \le t \le b$, whose trace lies in Ω, then the value which ω assigns to γ is defined by the formula

$$\omega(\gamma) = \int_a^b [A(\gamma(t))\phi'(t) + B(\gamma(t))\psi'(t)]\, dt. \tag{7-7}$$

The rule for computing $\omega(\gamma)$ can be stated thus: Given the differential form ω and a curve γ, we "evaluate ω on γ" by substituting into ω the expressions for x, y, dx, and dy which are obtained from the equations of γ, following the familiar custom of replacing dx by $\frac{dx}{dt}\, dt = \phi'(t)\, dt$, and dy by $\psi'(t)\, dt$; this results in an expression of the form $g(t)\, dt$, which is then used as an integrand to compute $\int_a^b g(t)\, dt$, where $[a, b]$ is the domain of γ. To put this in a more evident way, the value of $\omega(\gamma)$ is usually written

$$\int_\gamma \omega = \int_\gamma [A(x, y)\, dx + B(x, y)\, dy],$$

and one speaks of *integrating the differential form ω along the curve γ.* If we choose $A = 1$, $B = 0$, then $\omega = dx$, so that dx (and dy) are special 1-forms. For example, dx assigns to the smooth curve γ the value

$$\int_\gamma dx = \int_a^b \phi'(t)\, dt = \phi(b) - \phi(a)$$

which is the horizontal distance between the end points of γ. Since every 1-form can be expressed as a linear combination of dx and dy with function coefficients, dx and dy are called the **basic 1-forms** in the XY plane.

Let $\omega = xy\, dx - y^2\, dy$ and let γ be given by $x = 3t^2$, $y = t^3$, for $0 \le t \le 1$. On γ, we have

$$\begin{aligned} \omega &= (3t^2)(t^3)(6t\, dt) - (t^3)^2(3t^2\, dt) \\ &= (18t^6 - 3t^8)\, dt. \end{aligned}$$

Thus $$\int_\gamma \omega = \int_0^1 (18t^6 - 3t^8)\, dt = 18/7 - 1/3 = 47/21$$

Let us compute the integral of the same 1-form along the straight line from (0, 0) to (2, 4). The equation for this curve is $x = 2t$, $y = 4t$, $0 \le t \le 1$. On γ, $\omega = (2t)(4t)(2dt) - (4t)^2(4dt) = -48t^2\,dt$ so that

$$\int_\gamma \omega = \int_0^1 (-48t^2)\,dt = -16.$$

As we shall show in Theorem 2, $\int_{\gamma_1} \omega = \int_{\gamma_2} \omega$ whenever γ_1 and γ_2 are smoothly equivalent curves. In this last example, for instance, we may also use the parametrization $y = 2x$, $x = x$, $0 \le x \le 2$. Making this substitution instead, we have on γ

$$\omega = x(2x)\,dx - (2x)^2(2dx)$$
$$= -6x^2\,dx$$

and

$$\int_\gamma (xy\,dx - y^2\,dy) = \int_0^2 (-6x^2)\,dx = -16$$

in agreement with the previous calculation.

Certain general properties of 1-forms (line integrals) in the plane can be seen at once from (7-7). Reversal of the orientation of a curve changes the sign of the integral, since the direction of integration in the integral containing dt will be reversed. We may state this in the form

$$\int_{-\gamma} \omega = -\int_\gamma \omega.$$

If the curve γ is the union of a finite set of curves

$$\gamma = \gamma_1 + \gamma_2 + \cdots + \gamma_n,$$

then

$$\int_\gamma \omega = \int_{\gamma_1} \omega + \int_{\gamma_2} \omega + \cdots + \int_{\gamma_n} \omega$$

As an example, let us compute the integral of $\omega = xy\,dx + y^2\,dy$ along the closed polygonal path which forms the edge of the unit square, $0 \le x \le 1, 0 \le y \le 1$ (see Fig. 7-5). We write $\gamma = \gamma_1 + \gamma_2 + \gamma_3 + \gamma_4$, where these are the four sides of the square. We evaluate each of the line integrals $\int_{\gamma_i} \omega$ separately. On γ_1, $y = 0$ and $x = x$, with x going from 0 to 1; thus, on γ_1, $\omega = 0\,dx + 0 = 0$ and $\int_{\gamma_1} \omega = 0$. On γ_2, $x = 1$ and $y = y$, with y going from 0 to 1; thus, $\omega = (1)(y)0 + y^2\,dy$ and $\int_{\gamma_2} \omega = \int_0^1 y^2\,dy = \frac{1}{3}$. On γ_3, $y = 1$ and $x = x$, with x going from 1

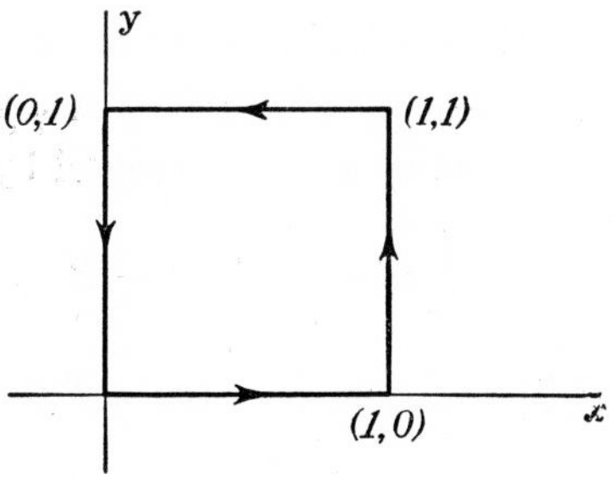

FIG. 7-5

to 0 because of the orientation of γ_3; thus, $\omega = (x)(1)\,dx + (1)0 = x\,dx$, and $\int_{\gamma_3} \omega = \int_1^0 x\,dx = -\frac{1}{2}$.† Finally, on γ_4, $x = 0$ and $y = y$, with y going from 1 to 0, so that $\omega = 0 + y^2\,dy$ and $\int_{\gamma_4} \omega = \int_1^0 y^2\,dy = -\frac{1}{3}$. Adding these, we have

$$\int_\gamma \omega = 0 + \tfrac{1}{3} - \tfrac{1}{2} - \tfrac{1}{3} = -\tfrac{1}{2}.$$

Integration of a 1-form is especially simple if it involves only one of the variables. For example, let $\omega = A(x)\,dx$ and let γ be a smooth curve whose starting point is (x_0, y_0) and whose last point is (x_1, y_1), given by $x = \phi(t)$, $y = \psi(t)$, $0 \le t \le 1$. On γ we have

$$\omega = A(\phi(t))\phi'(t)\,dt$$

so that

$$\int_\gamma \omega = \int_0^1 A(\phi(t))\phi'(t)\,dt.$$

Making the substitution $x = \phi(t)$, this becomes merely

$$\int_\gamma \omega = \int_{x_0}^{x_1} A(x)\,dx.$$

(In particular, we note that the value of $\int_\gamma \omega$ in this case depends only upon the location of the end points of γ and not upon the rest of the trace of the curve.) Comparable statements can be made for 1-forms

$$\omega = B(y)\,dy$$

(see Exercises 6 and 7).

The general 1-form (line integral) in 3-space is

$$\omega = A(x, y, z)\,dx + B(x, y, z)\,dy + C(x, y, z)\,dz,$$

and the method of evaluating $\omega(\gamma) = \int_\gamma \omega$ for a curve γ is the same. If γ is given by $x = \phi(t)$, $y = \psi(t)$, $z = \theta(t)$ for $0 \le t \le 1$, then we *define* the value of the line integral by

$$\begin{aligned} \int_\gamma \omega &= \int_\gamma A\,dx + B\,dy + C\,dz \\ &= \int_0^1 A(\phi(t), \psi(t), \theta(t))\frac{dx}{dt}\,dt \qquad \text{(7-8)} \\ &\quad + \int_0^1 B(\phi(t), \psi(t), \theta(t))\frac{dy}{dt}\,dt + \int_0^1 C(\phi(t), \psi(t), \theta(t))\frac{dz}{dt}\,dt. \end{aligned}$$

† Alternatively, γ_3 could be given by $x = 1 - t$, $y = 1$ for $0 \le t \le 1$, so that $\omega = (1 - t)(1)(-dt) + 0 = (t - 1)\,dt$ and $\int_{\gamma_3} \omega = \int_0^1 (t - 1)\,dt = -\frac{1}{2}$.

As an illustration, let $\omega = xy\,dx - y\,dy + 3zy\,dz$ and γ be: $x = t^2$, $y = t$, $z = -t^3$. On γ, we have

$$\omega = (t^2)(t)(2t\,dt) - (t)(dt) + 3(-t^3)(t)(-3t^2\,dt) = (9t^6 + 2t^4 - t)\,dt.$$

If the domain of γ is [0, 1], then

$$\int_\gamma \omega = \int_0^1 (9t^6 + 2t^4 - t)\,dt = 9/7 + 2/5 - 1/2.$$

Let us turn now to the theory of 2-forms. These will be a special class of surface-functionals. In the case of 2-forms in the plane, the theory is especially simple. As defined in Chap. 6, a surface in n-space is a mapping from a region D in the parameter plane into n-space. When $n = 2$, the notion of surface degenerates into the ordinary notion of a transformation T of the plane into itself, and a smooth surface is such a transformation which is of class C' and whose Jacobian is never zero. A simple smooth surface (surface element) is thus a one-to-one continuous transformation with nonzero Jacobian, which maps a region D of the (u, v) plane into a region in the (x, y) plane. Since the Jacobian is continuous, it must be always positive in D, or always negative in D; in the former case, T is orientation preserving, and in the latter, orientation reversing. We may thus identify such a surface with its trace in the (x, y) plane, oriented according to the sign of the Jacobian of T. The notion of "surface" becomes simply that of an oriented region in the plane. We recall the device which was used at the end of Sec. 7.1, and adopt the following definition for 2-forms in the plane.

Definition. *The general continuous 2-form in the XY plane is a region-functional denoted by*

(7-9) $$\omega = A(x, y)\,dxdy$$

where the function A is continuous. If Ω is a region (having area) in the domain of definition of A, then the value which ω assigns to Ω is defined by

$$\omega(\Omega) = \iint_\Omega A(x, y)\,dxdy.$$

In line with our previous discussion, it is also natural to consider expressions of the form $A(x, y)\,dydx$; this is also a 2-form, but by means of the convention that $dydx = -dxdy$, we may replace it by $-A(x, y)\,dxdy$ which is again of the form (7-9). The general 2-form in the plane becomes merely the oriented double integral which we discussed in Sec. 7.1.

The situation in 3-space is more complicated. In addition to the basic 2-form $dxdy$, we also have $dydz$ and $dzdx$; moreover, their coefficients may be functions of three variables. Thus, the general 2-form in space becomes

$$\omega = A(x, y, z)\, dydz + B(x, y, z)\, dzdx + C(x, y, z)\, dxdy.$$

This is a surface-functional, and the value which it assigns to a surface Σ is denoted by $\iint_{\Sigma} \omega$. However, we cannot explain the meaning of this symbol further, nor the method for evaluating it, without some additional machinery.

We complete the roster of differential forms in the plane by defining a 0-form to be merely any continuous function (= point function). In space, we must also define 3-forms.

Definition. *The general continuous 3-form in XYZ space is a region-functional denoted by*

$$\omega = A(x, y, z)\, dxdydz$$

where the function A is continuous. If Ω is a subset (having volume) of the domain of definition of A, then the value which ω assigns to Ω is defined by

$$\omega(\Omega) = \iiint_{\Omega} A(x, y, z)\, dxdydz.$$

Thus, the 3-forms in space are oriented triple integrals; a 3-form in which the order is not $dxdydz$ can be reduced to this form by permuting pairs. The 3-form $C(x, y, z)\, dydzdx$ is the same as $-C(x, y, z)\, dydxdz$ and as $C(x, y, z)\, dxdydz$.

We next introduce an algebraic structure into the system of differential forms by defining **addition** and **multiplication** of forms. Any two forms of the same class are added by combining coefficients of like terms. For example,

$$(x^2\, dx + xy^2\, dy) + (dx - 3y\, dy) = (x^2 + 1)\, dx + (xy^2 - 3y)\, dy$$

$$(2x + y)\, dxdy + (xy - y)\, dxdy = (2x + xy)\, dxdy$$

$$(3dx + xyz\, dy - xz\, dz) + (y\, dx - dz) = (3 + y)\, dx + xyz\, dy - (xz + 1)\, dz.$$

When two terms contain the same differentials, but in different orders, they must be brought into agreement before adding their coefficients, using the convention:

$$\begin{aligned} dxdy &= -dydx \\ dydz &= -dzdy \\ dzdx &= -dxdz \end{aligned} \tag{7-10}$$

For example,

$$(x\,dydz + y^2\,dxdy + z\,dxdz) + (3dydz - z\,dydx + x^2\,dzdx)$$
$$= (x\,dydz + 3dydz) + (y^2\,dxdy - z\,dydx) + (z\,dxdz + x^2\,dzdx)$$
$$= (x + 3)\,dydz + (y^2 + z)\,dxdy + (z - x^2)\,dxdz.$$

Multiplication of differential forms is governed by the rules set forth in (7-10) and the following:

$$dxdx = dydy = dzdz = 0. \tag{7-11}$$

Except for these conventions, and the necessity of preserving the order of factors, multiplication can be performed as in elementary algebra.† For example,

$$\begin{aligned}(2dx + 3xy\,dy)(dx) &= 2(dxdx) + (3xy)(dydx)\\ &= 0 + (3xy)(-dxdy)\\ &= -3xy\,dxdy\end{aligned}$$

$$\begin{aligned}&(2dx + 3xy\,dy)(x\,dx - y\,dy)\\ &\quad= (2x)(dxdx) + (3x^2y)(dydx) + (-2y)(dxdy) + (-3xy^2)(dydy)\\ &\quad= 0 + (3x^2y)(-dxdy) + (-2y)(dxdy) + 0\\ &\quad= -(3x^2y + 2y)\,dxdy.\end{aligned}$$

Taking a somewhat more complicated example involving three variables,

$$\begin{aligned}&(x\,dx - z\,dy + y^2\,dz)(x^2\,dydz + 2dzdx - y\,dxdy)\\ &\qquad= x^3\,dxdydz + 2x\,dxdzdy - xy\,dxdxdy\\ &\qquad\quad - x^2z\,dydydz - 2z\,dydzdx + yz\,dydxdy\\ &\qquad\quad + y^2x^2\,dzdydz + 2y^2\,dzdzdx - y^3\,dzdxdy\\ &\qquad= x^3\,dxdydz - 2z\,dydzdx - y^3\,dzdxdy\\ &\qquad= (x^3 - 2z - y^3)\,dxdydz.\end{aligned}$$

Such computations may be shortened by observing that any term which contains a repetition of one of the basic differential forms dx, dy, dz will be zero. Accordingly, the product of two 2-forms in space, or in the plane, and the product of a 1-form and a 2-form in the plane are automatically zero. In general, the product of a k-form and an m-form is a $k + m$-form; if $k + m$ is larger than n, the number of variables, then there will be repetitions, and such a product will be zero. Since a 0-form is merely a function, multiplication by a 0-form does not affect the degree of a form. For example,

$$(3x^2y)(x\,dx - xy\,dy) = 3x^3y\,dx - 3x^3y^2\,dy.$$

Finally we define a notion of **differentiation** for forms. In general, if ω

† Stated in somewhat more technical language, what we are saying is that the system of differential forms in 3-space is a linear associative algebra with basis elements 1, dx, dy, dz, $dxdy$, $dydz$, $dzdx$, $dxdydz$, whose coefficient space is the class of continuous functions, and whose multiplication table is specified by giving the relations (7-10) and (7-11) which hold for the generators dx, dy, dz.

is a k-form, its derivative $d\omega$ will be a $k + 1$-form. We give the definition of $d\omega$ for forms in 3-space.

Definition. (i) *If A is a 0-form (function) of class C' then dA is the 1-form*

$$dA = \frac{\partial A}{\partial x}\,dx + \frac{\partial A}{\partial y}\,dy + \frac{\partial A}{\partial z}\,dz$$

(ii) *If ω is a 1-form $A\,dx + B\,dy + C\,dz$ whose coefficients are functions of class C', then $d\omega$ is the 2-form*

$$d\omega = (dA)\,dx + (dB)\,dy + (dC)\,dz.$$

(iii) *If ω is a 2-form $A\,dydz + B\,dzdx + C\,dxdy$ whose coefficients are of class C', then $d\omega$ is the 3-form*

$$d\omega = (dA)\,dydz + (dB)\,dzdx + (dC)\,dxdy.$$

In (ii) and (iii), $d\omega$ is to be computed by evaluating dA, dB, and dC, and then computing the indicated products. Since dA is a 1-form, $(dA)\,dx$ is indeed a 2-form and $(dA)\,dydz$ a 3-form. The derivative of a 3-form may be computed in the same fashion, but since it will be a 4-form in three variables, it will automatically be zero. Differentiation of forms in two variables is done in the same fashion. Some examples will illustrate the technique.

Form	*Derivative*
$A = x^2y$	$dA = 2xy\,dx + x^2\,dy$
$A = xy + yz$	$dA = y\,dx + (x + z)\,dy + y\,dz$
$\omega = x^2y\,dx$	$d\omega = d(x^2y)\,dx$
	$= (2xy\,dx + x^2\,dy)\,dx$
	$= -x^2\,dxdy$
$\omega = (xy + yz)\,dx$	$d\omega = d(xy + yz)\,dx$
	$= (y\,dx + (x + z)dy + y\,dz)\,dx$
	$= (x + z)\,dydx + y\,dzdx$
$\omega = x^2y\,dydz - xz\,dxdy$	$d\omega = d(x^2y)\,dydz - d(xz)\,dxdy$
	$= (2xy\,dx + x^2\,dy)\,dydz - (z\,dx + x\,dz)\,dxdy$
	$= 2xy\,dxdydz - x\,dzdxdy$
	$= (2xy - x)\,dxdydz$

This extensive barrage of definitions is justified and partly motivated by the following result.

Theorem 1. *If $u = f(x, y)$ and $v = g(x, y)$, then*

$$dudv = \frac{\partial(u, v)}{\partial(x, y)}\,dxdy.$$

We have $du = f_1\,dx + f_2\,dy$ and $dv = g_1\,dx + g_2\,dy$ so that

$$\begin{aligned} du\,dv &= (f_1\,dx + f_2\,dy)(g_1\,dx + g_2\,dy) \\ &= f_1g_1\,dxdx + f_1g_2\,dxdy + f_2g_1\,dydx + f_2g_2\,dydy \\ &= f_1g_2\,dxdy + f_2g_1\,dydx = (f_1g_2 - f_2g_1)\,dxdy \\ &= \begin{vmatrix} f_1 & f_2 \\ g_1 & g_2 \end{vmatrix}\,dxdy = \frac{\partial(u, v)}{\partial(x, y)}\,dxdy. \quad \blacksquare \end{aligned}$$

Recalling that the theorem on transformation of multiple integrals requires one to replace $dudv$ by $\partial(u, v)/\partial(x, y)\, dxdy$ when making the substitution $u = f(x, y)$, $v = g(x, y)$, this theorem makes it possible to carry out such substitutions by the same routine procedure that one uses in singlefold integrals. For example, in Sec. 6.1, we considered the integral $\iint_{D^*} \exp (x - y)/(x + y)\, dxdy$, where D^* is the triangle bounded by $x = 0$, $y = 0$, $x + y = 1$. We set $u = x - y$, $v = x + y$, which maps D^* onto another triangle D with vertices $(0, 0)$, $(1, 1)$, $(-1, 1)$. We have $du = dx - dy$, $dv = dx + dy$, so that

$$dudv = (dx - dy)(dx + dy) = dxdy - dydx = 2dxdy.$$

Accordingly, we have

$$\iint_{D^*} \exp\left(\frac{x-y}{x+y}\right) dxdy = \iint_{D} e^{u/v}\tfrac{1}{2}dudv,$$

from which one may proceed as before to complete the problem.

We are at last ready to explain the meaning to be attached to a 2-form in 3-space, or more generally, a k-form in n-space.

Definition. *The general continuous 2-form in space is a surface-functional denoted by*

$$\omega = A(x, y, z)\, dydz + B(x, y, z)\, dzdx + C(x, y, z)\, dxdy$$

where A, B, and C are continuous functions defined in a region Ω. Let Σ be a smooth surface with domain D defined by

$$\begin{cases} x = \phi(u, v) \\ y = \psi(u, v) \\ z = \theta(u, v) \end{cases} \qquad (u, v) \in D$$

whose trace lies in Ω. Then, the value which ω assigns to Σ is defined by

$$\iint_{\Sigma} \omega = \iint_{D} \{A(\Sigma(u, v))\, d\psi d\theta + B(\Sigma(u, v))\, d\theta d\phi + C(\Sigma(u, v))\, d\phi d\psi\}$$

We note that again, $\iint_{\Sigma} \omega$ is computed by a straightforward process of substitution; ω is evaluated on the surface by using the equation for Σ, and the operations of differentiation and multiplication for differential forms. For example, let $\omega = xy\, dydz + x\, dzdx + 3zx\, dxdy$, and let Σ be the surface

$$\begin{cases} x = u + v \\ y = u - v \\ z = uv \end{cases} \qquad \begin{matrix} 0 \le u \le 1 \\ 0 \le v \le 1 \end{matrix}$$

On Σ, we have

$$\begin{aligned} dydz &= (du - dv)(v\,du + u\,dv) = (u + v)\,dudv \\ dzdx &= (v\,du + u\,dv)(du + dv) = (v - u)\,dudv \\ dxdy &= (du + dv)(du - dv) = -2dudv \end{aligned}$$

and $\omega = (u + v)(u - v)(u + v)\,dudv + (u + v)(v - u)\,dudv$
$\qquad + 3uv(u + v)(-2)\,dudv$

$$= (u^3 - 5u^2v - 7uv^2 - v^3 + v^2 - u^2)\,dudv$$

so that

$$\begin{aligned} \iint_\Sigma \omega &= \int_0^1 du \int_0^1 (u^3 - 5u^2v - 7uv^2 - v^3 + v^2 - u^2)\,dv \\ &= \int_0^1 (u^3 - \tfrac{7}{2}u^2 - \tfrac{7}{3}u + \tfrac{1}{12})\,du \\ &= -2. \end{aligned}$$

Again, let ω be the same 2-form, and let Σ be the surface given by $z = x^2 + y^2$, with $0 \leq x \leq 1$, $0 \leq y \leq 1$. On Σ, $dz = 2x\,dx + 2y\,dy$ so that

$$\begin{aligned} dydz &= dy\,(2x\,dx + 2y\,dy) = -2x\,dxdy \\ dzdx &= (2x\,dx + 2y\,dy)\,dx = -2y\,dxdy \end{aligned}$$

and on Σ we have

$$\begin{aligned} \omega &= xy\,dydz + x\,dzdx + 3zx\,dxdy \\ &= (xy)(-2x\,dxdy) + x(-2y\,dxdy) + 3(x^2 + y^2)x\,dxdy \\ &= (3x^3 + 3xy^2 - 2x^2y - 2xy)\,dxdy. \end{aligned}$$

Thus, the integral of this 2-form over Σ is

$$\begin{aligned} \iint_\Sigma \omega &= \int_0^1 dx \int_0^1 (3x^3 + 3xy^2 - 2x^2y - 2xy)\,dy \\ &= \int_0^1 (3x^3 - x^2)\,dx = \tfrac{5}{12}. \end{aligned}$$

When two surfaces are parametrically equivalent, then a 2-form will assign the same value to both. This, together with the analogous statement for line integrals, is the content of the next theorem.

Theorem 2. (i) *If γ_1 and γ_2 are smoothly equivalent curves and ω is a continuous 1-form defined on the trace of the curves, then* $\int_{\gamma_1} \omega = \int_{\gamma_2} \omega$.

(ii) *If Σ_1 and Σ_2 are smoothly equivalent surfaces, and ω is a continuous 2-form defined on their trace, then* $\iint_{\Sigma_1} \omega = \iint_{\Sigma_2} \omega$.

For (i), let us consider the 1-form $\omega = A(x, y, z)\,dx$. We may assume that $\gamma_2(t) = \gamma_1(f(t))$, where f is of class C', and maps the interval $[\alpha, \beta]$, which is the domain of γ_2, onto the interval $[a, b]$, which is the domain of γ_1. If we have $x = \phi(t)$ on γ_1, then $x = \phi(f(t))$ on γ_2. Computing the integral of ω along γ_2, we have

$$\int_{\gamma_2} \omega = \int_\alpha^\beta A(\gamma_2(t)) \frac{dx}{dt}\, dt$$
$$= \int_\alpha^\beta A(\gamma_1(f(t)))\ \phi'(f(t))\ f'(t)\ dt.$$

In this ordinary definite integral, make the substitution $s = f(t)$, and obtain

$$\int_{\gamma_2} \omega = \int_a^b A(\gamma_1(s))\phi'(s)\ ds = \int_{\gamma_1} \omega.$$

Similarly, one can show the same relation for the 1-forms $B\ dy$ and $C\ dz$, and by addition, obtain $\int_{\gamma_2} \omega = \int_{\gamma_1} \omega$ for a general 1-form ω.

For (ii), we consider first a 2-form $\omega = A(x, y, z)\ dxdy$. Let Σ_1 be a surface with domain D_1 on which we have $x = \phi(r, s)$, $y = \psi(r, s)$, $z = \theta(r, s)$ and let Σ_2 be a surface with domain D_2 which is smoothly equivalent to Σ_1; we may therefore assume that we have

$$\Sigma_2(u, v) = \Sigma_1(T(u, v)),$$

where $T(u, v) = (r, s)$ describes a C' transformation T mapping D_2 onto D_1, one-to-one, orientation preserving. Using the result of Theorem 1, we evaluate ω on Σ_2:

$$\omega = A(\Sigma_2(u, v))\ dxdy = A(\Sigma_2(u, v)) \frac{\partial(x, y)}{\partial(u, v)}\ dudv$$
$$= A(\Sigma_1(T(u, v))) \frac{\partial(x, y)}{\partial(u, v)}\ dudv.$$

Thus,

$$\iint_{\Sigma_2} \omega = \iint_{D_2} A(\Sigma_1(T(u, v))) \frac{\partial(x, y)}{\partial(u, v)}\ dudv.$$

In this, let us make the transformation of coordinates $(r, s) = T(u, v)$. Again applying Theorem 1, we have

$$\iint_{\Sigma_2} \omega = \iint_{D_1} A(\Sigma_1(r, s)) \frac{\partial(x, y)}{\partial(u, v)} \frac{\partial(u, v)}{\partial(r, s)}\ drds.$$

However, by the chain rule for differentiation,

$$\frac{\partial(x, y)}{\partial(u, v)} \frac{\partial(u, v)}{\partial(r, s)} = \frac{\partial(x, y)}{\partial(r, s)} = \begin{vmatrix} \phi_1 & \phi_2 \\ \psi_1 & \psi_2 \end{vmatrix}$$

so that

$$\iint_{\Sigma_2} \omega = \iint_{D_1} A(\Sigma_1(r, s)) \frac{\partial(x, y)}{\partial(r, s)}\ drds$$

The expression $\partial(x, y)/\partial(r, s)\, drds$ is, again by Theorem 1, equivalent to $dxdy$ on Σ_1, so that we finally obtain

$$\iint_{\Sigma_2} \omega = \iint_{\Sigma_1} A(x, y, z)\, dxdy = \iint_{\Sigma_1} \omega.$$

Again, the theorem may be completed by considering the 2-forms $B\, dydz$ and $C\, dzdx$, adding the results to arrive at the general case. ∎

So far, we have given no motivation for the consideration of integrals of 1-forms and of 2-forms. This will be done in Sec. 7.3, against a background of classical vector analysis. We shall show that the value which a 1-form ω assigns to the curve γ can also be obtained by integrating a certain function f, constructed from both ω and γ, along the curve γ. Similarly, the value which a 2-form ω assigns to the surface Σ can be obtained by integrating a function F over the surface Σ, where again F depends both upon ω and Σ. These integrations are carried out as in Sec. 7.1. The functions f and F which arise are defined only on the curve and on the surface; however, they arise from "vector-valued" functions in a manner which is physically significant, and which leads to important physical interpretations of the integrals involved.

As we have indicated, $\int_\gamma \omega$ may be called either a **line integral,** or the integral of a 1-form, along the curve γ. The more common name which is given to the integral of a 2-form over a surface is **"surface integral."** In using these names, it should be kept in mind that a line integral is not entirely equivalent with the concept of the integral of a function along a curve, nor is "surface integral" equivalent to "integral of a function over a surface." The difference lies in the fact that the latter, for example, has the form $F(\Sigma) = \iint_\Sigma f$ where f is fixed, whereas $\omega(\Sigma) = \iint_\Sigma \omega$ cannot be expressed in this fashion without letting f depend upon Σ (see Theorems 4 and 5, Sec. 7.3).

EXERCISES

1. Evaluate $\int_\gamma (x\, dx + xy\, dy)$ where

(*a*) γ is the line $x = t$, $y = t$, $0 \le t \le 1$.

(*b*) γ is the portion of the parabola $y = x^2$ from $(0, 0)$ to $(1, 1)$.

(*c*) γ is the portion of the parabola $x = y^2$ from $(0, 0)$ to $(1, 1)$.

(*d*) γ is the polygon whose successive vertices are $(0, 0)$, $(1, 0)$, $(0, 1)$, $(1, 1)$.

2. Evaluate $\int_\gamma (y\, dx - x\, dy)$ where

(*a*) γ is the closed curve $x = t^2 - 1$, $y = t^3 - t$, $-1 \le t \le 1$.

(*b*) γ is the straight line from $(0, 0)$ to $(2, 4)$.

(*c*) γ is the portion of the parabola $y = x^2$ from $(0, 0)$ to $(2, 4)$.

(*d*) γ is the polygon whose successive vertices are $(0, 0)$, $(-2, 0)$, $(-2, 4)$, $(2, 4)$.

3. Evaluate $\int_\gamma (y\,dx + x\,dy)$ for the curves given in Exercise 2.

4. Evaluate $\int_\gamma (z\,dx + x^2\,dy + y\,dz)$ where

(*a*) γ is the straight line from (0, 0, 0) to (1, 1, 1).

(*b*) γ is the portion of the *twisted cubic* $x = t$, $y = t^2$, $z = t^3$ from (0, 0, 0) to (1, 1, 1).

(*c*) γ is the portion of the *helix* $x = \cos t$, $y = \sin t$, $z = t$, for $0 \leq t \leq 2\pi$.

(*d*) γ is the closed polygon whose successive vertices are (0, 0, 0), (2, 0, 0), (2, 3, 0), (0, 0, 1), (0, 0, 0).

5. Evaluate $\int_\gamma (2x\,dx + z\,dy + y\,dz)$ for the curves given in Exercise 4.

6. If $\omega = B(y)\,dy$, show that $\int_\gamma \omega = \int_{y_0}^{y_1} B(y)\,dy$ for any smooth curve γ which starts at (x_0, y_0) and ends at (x_1, y_1).

7. If $\omega = A(x)\,dx + B(y)\,dy$, show that $\int_\gamma \omega = 0$ for any closed curve γ.

8. Verify the following:

(*a*) $(3x\,dx + 4y\,dy)(3x^2\,dx - dy) = -(3x + 12x^2y)\,dxdy$.

(*b*) $(3x^2\,dx - dy)(3x\,dx + 4y\,dy) = (3x + 12x^2y)\,dxdy$.

(*c*) $(x\,dy - yz\,dz)(y\,dx + xy\,dy - z\,dz) = (xy^2z - xz)\,dydz - y^2z\,dzdx - xy\,dxdy$.

(*d*) $(x^2\,dydz + yz\,dxdy)(3dx - dz) = (3x^2 - yz)\,dxdydz$.

(*e*) $(dxdy - dydz)(dx + dy + dz) = 0$.

(*f*) $(dx - x\,dy + yz\,dz)(x\,dx - x^2\,dy + xyz\,dz) = 0$.

9. Show that

$$(A\,dx + B\,dy + C\,dz)(a\,dx + b\,dy + c\,dz) = \begin{vmatrix} B & C \\ b & c \end{vmatrix} dydz + \begin{vmatrix} C & A \\ c & a \end{vmatrix} dzdx + \begin{vmatrix} A & B \\ a & b \end{vmatrix} dxdy.$$

10. Show that

$(A\,dx + B\,dy + C\,dz)(a\,dydz + b\,dzdx + c\,dxdy) = (aA + bB + cC)\,dxdydz$.

11. Evaluate df if (*a*) $f(x, y, z) = x^2yz$; (*b*) $f(x, y) = \log(x^2 + y^2)$.

12. Let $x = \phi(u, v, w)$, $y = \psi(u, v, w)$, $z = \theta(u, v, w)$. Show that

$$dxdydz = \frac{\partial(x, y, z)}{\partial(u, v, w)}\,dudvdw.$$

13. Evaluate $d\omega$ where

(*a*) $\omega = x^2y\,dx - yz\,dz$

(*b*) $\omega = 3x\,dx + 4xy\,dy$

(*c*) $\omega = 2xy\,dx + x^2\,dy$

(*d*) $\omega = e^{xy}\,dx - x^2y\,dy$

(*e*) $\omega = x^2y\,dydz - xz\,dxdy$

(*f*) $\omega = x^2z\,dydz + y^2z\,dzdx - xy^2\,dxdy$

(*g*) $\omega = xz\,dydx + xy\,dzdx + 2yz\,dydz$

14. If $\omega = A(x, y, z)\,dx + B(x, y, z)\,dy + C(x, y, z)\,dz$, show that

$$d\omega = (C_2 - B_3)\,dydz + (A_3 - C_1)\,dzdx + (B_1 - A_2)\,dxdy.$$

15. If $\omega = A(x, y, z)\,dydz + B(x, y, z)\,dzdx + C(x, y, z)\,dxdy$, show that

$$d\omega = (A_1 + B_2 + C_3)\,dxdydz.$$

16. Evaluate $\iint_\Sigma (x\,dydz + y\,dxdy)$, where

(*a*) Σ is the surface described by $x = u + v$, $y = u^2 - v^2$, $z = uv$, $0 \leq u \leq 1$, $0 \leq v \leq 1$.

(*b*) Σ is the portion of the cylinder $x^2 + y^2 = 1$ with $0 \leq z \leq 1$, oriented so that the normal is outward (away from the Z axis).

(*c*) Σ is the boxlike surface which is the union of five squares, each side of length one (see Fig. 7-6).

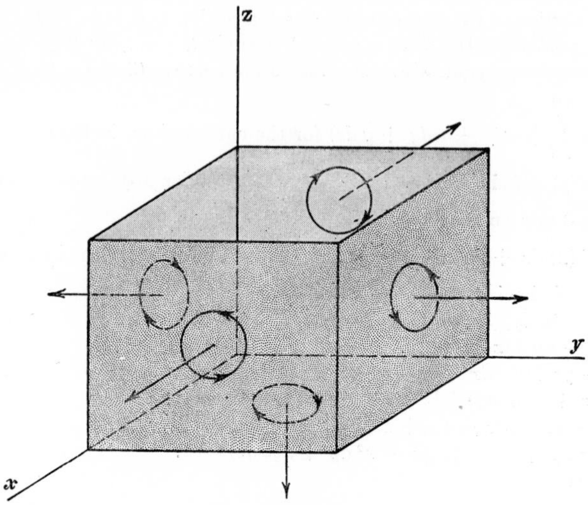

FIG. 7-6

17. Verify the following calculations with forms in four variables:

(*a*) $(dx + dy - dz + dw)(dxdy + 2dzdw) = 2dxdzdw + 2dydzdw - dxdydz + dxdydw.$

(*b*) $(dxdy + dydz - dzdw)(x\,dxdy + y\,dzdw) = (y - x)\,dxdydzdw.$

(*c*) $d(x^2y\,dydw + yw^2\,dxdz + xyzw\,dxdy) = (xyw - w^2)\,dxdydz + (2xy + xyz)\,dxdydw + 2yw\,dxdzdw.$

(*d*) $dx\,dy\,dz\,dw = \dfrac{\partial(x, y, z, w)}{\partial(r, s, t, u)}\,dr\,ds\,dt\,du$

when $x = \phi(r, s, t, u)$, $y = \psi(r, s, t, u)$, $z = \theta(r, s, t, u)$, $w = \chi(r, s, t, u)$.

18. Evaluate $\iint_{\Sigma} (xy\,dydz + yz\,dxdw)$, where Σ is the two-dimensional surface in 4-space described by $x = r^2 + s^2$, $y = r - s$, $z = rs$, $w = r + s$, and (r, s) obeys $0 \leq r \leq 1$, $0 \leq s \leq 1$.

7.3. Vector Analysis

Since the purpose of this section is only to point out the connections between the system of differential forms, and that of vector analysis, we shall not attempt to develop the theory of the latter in complete detail.† We shall begin with the coordinate approach, and discuss the coordinate-free geometric treatment later.

† Many excellent books deal with vector analysis and its applications. A thorough treatment may be found in L. Brand, "Vector and Tensor Analysis," John Wiley & Sons, Inc., New York, 1947.

As was seen in Sec. 1.1, addition of points is defined for points of the plane, or of space, or, in general, for points in E^n. If $p = (x_1, x_2, \ldots, x_n)$ and $q = (y_1, y_2, \ldots, y_n)$, then

$$p + q = (x_1 + y_1, x_2 + y_2, \ldots, x_n + y_n).$$

We also defined the product of a point p by a real number λ as the point given by

$$\lambda p = (\lambda x_1, \lambda x_2, \ldots, \lambda x_n).$$

It is natural to ask if there is a useful definition of multiplication for points such that the product of two points in E^n is again a point in E^n and such that the customary rules which govern the algebra of real numbers still hold for points. The **inner product** (also called scalar or dot product) of two points, which was defined by

$$p \cdot q = x_1y_1 + x_2y_2 + \cdots + x_ny_n$$

is not suitable, since the inner product of two points is a number (scalar) and not a point.

It is well known that suitable multiplications exist when $n = 2$. For example, one may define the product of two points in the plane by the formula

$$(x_1, x_2)(y_1, y_2) = (x_1y_1 - x_2y_2, x_1y_2 + x_2y_1). \tag{7-12}$$

Upon checking the various algebraic rules, it is found that under this definition for multiplication, and the previous definition of addition, E^2 becomes what is called a field (see Appendix). The motivation for (7-12) may be seen by making the correspondence $(a, b) \leftrightarrow a + bi$ between the plane and the field of all complex numbers. If $p = (x_1, x_2)$ corresponds to $z = x_1 + ix_2$ and $q = (y_1, y_2)$ corresponds to $w = y_1 + iy_2$, then we see that

$$zw = (x_1 + ix_2)(y_1 + iy_2) = (x_1y_1 - x_2y_2) + i(x_1y_2 + x_2y_1),$$

which corresponds to the point which is given as the product of p and q.

With this example in mind, one may attempt to find a similar definition for multiplication of points in 3-space. By algebraic methods, it can be shown that no such formula exists (still requiring that the ordinary algebraic rules remain valid). However, going to the next higher dimension, Hamilton (1843) discovered that a definition for multiplication of points in E^4 could be given which yields a system obeying all the algebraic rules which apply to real numbers (i.e., the field axioms) except one; multiplication is no longer commutative, so that (pq) and (qp) may be different points. This system is called the algebra of **quaternions.** It was soon seen that it could be used to great advantage in the theory of mechanics. By restricting points to a particular 3-space embedded in E^4, Gibbs and others developed a modification of the algebra of quaternions which was called **vector analysis,** and which gained widespread acceptance and importance, particularly in physics.

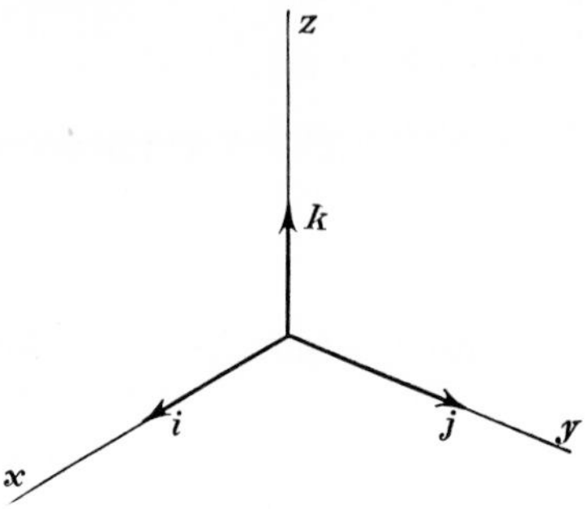

FIG. 7-7

Let $\mathbf{i} = (1, 0, 0)$, $\mathbf{j} = (0, 1, 0)$, $\mathbf{k} = (0, 0, 1)$. Any point in 3-space can be expressed in terms of these three. If $p = (a, b, c)$, then

$$p = a\mathbf{i} + b\mathbf{j} + c\mathbf{k}.$$

We define a multiplication operation $\times$ for points in E^3 by first defining it on the basis elements **i**, **j**, **k**:

$$\mathbf{i} \times \mathbf{i} = \mathbf{j} \times \mathbf{j} = \mathbf{k} \times \mathbf{k} = 0 \tag{7-13}$$

$$\begin{aligned} \mathbf{i} \times \mathbf{j} &= -\mathbf{j} \times \mathbf{i} = \mathbf{k} \\ \mathbf{j} \times \mathbf{k} &= -\mathbf{k} \times \mathbf{j} = \mathbf{i} \\ \mathbf{k} \times \mathbf{i} &= -\mathbf{i} \times \mathbf{k} = \mathbf{j} \end{aligned} \tag{7-14}$$

(Note that the cyclic order $\mathbf{i}:\mathbf{j}:\mathbf{k}:\mathbf{i}:\mathbf{j}$, in which product of any neighboring pair in order is the next, is consistent with the positive orientation of the axes as shown in Fig. 7-7.)

We may use these equations, together with the distributive law, to obtain a product for any two points. We have

$$\begin{aligned} &(x_1\mathbf{i} + x_2\mathbf{j} + x_3\mathbf{k}) \times (y_1\mathbf{i} + y_2\mathbf{j} + y_3\mathbf{k}) \\ &\quad = (x_1y_1)(\mathbf{i} \times \mathbf{i}) + (x_1y_2)(\mathbf{i} \times \mathbf{j}) + (x_1y_3)(\mathbf{i} \times \mathbf{k}) + (x_2y_1)(\mathbf{j} \times \mathbf{i}) \\ &\qquad + (x_2y_2)(\mathbf{j} \times \mathbf{j}) + (x_2y_3)(\mathbf{j} \times \mathbf{k}) + (x_3y_1)(\mathbf{k} \times \mathbf{i}) + (x_3y_2)(\mathbf{k} \times \mathbf{j}) \\ &\qquad + (x_3y_3)(\mathbf{k} \times \mathbf{k}) \\ &\quad = (x_1y_2 - x_2y_1)\mathbf{k} + (x_3y_1 - x_1y_3)\mathbf{j} + (x_2y_3 - x_3y_2)\mathbf{i}. \end{aligned}$$

We therefore adopt the following definition for the **cross product** of two points. (Other names are vector product and outer product.)

Definition. *If* $p = (x_1, x_2, x_3) = x_1\mathbf{i} + x_2\mathbf{j} + x_3\mathbf{k}$ *and*

$$q = (y_1, y_2, y_3) = y_1\mathbf{i} + y_2\mathbf{j} + y_3\mathbf{k},$$

then

$$p \times q = (x_2y_3 - x_3y_2)\mathbf{i} + (x_3y_1 - x_1y_3)\mathbf{j} + (x_1y_2 - x_2y_1)\mathbf{k}$$

It is seen that the coordinates of $p \times q$ have simple expressions as determinants, so that we may also write

$$(7\text{-}15)\qquad p \times q = \begin{vmatrix} x_2 & x_3 \\ y_2 & y_3 \end{vmatrix} \mathbf{i} + \begin{vmatrix} x_3 & x_1 \\ y_3 & y_1 \end{vmatrix} \mathbf{j} + \begin{vmatrix} x_1 & x_2 \\ y_1 & y_2 \end{vmatrix} \mathbf{k},$$

or in an even more abbreviated form,

$$p \times q = \begin{vmatrix} \mathbf{i} & \mathbf{j} & \mathbf{k} \\ x_1 & x_2 & x_3 \\ y_1 & y_2 & y_3 \end{vmatrix}.$$

(where we expand by the top row).

As indicated, such a multiplication operation defined on E^3 cannot obey all the rules of ordinary algebra. In particular, $\times$ is not an associative product; it is not in general true that $p \times (q \times r) = (p \times q) \times r$. For example, $(\mathbf{i} \times \mathbf{i}) \times \mathbf{k} = \mathbf{0} \times \mathbf{k} = \mathbf{0}$, but

$$\mathbf{i} \times (\mathbf{i} \times \mathbf{k}) = \mathbf{i} \times (-\mathbf{j}) = -\mathbf{k}.\dagger$$

To make up for this, the operations of vector analysis have simple geometrical interpretations.

Let us consider the collection of all directed line segments in 3-space. Each may be represented as an ordered pair of points $\overrightarrow{PQ}$; P is called the initial point, and Q the terminal point. We use these to define the notion of a vector or, rather, the separate notions of a bound vector and a free vector. A **bound vector v** at the point P (or having P as its point of application) is simply a directed line segment of the form $\overrightarrow{PQ}$. Any bound vector at P is completely specified by giving the terminal point Q. The length of $\mathbf{v}$ is denoted by $|\mathbf{v}|$ and is $|P - Q|$; the direction of $\mathbf{v}$ is the direction of the line from P toward Q, and thus has direction components $Q - P$ or direction cosines $(Q - P)/|Q - P|$. Two bound vectors are the same if and only if they have the same point of application, and have the same length and direction, so that their terminal points coincide.

In contrast, *any* two directed line segments which have the same length and direction are said to represent the same free vector. A **free vector v** thus appears as a collection of directed line segments having the same length and direction, without regard to the location of their initial points.

† Multiplication of quaternions is, however, associative. A point in E^4 can be written in the form $(a, b, c, d) = a\mathbf{i} + b\mathbf{j} + c\mathbf{k} + d\mathbf{1}$ where $\mathbf{i}$, $\mathbf{j}$, $\mathbf{k}$, and $\mathbf{1}$ are the four basis points on the axes. Multiplication is defined by (7-14) along with

$$\mathbf{i}^2 = \mathbf{j}^2 = \mathbf{k}^2 = -\mathbf{1}.$$

If $p = x_1\mathbf{i} + x_2\mathbf{j} + x_1\mathbf{k}$ and $q = y_1\mathbf{i} + y_2\mathbf{j} + y_3\mathbf{k}$, then the product of p and q as quaternions, taken in that order, turns out to be $p \times q - (p \cdot q)\mathbf{1}$. (See G. Birkhoff and S. MacLane, "Survey of Modern Algebra," pp. 236–238, The Macmillan Company, New York, 1953, or W. R. Hamilton, "Lectures on Quaternions," 1853.)

Any two such segments can be carried into one another by a translation† of 3-space. If we call such segments "equivalent," then a free vector **v** is an equivalence class of directed line segments, any of which may be said to represent the vector **v**. Among these, there is only one whose initial point is the origin. Thus, each free vector **v** may be prescribed completely by a single directed line segment of the form $\overrightarrow{\mathbf{0}p}$, and hence by the terminal point p alone. The coordinates of p are called the

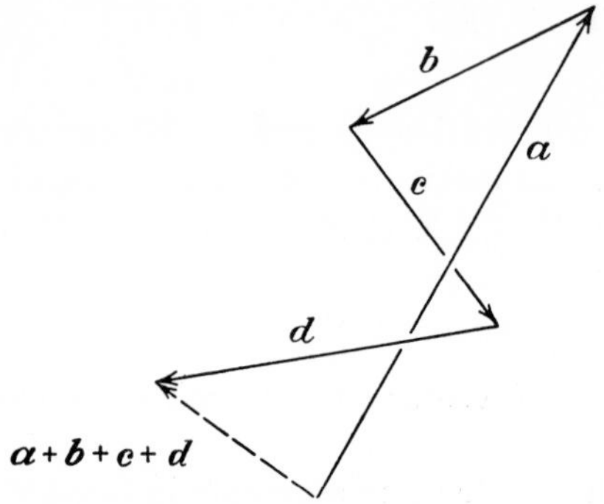

FIG. 7-8

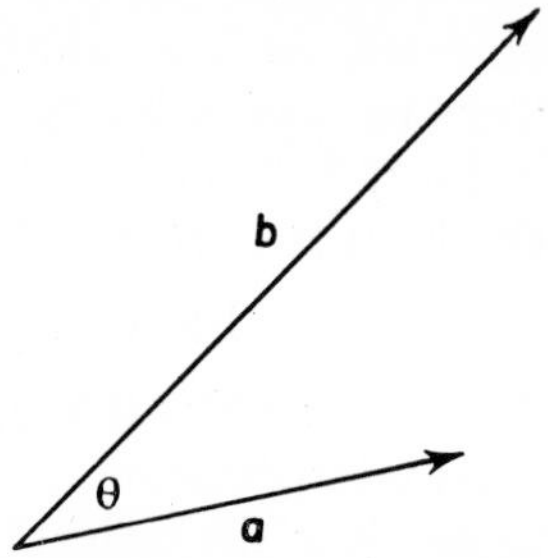

FIG. 7-9. $\mathbf{a}\cdot\mathbf{b} = |\mathbf{a}|\,|\mathbf{b}|\cos\theta$.

components of **v**, and are sometimes enclosed within square brackets, rather than in parentheses, in order to make a distinction between the vector itself and $\overrightarrow{\mathbf{0}p}$ which is only one of the directed line segments composing **v**; all of these have the form $\overrightarrow{PQ}$, where $Q = P + p$. Vector analysis is chiefly the theory of free vectors, and we shall omit the qualifying adjective in the future. However, bound vectors will occasionally make their appearance, particularly when it is convenient to represent a free vector by a line segment whose initial point is required to lie on a certain curve or surface.

The operations of forming the sum, the inner product, and the cross product of points yield at once corresponding operations for vectors. The sum of any finite number of vectors may be formed by placing them (i.e., representative directed line segments) in juxtaposition, head to tail, and constructing the directed line segment which goes from the initial point of the first to the terminal point of the last (Fig. 7-8). The inner product $\mathbf{a} \cdot \mathbf{b}$ of vectors **a** and **b** is the number $|\mathbf{a}|\,|\mathbf{b}|\cos\theta$, where θ is the angle between the vectors (Fig. 7-9). Finally, the cross product of two vectors **a** and **b** is the vector $\mathbf{c} = \mathbf{a} \times \mathbf{b}$ which is orthogonal to both **a** and **b**, whose length is $|\mathbf{a}|\,|\mathbf{b}|\sin\theta$, and such that the trihedral **a**, **b**, **c** is right-handed. To prove this statement, we first observe that two

† A rigid motion of space which may shift the origin, but which does not alter the direction of the coordinate axes.

vectors **u** and **v** are orthogonal if and only if $\mathbf{u} \cdot \mathbf{v} = 0$. Let **a** and **b** be represented by the points (a_1, a_2, a_3) and (b_1, b_2, b_3). Then, their cross product **c** will be represented, according to (7-15) by the point

$$\left(\begin{vmatrix} a_2 & a_3 \\ b_2 & b_3 \end{vmatrix}, \quad \begin{vmatrix} a_3 & a_1 \\ b_3 & b_1 \end{vmatrix}, \quad \begin{vmatrix} a_1 & a_2 \\ b_1 & b_2 \end{vmatrix} \right)$$

so that

$$\begin{aligned} \mathbf{c} \cdot \mathbf{a} &= \begin{vmatrix} a_2 & a_3 \\ b_2 & b_3 \end{vmatrix} a_1 + \begin{vmatrix} a_3 & a_1 \\ b_3 & b_1 \end{vmatrix} a_2 + \begin{vmatrix} a_1 & a_2 \\ b_1 & b_2 \end{vmatrix} a_3 \\ &= \begin{vmatrix} a_1 & a_2 & a_3 \\ a_1 & a_2 & a_3 \\ b_1 & b_2 & b_3 \end{vmatrix} = 0. \end{aligned}$$

Similarly, $\mathbf{c} \cdot \mathbf{b} = 0$, so that $\mathbf{a} \times \mathbf{b}$ is orthogonal to **a** and to **b**. To find the length of **c**, we recall that (see page 237)

$$\begin{aligned} |\mathbf{c}|^2 &= \begin{vmatrix} a_2 & a_3 \\ b_2 & b_3 \end{vmatrix}^2 + \begin{vmatrix} a_3 & a_1 \\ b_3 & b_1 \end{vmatrix}^2 + \begin{vmatrix} a_1 & a_2 \\ b_1 & b_2 \end{vmatrix}^2 \\ &= (a_1^2 + a_2^2 + a_3^2)(b_1^2 + b_2^2 + b_3^2) - (a_1b_1 + a_2b_2 + a_3b_3)^2 \\ &= |\mathbf{a}|^2|\mathbf{b}|^2 - (\mathbf{a} \cdot \mathbf{b})^2. \end{aligned}$$

Using the formula for $\mathbf{a} \cdot \mathbf{b}$, we obtain

$$\begin{aligned} |\mathbf{c}|^2 &= |\mathbf{a}|^2|\mathbf{b}|^2 - (|\mathbf{a}|\,|\mathbf{b}| \cos \theta)^2 \\ &= |\mathbf{a}|^2|\mathbf{b}|^2(1 - \cos^2 \theta) \\ &= |\mathbf{a}|^2|\mathbf{b}|^2 \sin^2 \theta \end{aligned}$$

so that $|\mathbf{c}| = |\mathbf{a} \times \mathbf{b}| = |\mathbf{a}|\,|\mathbf{b}| \sin \theta$. (We also note that this number is the area of the parallelogram having **a** and **b** for consecutive sides, as

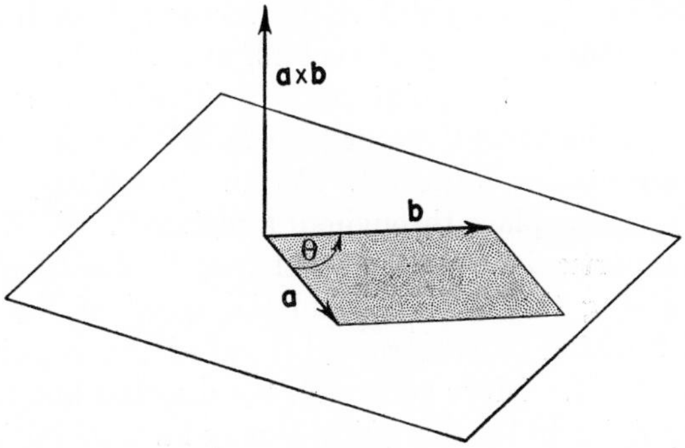

FIG. 7-10

shown in Fig. 7-10.) When **a** and **b** are chosen from among the basis vectors **i**, **j**, **k**, it is clear from the table (7-14) that **a**, **b**, and $\mathbf{a} \times \mathbf{b}$ form a positively oriented trihedral; for the general case, see Exercise 3.

The fact that the definitions of sum, inner product, and cross product, given originally in terms of the coordinates of the points, can also be given solely in geometrical terms means that these operations have an invariant quality which lends itself to the statement of physical laws. This invariance is inherent also in the coordinate definitions. The inner product of two points, p and q, is an algebraic function of their coordinates whose value is unchanged if the underlying 3-space is subjected to any orthogonal linear transformation (rotation) resulting in new coordinates for p and q.

We may also consider functions $\mathbf{f}$ whose values are vectors. These will be called **vector-valued** functions or **vector fields**, and will assign to each point p in the domain of definition D a vector $\mathbf{v}$. If $\mathbf{v}$ is represented by the point in space whose coordinates are the components of $\mathbf{v}$, then $\mathbf{f}$ is nothing more than a function from D into E^3, that is, a transformation from the set D into E^3. When D is an interval on the line, or a region in the plane, then this interpretation coincides with the notion of curve or surface, respectively; one speaks of the curve or surface as being traced by the end point of the vector $\mathbf{f}(t)$, or $\mathbf{f}(s, t)$. We may also make use of the mobility of vectors, and say that a vector-valued function $\mathbf{V}$ assigns to each point $p \in D$ a directed line segment whose initial point is p; the term "vector field in D" is more commonly used when this interpretation is meant. As an illustration, suppose that a flow of liquid is taking place throughout a region D. At each point of D, the liquid has a particular velocity which may be described by a directed line segment giving the direction and the speed of the motion. The vector-valued function so constructed is called the velocity field of the liquid (see Fig. 7-11). More generally, the directed line segment associated with the point p in the domain of $\mathbf{V}$ may have its initial point not at p, but at some other point determined by p. As an example of this, let $\mathbf{g}$ be a vector-valued function defined on an interval $a \leq t \leq b$, and whose end point describes a curve. Its derivative, $\mathbf{g}'(t)$, is a vector which we may represent by the directed line segment whose initial point is the point $\mathbf{g}(t)$ lying on the curve; this gives the customary picture of a curve and its tangent vectors (Fig. 7-12).

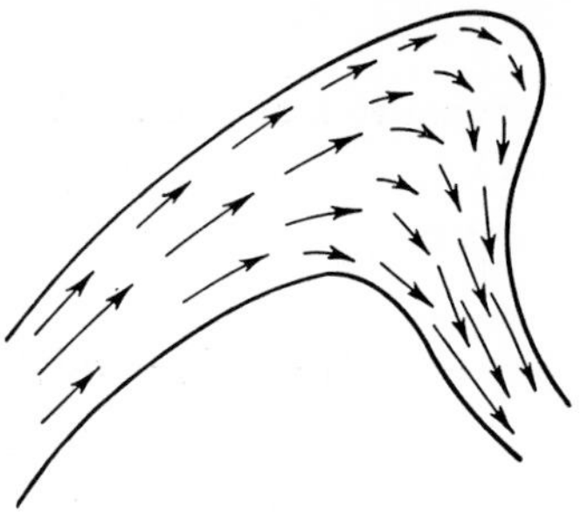

FIG. 7-11

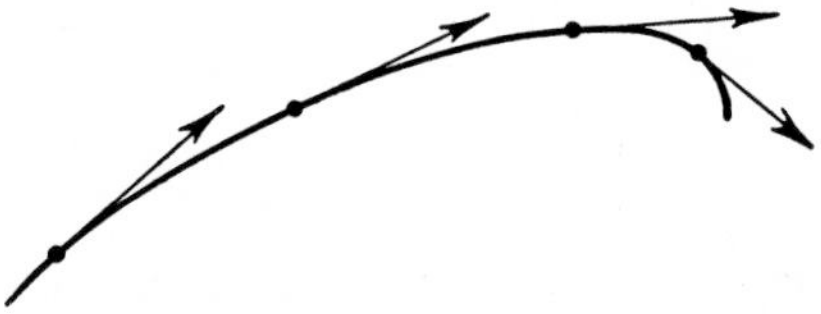

FIG. 7-12. Graph of a curve and its associated tangent vectors.

We may associate with any (**scalar**) function f of three variables which is of class C' a particular vector-valued function called the **gradient** of f.

Definition. *If f is of class C', then its gradient is the vector-valued function*

$$\begin{aligned}\text{grad }(f) &= f_1\mathbf{i} + f_2\mathbf{j} + f_3\mathbf{k}\\ &= \frac{\partial f}{\partial x}\mathbf{i} + \frac{\partial f}{\partial y}\mathbf{j} + \frac{\partial f}{\partial z}\mathbf{k}\\ &= \nabla f\end{aligned}$$

In explanation of the last symbol, ∇ is to be thought of as the vector differential operator

$$\nabla = \mathbf{i}\frac{\partial}{\partial x} + \mathbf{j}\frac{\partial}{\partial y} + \mathbf{k}\frac{\partial}{\partial z}. \tag{7-16}$$

The gradient of f at a point p may be represented by a directed line segment with initial point at p. If we take any unit vector

$$\mathbf{b} = b_1\mathbf{i} + b_2\mathbf{j} + b_3\mathbf{k},$$

then

$$\nabla f \cdot \mathbf{b} = f_1b_1 + f_2b_2 + f_3b_3. \tag{7-17}$$

The differential of f (see Sec. 5.3) was $[f_1, f_2, f_3]$ so that the expression in (7-17) is the same as the value of the directional derivative of f at p in the direction (b_1, b_2, b_3). If $\mathbf{v}$ is any vector, and $\mathbf{b}$ is a unit vector, then $\mathbf{v} \cdot \mathbf{b} = |\mathbf{v}| \cos \theta$ is the component of $\mathbf{v}$ in the direction $\mathbf{b}$ (see Fig. 7-13). Its greatest value is $|\mathbf{v}|$ and is obtained when $\mathbf{b}$ is parallel to $\mathbf{v}$. Applying this remark to the present case, we see that the following statement is true: the gradient of f at p is a vector whose component in the direction $\mathbf{b}$ is the directional derivative of f at p in the direction $\mathbf{b}$, and the gradient itself points in the direction of the greatest rate of increase of f. (The gradient is thus invariant under changes of axes.)

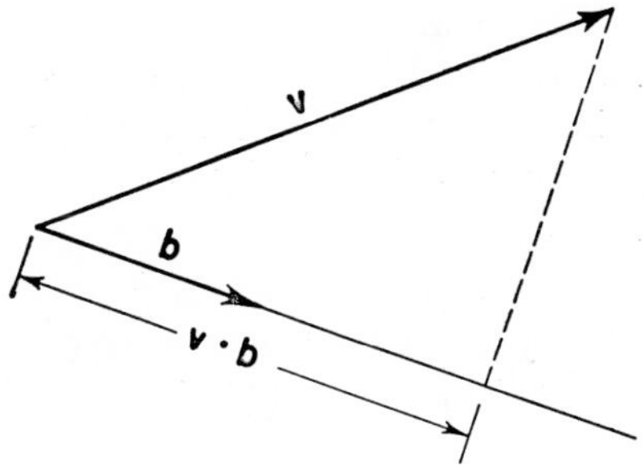

FIG. 7-13

With any vector field $\mathbf{V}$ of class C', one may associate two other functions. The first is called the **divergence** of $\mathbf{V}$ and is an ordinary scalar function.

Definition. *If $\mathbf{V} = A\mathbf{i} + B\mathbf{j} + C\mathbf{k}$, where A, B, and C are (scalar) functions of class C' defined in a region Ω, then the divergence of $\mathbf{V}$ is*

$$\begin{aligned} \operatorname{div}(\mathbf{V}) &= A_1 + B_2 + C_3 \\ &= \frac{\partial A}{\partial x} + \frac{\partial B}{\partial y} + \frac{\partial C}{\partial z} \qquad (7\text{-}18) \\ &= \nabla \cdot \mathbf{V}. \end{aligned}$$

We shall later recast this in a form which makes evident the geometrical invariance of the divergence (Sec. 7.5). At the moment, we give only the following algebraic justification. We may view **V** as defining a transformation from (x, y, z) space into (r, s, t) space by means of the equations

$$\begin{cases} r = A(x, y, z) \\ s = B(x, y, z) \\ t = C(x, y, z). \end{cases}$$

The differential of this transformation is represented by the matrix

$$\begin{bmatrix} \frac{\partial A}{\partial x} & \frac{\partial A}{\partial y} & \frac{\partial A}{\partial z} \\ \frac{\partial B}{\partial x} & \frac{\partial B}{\partial y} & \frac{\partial B}{\partial z} \\ \frac{\partial C}{\partial x} & \frac{\partial C}{\partial y} & \frac{\partial C}{\partial z} \end{bmatrix}$$

and the divergence of V is the trace of this matrix, that is, the sum of the diagonal entries. This is known to be one of the invariants of a matrix, under the orthogonal group of rotations of 3-space (see Exercise 12).

The second function associated with a vector field **V** is a vector-valued function and is called the **curl** of **V**.

Definition. *If* $\mathbf{V} = A\mathbf{i} + B\mathbf{j} + C\mathbf{k}$ *where* A, B *and* C *are (scalar) functions of class* C' *defined in a region* Ω, *then the curl of* **V** *is the vector-valued function:*

$$\begin{aligned} \operatorname{curl}(\mathbf{V}) &= (C_2 - B_3)\mathbf{i} + (A_3 - C_1)\mathbf{j} + (B_1 - A_2)\mathbf{k} \\ &= \left(\frac{\partial C}{\partial y} - \frac{\partial B}{\partial z}\right)\mathbf{i} + \left(\frac{\partial A}{\partial z} - \frac{\partial C}{\partial x}\right)\mathbf{j} + \left(\frac{\partial B}{\partial x} - \frac{\partial A}{\partial y}\right)\mathbf{k} \qquad (7\text{-}19) \\ &= \nabla \times \mathbf{V}. \end{aligned}$$

The last expression is to be regarded as a convenient formula for the curl of **V** and may be written as

$$\nabla \times \mathbf{V} = \begin{vmatrix} \mathbf{i} & \mathbf{j} & \mathbf{k} \\ \frac{\partial}{\partial x} & \frac{\partial}{\partial y} & \frac{\partial}{\partial z} \\ A & B & C \end{vmatrix}$$

The invariant nature of this will also be shown later on.

Many of the most important postulates of physical theory find their simplest statements in vector equations. To cite only one example, one form of the Maxwell equations is:

$$\text{(7-20)} \qquad \begin{aligned} &\operatorname{div}(\mathbf{E}) = \rho \qquad &\operatorname{curl}(\mathbf{E}) = -\frac{\partial \mathbf{H}}{\partial t} \\ &\operatorname{div}(\mathbf{H}) = 0 \qquad &\operatorname{curl}(\mathbf{H}) = 4\pi\left(\mathbf{J} + \frac{\partial \mathbf{E}}{\partial t}\right) \end{aligned}$$

One of the chief tools in the use of vector analysis in such applications is a knowledge of certain standard identities. In the list below, we give a number of these. All can be verified directly by substitution and computation.

If $\mathbf{a} = a_1\mathbf{i} + a_2\mathbf{j} + a_3\mathbf{k}$, $b = b_1\mathbf{i} + b_2\mathbf{j} + b_3\mathbf{k}$, and $\mathbf{c} = c_1\mathbf{i} + c_2\mathbf{j} + c_3\mathbf{k}$, then

$$\text{(7-21)} \qquad \begin{aligned} (\mathbf{a} \times \mathbf{b}) \cdot \mathbf{c} &= (\mathbf{b} \times \mathbf{c}) \cdot \mathbf{a} = (\mathbf{c} \times \mathbf{a}) \cdot \mathbf{b} \\ &= \begin{vmatrix} a_1 & a_2 & a_3 \\ b_1 & b_2 & b_3 \\ c_1 & c_2 & c_3 \end{vmatrix} \end{aligned}$$

$$\text{(7-22)} \qquad \mathbf{a} \times (\mathbf{b} \times \mathbf{c}) = (\mathbf{a} \cdot \mathbf{c})\mathbf{b} - (\mathbf{a} \cdot \mathbf{b})\mathbf{c}$$

If f is a scalar function of class C'', then

$$\text{(7-23)} \qquad \operatorname{curl}(\operatorname{grad}(f)) = \nabla \times \nabla f = \mathbf{0}$$

$$\text{(7-24)} \qquad \begin{aligned} \operatorname{div}(\operatorname{grad}(f)) &= \nabla \cdot \nabla f = \nabla^2 f \\ &= \frac{\partial^2 f}{\partial x^2} + \frac{\partial^2 f}{\partial y^2} + \frac{\partial^2 f}{\partial z^2} \end{aligned}$$

If $\mathbf{V} = A\mathbf{i} + B\mathbf{j} + C\mathbf{k}$ is a vector field with components of class C'' then

$$\text{(7-25)} \qquad \operatorname{div}(\operatorname{curl}(\mathbf{V})) = \nabla \cdot (\nabla \times \mathbf{V}) = \mathbf{0}$$

$$\text{(7-26)} \qquad \begin{aligned} \operatorname{curl}(\operatorname{curl}(V)) &= \nabla \times (\nabla \times \mathbf{V}) \\ &= \nabla(\nabla \cdot \mathbf{V}) - [\nabla^2 A\mathbf{i} + \nabla^2 B\mathbf{j} + \nabla^2 C\mathbf{k}] \\ &= \operatorname{grad}(\operatorname{div}(\mathbf{V})) - \nabla^2\mathbf{V}. \end{aligned}$$

If $\mathbf{F}$ and $\mathbf{G}$ are both vector-valued functions of class C', then

$$\text{(7-27)} \qquad \operatorname{div}(\mathbf{F} \times \mathbf{G}) = \nabla \cdot (\mathbf{F} \times \mathbf{G}) = \mathbf{G} \cdot (\nabla \times \mathbf{F}) - \mathbf{F} \cdot (\nabla \times \mathbf{G}).$$

Let us now compare the system of vector analysis, as sketched above, with the system of differential forms in three variables. We notice first that there is a certain formal similarity between the multiplication table for the vector units **i**, **j**, **k** given in (7-13) and (7-14) and the corresponding table for the basic differential forms dx, dy, and dz given in (7-10) and (7-11). In the latter, however, we do not have the identification $dxdy = dz$ which corresponds to the relation $\mathbf{i} \times \mathbf{j} = \mathbf{k}$. This suggests that we correspond elements in pairs:

$$\left.\begin{matrix} dx \\ dydz \end{matrix}\right. \leftrightarrow \mathbf{i} \qquad \left.\begin{matrix} dy \\ dzdx \end{matrix}\right. \leftrightarrow \mathbf{j} \qquad \left.\begin{matrix} dz \\ dxdy \end{matrix}\right. \leftrightarrow \mathbf{k}$$

To complete these, and take into account 0-forms and 3-forms, we adjoin one more correspondence

$$\left.\begin{matrix} 1 \\ dxdydz \end{matrix}\right. \leftrightarrow \mathbf{1}$$

With these, we can set up a two-to-one correspondence between differential forms, and vector- and scalar-valued functions. To any 1-form or 2-form will correspond a vector function, and to any 0-form or 3-form will correspond a scalar function. The method of correspondence is indicated below:

$$\left.\begin{matrix} A\,dx + B\,dy + C\,dz \\ A\,dydz + B\,dzdx + C\,dxdy \end{matrix}\right\} \leftrightarrow A\mathbf{i} + B\mathbf{j} + C\mathbf{k}$$

$$\left.\begin{matrix} f(x, y, z) \\ f(x, y, z)\,dxdydz \end{matrix}\right\} \leftrightarrow f(x, y, z)$$

In the opposite direction, we see that a vector-valued function corresponds to both a 1-form and to a 2-form, and a scalar function to a 0-form, and a 3-form. To see the effect of this relationship, let

$$\mathbf{V} = A\mathbf{i} + B\mathbf{j} + C\mathbf{k} \qquad \text{and} \qquad \mathbf{W} = a\mathbf{i} + b\mathbf{j} + c\mathbf{k}$$

Corresponding to $\mathbf{V}$, we choose the 1-form

$$\nu = A\,dx + B\,dy + C\,dz$$

and corresponding to $\mathbf{W}$, both the 1-form and 2-form

$$\begin{aligned} \omega &= a\,dx + b\,dy + c\,dz \\ \omega^* &= a\,dydz + b\,dzdx + c\,dxdy \end{aligned}$$

As shown in Exercises 9 and 10, Sec. 7.2,

$$\begin{aligned} \nu\omega &= \begin{vmatrix} B & C \\ b & c \end{vmatrix} dydz + \begin{vmatrix} C & A \\ c & a \end{vmatrix} dzdx + \begin{vmatrix} A & B \\ a & b \end{vmatrix} dxdy \\ \nu\omega^* &= (aA + bB + cC)\,dxdydz \end{aligned}$$

Reversing the direction of correspondence, and comparing these with (7-15), we see that $\nu\omega$ corresponds to $\mathbf{V} \times \mathbf{W}$ and $\nu\omega^*$ to $\mathbf{V} \cdot \mathbf{W}$. Thus, single notion of multiplication among differential forms corresponds both to the inner product and the cross product among vectors.

What vector operations correspond to differentiation of forms? Let us start with a scalar function f, go to the corresponding 0-form f, and apply d. We obtain the 1-form

$$df = f_1\,dx + f_2\,dy + f_3\,dz$$

which in turn corresponds to the vector function $f_1\mathbf{i} + f_2\mathbf{j} + f_3\mathbf{k}$, the gradient of f. Again, let us start from a vector-valued function

$$\mathbf{V} = A\mathbf{i} + B\mathbf{j} + C\mathbf{k},$$

go to the corresponding 1-form $\omega = A\,dx + B\,dy + C\,dz$, and again apply d. We obtain 2-form which was shown in Exercise 14, Sec. 7.2, to be

$$d\omega = (C_2 - B_3)\,dydz + (A_3 - C_1)\,dzdx + (B_1 - A_2)\,dxdy.$$

Upon comparing this with (7-19), we see that this corresponds to the vector function curl ($\mathbf{V}$). Finally, if we correspond to $\mathbf{V}$ the 2-form

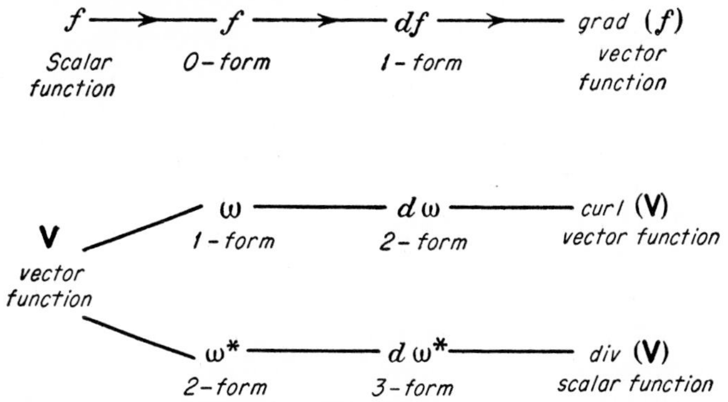

FIG. 7-14

$\omega^* = A\,dydz + B\,dzdx + C\,dxdy$, and apply d, we obtain the 3-form $(A_1 + B_2 + C_3)\,dxdydz$ which corresponds in turn to the scalar function div ($\mathbf{V}$). Briefly, then, the single operation of differentiation in the system of differential forms corresponds in turn to the operations of taking the gradient of a scalar and taking the curl and the divergence of a vector. This is indicated schematically in Fig. 7-14.

Some of the identities in the list given earlier correspond to simple statements about forms.

Theorem 3. *If ω is any differential form of class C'', then* $dd\omega = 0$.

This holds in general when ω is a k-form in n variables. We shall prove it when ω is a 1-form in three variables. Let $\omega = A(x, y, z)\,dx$. Then

$$d\omega = d(A)\,dx = \frac{\partial A}{\partial x}\,dxdx + \frac{\partial A}{\partial y}\,dydx + \frac{\partial A}{\partial z}\,dzdx$$
$$= \frac{\partial A}{\partial y}\,dydx + \frac{\partial A}{\partial z}\,dzdx,$$

and
$$dd\omega = d\left(\frac{\partial A}{\partial y}\right)dydx + d\left(\frac{\partial A}{\partial z}\right)dzdx$$
$$= \frac{\partial^2 A}{\partial z \partial y}\,dzdydx + \frac{\partial^2 A}{\partial y \partial z}\,dydzdx = 0$$

using the equality of the mixed derivatives and the fact that

$$dydzdx = -dzdydx.$$

A similar argument holds for $B\,dy$ and $C\,dz$. ▌ (See also Exercise 18.)

Using the relations shown in Fig. 7-14, we see that the statement $ddf = 0$, holding for a 0-form f, corresponds to the vector identity curl (grad f) $= 0$ [see (7-23)] and the statement $dd\omega = 0$, holding for a 1-form, to the vector identity div (curl **V**) $= 0$ [see (7-25)].

Our final connections between vector analysis and differential forms will be made by relating the integral of a form to integrals of certain scalar functions which are obtained by vector operations.

Theorem 4. *Let* $\mathbf{F} = A\mathbf{i} + B\mathbf{j} + C\mathbf{k}$ *define a continuous vector field in a region* Ω *of space, and let* $\omega = A\,dx + B\,dy + C\,dz$ *be the corresponding 1-form. Let* γ *be a smooth curve lying in* Ω. *Let* F_T *be the scalar function defined on the trace of* γ *whose value at a point* p *is the component of* $\mathbf{F}$ *in the direction of the tangent to* γ *at* p. *Then,*

$$\int_\gamma F_T\,ds = \int_\gamma \omega = \int_\gamma (A\,dx + B\,dy + C\,dz)$$

The first integral is the integral of a numerical-valued function along the curve γ, as discussed in Sec. 7.1. It should be noticed that the function F_T is defined only for points on γ, although **F** is defined throughout Ω. We may assume† that γ is parametrized by arc length, so that the tangent vector to γ at $p = \gamma(s)$ is $\mathbf{v} = \gamma'(s)$ and $|\mathbf{v}| = 1$. The component of **F** along **v** is then

$$F_T = \mathbf{F}\cdot\mathbf{v}$$
$$= (A\mathbf{i} + B\mathbf{j} + C\mathbf{k})\cdot\left(\frac{dx}{ds}\mathbf{i} + \frac{dy}{ds}\mathbf{j} + \frac{dz}{ds}\mathbf{k}\right)$$
$$= A\frac{dx}{ds} + B\frac{dy}{ds} + C\frac{dz}{ds}$$

and
$$\int_\gamma F_T\,ds = \int_0^l \left(A\frac{dx}{ds} + B\frac{dy}{ds} + C\frac{dz}{ds}\right)ds.$$

† Since smoothly equivalent curves will give the same value to the integrals in the statement of the theorem.

Comparing this with the definition of the integral of a 1-form (7-8), we see that

$$\int_\gamma F_T\,ds = \int_\gamma \omega. \quad ∎$$

The situation for integrals of 2-forms is similar.

Theorem 5. *Let* $\mathbf{F} = A\mathbf{i} + B\mathbf{j} + C\mathbf{k}$ *define a continuous vector field in a region* Ω, *and let* $\omega = A\,dydz + B\,dzdx + C\,dxdy$ *be the corresponding 2-form. Let* Σ *be a smooth surface lying in* Ω. *Let* F_N *be the scalar function defined on the trace of* Σ *whose value at a point* p *is the component of* $\mathbf{F}$ *in the direction of the normal to* Σ *at* p. *Then*

$$\iint_\Sigma F_N\,dA = \iint_\Sigma \omega = \iint_\Sigma (A\,dydz + B\,dzdx + C\,dxdy).$$

Let Σ have domain D in the (u, v) plane. By (6-29) the normal to Σ at the point $p = \Sigma(u, v)$ is

$$\mathbf{n}(u, v) = \left(\frac{\partial(y, z)}{\partial(u, v)}, \frac{\partial(z, x)}{\partial(u, v)}, \frac{\partial(x, y)}{\partial(u, v)}\right)$$

so that the normal component of $\mathbf{F}$ at p is

$$F_N = \frac{\mathbf{F}\cdot\mathbf{n}}{|\mathbf{n}|} = \frac{A\dfrac{\partial(y, z)}{\partial(u, v)} + B\dfrac{\partial(z, x)}{\partial(u, v)} + C\dfrac{\partial(x, y)}{\partial(u, v)}}{|\mathbf{n}(u, v)|}.$$

Thus, according to the definition given in (7-3)

$$\iint_\Sigma F_N\,dA = \iint_D F_N(\Sigma(u, v))\,|\mathbf{n}(u, v)|\,dudv$$

$$= \iint_D \left(A\frac{\partial(y, z)}{\partial(u, v)} + B\frac{\partial(z, x)}{\partial(u, v)} + C\frac{\partial(x, y)}{\partial(u, v)}\right) dudv$$

Using Theorem 1, Sec. 7.2, this may be written as

$$\iint_\Sigma F_N\,dA = \iint_\Sigma A\,dydz + B\,dzdx + C\,dxdy = \iint_\Sigma \omega. \quad ∎$$

To show how such integrals arise, let $\mathbf{V}$ be the vector-valued function which describes the velocity field of a liquid which is flowing throughout a region Ω, and let $\mathbf{F} = \rho\mathbf{V}$, where ρ is the scalar function which gives the density distribution of the liquid in Ω. Let Σ be a smooth orientable surface (for example, a portion of the surface of a sphere) lying in Ω. At any point on Σ, F_N measures the rate of flow of mass across Σ in the direction of the normal. The integral $\iint_\Sigma F_N\,dA$ is then the total mass of fluid which passes through Σ, per unit time. Again, let γ be a smooth curve lying in Ω. At a point lying on γ, V_T is the component of the velocity of the fluid taken in the direction of the tangent to γ. The integral $\int_\gamma V_T\,ds$ is then a measure of the extent to which the motion of the fluid is a flow *along* the curve γ. If γ is a closed curve, then $\int_\gamma V_T$ is called the circulation around γ.

Integrals of the same sort also arise in mechanics, especially in connection with the notion of work, in thermodynamics, and in electromagnetic theory.†

EXERCISES

1. Let $\mathbf{a} = 2\mathbf{i} - 3\mathbf{j} + \mathbf{k}$, $\mathbf{b} = \mathbf{i} - \mathbf{j} + 3\mathbf{k}$, $\mathbf{c} = \mathbf{i} - 2\mathbf{j}$. Compute the vectors $(\mathbf{a} \times \mathbf{b}) \cdot \mathbf{c}$, $\mathbf{a} \times (\mathbf{b} \times \mathbf{c})$, $(\mathbf{a} \times \mathbf{b}) \times \mathbf{c}$, $\mathbf{a} \times (\mathbf{a} \times \mathbf{b})$, $(\mathbf{a} + \mathbf{b}) \times (\mathbf{b} + \mathbf{c})$, $(\mathbf{a} \cdot \mathbf{b})\mathbf{c} - (\mathbf{a} \cdot \mathbf{c})\mathbf{b}$.

2. Assuming the law of cosines for a triangle embedded in 3-space, show that $\mathbf{a} \cdot \mathbf{b} = |\mathbf{a}|\,|\mathbf{b}| \cos\theta$.

3. Three points $p_j = (x_j, y_j, z_j)$ which do not lie in a plane through the origin, determine a trihedral with sides $\overrightarrow{\mathbf{0}p_1}$, $\overrightarrow{\mathbf{0}p_2}$, $\overrightarrow{\mathbf{0}p_3}$ which has positive orientation if and only if

$$\begin{vmatrix} x_1 & y_1 & z_1 \\ x_2 & y_2 & z_2 \\ x_3 & y_3 & z_3 \end{vmatrix} > 0.$$

Using this, show that the vectors $\mathbf{a}$, $\mathbf{b}$, and $\mathbf{a} \times \mathbf{b}$ form a trihedral having positive orientation, unless $\mathbf{a}$ and $\mathbf{b}$ are parallel.

4. Given vectors $\mathbf{a}$ and $\mathbf{b}$, and a real number k, is there a vector $\mathbf{v}$ such that $\mathbf{a} \times \mathbf{v} = \mathbf{b}$ and $\mathbf{a} \cdot \mathbf{v} = k$?

5. Define a sequence of vectors $\{p_n\}$ by $p_1 = \mathbf{a}$, $p_2 = \mathbf{i}$, $p_3 = \mathbf{a} \times \mathbf{i}$, $p_4 = \mathbf{a} \times p_3$, and in general, $p_{n+1} = \mathbf{a} \times p_n$. What is the ultimate behavior of the sequence?

6. If $\mathbf{f}$ and $\mathbf{g}$ are vector-valued functions of a single variable, show that

$$\frac{d}{dt}(\mathbf{f} \cdot \mathbf{g}) = \left(\frac{d}{dt}\mathbf{f}\right) \cdot \mathbf{g} + \mathbf{f} \cdot \left(\frac{d}{dt}\mathbf{g}\right)$$

and

$$\frac{d}{dt}(\mathbf{f} \times \mathbf{g}) = \left(\frac{d}{dt}\mathbf{f}\right) \times \mathbf{g} + \mathbf{f} \times \left(\frac{d}{dt}\mathbf{g}\right)$$

7. If $\mathbf{f}$ is a vector-valued function of one variable, and $|\mathbf{f}(t)| = 1$ for all t, show that $\mathbf{f}(t)$ and $\mathbf{f}'(t)$ are always orthogonal. Does this have a simple geometric interpretation?

8. Show that the curvature of a curve γ at the point $\gamma(c)$ is

$$k = \frac{|\gamma'(c) \times \gamma''(c)|}{|\gamma'(c)|^3}$$

9. Show that the normal to the surface Σ can be defined by (see (6-29))

$$\mathbf{n} = \Sigma_u \times \Sigma_v$$

† See J. C. Slater and N. H. Frank, "Introduction to Theoretical Physics," 1933, J. A. Stratton, "Electromagnetic Theory," 1941, and P. M. Morse and H. Feshbach, "Methods of Theoretical Physics," 1953, all published by McGraw-Hill Book Company, Inc., New York.

10. Find the gradient vector for f where

(*a*) $f(x, y) = x^2 + y^2$ (*b*) $f(x, y, z) = xyz$.

11. Show that the gradient vectors for f are orthogonal to the level surfaces

$$f(x, y, z) = c.$$

***12.** Let A be the square matrix $[a_{ij}]$ and let B be a nonsingular matrix. Set $A^* = B^{-1}AB$. Show that the trace of A (the sum of the diagonal entries) is the same as that of A^*.

13. Verify identities (7-21) and (7-22).

14. Verify identities (7-23) and (7-25).

15. (*a*) Verify identity (7-24).

(*b*) Show that if f and g are scalar functions of class C'', then

$$\nabla^2(fg) = f\nabla^2 g + g\nabla^2 f + 2(\text{grad } f \cdot \text{grad } g).$$

16. Verify (7-26).

17. Verify (7-27).

18. Prove Theorem 3 when ω is a 0-form, and when ω is a 2-form in four variables.

19. Show that div (grad $f \times$ grad g) $= 0$.

7.4. The Theorems of Green, Gauss, and Stokes

The important theorems which form the subject of this section deal with certain relations among line integrals, surface integrals, and volume integrals. In the language of differential forms, they connect an integral of a differential form ω with an integral of its derivative $d\omega$. We start by giving general statements for these theorems.

Green's Theorem. *Let D be a suitably well-behaved region in the plane whose boundary is a curve ∂D. Let ω be a 1-form of class C' defined in D. Then*

$$\int_{\partial D} \omega = \iint_D d\omega.$$

Stokes' Theorem. *Let Σ be a suitably well-behaved orientable surface whose boundary is a curve $\partial\Sigma$. Let ω be a 1-form of class C' defined on Σ. Then*

$$\int_{\partial\Sigma} \omega = \iint_\Sigma d\omega.$$

Divergence Theorem (Gauss). *Let R be a suitably well-behaved region in space whose boundary ∂R is a surface. Let ω be a 2-form of class C' defined on R. Then*

$$\iint_{\partial R} \omega = \iiint_R d\omega$$

The qualification "suitably well behaved" which occurs in each statement is inserted to indicate that it is convenient to impose some restrictions upon the regions, surfaces, and curves on which the integration is carried out. The exact nature of these restrictions is chiefly dependent upon the tools which are employed to prove the theorem. In most of the simpler applications of these theorems, one encounters only the nicest of curves and surfaces; for these, the proofs which we shall give are sufficient.†

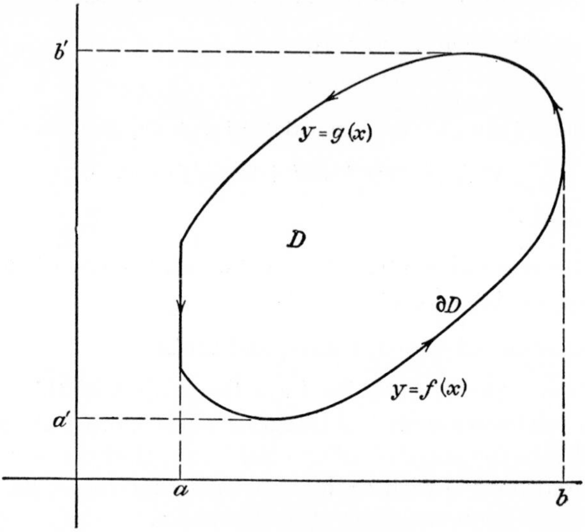

FIG. 7-15

Let us begin by proving a special case of Green's theorem.

Theorem 6. *Let D be a closed convex region in the plane and let $\omega = A(x, y)\,dx + B(x, y)\,dy$ with A and B of class C' in D. Then,*

$$\int_{\partial D} A\,dx + B\,dy = \iint_D d\omega = \iint_D \left(\frac{\partial B}{\partial x} - \frac{\partial A}{\partial y}\right) dxdy.$$

The assumption that D is convex allows us to describe D in two ways (see Fig. 7-15). If the projection of D onto the horizontal axis is the closed interval $[a, b]$, then D is the set of all points (x, y) such that

$$\begin{gathered} a \leq x \leq b \\ f(x) \leq y \leq g(x) \end{gathered} \tag{7-28}$$

where g and f are the continuous functions whose graphs form the top and bottom pieces of the boundary of D. Likewise, if $[a', b']$ is the pro-

† More general proofs may be found in O. D. Kellogg, "Foundations of Potential Theory," Frederick Ungar Publishing Co., New York, 1940, and in the recent periodical literature.

jection of D upon the vertical axis, D is the set of points (x, y) such that

$$\begin{aligned} a' \le y \le b' \\ F(y) \le x \le G(y). \end{aligned} \tag{7-29}$$

Since $\int_{\partial D} \omega = \int_{\partial D} A\,dx + \int_{\partial D} B\,dy$, we may treat each part separately. Suppose that $\omega = A(x, y)\,dx$. On γ_1, the lower part of ∂D, $y = f(x)$, $a \le x \le b$, and $\omega = A(x, f(x))\,dx$.

Thus $$\int_{\gamma_1} \omega = \int_a^b A(x, f(x))\,dx.$$

On γ_2, the upper part of ∂D, $y = g(x)$ and x goes from b to a. Thus, $\omega = A(x, g(x))\,dx$ and

$$\int_{\gamma_2} \omega = \int_b^a A(x, g(x))\,dx = -\int_a^b A(x, g(x))\,dx.$$

On the vertical parts of ∂D, if any, $\omega = 0$. Adding, we find

$$\int_{\partial D} \omega = \int_{\partial D} A\,dx = \int_a^b [A(x, f(x)) - A(x, g(x))]\,dx.$$

On the other hand, $d\omega = d(A(x, y)\,dx) = A_2(x, y)\,dydx$ so that

$$\begin{aligned} \iint_D d\omega &= \iint_D A_2(x, y)\,dydx \\ &= -\iint_D A_2(x, y)\,dxdy \\ &= -\int_a^b dx \int_{f(x)}^{g(x)} A_2(x, y)\,dy \\ &= -\int_a^b [A(x, g(x)) - A(x, f(x))]\,dx. \end{aligned}$$

Comparing the two results, we have $\int_{\partial D} \omega = \iint_D d\omega$. A similar computation, using (7-29), shows that the same relation holds if $\omega = B(x, y)\,dy$, and adding these, we obtain the formula for a general 1-form. ∎

In generalizing this theorem, we first remark that the proof used only the fact that D could be described both in the form (7-28) and in the form (7-29). Such regions need not be convex, as is shown by the region given by: $x \ge 0$, $y \le x^2$, $y \ge 2x^2 - 1$. For such regions, we shall use the term "standard region." Suppose now that D is itself not standard, but is the union of a finite number of standard regions such as shown in Fig. 7-16. Green's theorem holds for each of the regions D_j so that

$$\int_{\partial D_j} \omega = \iint_{D_j} d\omega$$

and adding, we have

$$\int_{\partial D_1} \omega + \int_{\partial D_2} \omega + \cdots + \int_{\partial D_n} \omega = \iint\limits_{D_1} d\omega + \iint\limits_{D_2} d\omega + \cdots + \iint\limits_{D_n} d\omega$$
$$= \iint\limits_{D} d\omega$$

However, in adding the line integrals on the left, only the terms which arise from parts of the boundary of D will remain. A curve γ which forms a portion of ∂D_j but not of ∂D will also appear as part of the boundary of one of the other standard regions; moreover, it will appear with

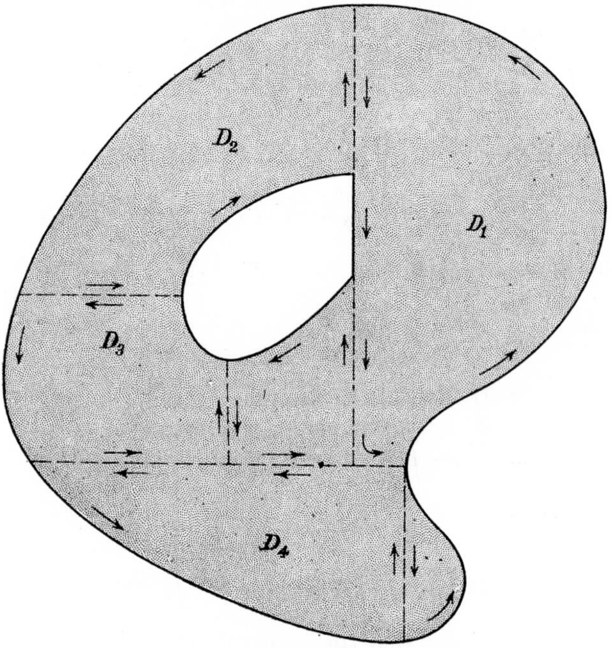

FIG. 7-16

the opposite orientation, so that the sum of the corresponding line integrals will be $\int_\gamma \omega + \int_{-\gamma} \omega = 0$. This type of argument shows that Green's theorem is valid for regions D which can be expressed as the union of a finite number of standard regions. Finally, one may extend the theorem still further by considering regions D which are the limits, in a suitable sense, of such regions.

One may also generalize Theorem 6 in another way. Let T be a continuous transformation from the (u, v) plane into the (x, y) plane which maps a set D onto a set D^*. Suppose that Green's theorem is valid for the set D. Does it then hold for the set D^*? To obtain an answer for this question, we must discuss the behavior of differential forms under a general transformation. Let us assume that T is one-to-one and of class C'' in D, and is given by

$$\begin{cases} x = \phi(u, v) \\ y = \psi(u, v). \end{cases}$$

We use these equations to transform any differential form in the XY plane into a differential form in the UV plane. To effect the transformation, we replace x and y wherever they appear by ϕ and ψ, respectively. For example, a 0-form $f(x, y)$ is transformed into the 0-form

$$f^*(u, v) = f(\phi(u, v), \psi(u, v)),$$

a 1-form $\omega = A(x, y)\, dx + B(x, y)\, dy$ is transformed into the 1-form

$$\begin{aligned} \omega^* &= A^*(u, v)\, d\phi + B^*(u, v)\, d\psi \\ &= A^*(u, v)[\phi_1(u, v)\, du + \phi_2(u, v)\, dv] \\ &\qquad + B^*(u, v)[\psi_1(u, v)\, du + \psi_2(u, v)\, dv] \\ &= [A^*(u, v)\phi_1(u, v) + B^*(u, v)\psi_1(u, v)]\, du \\ &\qquad + [A^*(u, v)\phi_2(u, v) + B^*(u, v)\psi_2(u, v)]\, dv \end{aligned}$$

where A^* and B^* are the 0-forms obtained by transforming A and B.

As an illustration, let T be given by $x = u^2 + v$, $y = v$, and let

$$\omega = xy\, dx.$$

Then,

$$\begin{aligned} \omega^* &= (u^2 + v)(v)\, d(u^2 + v) \\ &= (u^2v + v^2)(2u\, du + dv) \\ &= 2(u^3v + uv^2)\, du + (u^2v + v^2)\, dv. \end{aligned}$$

Consider the 2-form $d\omega = d(xy)\, dx = (x\, dy + y\, dx)\, dx = x\, dydx$. If we transform this by T, we obtain a 2-form

$$\begin{aligned} (d\omega)^* &= (u^2 + v)(dv)(2u\, du + dv) \\ &= 2u(u^2 + v)\, dvdu. \end{aligned}$$

Let us also differentiate the 1-form ω^*.

$$\begin{aligned} d(\omega^*) &= 2(3u^2v\, du + u^3\, dv + v^2\, du + 2uv\, dv)\, du \\ &\qquad + (2uv\, du + u^2\, dv + 2v\, dv)\, dv \\ &= 2(u^3 + 2uv)\, dvdu + 2uv\, dudv \\ &= (2u^3 + 4uv - 2uv)\, dvdu = 2u(u^2 + v)\, dvdu. \end{aligned}$$

We have also shown—at least for this example—that

$$(d\omega)^* = d(\omega^*). \tag{7-30}$$

This relation, which holds in general, is of great importance in the theory of differential forms. Assuming the validity of this, for the moment, we may obtain another extension of Theorem 6.

Theorem 7. *Let T be a transformation which is one-to-one and of class C'' in a closed bounded region D, mapping D onto D^*. Then, if Green's theorem holds for D, it holds for D^*.*

We take D as a set in the (u, v) plane whose boundary is a curve γ. T carries D into the set D^* in the (x, y) plane, and γ into the boundary γ^* of D^*. Let ω be any 1-form in the (x, y) plane of class C', and let T transform ω into the 1-form ω^*. T will also transform the 2-form $d\omega$ into a 2-form $(d\omega)^*$ in u and v. The results in Sec. 7.1 dealing with transformation of integrals give at once the formulas

(7-31)
$$\int_\gamma \omega^* = \int_{\gamma^*} \omega$$
$$\iint_D (d\omega)^* = \iint_{D^*} d\omega$$

By assumption, Green's theorem holds in D; thus, applying it to the 1-form ω^*,

(7-32)
$$\int_\gamma \omega^* = \iint_D d(\omega^*).$$

By the fundamental relation (7-30), $d(\omega^*) = (d\omega)^*$. Combining this with (7-31) and (7-32),

$$\int_{\gamma^*} \omega = \int_\gamma \omega^* = \iint_D (d\omega)^* = \iint_{D^*} d\omega$$

and Green's theorem holds for D^*. ▮

This can be used to give another proof of Theorem 6 (see Exercise 13).

The crucial step in the argument is the use of the relation (7-30). The proof of this is our next order of business, and shows that the differentiation operator d is **invariant** under change of variables.

Theorem 8. *If ω is a differential form of class C', then*

(7-33)
$$(d\omega)^* = d(\omega^*).$$

We shall prove this in a somewhat wider context than that which was used in the previous theorem. Let T be a transformation of class C'' from (u, v) space into (x, y, z) space, described by

$$\begin{cases} x = \phi(u, v) \\ y = \psi(u, v) \\ z = \theta(u, v). \end{cases}$$

In the same fashion as before, we may use T to transform differential forms in the variables x, y, z into forms in u, v, and we shall use ω^* to denote the form obtained by transforming ω. To begin with, suppose that ω is a 0-form $f(x, y, z)$. Its transform ω^* will then be the 0-form

$$\omega^* = f^*(u, v) = f(\phi(u, v), \psi(u, v), \theta(u, v)).$$

Differentiating this, we obtain the 1-form

$$d(\omega^*) = (f_1\phi_1 + f_2\psi_1 + f_3\theta_1)\, du + (f_1\phi_2 + f_2\psi_2 + f_3\theta_2)\, dv.$$

If we differentiate ω *before* transforming, we obtain the 1-form

$$d\omega = f_1\, dx + f_2\, dy + f_3\, dz$$

and the transform of this is the 1-form

$$\begin{aligned}(d\omega)^* &= f_1(\phi_1\, du + \phi_2\, dv) + f_2(\psi_1\, du + \psi_2\, dv) + f_3(\theta_1\, du + \theta_2\, dv)\\ &= (f_1\phi_1 + f_2\psi_1 + f_3\theta_1)\, du + (f_1\phi_2 + f_2\psi_2 + f_3\theta_2)\, dv\end{aligned}$$

This agrees with the expression for $d(\omega^*)$, and we have shown that the relation $d(\omega^*) = (d\omega)^*$ holds for 0-forms.

Let us suppose now that ω is the 1-form $A(x, y, z)\, dx$. Its transform will be the 1-form

$$\begin{aligned}\omega^* &= A[\phi_1\, du + \phi_2\, dv]\\ &= A\phi_1\, du + A\phi_2\, dv.\end{aligned}$$

Differentiating this, we obtain the 2-form

$$\begin{aligned}d(\omega^*) &= \left[\frac{\partial}{\partial u}(A\phi_1)\, du + \frac{\partial}{\partial v}(A\phi_1)\, dv\right] du\\ &\qquad + \left[\frac{\partial}{\partial u}(A\phi_2)\, du + \frac{\partial}{\partial v}(A\phi_2)\, dv\right] dv\\ &= \left[\frac{\partial}{\partial u}(A\phi_2) - \frac{\partial}{\partial v}(A\phi_1)\right] dudv\\ &= \left[A\phi_{12} + \phi_2\frac{\partial A}{\partial u} - A\phi_{21} - \phi_1\frac{\partial A}{\partial v}\right] dudv\\ &= \left[\phi_2\frac{\partial A}{\partial u} - \phi_1\frac{\partial A}{\partial v}\right] dudv\end{aligned}$$

making use of the fact that T is of class C'' and thus $\phi_{12} = \phi_{21}$. We compute $\partial A/\partial u$ and $\partial A/\partial v$ by the chain rule.

$$\begin{aligned}\frac{\partial A}{\partial u} &= A_1\phi_1 + A_2\psi_1 + A_3\theta_1\\ \frac{\partial A}{\partial v} &= A_1\phi_2 + A_2\psi_2 + A_3\theta_2\end{aligned}$$

so that

$$\phi_2 \frac{\partial A}{\partial u} - \phi_1 \frac{\partial A}{\partial v} = \phi_2[A_1\phi_1 + A_2\psi_1 + A_3\theta_1] - \phi_1[A_1\phi_2 + A_2\psi_2 + A_3\theta_2]$$
$$= A_2(\psi_1\phi_2 - \psi_2\phi_1) + A_3(\theta_1\phi_2 - \theta_2\phi_1).$$

Thus
$$d(\omega^*) = \left\{ A_2 \begin{vmatrix} \psi_1 & \psi_2 \\ \phi_1 & \phi_2 \end{vmatrix} + A_3 \begin{vmatrix} \theta_1 & \theta_2 \\ \phi_1 & \phi_2 \end{vmatrix} \right\} dudv.$$

If, on the other hand, we differentiate ω before transforming, we have

$$d\omega = (A_1\, dx + A_2\, dy + A_3\, dz)\, dx$$
$$= A_2\, dydx + A_3\, dzdx.$$

If we transform this, and use Theorem 1, we have

$$dydx = \frac{\partial(y, x)}{\partial(u, v)}\, dudv = \begin{vmatrix} \psi_1 & \psi_2 \\ \phi_1 & \phi_2 \end{vmatrix} dudv$$
$$dzdx = \frac{\partial(z, x)}{\partial(u, v)}\, dudv = \begin{vmatrix} \theta_1 & \theta_2 \\ \phi_1 & \phi_2 \end{vmatrix} dudv$$

so that

$$(d\omega)^* = \left\{ A_2 \begin{vmatrix} \psi_1 & \psi_2 \\ \phi_1 & \phi_2 \end{vmatrix} + A_3 \begin{vmatrix} \theta_1 & \theta_2 \\ \phi_1 & \phi_2 \end{vmatrix} \right\} dudv.$$

Since this agrees with the expression for $d(\omega^*)$, we have shown that $d(\omega^*) = (d\omega)^*$ holds when $\omega = A(x, y, z)\, dx$. A similar computation shows that the relation is valid also for the 1-forms $B\, dy$ and $C\, dz$, and we have thus shown that it holds for any 1-form.

A comparable direct verification may also be made when ω is a 2-form such as $A(x, y, z)\, dydz$. Rather than carry this out, we shall outline an inductive method which proves the theorem for differential forms in n variables. We make use of two special formulas. Forms are transformed by T by replacing $x, y, z, \ldots$ wherever they occur by $\phi, \psi, \theta, \ldots$, and then simplifying the result by means of the algebra of forms. Thus, if α and β are any two forms, then

$$(\alpha\beta)^* = \alpha^*\beta^*. \tag{7-34}$$

The second formula expresses the manner in which the differentiation operator acts on products of forms. If α is a k-form and β any form, then it may be shown that

$$d(\alpha\beta) = (d\alpha)\beta + (-1)^k \alpha\, (d\beta) \tag{7-35}$$

(see Exercise 16). Suppose that we know that the invariance relation (7-33) holds for the forms α and β, and let $\omega = \alpha\beta$. By (7-34), we have $\omega^* = \alpha^*\beta^*$, and since α^* is also a k-form, we apply (7-35) to obtain

$$d(\omega^*) = (d\alpha^*)\beta^* + (-1)^k\alpha^*(d\beta^*)$$

Since the theorem is valid for α and β, we have $d(\alpha^*) = (d\alpha)^*$ and

$d(\beta^*) = (d\beta)^*$. Making these replacements,

$$\begin{aligned} d(\omega^*) &= (d\alpha)^*\beta^* + (-1)^k\alpha^*(d\beta)^* \\ &= [(d\alpha)\beta + (-1)^k\alpha(d\beta)]^* \\ &= [d(\alpha\beta)]^* = (d\omega)^*. \end{aligned}$$

Thus, the invariance relation (7-33) holds for the form $\alpha\beta$. We have shown that it holds for 0-forms. It is easily seen that it holds for any of the basic forms dx, dy, dz, ... Since every differential form is built up from these by multiplication and addition, the relation (7-33) is valid for any differential form of class C'. ▮

This fundamental relation, and the technique used in Theorem 7 can be combined to obtain another proof for the formula for change of variable in double integrals.

Theorem 9. *Let T be a transformation of class C'' defined by*

$$x = \phi(u, v), \qquad y = \psi(u, v)$$

which maps a closed region D onto a region D^*. We assume that D and D^* are finite unions of standard regions, and that T is one-to-one on the boundary of D and maps it into the boundary of D^*. Let f be continuous in D^*. Then,

$$\iint_{D^*} f(x, y)\, dxdy = \iint_D f(\phi(u, v), \psi(u, v)) \frac{\partial(x, y)}{\partial(u, v)}\, dudv.$$

As we have seen in Sec. 6.1, the difficult step is to show that this holds when $f(p)$ is constantly 1:

$$\iint_{D^*} dxdy = A(D^*) = \iint_D \frac{\partial(x, y)}{\partial(u, v)}\, dudv.$$

Consider the special 1-form $\omega = x\, dy$. This is chosen because $d\omega = dxdy$ so that by Green's theorem,

$$A(D^*) = \iint_{D^*} d\omega = \int_{\partial D^*} \omega$$

Writing this as an ordinary singlefold definite integral, and applying the formula for change of variable in this case (Sec. 3.2, Corollary to Theorem 7), we obtain

$$A(D^*) = \int_{\partial D} \omega^*$$

Applying Green's theorem to D, and the fundamental invariance relation (7-33), we have

$$A(D^*) = \iint_D d(\omega^*) = \iint_D (d\omega)^*$$

Since $d\omega = dxdy$, $(d\omega)^* = d\phi d\psi = \begin{vmatrix} \phi_1 & \phi_2 \\ \psi_1 & \psi_2 \end{vmatrix} dudv = \dfrac{\partial(x, y)}{\partial(u, v)}\, dudv.$ ▮

We note that this form of the change-of-variable theorem is in certain respects more general than that obtained in Sec. 6.1. Here, the Jacobian of T is not required to have constant sign, provided that the integral for $A(D^*)$ is understood to be an oriented integral. To offset this, the transformation T was required to be of class C''.

Next, we proceed to give a proof of Stokes' theorem by reducing it to an application of Green's theorem.

Theorem 10. *Let Σ be a smooth surface of class C'' whose domain D is a standard region, or a finite union of standard regions, in the UV plane. Let*

$$\omega = A\,dx + B\,dy + C\,dz$$

where A, B, and C are of class C' on Σ. Then,

$$\int_{\partial\Sigma} A\,dx + B\,dy + C\,dz = \iint_{\Sigma} \left(\frac{\partial C}{\partial y} - \frac{\partial B}{\partial z}\right) dydz + \left(\frac{\partial A}{\partial z} - \frac{\partial C}{\partial x}\right) dzdx + \left(\frac{\partial B}{\partial x} - \frac{\partial A}{\partial y}\right) dxdy$$

The line integral on the left is $\int_{\partial\Sigma} \omega$, while the surface integral on the right is $\iint_{\Sigma} d\omega$. It should be noticed that this becomes Green's theorem if the surface Σ is taken as the region D in the XY plane; $C = 0$ and $dz = 0$ so that the differential form in the right-hand integral becomes $\left(\frac{\partial B}{\partial x} - \frac{\partial A}{\partial y}\right) dxdy$. The proof of the theorem is almost immediate. By assumption, Σ is described by a set of equations $x = \phi(u, v)$, $y = \psi(u, v)$, $z = \theta(u, v)$ for $(u, v) \in D$ which define a transformation of class C''. Moreover, D is a region to which Green's theorem applies. If we use the transformation Σ to transform ω, we obtain a 1-form ω^* in u and v. Applying the method used in Theorem 7, Green's theorem in D, and the fundamental relation (7-33), we have

$$\int_{\partial\Sigma} \omega = \int_{\partial D} \omega^* = \iint_{D} d(\omega^*) = \iint_{D} (d\omega)^* = \iint_{\Sigma} d\omega$$

which, as we have seen, is the conclusion of Stokes' theorem. ∎

By allowing D to be a union of finite number of standard regions, we admit surfaces Σ which may have a finite number of "holes" (see Fig. 7-17). In computing $\int_{\partial\Sigma} \omega$, we must of course integrate around all the separate curves which comprise the boundary of Σ, each in its proper orientation. The theorem may also be extended to a surface (differentiable manifold) which is obtained by piecing together simple surface elements; however, it is necessary that it be orientable. The Möebius strip is a nonorientable manifold M which can be represented as the

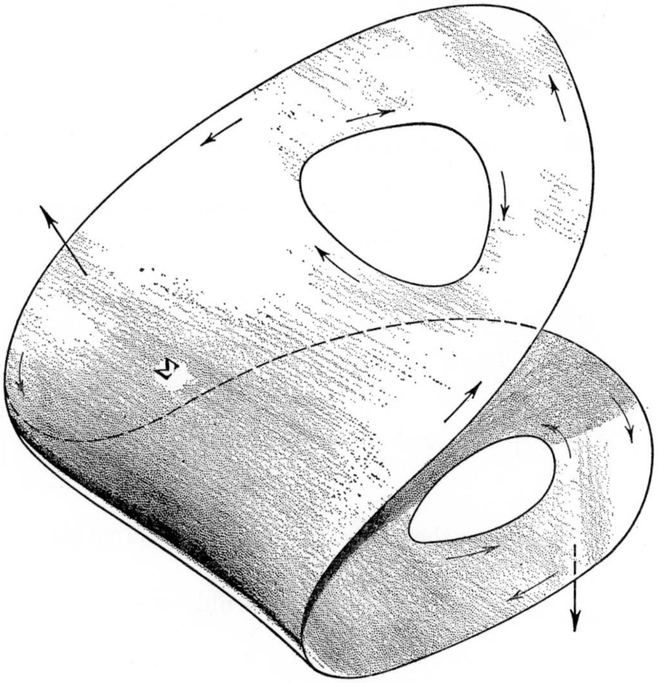

FIG. 7-17

union of two simple surface elements Σ_1 and Σ_2. To each of these, Stokes' theorem may be applied, and for a suitable 1-form ω

$$\int_{\partial\Sigma_1} \omega = \iint_{\Sigma_1} d\omega$$

$$\int_{\partial\Sigma_2} \omega = \iint_{\Sigma_2} d\omega$$

Adding these, however, we do not get the integral of ω around the simple closed curve Γ which forms the edge of the Möebius strip (see Fig. 7-18). Since M is nonorientable, no consistent orientations of Σ_1 and Σ_2 can be found, and one of the "inside" edges of Σ_1 will be traced twice in the *same* direction and the integral of ω along it will not in general drop out. (Note also that the edge of the strip is not traced in a consistent fashion.)

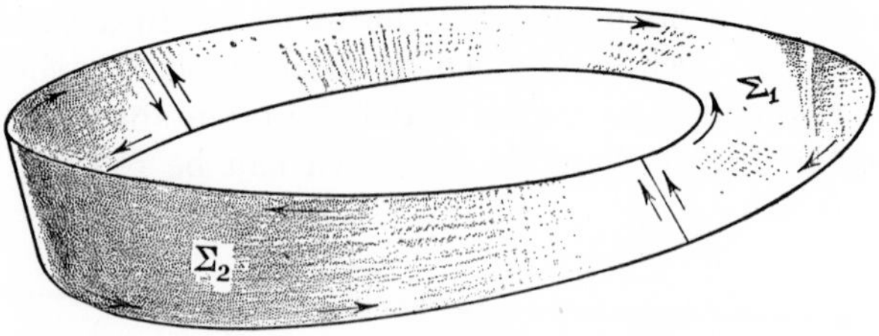

FIG. 7-18

Turning finally to the divergence theorem, we prove it first for the case of a cube.

Theorem 11. *Let R be a cube in (x, y, z) space with faces parallel to the coordinate planes. Let ω be a 2-form*

$$\omega = A\,dydz + B\,dzdx + C\,dxdy$$

with A, B, and C of class C' in R. Then,

$$\text{(7-36)} \quad \iint\limits_{\partial R} A\,dydz + B\,dzdx + C\,dxdy = \iiint\limits_{R} \left[\frac{\partial A}{\partial x} + \frac{\partial B}{\partial y} + \frac{\partial C}{\partial z}\right] dxdydz$$

The surface integral on the left is $\iint\limits_{\partial R} \omega$ and the volume integral on the right is $\iiint\limits_{R} d\omega$. Let us suppose that R is the unit cube having as opposite vertices the origin and $(1, 1, 1)$ (see Fig. 7-19). We may consider the separate terms in ω individually; suppose that $\omega = A(x, y, z)\,dydz$. Since $d\omega = A_1(x, y, z)\,dxdydz$

$$\begin{aligned}\iiint\limits_{R} d\omega &= \iiint\limits_{R} A_1(x, y, z)\,dxdydz \\ &= \int_0^1 dy \int_0^1 dz \int_0^1 A_1(x, y, z)\,dx \\ &= \int_0^1 dy \int_0^1 dz[A(1, y, z) - A(0, y, z)]\end{aligned}$$

On the other hand, we see that $\omega = 0$ on ∂R, except on the front and back faces. These have opposite orientations. On the front face, Σ_1, the orientation is the same as the YZ plane, and $\omega = A(1, y, z)\,dydz$. On the back face, the orientation is reversed, so that

$$\omega = A(0, y, z)\,dzdy = -A(0, y, z)\,dydz.$$

In each case, the parameter (y, z) covers the positively oriented unit square S in the YZ plane. Thus,

$$\begin{aligned}\iint_{\partial R} \omega &= \iint_{\Sigma_1} \omega + \iint_{\Sigma_2} \omega \\ &= \iint_S A(1, y, z)\, dydz - \iint_S A(0, y, z)\, dydz \\ &= \int_0^1 dy \int_0^1 dz[A(1, y, z) - A(0, y, z)]. \quad \blacksquare\end{aligned}$$

The line of argument used in Theorem 7 may now be used again to establish the divergence theorem for a more general class of regions R (see also Exercise 5).

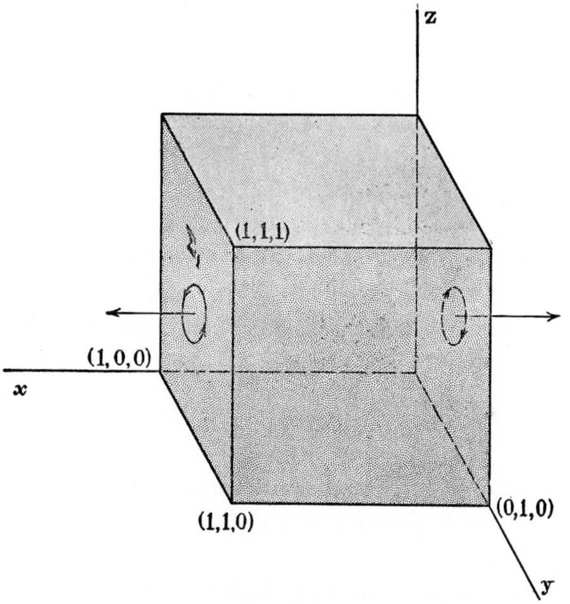

FIG. 7-19

Theorem 12. *The divergence theorem* (7-36) *holds for any region R which is the image of a closed cube under a one-to-one transformation of class C''.*

Again, we can combine regions together into more complicated regions (e.g., having cavities) and apply the divergence theorem to each. The surface integrals over the interface surfaces will cancel each other, since the common boundary will have opposite orientations, and only the surface integral over the boundary of the region itself will be left (see Fig. 7-20).

If we make use of the results in Sec. 7.3, especially Theorems 4 and 5, then we can recast these integral theorems in vector form. Let $\mathbf{F}$ be a vector field of class C' throughout a region in space.

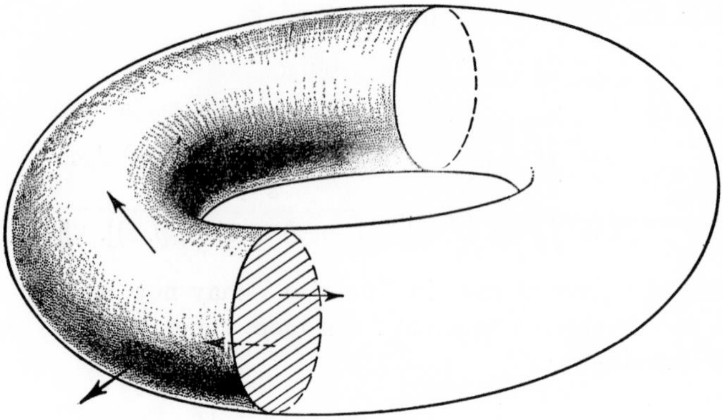

FIG. 7-20

Divergence Theorem. *Let R be a suitably well-behaved region in space whose boundary is a surface ∂R. Then*

$$\iiint_R \operatorname{div}(\mathbf{F}) = \iint_{\partial R} F_N$$

Stated verbally: The integral of div ($\mathbf{F}$) *throughout R is equal to the integral of the normal component of* $\mathbf{F}$ *over the boundary of R.*

Stokes' Theorem. *Let Σ be a suitably well-behaved orientable surface whose boundary is a curve $\partial\Sigma$. Then,*

$$\iint_\Sigma \operatorname{curl}(\mathbf{F})_N = \int_{\partial\Sigma} F_T$$

Stated verbally: The integral of the normal component of the curl of $\mathbf{F}$ *over a surface is equal to the integral of the tangential component of* $\mathbf{F}$ *around the boundary of the surface.*

These may be used to obtain physical interpretations for div ($\mathbf{F}$) and curl ($\mathbf{F}$). As in Sec. 7.3, let $\mathbf{V}$ be the velocity field of a fluid in motion, and let ρ be the density function; both may depend upon time. Let $\mathbf{F} = \rho\mathbf{V}$; this is the vector function which specifies the mass flow distribution. Let R be a closed bounded region of space to which the divergence theorem applies, e.g., a cube or a sphere. At any point p on the boundary of R, F_N is the normal component of $\mathbf{F}$, and therefore measures the rate of flow of mass out of R at p. The surface integral $\iint_{\partial R} F_N$ is then the total mass per unit time which leaves R through ∂R. Let us suppose that there is no creation or destruction of mass within R, i.e., no "sources" or "sinks." Then, $\iint_{\partial R} F_N$ must also be exactly the rate of decrease of the total mass within R:

$$\iint_{\partial R} F_N = -\frac{d}{dt}\iiint_R \rho.$$

If we apply the divergence theorem to the left side, and assume that $\frac{\partial \rho}{\partial t}$ is continuous so that we can move the time differentiation inside, we obtain

$$\iiint_R \operatorname{div}(\mathbf{F}) = -\iiint_R \frac{\partial \rho}{\partial t}$$

Since this relation must hold for all choices of R, we may conclude that the integrands are everywhere equal. Thus, we arrive at what is called the "equation of continuity":

$$\operatorname{div}(\mathbf{F}) = \operatorname{div}(\rho\mathbf{V}) = -\frac{\partial \rho}{\partial t}$$

If the fluid is incompressible, then $\operatorname{div}(\mathbf{V}) = 0$.

To obtain an interpretation for curl $(\mathbf{V})$, let $\mathbf{b}$ be a unit vector with initial point at a point p_0, and choose Σ as a circular disk of radius r, center p_0, having $\mathbf{b}$ as its normal (see Fig. 7-21). If p is a point of the circle C which forms the boundary of Σ, then V_T at p is the component of the velocity field along C, and $\int_C V_T = \int_{\partial\Sigma} V_T$ is a number which measures the extent to which the motion of the fluid is a rotation around C. By Stokes' theorem,

$$\int_C V_T = \iint_\Sigma \operatorname{curl}(\mathbf{V})_N$$

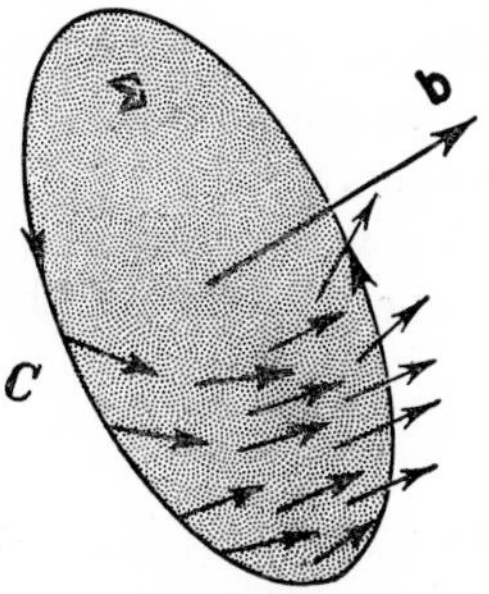

FIG. 7-21

By the mean value theorem, the right side may be replaced by $\pi r^2 h$, where h is the value of curl $(\mathbf{V})_N$ at some point p of Σ. Divide both sides by πr^2, and let $r \to 0$. The point p must approach p_0 so that h approaches curl $(\mathbf{V})_N$ computed at p_0. Thus, we obtain

$$\operatorname{curl}(\mathbf{V})_N = \lim_{r\to 0} \frac{1}{\pi r^2}\int_{\partial\Sigma} V_T$$

The right side may be interpreted as a number which measures the rotation of the fluid at the point p_0 in the plane normal to $\mathbf{b}$, per unit area. Since the normal to Σ remains constantly $\mathbf{b}$,

$$\operatorname{curl}(\mathbf{V})_N = \operatorname{curl}(\mathbf{V}) \cdot \mathbf{b}.$$

Thus, curl (**V**) · **b** measures the rotation of the fluid about the direction b. It will be greatest when **b** is chosen parallel to curl (**V**). Thus, curl (**V**) is a vector field which can be interpreted as specifying the axis of rotation and the magnitude (angular velocity) of that rotation, at each point in space. For example, if **V** is the velocity field for a rigid body rotating at constant angular velocity ω about a fixed axis **b**, then curl (**V**) $= 2\omega\mathbf{b}$. The motion of a fluid is said to be **"irrotational"** if curl (**V**) $\equiv 0$.

We may also use the integral theorems to arrive at expressions for div (**F**) and curl (**F**) having a form which is free of the coordinate appearance of the original definitions for these quantities. By the same line of argument that has been used above, one may arrive at the formulas

$$\operatorname{div}(\mathbf{F})\Big|_{p_0} = \lim_{r\downarrow 0} \frac{1}{\mathrm{v}(R)} \iint_{\partial R} F_N$$

$$\operatorname{curl}(\mathbf{F})\Big|_{p_0} \cdot \mathbf{b} = \lim_{\Sigma\downarrow p_0} \frac{1}{A(\Sigma)} \int_{\partial\Sigma} F_T$$

where $\mathrm{v}(R)$ is the volume of R and $A(\Sigma)$ the area of Σ, and R and Σ are thought of as closing down on the point p_0 in such a fashion that the normals to Σ are always parallel to **b**, and Stoke's theorem and the divergence theorem always apply.

Line integrals also arise in another natural way. Let **F** be a vector-valued function which describes a force field throughout a region of space. The work done by the force in moving a particle along a curve γ is defined to be the value of the line integral

$$W = \int_\gamma F_T$$

In particular, if γ is a closed path which forms the boundary of a smooth orientable surface Σ, then we may apply Stokes' theorem, and obtain

$$W = \iint_\Sigma \operatorname{curl}(\mathbf{F})_N$$

If **F** should be such that curl (**F**) $\equiv 0$, then $W = 0$. In this case, the work done by **F** around any such closed path is zero. Such force fields are given the name **conservative**; an example is the Newtonian gravitational field of a particle.

EXERCISES

1. Verify Green's theorem for $\omega = x\,dx + xy\,dy$ with D as the unit square with opposite vertices at (0, 0), (1, 1).

2. Apply Green's theorem to evaluate the integral of $(x - y^3)\,dx + x^3\,dy$ around the circle $x^2 + y^2 = 1$.

3. Verify Stoke's theorem with $\omega = x\,dz$ and with Σ as the surface described by $x = uv$, $y = u + v$, $z = u^2 + v^2$ for (u, v) in the triangle with vertices $(0, 0)$, $(1, 0)$, $(1, 1)$.

4. Carry out the details needed to show that the special case of Green's theorem stated in Theorem 6 holds for $\omega = B(x, y)\,dy$.

5. Prove the divergence theorem directly when R is the solid sphere

$$x^2 + y^2 + z^2 \leq 1.$$

6. (*a*) Show that the area of a region D to which Green's theorem applies may be given by

$$A(D) = \tfrac{1}{2} \int_{\partial D} (x\,dy - y\,dx)$$

(*b*) Apply this to find the area bounded by the ellipse $x = a\cos\theta$, $y = b\sin\theta$, $0 \leq \theta \leq 2\pi$.

7. Use Exercise 6 to find the area inside the loop of the folium of Descartes, described by $x = 3at/(1 + t^3)$, $y = 3at^2/(1 + t^3)$.

8. Let D be the region inside the square $|x| + |y| = 4$ and outside the circle $x^2 + y^2 = 1$. Using the relation in Exercise 6, find the area of D.

9. Find a 1-form ω for which $d\omega = (x^2 + y^2)\,dxdy$, and use this to evaluate

$$\iint_D (x^2 + y^2)\,dxdy$$

when D is the region described in Exercise 8.

10. Show that the volume of a suitably well-behaved region R in space is given by the formula

$$\mathrm{v}(R) = \tfrac{1}{3} \iint_{\partial R} x\,dydz + y\,dzdx + z\,dxdy$$

11. (*a*) Show that the moment of inertia of a solid R about the z axis can be expressed in the form

$$I = (\tfrac{1}{4}) \iint_{\partial R} (x^3 + 3xy^2)\,dydz + (3x^2y + y^3)\,dzdx$$

(*b*) Use this to find the moment of inertia of a sphere about a diameter.

12. Verify the invariance relation $(d\omega)^* = d(\omega^*)$ when $\omega = x\,dydz$ and T is the transformation $x = u + v - w$, $y = u^2 - v$, $z = v + w^2$.

13. Assuming Green's theorem for rectangles, prove it for a region of the type described by (7-28) with $\omega = A(x, y)\,dx$ by means of the transformation $x = u$, $y = f(u)v + g(u)(1 - v)$, $a \leq u \leq b$, $0 \leq v \leq 1$.

14. Verify the differentiation formula (7-35) when α and β are 0-forms in x, y, z.

15. Verify (7-35) for $\alpha = A(x, y, z)\,dz$ and $\beta = B(x, y, z)\,dy$.

***16.** Prove the formula for general forms α and β. (*Hint:* Proceed by induction on the degree of the form α, starting with α a 0-form, and a 1-form.)

17. Let $\mathbf{V}$ be the velocity field of the particles of a rigid body which is rotating about a fixed axis in the direction of the unit vector $\mathbf{b}$, at an angular velocity of ω. Show that div $(\mathbf{V}) = 0$ and curl $(\mathbf{V}) = 2\omega\mathbf{b}$.

18. Using **n** for a general normal vector on a surface and **T** for a general tangent vector to a curve, Stokes' theorem and the divergence theorem may be expressed by

$$\iint_{\Sigma} (\nabla \times \mathbf{F}) \cdot \mathbf{n} = \int_{\partial\Sigma} \mathbf{F} \cdot \mathbf{T}$$

$$\iiint_{R} \nabla \cdot \mathbf{F} = \iint_{\partial R} \mathbf{F} \cdot \mathbf{n}$$

When D is a region in the plane, and **n** and **T** are used for the (outward) normal vector and the tangent vector for the curve ∂D, and when $\mathbf{F} = A\mathbf{i} + B\mathbf{j}$ is a vector field in the plane, show that Green's theorem may be put into either of the forms

$$\iint_{D} \nabla \cdot \mathbf{F} = \int_{\partial D} \mathbf{F} \cdot \mathbf{n}$$

$$\iint_{D} (\nabla \times \mathbf{F}) \cdot \mathbf{k} = \int_{\partial D} \mathbf{F} \cdot \mathbf{T}$$

19. The theorems of this section are special cases of a generalized Stokes' theorem, applying to k-forms in n variables, which may be stated in the form $\omega(\partial M) = d\omega(M)$, or equivalently

$$\underbrace{\int \cdots \int_{\partial M}}_{k} \omega = \underbrace{\int \cdots \int_{M}}_{k+1} d\omega$$

where M is a $k + 1$ dimensional manifold and ω is a k-form. Assuming this, obtain the following special cases:

(*a*) If M is a region in 4-space, and ∂M is its three-dimensional boundary, then

$$\iiint_{\partial M} \{A\, dydzdw + B\, dxdzdw + C\, dxdydw + D\, dxdydz\}$$
$$= \iiiint_{M} \left\{\frac{\partial A}{\partial x} + \frac{\partial B}{\partial y} + \frac{\partial C}{\partial z} + \frac{\partial D}{\partial w}\right\} dxdydzdw.$$

(*b*) If Σ is a two-dimensional surface in 4-space bounded by a curve $\partial\Sigma$, then

$$\int_{\partial\Sigma} \{A\, dx + B\, dy + C\, dz + D\, dw\}$$
$$= \iint_{\Sigma} \left\{\left(\frac{\partial B}{\partial x} - \frac{\partial A}{\partial y}\right) dxdy + \left(\frac{\partial C}{\partial x} - \frac{\partial A}{\partial z}\right) dxdz + \left(\frac{\partial D}{\partial x} - \frac{\partial A}{\partial w}\right) dxdw\right.$$
$$\left. + \left(\frac{\partial C}{\partial y} - \frac{\partial B}{\partial z}\right) dydz + \left(\frac{\partial D}{\partial y} - \frac{\partial B}{\partial w}\right) dydw + \left(\frac{\partial D}{\partial z} - \frac{\partial C}{\partial w}\right) dzdw\right\}$$

7.5. Independence of Path, and Exact Differential Forms

In this section, we shall discuss the properties of a special class of differential forms.

Definition. *A 1-form ω is said to be exact in a region Ω if there is a function f which is defined and of class C' in Ω, and such that $df = \omega$.*

For example, the 1-form $2xy\,dx + x^2\,dy + 2z\,dz$ is exact since this is precisely $d(x^2y + z^2)$. If ω is exact, and $\omega = df$, then ω is also dg, where g differs from f by a constant function.

Theorem 13. *Let ω be exact in a region Ω, with $\omega = df$ there. Let γ be any smooth curve in Ω which goes from a point p_0 to a point p_1. Then,*

$$\int_\gamma \omega = \int_\gamma df = f(p_1) - f(p_0)$$

Let γ be given by $x = \phi(t)$, $y = \psi(t)$, $z = \theta(t)$, $0 \le t \le 1$. Since $\omega = df$, we have

$$\omega = f_1(x, y, z)\,dx + f_2(x, y, z)\,dy + f_3(x, y, z)\,dz,$$

so that on γ,

$$\omega = \{f_1(\gamma(t))\phi'(t) + f_2(\gamma(t))\psi'(t) + f_3(\gamma(t))\theta'(t)\}\,dt.$$

But, this can also be written as

$$\omega = \frac{d}{dt}\{f(\gamma(t))\}\,dt$$

so that

$$\begin{aligned}\int_\gamma \omega &= \int_0^1 \frac{d}{dt}\{f(\gamma(t))\}\,dt\\ &= f(\gamma(1)) - f(\gamma(0))\\ &= f(p_1) - f(p_0). \quad \blacksquare\end{aligned}$$

Corollary. *If ω is an exact 1-form in a region Ω, then $\int_\gamma \omega = 0$ for every closed γ lying in Ω.*

For, if γ is closed, then $p_0 = p_1$, and $f(p_1) = f(p_0)$. $\blacksquare$

A special name is given to the type of behavior described in the corollary.

Definition. *A line integral $\int_\gamma \omega$ is said to be independent of path in a region Ω if its value is the same along any other curve lying in Ω which joins the same points (in the same order). Equivalently, $\int_\gamma \omega = 0$ for every closed curve γ lying in Ω.*

The equivalence arises from the fact that if γ_1 and γ_2 are two curves lying in Ω which have common end points, then the union of γ_1 and $-\gamma_2$ is a closed curve lying in Ω. Using this terminology, the corollary above states that any exact 1-form yields line integrals that are independent of path. We may use this to test a 1-form for exactness. For example, $\omega = y\,dx$ is not exact in the first quadrant since its integral along the straight line from (0, 0) to (1, 1) is $\int_0^1 x\,dx = \frac{1}{2}$, while its integral along the parabola $y = x^2$ which also joins (0, 0) to (1, 1) is $\int_0^1 x^2\,dx = \frac{1}{3}$.

This would be a difficult test to apply in some cases since it depends upon a comparison between the numerical value of line integrals. An alternate procedure may also be used.

Theorem 14. *If ω is an exact 1-form of class C'' in Ω, then it is necessary that $d\omega = 0$ throughout Ω. In particular:*

(i) *If $\omega = A(x, y)\,dx + B(x, y)\,dy$ is exact in a region D in which A and B are of class C'', then it is necessary that $\dfrac{\partial A}{\partial y} = \dfrac{\partial B}{\partial x}$ throughout D.*

(ii) *If $\omega = A(x, y, z)\,dx + B(x, y, z)\,dy + C(x, y, z)\,dz$ is exact in a region Ω in which A, B, and C are of class C'', then it is necessary that throughout Ω,*

$$\frac{\partial C}{\partial y} = \frac{\partial B}{\partial z}, \qquad \frac{\partial A}{\partial z} = \frac{\partial C}{\partial x}, \qquad \frac{\partial B}{\partial x} = \frac{\partial A}{\partial y}. \tag{7-37}$$

This is an immediate deduction from Theorem 3. There, it was shown that $dd\omega = 0$ for any differential form of class C''. If ω is exact, then $\omega = df$ in Ω, so that $d\omega = ddf = 0$ in Ω. ▌

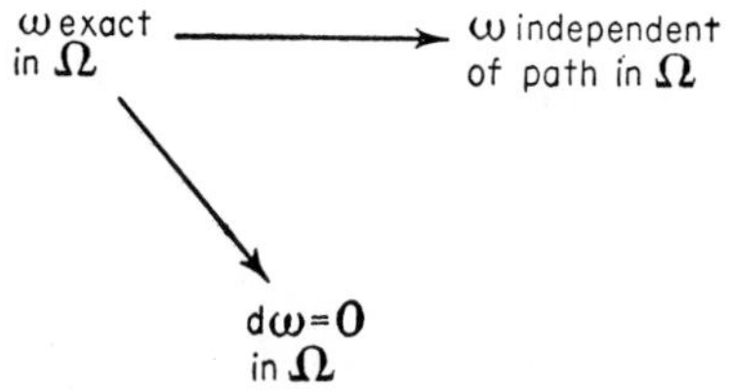

FIG. 7-22

A differential form which has the property that $d\omega = 0$ in a region Ω is sometimes said to be **closed.** The connections between this, and the property of being exact, and of being independent of path, is shown schematically in Fig. 7-22 (assuming that ω is of class C''). Contrasting these, the condition on the left is a local property which may be tested by examining the coefficients of the differential form, and checking Eqs. (7-37); the condition on the right is one which requires a treatment of the differential form "in the large" by integrating it over various curves. It is natural to seek a connection between these conditions.

Theorem 15. *If ω is a 1-form which is of class C' and obeys the condition $d\omega = 0$ in a convex region Ω, then ω is exact in Ω.*

Let us assume that $\omega = A\,dx + B\,dy + C\,dz$, and that Eqs. (7-37) hold throughout a convex region Ω in space which contains the origin $(0, 0, 0)$. We construct a function f by integrating ω along a polygon joining $(0, 0, 0)$ to (x, y, z) within Ω (see Fig. 7-23). Let

$$f(x, y, z) = \int_0^x A(t, 0, 0)\,dt + \int_0^y B(x, t, 0)\,dt + \int_0^z C(x, y, t)\,dt.$$

We wish to show that $\omega = df$. Computing the partial derivatives of f, and using Eqs. (7-37), we have

$$\begin{aligned}
f_3(x, y, z) &= C(x, y, z) \\
f_2(x, y, z) &= B(x, y, 0) + \int_0^z C_2(x, y, t)\, dt \\
&= B(x, y, 0) + \int_0^z B_3(x, y, t)\, dt \\
&= B(x, y, 0) + [B(x, y, z) - B(x, y, 0)] \\
&= B(x, y, z) \\
f_1(x, y, z) &= A(x, 0, 0) + \int_0^y B_1(x, t, 0)\, dt + \int_0^z C_1(x, y, t)\, dt \\
&= A(x, 0, 0) + \int_0^y A_2(x, t, 0)\, dt + \int_0^z A_3(x, y, t)\, dt \\
&= A(x, 0, 0) + [A(x, y, 0) - A(x, 0, 0)] \\
&\qquad + [A(x, y, z) - A(x, y, 0)] \\
&= A(x, y, z). \quad \blacksquare
\end{aligned}$$

For a general region, the best that this theorem gives is the following corollary.

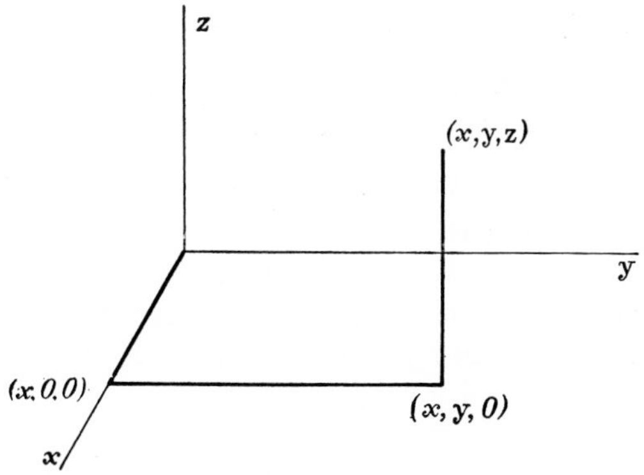

FIG. 7-23

Corollary. *If $d\omega = 0$ in an open region Ω, then ω is locally exact in Ω, that is, about any point p there is a neighborhood in which ω has the form $\omega = df$.*

As the point p moves around in Ω, the function f may change, and it may not be possible to find a single function such that $\omega = df$ throughout all of Ω. For example, consider the 1-form

(7-38) $$\omega = \frac{x}{x^2 + y^2}\, dy - \frac{y}{x^2 + y^2}\, dx$$

in the open ring $D = \{\text{all } (x, y) \text{ with } 1 \leq x^2 + y^2 \leq 4\}$. Direct computation shows that $d\omega = 0$ in D, so that ω is locally exact in D. However, ω is not exact in D, for if we compute the integral of ω around a circular path, $x = r \cos \theta$, $y = r \sin \theta$, lying in D, we obtain

$$\int_\gamma \omega = \int_0^{2\pi} \left\{ \frac{(r \cos \theta)}{r^2} (r \cos \theta) - \frac{(r \sin \theta)}{r^2} (-r \sin \theta) \right\} d\theta$$
$$= \int_0^{2\pi} (\cos^2 \theta + \sin^2 \theta)\, d\theta = 2\pi \neq 0.$$

If ω were exact in D, then by the corollary to Theorem 13, $\int_\gamma \omega$ would have to be zero. As we shall see later, the clue to this behavior lies in the nature of the set D.

Referring again to the diagram of Fig. 7-22, we see that Theorem 15 shows that the condition $d\omega = 0$ in a convex region Ω implies exactness, and therefore independence of path in Ω. A similar technique will prove the converse, for a general region Ω.

Theorem 16. *If ω is independent of path in an open connected set Ω, then ω is exact in Ω, and therefore obeys $d\omega = 0$.*

Choose any point $p_0 \in \Omega$. By assumption, Ω is connected so that any point $p \in \Omega$ can be joined to p_0 by a smooth curve γ lying in Ω. Define a function f in Ω by setting $f(p) = \int_\gamma \omega$. Since ω yields line integrals that are independent of path, it does not matter what curve γ we choose, so long as it lies in Ω and goes from p_0 to p. We again wish to show that $\omega = df$, and for this, we need the partial derivatives of f. If p_1 and $p_1 + \Delta p$ are points of Ω, and β is any curve in Ω from p_1 to $p_1 + \Delta p$, then choosing a curve γ from p_0 to p_1, we have

$$f(p_1 + \Delta p) = \int_\gamma \omega + \int_\beta \omega$$
$$= f(p_1) + \int_\beta \omega.$$

To compute $f_1(p_1)$, the partial derivative of f in the direction of the X axis, we take $\Delta p = (h, 0, 0)$ and compute

$$\lim_{h \to 0} \frac{f(p_1 + \Delta p) - f(p_1)}{h} = \lim_{h \to 0} \frac{1}{h} \int_\beta \omega$$

For β, we choose the straight line from p_1 to $p_1 + \Delta p$ whose equation is $x = x_1 + ht$, $y = y_1$, $z = z_1$; $0 \le t \le 1$. If $\omega = A\,dx + B\,dy + C\,dz$, then on β, $\omega = A(x_1 + ht, y_1, z_1)h\,dt$ and

$$\frac{f(p_1 + \Delta p) - f(p_1)}{h} = \int_0^1 A(x_1 + ht, y_1, z_1)\, dt.$$

Letting h approach 0, and using the fact that A is continuous

$$f_1(p_1) = \lim_{h \to 0} \int_0^1 A(x_1 + ht, y_1, z_1)\, dt$$
$$= \int_0^1 A(x_1, y_1, z_1)\, dt = A(x_1, y_1, z_1)$$

In a similar fashion, we find $f_2(p_1) = B(p_1)$ and $f_3(p_1) = C(p_1)$ so that $\omega = df$ in Ω.† ▌

The state of our knowledge to this point is shown by the solid lines in Fig. 7-24, again assuming that ω is of class C''. To round these out, we characterize the regions for which complete equivalence holds.

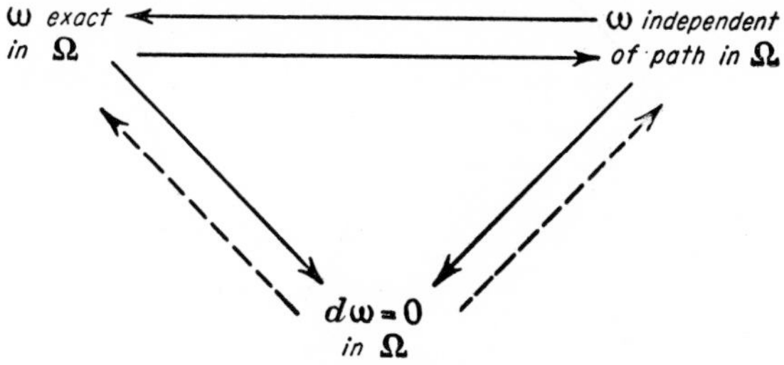

FIG. 7-24

Definition. *An open region Ω is said to be simply connected if and only if every continuous closed curve γ lying in Ω is the boundary of a continuous orientable surface lying wholly in Ω.*

Since any closed curve in Ω can be regarded as a mapping from the boundary of a unit circle into Ω, this can be put more precisely as follows: *Ω is simply connected if and only if every continuous mapping of the boundary of the unit disk into Ω can be extended to give a continuous mapping of the disk itself into Ω.* This has an equivalent formulation which can be visualized easily: a region Ω is simply connected if every continuous closed curve lying in Ω can be contracted to a point without passing outside of Ω. In the plane, a region whose boundary is a simple closed curve is **simply connected,** while one whose boundary consists of several closed curves is **multiply connected.** (See Fig. 7-25. In this example, γ cannot be contracted to a point without passing outside D.) In space, the region bounded by a torus surface is multiply connected, since a closed curve which encircles the hole cannot be closed down to a point. On the other hand, the region between two concentric spheres is simply connected.

† It is interesting to observe that the proof of this theorem used only the assumption that $\int_\gamma \omega = 0$ for closed polygonal paths γ with segments parallel to the axes; by Theorem 13, we can then conclude that this holds for any closed curve γ, lying in the region.

Theorem 17. *Let Ω be a simply connected open region and let ω be a 1-form of class C' in Ω such that $d\omega = 0$ everywhere in Ω. Then, ω is independent of path, and thus exact, in Ω.*

We shall assume that every closed polygon γ lying in Ω is the boundary of a surface Σ of class C'' which also lies in Ω. The surface Σ must be

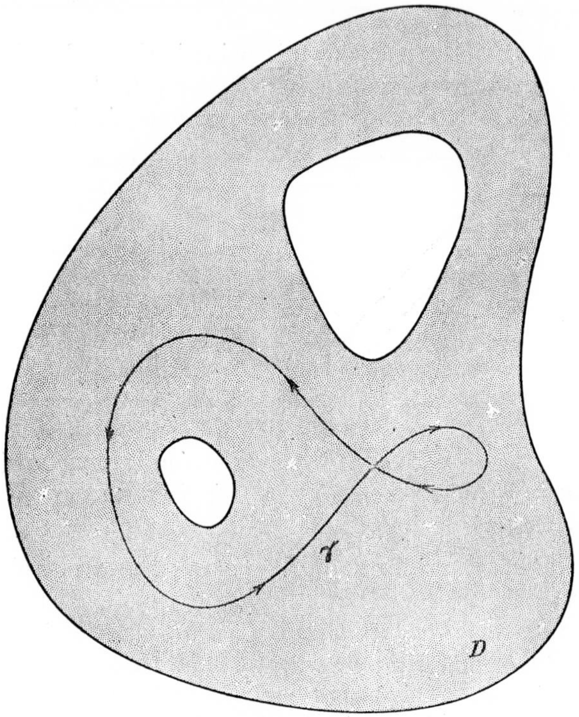

FIG. 7-25. Multiply connected region in the plane.

allowed to have multiple points (for example, if γ is a knotted curve) but is orientable, and sufficiently well behaved to apply Stokes' theorem. If we do so, then we have

$$\int_\gamma \omega = \iint_\Sigma d\omega = 0.$$

This holds for any closed polygonal path in Ω, and the result follows at once by Theorem 16. ∎

Corollary. *If Ω is a simply connected region in space, then any 1-form ω of class C'' which is locally exact in Ω, is exact.*

Referring to Fig. 7-24, we have shown that the implications indicated by the dotted lines hold when Ω is simply connected. Starting at the upper left, the fact that ω is locally exact in Ω implies that $d\omega = 0$ throughout Ω; this in turn implies that ω is independent of path in Ω, and therefore exact in Ω.

When a 1-form ω is known to be exact, and thus of the form df, the function f may be found by integrating ω along any convenient path from some point p_0 to $p = (x, y, z)$; it will be unique, up to an additive constant. For example, consider the 1-form $\omega = 2xy^3\,dx + 3x^2y^2\,dy$. Checking for exactness, we find that $d\omega = 6xy^2\,dydx + 6xy^2\,dxdy = 0$. To find f, we integrate from (0, 0) to (x, y). If we choose the solid broken line shown in Fig. 7-26, we obtain

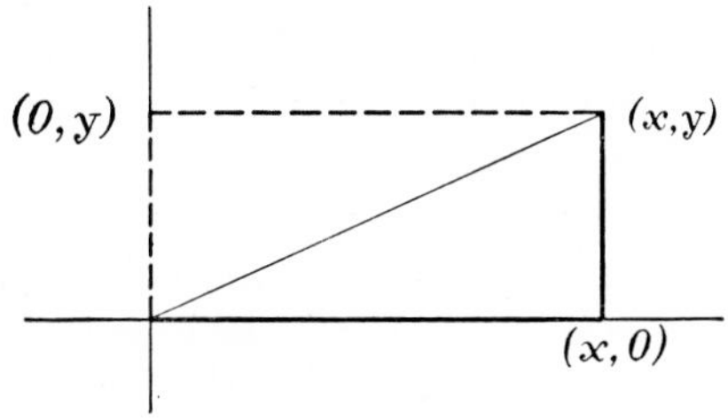

FIG. 7-26

$$f(x, y) = \int_0^x 0\,dx + \int_0^y 3x^2y^2\,dy = x^2y^3.$$

We may also use the dotted broken line, and obtain

$$f(x, y) = \int_0^y 0\,dy + \int_0^x 2xy^3\,dx = x^2y^3.$$

Finally, if we use the straight line joining (0, 0) and (x, y), we have

$$\begin{aligned} f(x, y) &= \int_0^1 \{2(xt)(yt)^3d(xt) + 3(xt)^2(yt)^2d(yt)\} \\ &= \int_0^1 \{(2xy^3)(x)t^4\,dt + (3x^2y^2)(y)t^4\,dt\} \\ &= x^2y^3 \int_0^1 5t^4\,dt = x^2y^3. \end{aligned}$$

When the coefficients in ω have special properties, other methods may be used to find f (see Exercise 5).

The study of differential equations also leads to the consideration of exact differential forms. One says that a curve γ in the plane is a solution of the first order "differential equation"

(7-39) $$A(x, y)\,dx + B\,(x, y)\,dy = 0$$

if the 1-form $\omega = A\,dx + B\,dy$ is zero on γ. If ω is exact, and $\omega = df$, then the level curves of f are solutions for (7-39). An "integrating factor" for the equation (7-39) is a function g such that $g\omega$ is an exact 1-form. Computing $d(g\omega)$, and requiring that this vanish, one is led to a partial differential equation for g. General existence theorems in the theory of differential equations show that, provided A and B are sufficiently well behaved, the equation (7-39) always admits integrating factors. The situation is somewhat different in the case of forms in three or more variables. A curve γ in 3-space is said to be a solution of the "total differential equation" (or **Pfaffian** equation)

$$A(x, y, z)\,dx + B(x, y, z)\,dy + C(x, y, z)\,dz = 0 \tag{7-40}$$

if the 1-form $\omega = A\,dx + B\,dy + C\,dz$ is zero on γ. When ω is exact, and has the form $\omega = df$, then any curve lying on the level surfaces of f will be a solution of (7-40). Since this is a very special type of possible behavior for the solution curves of such an equation, it is plausible that only certain Pfaffian equations admit integrating factors. The analysis supports this. If g is an integrating factor for ω, then we may assume that $d(g\omega) = 0$. Using the formula (7-35) for differentiating a product, we obtain

$$(dg)\omega + g(d\omega) = 0.$$

It is easily seen that $\omega\omega = 0$; thus, if we multiply this equation on the right by ω, we obtain as a necessary condition

$$g(d\omega)\omega = 0$$

Dividing by the function g, we obtain the condition $(d\omega)\omega = 0$. In terms of the coefficients of ω, this shows that a necessary condition that (7-40) have an integrating factor is that

$$\left(\frac{\partial C}{\partial y} - \frac{\partial B}{\partial z}\right)A + \left(\frac{\partial A}{\partial z} - \frac{\partial C}{\partial x}\right)B + \left(\frac{\partial B}{\partial x} - \frac{\partial A}{\partial y}\right)C = 0.$$

It may also be shown that if this condition holds, and one imposes reasonable restrictions on A, B, and C, then an integrating factor for (7-40) exists.†

The notions of exactness and of independence of path may also be given in vector form. Using the "dictionary" in Sec. 7.3, we may recast our results in the following form.

Theorem 18. *Let* $\mathbf{F}$ *be a vector field which is of class* C'' *and obeys the condition* curl $(\mathbf{F}) = 0$ *throughout a simply connected region of space* Ω. *Then, there is a scalar function* f, *unique up to additive constants, such that in* Ω

$$\mathbf{F} = \text{grad}\ (f)$$

Moreover, if γ *is any smooth curve lying in* Ω *and going from* p_0 *to* p_1, *then*

$$\int_\gamma F_T = f(p_1) - f(p_0).$$

† See E. L. Ince, "Ordinary Differential Equations," Dover Publications, New York, 1944, or L. R. Ford, "Differential Equations," 2d ed., McGraw-Hill Book Company, Inc., New York, 1955.

The function f is called the **potential** for the vector field **F**. When the condition curl (**F**) $= 0$ is translated by saying that **F** specifies an "irrotational" velocity field, then f is called the velocity potential. If **F** specifies a force field, then **F** is said to be **conservative** when curl (**F**) $= 0$; in this case, it is customary to set $U = -f$ and call this the **potential energy.** If γ is a curve from p_0 to p_1, then

$$\int_\gamma F_T = U(p_0) - U(p_1).$$

This is interpreted as meaning that the work done by the field in moving a particle from p_0 to p_1 is independent of the path chosen, and is equal to the loss in potential energy.

There is also a corresponding theory dealing with exactness of 2-forms.

Definition. *A 2-form σ is exact in Ω if there is a 1-form ω of class C' in Ω such that $\sigma = d\omega$.*

There is more freedom in the choice of ω in this case. If σ is exact, and ω is a 1-form with $\sigma = d\omega$, then any exact 1-form may be added to ω. For example, σ is also given as $d(\omega + df)$, where f is a function of class C''.

What corresponds to the notion of independence of path for 2-forms? An answer is supplied by Stokes' theorem.

Theorem 19. *If σ is exact in Ω and Σ_1 and Σ_2 are two smooth orientable surfaces lying in Ω and having the same curve γ as boundary, then*

$$\iint_{\Sigma_1} \sigma = \iint_{\Sigma_2} \sigma.$$

For, if $\sigma = d\omega$, then, by Stokes' theorem,

$\iint_\Sigma \sigma = \iint_\Sigma d\omega = \int_{\partial\Sigma} \omega$ for both choices of Σ. ▌

Corollary. *If σ is exact in Ω, then $\iint_\Sigma \sigma = 0$ for any smooth orientable closed surface Σ in Ω.*

We can also test a 2-form for exactness by examining its coefficients.

Theorem 20. *If $\sigma = A\,dydz + B\,dzdx + C\,dxdy$ is exact and of class C'' in Ω, then $d\sigma = 0$ there; that is,*

$$\frac{\partial A}{\partial x} + \frac{\partial B}{\partial y} + \frac{\partial C}{\partial z} = 0.$$

This also comes at once from Theorem 3; if $\sigma = d\omega$, then

$$d\sigma = dd\omega = 0. \;\blacksquare$$

We are again able to prove a local converse to this.

Theorem 21. *If σ is a 2-form which is of class C' and obeys the condition $d\sigma = 0$ in a convex region Ω, then σ is exact in Ω.*

If $\sigma = A\,dydz + B\,dzdx + C\,dxdy$, then we shall assume that $A_1 + B_2 + C_3$ is identically zero in a convex region Ω containing the origin $(0, 0, 0)$. We shall find a 1-form ω such that $d\omega = \sigma$. Because of the latitude that exists in the choice of ω, it will turn out to be possible to find a solution of the form $\omega = a(x, y, z)\,dx + b(x, y, z)\,dy$. The requirement $d\omega = \sigma$ imposes the following three conditions on the coefficients of ω:

$$\frac{\partial a}{\partial z} = B, \qquad \frac{\partial b}{\partial z} = -A, \qquad \frac{\partial b}{\partial x} - \frac{\partial a}{\partial y} = C. \tag{7-41}$$

Integrating the first two with respect to z, and supplying an arbitrary function of (x, y) in the integral of the first, we are led to try the following

$$\begin{aligned} a(x, y, z) &= \int_0^z B(x, y, t)\,dt - \int_0^y C(x, s, 0)\,ds \\ b(x, y, z) &= -\int_0^z A(x, y, t)\,dt. \end{aligned}$$

These clearly satisfy the first two equations in (7-41). To see that the third holds as well, we differentiate with respect to y and x, respectively, obtaining

$$\begin{aligned} \frac{\partial a}{\partial y} &= \int_0^z B_2(x, y, t)\,dt - C(x, y, 0) \\ \frac{\partial b}{\partial x} &= -\int_0^z A_1(x, y, t)\,dt \end{aligned}$$

Accordingly,

$$\frac{\partial b}{\partial x} - \frac{\partial a}{\partial y} = -\int_0^z [A_1(x, y, t) + B_2(x, y, t)]\,dt + C(x, y, 0)$$

But, $A_1 + B_2 + C_3 = 0$, so that the right side becomes

$$\begin{aligned} \int_0^z C_3(x, y, t)\,dt + C(x, y, 0) &= [C(x, y, z) - C(x, y, 0)] + C(x, y, 0) \\ &= C(x, y, z) \end{aligned}$$

and all of the equations in (7-41) are satisfied. ▌ (We shall also give another treatment of this in Exercise 2, Sec. 7.6.)

Corollary. *If a 2-form σ satisfies the condition $d\sigma = 0$ throughout an open region Ω, then σ is locally exact in Ω.*

This means again that in some neighborhood of any point of Ω, there is defined a 1-form ω such that σ is the derivative of ω in this neighborhood. The various 1-forms ω may not piece together to give a 1-form whose derivative is σ everywhere in Ω. For example, the 2-form

$$\sigma = \frac{x\,dydz + y\,dzdx + z\,dxdy}{(x^2 + y^2 + z^2)^{3/2}} \tag{7-42}$$

is of class C' in all of space, except at the origin, and direct calculation shows that $d\sigma = 0$ in this whole set. Thus, σ is locally exact everywhere except at the origin. However, σ is not exact in this set, for if one computes the surface integral $\iint_\Sigma \sigma$, where Σ is the unit sphere:

$$x = \sin\phi\cos\theta,\ y = \sin\phi\sin\theta,\ z = \cos\phi,\ 0 \le \phi \le \pi,\ 0 \le \theta \le 2\pi,$$

the value does not turn out to be zero! It will be noticed that the region Ω involved in this example is simply connected. It is natural to ask for the corresponding property, which, if possessed by Ω, will ensure that any 2-form that is locally exact in Ω must also be exact. Such a property can be found; however, an adequate discussion would take us far afield (see Exercise 16). It will be seen in Exercise 8 that it is sufficient if Ω is "star-shaped" with respect to the origin; this is an improvement on convexity, but it is far from the best possible.

These results on exact 2-forms may also be cast into vector form. Let $\mathbf{F}$ be a vector field described by $\mathbf{F} = A\mathbf{i} + B\mathbf{j} + C\mathbf{k}$. Referring again to Sec. 7.3, we see that its corresponding 2-form is exact if and only if we can write $\mathbf{F} = \text{curl}\,(\mathbf{V})$, where $\mathbf{V}$ is another vector field. Since $\text{div}\,(\text{curl}\,(\mathbf{V})) = 0$, a necessary condition on $\mathbf{F}$ is that $\text{div}\,(\mathbf{F}) = 0$. Such a field is said to be **solenoidal,** or divergence free. The velocity field of an incompressible fluid is solenoidal.

Theorem 22. *If* $\mathbf{F}$ *is a solenoidal vector field of class* C'*, then in any convex set,* $\mathbf{F}$ *is of the form* $\mathbf{F} = \text{curl}\,(\mathbf{V})$.

EXERCISES

1. For each of the following 1-forms ω, find if possible a function f such that $\omega = df$.
(*a*) $\omega = (3x^2y + 2xy)\,dx + (x^3 + x^2 + 2y)\,dy$
(*b*) $\omega = (xy\cos xy + \sin xy)\,dx + (x^2\cos xy + y^2)\,dy$
(*c*) $\omega = (2xyz^3 + z)\,dx + x^2z^3\,dy + (3x^2yz^2 + x)\,dz$
(*d*) $\omega = x^2\,dy + 3xz\,dz$

2. (*a*) By differentiating $tg(xt, yt, zt)$ with respect to t, show that

$$g(x, y, z) = \int_0^1 g(xt, yt, zt)\,dt + \int_0^1 [xg_1(xt, yt, zt) + yg_2(xt, yt, zt) + zg_3(xt, yt, zt)]t\,dt$$

(*b*) A region Ω in space is said to be star-shaped with respect to the origin if the line segment $\overline{0P}$ lies in Ω whenever the end point P lies in Ω. Let Ω be star-shaped, and let $\omega = A\,dx + B\,dy + C\,dz$ obey $d\omega = 0$ in Ω. Obtain an alternate proof of

Theorem 15 by showing that $\omega = df$, where f is defined in Ω by the explicit formula

$$f(x, y, z) = \int_0^1 [xA(xt, yt, zt) + yB(xt, yt, zt) + zC(xt, yt, zt)]\, dt.$$

(c) Can this integral be regarded as a line integral of ω along a curve joining (0, 0, 0) to (x, y, z)?

3. Verify that the differential form given in Eq. (7-38) obeys $d\omega = 0$ throughout the ring D.

4. Consider the differential form

$$\omega = \frac{x\, dx + y\, dy}{x^2 + y^2}$$

Show that $d\omega = 0$ in the ring D. Is ω exact in D?

5. Recall that a function f is said to be homogeneous of degree k if

$$f(xt, yt, zt) = t^k f(x, y, z)$$

for all $t \geq 0$ and all (x, y, z) in a sphere about the origin. Let

$$\omega = A\, dx + B\, dy + C\, dz$$

be an exact 1-form whose coefficients are all homogeneous of degree k, $k \geq 0$. Show that $\omega = df$, where

$$f(x, y, z) = \frac{xA(x, y, z) + yB(x, y, z) + zC(x, y, z)}{k + 1}$$

6. If such exist, find integrating factors for the following differential forms:

(a) $(x^2 + 2y)\, dx - x\, dy$

(b) $3yz^2\, dx + xz^2\, dy + 2xyz\, dz$

(c) $xy\, dx + xy\, dy + yz\, dz$

7. (a) Show that the 2-form $\sigma = A\, dydz + B\, dzdx + C\, dxdy$ can also be expressed in the form $\sigma = \alpha\, dx + \beta\, dy$, where $\alpha = B\, dz - C\, dy$, $\beta = -A\, dz$.

(b) In the proof of Theorem 21, a 1-form $\omega = a\, dx + b\, dy$ was found such that $d\omega = \sigma$. Show that the coefficients of ω are given by the equations:

$$a(x, y, z) = \int_\gamma \alpha, \qquad b(x, y, z) = \int_\gamma \beta$$

where γ is the polygonal path from the origin to (x, y, z) that is shown in Fig. 7-23.

8. (a) By differentiating $t^2 g(xt, yt, zt)$ with respect to t, show that $g(x, y, z)$ may be given by

$$2\int_0^1 g(xt, yt, zt) t\, dt + \int_0^1 [xg_1(xt, yt, zt) + yg_2(xt, yt, zt) + zg_3(xt, yt, zt)] t^2\, dt.$$

(b) If $\sigma = A\, dydz + B\, dzdx + C\, dxdy$, show that

$$2\sigma = (B\, dz - C\, dy)\, dx + (C\, dx - A\, dz)\, dy + (A\, dy - B\, dx)\, dz.$$

(*c*) Let Ω be star-shaped with respect to the origin, and let $d\sigma = 0$ in Ω. Obtain an alternate proof of Theorem 21 by showing that $\sigma = d\omega$, where $\omega = a\,dx + b\,dy + c\,dz$, and where

$$a(x, y, z) = \int_0^1 [zB(xt, yt, zt) - yC(xt, yt, zt)]t\,dt$$

$$b(x, y, z) = \int_0^1 [xC(xt, yt, zt) - zA(xt, yt, zt)]t\,dt$$

$$c(x, y, z) = \int_0^1 [yA(xt, yt, zt) - xB(xt, yt, zt)]t\,dt$$

9. Let $\sigma = A\,dydz + B\,dzdx + C\,dxdy$, where the functions A, B, and C are homogeneous of degree k in a neighborhood of the origin. If σ is exact, show that $\sigma = d\omega$, where

$$\omega = \frac{(zB - yC)\,dx + (xC - zA)\,dy + (yA - xB)\,dz}{k + 2}$$

10. Show that the following 2-forms are exact by exhibiting each in the form $\sigma = d\omega$:

(*a*) $(3y^2z - 3xz^2)\,dydz + x^2y\,dzdx + (z^3 - x^2z)\,dxdy$

(*b*) $(2xz + z)\,dzdx + y\,dxdy$

11. Formulate a necessary condition that a 1-form in n variables be exact.

12. Verify the assertions made in connection with the 2-form given in Eq. (7-42).

13. Formulate a definition for "integrating factor" for 2-forms. Obtain a differential equation which must be satisfied by any integrating factor for the 2-form

$$\sigma = A\,dydz + B\,dzdx + C\,dxdy.$$

Using this, and Euler's differential equation for homogeneous functions (Exercise 12, Sec. 5.4), obtain the most general integrating factor for $x\,dydz + y\,dzdx + z\,dxdy$.

14. Using Theorem 8, Sec. 7.4, show that a transformation of class C'' carries exact forms into exact forms.

15. Let Ω be a region in space which can be mapped onto a star-shaped set by a one-to-one transformation of class C''. Show that any 2-form σ which satisfies the equation $d\sigma = 0$ in Ω is exact in Ω.

16. Let σ be a 2-form which obeys $d\sigma = 0$ in an open region Ω. Let Ω have the property that every simple smooth closed surface Σ lying in Ω is the complete boundary of a region R which is contained in Ω. Show that $\iint_\Sigma \sigma = 0$ for all such closed surfaces in Ω. Is this property true for the region bounded by a torus surface? For the region between two concentric spheres? Must σ then be exact in Ω?

7.6. Special Formulas

The results in Sec. 7.5 allow one to express a vector function which is irrotational or solenoidal (divergence free) in special forms, at least locally. This method is one that is employed frequently in physics. We illustrate it with a standard example based on the Maxwell equations (7-20). Dropping the constant 4π to simplify the discussion, let us suppose that **E** and **H** are vector functions of (x, y, z, t), representing the electric and magnetic fields, which obey the four equations:

$$\nabla \cdot \mathbf{E} = \rho \tag{7-43}$$

$$\nabla \cdot \mathbf{H} = 0 \tag{7-44}$$

$$\nabla \times \mathbf{E} + \frac{\partial \mathbf{H}}{\partial t} = 0 \tag{7-45}$$

$$\nabla \times \mathbf{H} - \frac{\partial \mathbf{E}}{\partial t} = \mathbf{J} \tag{7-46}$$

The scalar function ρ describes the distribution of charge, and the vector function $\mathbf{J}$ describes the distribution of current. If we regard ρ and $\mathbf{J}$ as known, we may seek a solution of these equations for $\mathbf{E}$ and $\mathbf{H}$. We shall show that this may be reduced to the solution of a standard partial differential equation, the inhomogeneous wave equation.

By (7-44), and Theorem 22, $\mathbf{H}$ can be represented locally in the form

$$\mathbf{H} = \nabla \times \mathbf{A} \tag{7-47}$$

where $\mathbf{A}$, the vector potential, may be altered by adding any vector function of the form ∇g, where g is a suitable scalar function. Putting this into (7-45), we have

$$\begin{aligned} 0 &= \nabla \times \mathbf{E} + \frac{\partial}{\partial t}(\nabla \times \mathbf{A}) \\ &= \nabla \times \left(\mathbf{E} + \frac{\partial \mathbf{A}}{\partial t}\right) \end{aligned}$$

By Theorem 18, a scalar function ϕ exists such that, locally at least,

$$\mathbf{E} + \frac{\partial \mathbf{A}}{\partial t} = \nabla(-\phi) = -\nabla \phi$$

(The negative sign is chosen only to improve the final appearance of our equations.) We may thus assume that $\mathbf{E}$ and $\mathbf{H}$ have the representations given in (7-47) and in

$$\mathbf{E} = -\nabla \phi - \frac{\partial \mathbf{A}}{\partial t} \tag{7-48}$$

Put these into (7-43) and (7-46), obtaining

$$\begin{aligned} \rho &= \nabla \cdot \left(-\nabla \phi - \frac{\partial \mathbf{A}}{\partial t}\right) \\ &= -\nabla^2 \phi - \frac{\partial}{\partial t}(\nabla \cdot \mathbf{A}) \end{aligned} \tag{7-49}$$

and

$$\begin{aligned} \mathbf{J} &= \nabla \times (\nabla \times \mathbf{A}) - \frac{\partial}{\partial t}\left(-\nabla \phi - \frac{\partial \mathbf{A}}{\partial t}\right) \\ &= \nabla \times (\nabla \times \mathbf{A}) + \nabla \frac{\partial \phi}{\partial t} + \frac{\partial^2 \mathbf{A}}{\partial t^2} \end{aligned}$$

Making use of the vector identity (7-26), this can be written as

$$\mathbf{J} = \nabla(\nabla \cdot \mathbf{A}) - \nabla^2\mathbf{A} + \nabla\frac{\partial \phi}{\partial t} + \frac{\partial^2 \mathbf{A}}{\partial t^2} \tag{7-50}$$

Turning (7-49) and (7-50) around, we have two equations to be satisfied by **A** and ϕ:

$$\nabla^2\phi = -\rho - \frac{\partial}{\partial t}(\nabla \cdot \mathbf{A})$$

$$\nabla^2\mathbf{A} - \frac{\partial^2\mathbf{A}}{\partial t^2} = -\mathbf{J} + \nabla\left(\nabla \cdot \mathbf{A} + \frac{\partial \phi}{\partial t}\right)$$

In the second, $\nabla^2\mathbf{A}$ is to be interpreted by writing $\mathbf{A} = a\mathbf{i} + b\mathbf{j} + c\mathbf{k}$ and applying ∇^2 to each component, obtaining

$$\nabla^2\mathbf{A} = \nabla^2(a)\mathbf{i} + \nabla^2(b)\mathbf{j} + \nabla^2(c)\mathbf{k}.$$

The second equation would assume a much simpler form if **A** and ϕ could be chosen so that

$$\nabla \cdot \mathbf{A} + \frac{\partial \phi}{\partial t} = 0. \tag{7-51}$$

In this case, our two equations would become

$$\nabla^2\phi - \frac{\partial^2\phi}{\partial t^2} = -\rho$$

and

$$\nabla^2\mathbf{A} - \frac{\partial^2\mathbf{A}}{\partial t^2} = -\mathbf{J}.$$

In the choice of **A**, we have a considerable amount of freedom. Suppose that $\mathbf{A}_0$ and ϕ_0 are particular choices which satisfy (7-47) and (7-48); if we add a vector of the form ∇g to $\mathbf{A}_0$, (7-47) will still hold, since

$$\begin{aligned}\nabla \times \mathbf{A} &= \nabla \times (\mathbf{A}_0 + \nabla g)\\ &= \nabla \times \mathbf{A}_0 + \nabla \times (\nabla g)\\ &= \nabla \times \mathbf{A}_0 = \mathbf{H},\end{aligned}$$

where we have used (7-23). If we modify $\mathbf{A}_0$ in this way, we must also modify ϕ in order to preserve (7-48). Putting $\phi = \phi_0 - \frac{\partial}{\partial t}g$, we have

$$\begin{aligned}-\nabla\phi - \frac{\partial \mathbf{A}}{\partial t} &= -\nabla\left(\phi_0 - \frac{\partial g}{\partial t}\right) - \frac{\partial}{\partial t}(\mathbf{A}_0 + \nabla g)\\ &= -\nabla\phi_0 + \nabla\left(\frac{\partial g}{\partial t}\right) - \frac{\partial}{\partial t}\mathbf{A}_0 - \frac{\partial}{\partial t}(\nabla g)\\ &= -\nabla\phi_0 - \frac{\partial}{\partial t}\mathbf{A}_0\\ &= \mathbf{E}.\end{aligned}$$

We next choose g, which is thus far unrestricted, so that (7-51) holds. This requires that we have

$$\nabla \cdot (\mathbf{A}_0 + \nabla g) + \frac{\partial}{\partial t}\left(\phi_0 - \frac{\partial g}{\partial t}\right) = 0$$

which implies that g must be chosen to satisfy the equation

$$\nabla^2 g - \frac{\partial^2 g}{\partial t^2} = -\left(\nabla \cdot \mathbf{A}_0 + \frac{\partial \phi_0}{\partial t}\right).$$

With this line of argument, the solution of Maxwell's equations may be reduced to the consideration of the special partial differential equation

$$\text{(7-52)} \qquad \nabla^2 \psi - \frac{\partial^2 \psi}{\partial t^2} = -h.$$

In coordinate form, this is

$$\frac{\partial^2 \psi}{\partial x^2} + \frac{\partial^2 \psi}{\partial y^2} + \frac{\partial^2 \psi}{\partial z^2} - \frac{\partial^2 \psi}{\partial t^2} + h = 0$$

and is called the **inhomogeneous wave equation.** Vector methods may also be used in discussing it. To illustrate the technique, we shall treat the special case in which ψ and h are independent of time. The differential equation reduces to

$$\nabla^2 \psi = -h$$

which is often called **Poisson's equation.** When h is identically zero, this becomes **Laplace's equation**

$$\nabla^2 \psi = 0.$$

The chief tool in the vector treatment of these equations are certain relations which may be derived from the divergence theorem, and which are called **Green's identities.** To obtain these, we start from the vector form of the divergence theorem

$$\text{(7-53)} \qquad \iiint_{\Omega} \nabla \cdot \mathbf{F} = \iint_{\partial\Omega} \mathbf{F} \cdot \mathbf{n} = \iint_{\partial\Omega} F_N$$

where the vector $\mathbf{n}$ in the second integral is the general unit normal on $\partial\Omega$. In our applications, Ω will be the region lying between two spheres. If we choose the vector function $\mathbf{F}$ to have a particular form, then we can obtain a number of special cases of this result which are quite useful. To illustrate this, let us first take $\mathbf{F}$ as a gradient field, $\mathbf{F} = \nabla g$. Since $\nabla \cdot (\nabla g) = \nabla^2 g$, and $\nabla g \cdot \mathbf{n}$ is the directional derivative of g in the direction **n**, (7-53) becomes

$$\iiint_{\Omega} \nabla^2 g = \iint_{\partial\Omega} D_{\mathbf{n}} g = \iint_{\partial\Omega} \frac{\partial g}{\partial \mathbf{n}} \tag{7-54}$$

where $\dfrac{\partial g}{\partial \mathbf{n}}$ is understood to mean the scalar function whose value at a point on the boundary of Ω is the directional derivative of g in the direction normal to the surface. (Briefly, $\partial g/\partial \mathbf{n}$ is the normal derivative of g.)

Again, if we choose $\mathbf{F} = f\nabla g$, and use the vector identity

$$\nabla \cdot (f\mathbf{V}) = \nabla f \cdot \mathbf{V} + f(\nabla \cdot \mathbf{V})$$

with $\mathbf{V} = \nabla g$, then

$$\nabla \cdot \mathbf{F} = \nabla f \cdot \nabla g + f\nabla^2 g$$

and (7-53) becomes Green's **first identity:**

$$\iiint_{\Omega} \nabla f \cdot \nabla g + \iiint_{\Omega} f\nabla^2 g = \iint_{\partial\Omega} f \frac{\partial g}{\partial \mathbf{n}} \tag{7-55}$$

We illustrate the use of these identities, by proving certain properties of the class of **harmonic functions.** Recall that a function g is said to be harmonic in a region Ω if it satisfies Laplace's equation, $\nabla^2 g = 0$, in Ω. In Theorem 14, Sec. 6.4, we proved by a different method that these functions were conditioned in a region by their values on the boundary; if g is harmonic in a bounded closed region Ω, and $g(p) \le M$ for all p on the boundary of Ω, then $g(p) \le M$ for all points p in Ω itself. As a deduction from this, in Exercise 16, Sec. 6.4, we found that two functions which are harmonic in Ω and which coincide on the boundary of Ω must coincide throughout Ω. The second of these results comes at once from (7-55). If we take $f = g$ and assume that g is harmonic in Ω, and that $g = 0$ on the boundary of Ω, then we have

$$\iiint_{\Omega} \nabla g \cdot \nabla g = \iiint_{\Omega} |\nabla g|^2 = 0.$$

Since $|\nabla g| \ge 0$, we must have $\nabla g = 0$ (assuming that g is of class C'') and g is constant in Ω. Since the boundary value of g is zero, $g = 0$ in Ω. If g and g^* were two functions, both harmonic in Ω, with $g(p) = g^*(p)$ for all points p on the boundary of Ω, then $g - g^*$ would be harmonic in Ω, and would have boundary value zero; by the previous argument, $g - g^*$ would be identically zero throughout Ω, so that $g = g^*$. By an analogous argument, it may be shown that if g and g^* are harmonic in Ω, and if their normal derivatives, $\partial g/\partial \mathbf{n}$ and $\partial g^*/\partial \mathbf{n}$, are equal on the boundary of Ω, then g and g^* differ at most by a constant in Ω (see Exercise 1). These results show that for a suitably well-behaved region Ω, the values of a harmonic function in Ω are determined completely by its values on $\partial\Omega$, and up to an additive constant, by the values of its normal derivative on $\partial\Omega$.

One may turn this around and ask the following question: Given a function f, defined on $\partial\Omega$, is there a function g which is harmonic in Ω and such that $g = f$ on $\partial\Omega$? This is called the **Dirichlet problem** for the region Ω. If Ω is suitably well behaved and f is continuous, then it has a solution, which, by the previous discussion, is unique. Correspondingly, given a function f defined on $\partial\Omega$, one may ask for a function g, harmonic in Ω, such that $\partial g/\partial \mathbf{n} = f$ on $\partial\Omega$. This is called **Neumann's problem** for Ω. There may exist no solutions, even though Ω is very well behaved and f is continuous; to see this, we resort again to Green's identities. If we apply (7-54) when g is harmonic in Ω, then we obtain

$$\iiint_{\Omega} \nabla^2 g = 0 = \iint_{\partial\Omega} \frac{\partial g}{\partial \mathbf{n}}$$

Thus, a necessary condition on the boundary-value function f in Neumann's problem is that its integral over the boundary of Ω be zero. Again, the previous discussion shows that if Neumann's problem has a solution g, and if Ω is sufficiently well behaved, then g is unique to within an additive constant.

Let us turn now to Poisson's equation:

$$\nabla^2\psi = -h$$

where h is assumed to be of class C'', and, for convenience, to vanish outside a bounded region. We shall seek a solution of this equation which obeys two additional conditions:

$$\lim_{|p|\to\infty} |\psi(p)| = 0 \tag{7-56}$$

$$\lim_{|p|\to\infty} |\text{grad } \psi(p)|\,|p| = 0 \tag{7-57}$$

The first may be translated as saying that ψ vanishes at infinity, and the second as saying that the partial derivatives of ψ vanish more rapidly than $1/|p| = (x^2 + y^2 + z^2)^{-1/2}$. If we can obtain such a solution of Poisson's equation, then any harmonic function can be added to it; conversely, if ψ and ψ^* are two solutions of Poisson's equation, then

$$\nabla^2(\psi - \psi^*) = \nabla^2\psi - \nabla^2\psi^* = h - h = 0,$$

so that $\psi - \psi^*$ is harmonic.

We begin by deriving Green's so-called **second identity.** Write (7-55) with f and g interchanged:

$$\iiint_{\Omega} \nabla g \cdot \nabla f + \iiint_{\Omega} g\nabla^2 f = \iint_{\partial\Omega} g \frac{\partial f}{\partial \mathbf{n}}.$$

Subtract this from (7-55); the first integral drops out, leaving

$$\text{(7-58)} \qquad \iiint_{\Omega} \{f\nabla^2 g - g\nabla^2 f\} = \iint_{\partial\Omega} \left\{f \frac{\partial g}{\partial \mathbf{n}} - g \frac{\partial f}{\partial \mathbf{n}}\right\}.$$

Theorem 23. *If ψ is a solution of the equation $\nabla^2\psi + h = 0$ which obeys the boundary conditions* (7-56) *and* (7-57), *then ψ is given at the point $p_0 = (x_0, y_0, z_0)$ by*

$$4\pi\psi(p_0) = \iiint \frac{h(p)}{|p - p_0|}\, dp = \iiint \frac{h(x, y, z)\, dxdydz}{[(x - x_0)^2 + (y - y_0)^2 + (z - z_0)^2]^{1/2}}$$

Let $\phi(p) = 1/|p - p_0|$. By direct computation, it is seen that $\nabla^2\phi = 0$ everywhere, except at the singularity p_0. Also,

$$\text{grad}\ \phi(p) = (p - p_0)/|p - p_0|^3$$

so that $|\text{grad}\ \phi(p)| = 1/|p - p_0|^2$. The function ϕ thus obeys the conditions (7-56) and (7-57) "at infinity." Let Ω be the region between two spheres with center p_0; we suppose that the larger has radius R, and the smaller has radius r. We apply Green's identity (7-58) with this choice of Ω, and with $f = \phi$ and $g = \psi$. Since ψ is assumed to be a solution of Poisson's equation, $\nabla^2 g = -h$. Since ϕ is harmonic in Ω, $\nabla^2 f = 0$. We therefore have

$$\text{(7-59)} \qquad -\iiint_{\Omega} \phi h = \iint_{\partial\Omega} \phi \frac{\partial\psi}{\partial \mathbf{n}} - \iint_{\partial\Omega} \psi \frac{\partial\phi}{\partial \mathbf{n}}$$

The boundary of Ω consists of two spherical surfaces, Σ_R and Σ_r. On the outside one, Σ_R, the normal $\mathbf{n}$ is directed away from p_0. If we employ spherical coordinates (ρ, θ, ϕ), with p_0 as origin, then "derivative in the direction of the normal" means $\frac{\partial}{\partial\rho}$, so that on Σ_R, $\phi(p) = \rho^{-1} = R^{-1}$

$$\frac{\partial\phi}{\partial \mathbf{n}} = \frac{\partial\phi}{\partial\rho} = \frac{\partial}{\partial\rho}(\rho^{-1}) = -\rho^{-2} = -R^{-2}$$

Similarly, on Σ_r, the normal is directed *toward* p_0, and $\frac{\partial}{\partial \mathbf{n}} = -\frac{\partial}{\partial\rho}$; thus

$\phi(p) = \rho^{-1} = r^{-1}$ and

$$\frac{\partial \phi}{\partial \mathbf{n}} = -\frac{\partial \phi}{\partial \rho} = -\frac{\partial}{\partial \rho}(\rho^{-1}) = \rho^{-2} = r^{-2}.$$

Using these, (7-59) becomes

$$0 = \iiint_{\Omega} h\phi + \frac{1}{R}\iint_{\Sigma_R} \frac{\partial \psi}{\partial \mathbf{n}} + \frac{1}{r}\iint_{\Sigma_r} \frac{\partial \psi}{\partial \mathbf{n}} + \frac{1}{R^2}\iint_{\Sigma_R} \psi - \frac{1}{r^2}\iint_{\Sigma_r} \psi. \tag{7-60}$$

We examine the behavior of each of these integrals as r approaches 0, and R increases. Estimating the first three surface integrals, we have

$$\begin{aligned}\left|\frac{1}{R}\iint_{\Sigma_R} \frac{\partial \psi}{\partial \mathbf{n}}\right| &\le \frac{1}{R}(\text{area of } \Sigma_R)(\text{maximum of } |\text{grad } \psi| \text{ on } \Sigma_R)\\ &\le 4\pi R\,(\max |\text{grad } \psi| \text{ on } \Sigma_R)\end{aligned}$$

$$\begin{aligned}\left|\frac{1}{r}\iint_{\Sigma_r} \frac{\partial \psi}{\partial \mathbf{n}}\right| &\le \frac{1}{r}(\text{area of } \Sigma_r)(\text{maximum of } |\text{grad } \psi| \text{ on } \Sigma_r)\\ &\le 4\pi r\,(\text{maximum of } |\text{grad } \psi| \text{ on } \Sigma_r)\end{aligned}$$

$$\begin{aligned}\left|\frac{1}{R^2}\iint_{\Sigma_R} \psi\right| &\le \frac{1}{R^2}(\text{area of } \Sigma_R)(\text{maximum of } |\psi| \text{ on } \Sigma_R)\\ &\le 4\pi\,(\text{maximum of } |\psi| \text{ on } \Sigma_R).\end{aligned}$$

Using (7-56) and (7-57), we see that all three approach zero, as $r \to 0$ and $R \to \infty$. Applying the mean value theorem to the remaining surface integral,

$$\begin{aligned}-\frac{1}{r^2}\iint_{\Sigma_r} \psi &= -\frac{4\pi r^2}{r^2}\psi(p^*)\\ &= -4\pi\psi(p^*)\end{aligned}$$

where p^* is some point lying on Σ_r. As $r \to 0$, $p^* \to p_0$

so that
$$\lim_{r \to 0} \frac{1}{r^2}\iint_{\Sigma_r} \psi = 4\pi\psi(p_0).$$

Accordingly, if we return to (7-60), we have

$$4\pi\psi(p_0) = \lim_{\substack{r \to 0\\ R \to \infty}} \iiint_{\Omega} h\phi = \iiint \frac{h(p)}{|p - p_0|}\,dp. \quad \blacksquare$$

Having thus obtained the necessary form of a solution of the Poisson equation, one may proceed to verify directly that this is a solution.†

† For details of this, and for an exposition of the general theory, the reader should consult O. D. Kellogg, "Foundations of Potential Theory," Frederick Ungar Publishing Co., New York, 1940.

The general wave equation (7-52) may be treated in a similar manner. The solution which is obtained has the form

$$\psi(x_0, y_0, z_0, t) = \iiint \frac{h(x, y, z, t - \rho)\, dxdydz}{\rho}$$

where $\rho = |p - p_0|$, assuming that ψ and h are independent of time for $t \leq 0$. The form of the integrand has a simple interpretation; at time t, the value of ψ is not determined by the *simultaneous* values of h throughout space, but rather by those values which could be "communicated" to p_0 by a signal which travels at speed 1, and which therefore left the point p at time $t - |p - p_0| = t - \rho$.†

EXERCISES

1. (*a*) If g is harmonic in Ω and the normal derivative of g on the boundary is zero, show that $\nabla g = 0$ in Ω.

(*b*) Let g and g^* be harmonic in Ω, and let $\dfrac{\partial g}{\partial \mathbf{n}} = \dfrac{\partial g^*}{\partial \mathbf{n}}$ on $\partial\Omega$. Show that $g^* = g + K$, where K is constant.

2. Let $\nabla \cdot \mathbf{F} = 0$ in a convex region Ω. Show that $\mathbf{F}$ can be expressed there in the form $\mathbf{F} = \nabla \times \mathbf{V}$, where $\nabla \cdot \mathbf{V} = 0$ and $\nabla^2\mathbf{V} = -\nabla \times \mathbf{F}$. (This reduces the problem of finding a 1-form ω with $d\omega = \sigma$ for a given exact 2-form σ, to the solution of Poisson's equation.)

3. Prove the following vector analogues for Green's identities.

(*a*) $$\iint\limits_{\partial\Omega} (\mathbf{F} \times \nabla \times \mathbf{G})_N = \iiint\limits_{\Omega} (\nabla \times \mathbf{F}) \cdot (\nabla \times \mathbf{G}) - \iiint\limits_{\Omega} \mathbf{F} \cdot (\nabla \times \nabla \times \mathbf{G})$$

(*b*) $$\iiint\limits_{\Omega} \{\mathbf{G} \cdot (\nabla \times \nabla \times \mathbf{F}) - \mathbf{F} \cdot (\nabla \times \nabla \times \mathbf{G})\} = \iint\limits_{\partial\Omega} \{(\mathbf{F} \times \nabla \times \mathbf{G})_N - (\mathbf{G} \times \nabla \times \mathbf{F})_N\}.$$

7.7. Calculus of Variations

In the extremal problems which were discussed in Chap. 6, one sought for the point at which a numerical-valued (point) function attained its greatest or least value. In this final section, we shall discuss very briefly the analogous type of problem for curve-functionals and surface-functionals. Let F be a curve-functional, defined on a class $\mathcal{C}$ of curves. A curve γ^* is said to be minimal for F and $\mathcal{C}$ if $F(\gamma^*) \leq F(\gamma)$ for every curve γ in $\mathcal{C}$. For example, if $\mathcal{C}$ is the class of smooth curves with end points P and Q, and $F(\gamma)$ is the length of γ, then the straight line between P and Q is a minimal curve. Another functional which might be used

† For details of this, and other applications of Green's identities, the reader is referred to the treatise by P. M. Morse and H. Feshbach, "Methods of Theoretical Physics," McGraw-Hill Book Company, Inc., New York, 1953.

would be $F(\gamma) = \int_\gamma \omega$ where ω is a prescribed 1-form, or $F(\gamma) = \int_\gamma f\,ds$, where f is a continuous function defined at all points in a region containing P and Q. A general class of curve-functionals which includes all of these is given by

$$F(\gamma) = \int_0^1 K(\gamma(t), \gamma'(t))\,dt \tag{7-61}$$

where for convenience, we have assumed that all of the curves have domain [0, 1]. To obtain $F(\gamma)$ equal to the length of γ, we may take $K(p, q) = |q|$; other special choices of K will yield the other special cases mentioned above. When we restrict the consideration to curves in 3-space, then γ may be given by a set of equations: $x = \phi(t)$, $y = \psi(t)$, $z = \theta(t)$, and (7-61) takes the form

$$F(\gamma) = \int_0^1 K(\phi(t), \psi(t), \theta(t), \phi'(t), \psi'(t), \theta'(t))\,dt \tag{7-62}$$

One may also regard F as a functional whose domain of definition is a class of triples of functions, and write

$$F(\phi, \psi, \theta) = \int_0^1 K(\phi, \psi, \theta, \phi', \psi', \theta').$$

The simplest case of this would be the functional described by

$$F(\phi) = \int_0^1 K(\phi(t), \phi'(t))\,dt \tag{7-63}$$

whose domain is a class of functions $\phi \in C'$ on [0, 1].

As in Sec. 6.4 where we discussed the theory of maxima and minima for point functions of several real variables, it is again easy to obtain necessary conditions which must be satisfied by extremals, but it is more difficult to obtain sufficient conditions which ensure that one has been found. In this section, we shall deal with a simplified theory and discuss only necessary conditions. In particular, the analogue for the fact that an extremal point for a point function f must be a critical point for f is that an extremal curve for F must satisfy the so-called **Euler differential equations.** To derive these, we start with the simplest case.

Suppose that a function ϕ_0 is minimal for the functional F given in (7-63) in the class $\mathcal{C}$ of all functions ϕ which belong to C' on [0, 1] and obey the end point restriction $\phi(0) = a$, $\phi(1) = b$. If ϕ is any member of $\mathcal{C}$, then $F(\gamma) \geq F(\gamma_0)$. Let β be any function of class C' on [0, 1] with $\beta(0) = \beta(1) = 0$, and set $\phi = \phi_0 + \lambda\beta$, where λ is a real number. This function is in the class $\mathcal{C}$, so that

$$F(\gamma_0 + \lambda\beta) \geq F(\phi_0) \text{ for all } \lambda, \ -\infty < \lambda < \infty.$$

Putting $g(\lambda) = F(\phi_0 + \lambda\beta)$, this asserts that g has its minimum value for

$\lambda = 0$. Returning to (7-63), we have

$$g(\lambda) = \int_0^1 K(\phi_0(t) + \lambda\beta(t), \phi_0'(t) + \lambda\beta'(t))\, dt.$$

A necessary condition is that $g'(0) = 0$. Computing this, we obtain

$$0 = \int_0^1 K_1(\phi_0, \phi_0')\beta + \int_0^1 K_2(\phi_0, \phi_0')\beta' \tag{7-64}$$

If K is of class C'', then we can integrate by parts in the second integral, obtaining

$$\begin{aligned}\int_0^1 K_2(\phi_0(t), \phi_0'(t))\, d\beta(t) &= K_2(\phi_0(t), \phi_0'(t))\beta(t)\Big|_0^1 \\ &\qquad - \int_0^1 \beta(t) \frac{d}{dt} K_2(\phi_0(t), \phi_0'(t))\, dt \\ &= -\int_0^1 \beta(t) \frac{d}{dt} K_2(\phi_0(t), \phi_0'(t))\, dt\end{aligned}$$

where we have used the end point conditions $\beta(0) = \beta(1) = 0$. With this, (7-64) becomes

$$0 = \int_0^1 \beta(t) \left\{K_1(\phi_0(t), \phi_0'(t)) - \frac{d}{dt} K_2(\phi_0(t), \phi_0'(t))\right\} dt$$

Moreover, this must hold for any choice of the function β.

Lemma. *If* $\int_0^1 \beta(t)k(t)\, dt = 0$ *for all choices of* β, *then* $k(t) = 0$ *for* $0 \le t \le 1$, *where* k *is any continuous function defined on* $[0, 1]$.

If k is not identically zero, then there is a point t_0, $0 < t_0 < 1$, with $k(t_0) \neq 0$. We may assume that $k(t_0)$ is positive, so that there is a neighborhood N about t_0 and a number $\delta > 0$ such that $k(t) > \delta$ for all $t \in N$. Choose β so that $\beta(t) = 0$ for t outside N, but with $\beta(t) > 0$ on a neighborhood of t_0. Then $\beta(t)k(t) \ge 0$ for all t in $[0, 1]$. Since

$$\int_0^1 \beta(t)k(t)\, dt = 0,$$

we must have $\beta(t)k(t) = 0$ for all t, including these points in N where $\beta(t) > 0$. Hence, $k(t_0) = 0$. ▌

Applying this lemma, we obtain the following necessary condition (Euler differential equation) to be satisfied by the extremal ϕ_0:

$$K_1(\phi_0(t), \phi_0'(t)) = \frac{d}{dt} K_2(\phi_0(t), \phi_0'(t)). \tag{7-65}$$

If we carry out the indicated differentiation with respect to t, then we obtain a nonlinear second-order differential equation for the extremal function ϕ_0:

$$K_1(\phi_0, \phi_0') = K_{12}(\phi_0, \phi_0')\phi_0' + K_{22}(\phi_0, \phi_0')\phi_0''.$$

The process we have used is sometimes described as "varying" ϕ_0; from this, one calls the whole approach the "variational" method. It has much in common with the concept of directional derivative for point functions. As $\lambda \to 0$, the functions $\phi_0 + \lambda\beta$ may be thought of as approaching ϕ_0 along the direction specified by β. If the functional F is minimal at ϕ_0, then its directional derivative in any direction from ϕ_0 must be zero. This again gives the Euler differential equation. The fact that we have assumed ϕ_0 to be a minimal function for F is not important; the same differential equation would be obtained if ϕ_0 were maximal for F. One may also obtain necessary conditions for an extremal to be maximal or to be minimal, analogous to those for a point function of several variables (see again Sec. 6.4).

Let us turn now to the more general functional F described by (7-62); writing

$$F(\phi, \psi, \theta) = \int_0^1 K(\phi, \psi, \theta, \phi', \psi', \theta')$$

we can vary each of the functions ϕ, ψ, and θ independently. If the triple $(\phi_0, \psi_0, \theta_0)$ is extremal (minimal, for example), then $F(\phi_0 + \lambda\beta, \psi_0, \theta_0)$, $F(\phi_0, \psi_0 + \lambda\beta, \theta_0)$, and $F(\phi_0, \psi_0, \theta_0 + \lambda\beta)$ will all exceed $F(\phi_0, \psi_0, \theta_0)$. The process which we carried out above may be applied to each, and we obtain three equations in place of (7-65):

$$K_1(\phi_0, \psi_0, \theta_0, \phi_0', \psi_0', \theta_0') = \frac{d}{dt} K_4(\phi_0, \psi_0, \theta_0, \phi_0', \psi_0', \theta_0')$$

$$K_2(\phi_0, \psi_0, \theta_0, \phi_0', \psi_0', \theta_0') = \frac{d}{dt} K_5(\phi_0, \psi_0, \theta_0, \phi_0', \psi_0', \theta_0')$$

$$K_3(\phi_0, \psi_0, \theta_0, \phi_0', \psi_0', \theta_0') = \frac{d}{dt} K_6(\phi_0, \psi_0, \theta_0, \phi_0', \psi_0', \theta_0')$$

In order to make the notation for these relations a little less cumbersome, it is usual to write (7-62) as

$$F(\gamma) = F(x, y, z) = \int_0^1 K(x, y, z, x', y', z')\, dt$$

so that the Euler equations become:

$$\text{(7-65}a\text{)} \qquad \begin{aligned} \frac{\partial K}{\partial x} &= \frac{d}{dt}\frac{\partial K}{\partial x'} \\ \frac{\partial K}{\partial y} &= \frac{d}{dt}\frac{\partial K}{\partial y'} \\ \frac{\partial K}{\partial z} &= \frac{d}{dt}\frac{\partial K}{\partial z'} \end{aligned}$$

In each of these, one must keep in mind that the differentiation with respect to t will involve contributions from each of the functions ϕ, ψ, θ, ϕ', ψ', θ'.

The corresponding questions for surface functionals may be treated in the same way. If $\mathcal{S}$ is a suitable class of smooth surfaces Σ, all having domain D, then an important class of functionals has the form

$$F(\Sigma) = \iint_D K(\Sigma, \Sigma_u, \Sigma_v).$$

When Σ is described by $x = \phi(u, v)$, $y = \psi(u, v)$, $z = \theta(u, v)$, then this may also be given as

$$F(\phi, \psi, \theta) = F(\Sigma) = \iint_D K(\phi, \psi, \theta, \phi_1, \psi_1, \theta_1, \phi_2, \psi_2, \theta_2). \tag{7-66}$$

We shall first study the simplest case, and consider the functional F which is defined by

$$\begin{aligned} F(\phi) &= \iint_D K(\phi(u, v), \phi_1(u, v), \phi_2(u, v))\, dudv \\ &= \iint_D K(\phi, \phi_1, \phi_2). \end{aligned}$$

Let $\mathcal{S}_f$ be the class of functions ϕ which are of class C'' in D, and which agree with a specified function f on the boundary of D. For convenience, we shall assume that D is a convex set whose boundary is the trace of a simple closed curve. Suppose that ϕ^* is minimal for F, on the class $\mathcal{S}_f$; we shall derive a partial differential equation which must be satisfied by ϕ^*. Note again that we are obtaining only a necessary condition.

Once more, we use the variational method. Consider the function $\phi = \phi^* + \lambda\beta$, where β is any function of class C'' in D whose value on the boundary of D is everywhere zero. Accordingly, ϕ also agrees with the given function f on the boundary of D, and thus belongs to the class $\mathcal{S}_f$. Since ϕ^* was assumed minimal, $F(\phi) \geq F(\phi^*)$ for every λ, $-\infty < \lambda < \infty$. Put

$$\begin{aligned} g(\lambda) &= F(\phi^* + \lambda\beta) \\ &= \iint_D K(\phi^* + \lambda\beta, \phi_1^* + \lambda\beta_1, \phi_2^* + \lambda\beta_2). \end{aligned}$$

This function must attain its minimum value for $\lambda = 0$, and we must have $g'(0) = 0$. Computing this, we obtain

$$(7\text{-}67)\quad 0 = \iint_D K_1(\phi^*, \phi_1^*, \phi_2^*)\beta + \iint_D \{K_2(\phi^*, \phi_1^*, \phi_2^*)\beta_1 + K_3(\phi^*, \phi_1^*, \phi_2^*)\beta_2\}.$$

The second integral can be thrown into a different form. Consider the 1-form $\omega = \beta K_2\, dv - \beta K_3\, du$. By Green's theorem, $\int_{\partial D} \omega = \iint_D d\omega$; moreover, β was chosen to vanish everywhere on the boundary of D, so that $\int_{\partial D} \omega = 0$; thus, $\iint_D d\omega = 0$. Differentiating we obtain

$$d\omega = \left[\beta_1 K_2 + \beta \frac{\partial}{\partial u} K_2 + \beta_2 K_3 + \beta \frac{\partial}{\partial v} K_3\right] dudv$$

so that

$$\iint_D \{K_2\beta_1 + K_3\beta_2\} = -\iint_D \left(\frac{\partial}{\partial u} K_2 + \frac{\partial}{\partial v} K_3\right)\beta.$$

Substituting this into (7-67), we have

$$0 = \iint_D \left\{K_1 - \frac{\partial}{\partial u} K_2 - \frac{\partial}{\partial v} K_3\right\} \beta.$$

This holds for every choice of the function β. By an argument analogous to that of the lemma, we may conclude that the integrand must be everywhere zero in D; the resulting equation is the Euler equation for the extremal function ϕ^*:

$$(7\text{-}68)\quad K_1(\phi^*, \phi_1^*, \phi_2^*) = \frac{\partial}{\partial u} K_2(\phi^*, \phi_1^*, \phi_2^*) + \frac{\partial}{\partial v} K_3(\phi^*, \phi_1^*, \phi_2^*)$$

For the more general function given in (7-66), the same process, applied to each coordinate function in turn, yields three equations. If we write $K(x, y, z, x_u, y_u, z_u, x_v, y_v, z_v)$ in place of $K(\phi, \psi, \theta, \phi_1, \psi_1, \theta_1, \phi_2, \psi_2, \theta_2)$, then these equations appear as

$$(7\text{-}69)\quad \begin{aligned} \frac{\partial K}{\partial x} &= \frac{\partial}{\partial u}\frac{\partial K}{\partial x_u} + \frac{\partial}{\partial v}\frac{\partial K}{\partial x_v} \\ \frac{\partial K}{\partial y} &= \frac{\partial}{\partial u}\frac{\partial K}{\partial y_u} + \frac{\partial}{\partial v}\frac{\partial K}{\partial y_v} \\ \frac{\partial K}{\partial z} &= \frac{\partial}{\partial u}\frac{\partial K}{\partial z_u} + \frac{\partial}{\partial v}\frac{\partial K}{\partial z_v} \end{aligned}$$

In carrying out the differentiation with respect to u, or v, it must be recalled that u and v are present in the functions which describe Σ.

For example, we give the first of the equations in (7-69) in this expanded form:

$$\begin{aligned} K_1 = K_{14}\frac{\partial x}{\partial u} + K_{17}\frac{\partial x}{\partial v} + K_{24}\frac{\partial y}{\partial u} + K_{27}\frac{\partial y}{\partial v} \\ + K_{34}\frac{\partial z}{\partial u} + K_{37}\frac{\partial z}{\partial v} \\ + K_{44}\frac{\partial^2 x}{\partial u^2} + (2K_{47})\frac{\partial^2 x}{\partial u \partial v} + K_{77}\frac{\partial^2 x}{\partial v^2} \\ + K_{54}\frac{\partial^2 y}{\partial u^2} + (K_{57} + K_{84})\frac{\partial^2 y}{\partial u \partial v} + K_{87}\frac{\partial^2 y}{\partial v^2} \\ + K_{64}\frac{\partial^2 z}{\partial u^2} + (K_{67} + K_{94})\frac{\partial^2 z}{\partial u \partial v} + K_{97}\frac{\partial^2 z}{\partial v^2}. \end{aligned}$$

We conclude by giving a number of simple standard examples of variational problems, and the manner in which the Euler equations are used.

Let us begin with the familiar problem of determining the curve of shortest length which joins two points. For this, we use the functional

$$F(\gamma) = \int_0^1 |\gamma'| = \int_0^1 \sqrt{(x')^2 + (y')^2}$$

which gives the length of the curve γ. The kernel of F is the function $K(x, y, x', y') = [(x')^2 + (y')^2]^{1/2}$. The corresponding Euler equations are

$$K_1 = \frac{d}{dt}K_3 \qquad K_2 = \frac{d}{dt}K_4$$

Since $K_1 = K_2 = 0$, these become merely

$$\frac{d}{dt}\left(\frac{x'}{\sqrt{(x')^2 + (y')^2}}\right) = 0, \qquad \frac{d}{dt}\left(\frac{y'}{\sqrt{(x')^2 + (y')^2}}\right) = 0.$$

From these, we conclude at once that

$$x'[(x')^2 + (y')^2]^{-1/2} \qquad \text{and} \qquad y'[(x')^2 + (y')^2]^{-1/2}$$

are constant. There then exist constants A and B such that $Ax' + By' = 0$. Integrating this, we find that the general solution of the Euler equations for this problem is the family of straight lines $Ax + By = C$. There is just one of these which passes through the two given points. Thus, we may conclude that among the class of smooth curves which join two points, the only possible minimal one is the straight line. It remains to be shown that the straight line is a minimum, for we have no guarantee that the minimum problem has a solution. (See Exercise 2, or the references given later in the section.)

Another example of an extremal problem which has a simple formulation is that of finding the surface of smallest area which has a prescribed curve (or curves) for its boundary. We first consider the special case of a surface of revolution, bounded by two circles. Let P and Q be two points in the upper half plane, and let γ be a smooth curve joining P to Q and remaining above the horizontal axis. Rotate this curve about this axis, obtaining a surface Σ which is bounded by the two circles traced out by the points P and Q. Holding P and Q fixed, what curve γ will give a surface of minimal area? The formula for the area of Σ is

$$F(\gamma) = 2\pi \int_0^1 y\sqrt{(x')^2 + (y')^2}\,dt$$

where γ is given by $x = X(t)$, $y = Y(t)$, and $\gamma(0) = P$, $\gamma(1) = Q$. Dropping the factor 2π, we have

$$K(x, y, x', y') = y\sqrt{(x')^2 + (y')^2}$$

so that the corresponding Euler equations (7-65a) become

$$0 = \frac{d}{dt}\left\{\frac{yx'}{\sqrt{(x')^2 + (y')^2}}\right\}$$
$$\sqrt{(x')^2 + (y')^2} = \frac{d}{dt}\left\{\frac{yy'}{\sqrt{(x')^2 + (y')^2}}\right\}.$$

From the first of these, we conclude that there is a constant A such that $yx' = A[(x')^2 + (y')^2]^{1/2}$. Squaring this, we obtain the differential equation

$$dx = \frac{A\,dy}{\sqrt{y^2 - A^2}}$$

whose solution is the family of all catenaries

$$y = A\cosh\left(\frac{x - c}{A}\right)$$

One is thus tempted to say that the surface of revolution of minimum area is that generated by the catenary which passes through P and Q. However, all that the above analysis has shown is that if there is a smooth curve which generates a surface of minimal area, it is obtained by revolving a catenary passing through P and Q. Moreover, it is easy to see that there may not always be a catenary passing through P and Q. For example, if $P = (1, H)$ and $Q = (-1, H)$, then $c = 0$ and

$$H = A\cosh\frac{1}{A}.$$

As A ranges over the set of all positive real numbers, $A\cosh(1/A)$ has a minimum value $\alpha > 0$ so that if $H < \alpha$, then there is no catenary from P to Q. Certainly, in this case, the surface of minimal area (if one exists) must be generated by a nonsmooth curve. It can be shown that the dotted curve in Fig. 7-27 is the only other contender. It generates a nonsmooth surface consisting of two disks joined by a thread. This surface can be minimal, even when there is a catenary from P to Q. However, in some cases, the catenary surface can afford a local minimum,

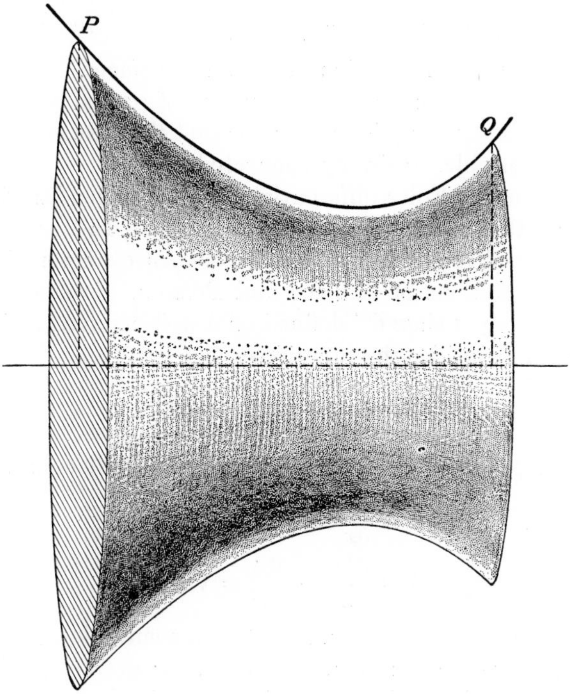

FIG. 7-27

even when it is not an absolute minimum; this means that it will yield a surface of smallest area among the surfaces which do not deviate much from it, although the disk surface will have a still smaller area.†

This simple case illustrates the type of behavior to be expected in the general minimal surface problem. One special case can be treated more easily. Suppose that we consider the class of surfaces Σ described by the parametric equations $x = u$, $y = v$, $z = f(u, v)$, $(u, v) \in D$, where D is a region in the plane bounded by a smooth curve. We also assume that f is of class C'' in D. The area of Σ is given by

$$F(f) = \iint_D \sqrt{1 + f_1^2 + f_2^2}$$

† For a full discussion of this and a proof that there is a minimum, see G. A. Bliss, "Calculus of Variations," *Carus Mathematical Monographs*, 1925.

Using (7-68), the Euler equation turns out to be

$$0 = \frac{\partial}{\partial u}\left[\frac{f_1}{(1 + f_1^2 + f_2^2)^{1/2}}\right] + \frac{\partial}{\partial v}\left[\frac{f_2}{(1 + f_1^2 + f_2^2)^{1/2}}\right]$$

which becomes

$$\frac{\partial^2 f}{\partial u^2}\left[1 + \left(\frac{\partial f}{\partial v}\right)^2\right] + \frac{\partial^2 f}{\partial v^2}\left[1 + \left(\frac{\partial f}{\partial u}\right)^2\right] = 2\,\frac{\partial f}{\partial u}\,\frac{\partial f}{\partial v}\,\frac{\partial^2 f}{\partial u \partial v}$$

the so-called differential equation of minimal surfaces.

In the general case, one is led to a system of partial differential equations; the situation is complicated by the fact that the surfaces involved need not be orientable, or simply connected.†

In many cases, the Euler differential equation coincides with one that is familiar and that has a well-developed theory. In this case, one may employ variational methods to advantage. An example of this is provided by the equations of Laplace and Poisson, discussed in Sec. 7.6. Let ϕ be a function of class C'' defined on a well-behaved region D in the (x, y) plane, and consider the functional

$$F(\phi) = \iint_D \{(\phi_x)^2 + (\phi_y)^2\}.$$

We have $K(\phi, \phi_x, \phi_y) = (\phi_x)^2 + (\phi_y)^2$ so that Euler's equation is

$$0 = \frac{\partial}{\partial x}(2\phi_x) + \frac{\partial}{\partial y}(2\phi_y)$$

or

$$0 = \frac{\partial^2 \phi}{\partial x^2} + \frac{\partial^2 \phi}{\partial y^2} = \nabla^2 \phi.$$

Thus, a function ϕ^* which minimizes $F(\phi)$ in a suitable class of functions ϕ must be a harmonic function. Suppose, for example, that we again consider the class of functions ϕ having prescribed boundary values on ∂D. It is natural to expect that the solution of Laplace's equation in this class (i.e., the solution of Dirichlet's problem) will minimize the functional F. This can be shown directly. Let ϕ^* be this function, and consider the function $\phi^* + \beta$, where β is of class C'' in D and vanishes on the boundary of D. We then have

$$F(\phi^* + \beta) = \iint_D \{(\phi_x^* + \beta_x)^2 + (\phi_y^* + \beta_y)^2\}$$

(7-70) $$= \iint_D \{(\phi_x^*)^2 + (\phi_y^*)^2\} + \iint_D \{(\beta_x)^2 + (\beta_y)^2\} + 2\iint_D \{\phi_x^*\beta_x + \phi_y^*\beta_y\}.$$

† For examples of this, and a discussion of the experimental approach through the use of soap films, see R. Courant and H. Robbins, "What Is Mathematics?" Oxford University Press, New York, 1941.

Consider the 1-form $\omega = \beta\phi_x^* \, dy - \beta\phi_y^* \, dx$; since $\beta = 0$ on ∂D, $\int_{\partial D} \omega = 0$. By Green's theorem, $\iint_D d\omega = 0$. Computing $d\omega$, we have

$$\begin{aligned} d\omega &= (\beta_x\phi_x^* + \beta_y\phi_y^* + \beta\nabla^2\phi^*) \, dxdy \\ &= (\beta_x\phi_x^* + \beta_y\phi_y^*) \, dxdy. \end{aligned}$$

Thus, the third integral in (7-70) has value zero, and we have the simple relation

$$F(\phi^* + \beta) = F(\phi^*) + F(\beta).$$

However, from its nature, $F(\beta) \geq 0$ for all β, with equality only if β is constant in D; since β is zero on ∂D, this happens only if $\beta \equiv 0$. Thus, we have shown that $F(\phi) \geq F(\phi^*)$ for any function ϕ in the class considered, and ϕ^* is indeed minimal. This fact can be used to obtain approximate solutions of the Dirichlet problem.†

EXERCISES

1. Let $F(\gamma) = \int_\gamma A(x, y) \, dx + B(x, y) \, dy$. Show that the Euler equations for this, in the class of smooth curves γ with fixed end points P and Q, are

$$0 = (A_2 - B_1) \frac{dx}{dt}, \qquad 0 = (A_2 - B_1) \frac{dy}{dt}.$$

2. Let $\omega = (xy - x^2/2) \, dy$, and $P = (0, 0)$, $Q = (1, 1)$. Show that $F(\gamma) = \int_\gamma \omega$ has no maximum or minimum in the class of smooth curves joining P to Q, if the curves are allowed to have multiple points. [*Hint:* $d\omega = (y - x) \, dxdy$, which is positive above the line $y = x$, and negative below. Use Green's theorem.]

3. (*Continuation*) Show that the straight line between P and Q is maximal for $F(\gamma)$ among all *simple* curves from P to Q.

4. (*Continuation*) Let $P = (0, 0)$ and $Q = (1, 2)$. Show that $F(\gamma)$ does not have a finite maximum for γ in the class of smooth simple curves joining P to Q.

5. Let $F(\phi) = \int_0^1 K(\phi, \phi', \phi'')$. In the class of functions ϕ with $\phi(0) = 0$, $\phi(1) = 1$, $\phi'(0) = a$, $\phi'(1) = b$, show that an extremal function must satisfy the equation

$$K_1(\phi, \phi', \phi'') - \frac{d}{dt} K_2(\phi, \phi', \phi'') + \frac{d^2}{dt^2} K_3(\phi, \phi', \phi'') = 0.$$

† For a discussion of this, see R. Weinstock, 'Calculus of Variations," McGraw-Hill Book Company, Inc., New York, 1952.

APPENDIX

FOUNDATIONS OF THE NUMBER SYSTEM

The real-number system underlies all of analysis. In the next few pages, we shall set forth its characteristic properties. We start with a definition: *The real numbers constitute a complete simply ordered field.*

We expand this concise statement by explaining the meaning of the terms involved.

Definition. *A field is a set R of elements a, b, x, . . . , together with two functions $+$ and $\cdot$, called "sum" and "product," which satisfy the following requirements:*

(F_1) **Closure.** *If a and b are in R, then their sum {product} is defined and is a unique element of R denoted by $a + b$ $\{a \cdot b\}$.*

(F_2) **Commutative.** *If a and b are in R, then*

$$\begin{aligned} a + b &= b + a \\ a \cdot b &= b \cdot a \end{aligned}$$

(F_3) **Associative.** *If a, b, and c are in R, then*

$$\begin{aligned} a + (b + c) &= (a + b) + c \\ a \cdot (b \cdot c) &= (a \cdot b) \cdot c \end{aligned}$$

(F_4) **Distributive.** *If a, b, and c are in R, then*

$$a \cdot (b + c) = (a \cdot b) + (a \cdot c)$$

(F_5) **Existence of neutral elements.** *There are special elements of R, denoted by 0 and 1, such that for any $x \varepsilon R$,*

$$x + 0 = x \text{ and } x \cdot 1 = x.$$

(F_6) **Inverses.** *For any $a \varepsilon R$, the equation $a + x = 0$ has a solution, and for any $a \varepsilon R$ except 0, the equation $a \cdot x = 1$ has a solution.*

In working with a field, it is customary to use certain abbreviations. For example, according to (F_6), there is an element x such that $a + x = 0$; moreover, this element is unique, for if $a + x' = 0$, then

$$\begin{aligned} x = x + 0 = x + (a + x') &= (x + a) + x' \\ &= (a + x) + x' = 0 + x' = x' + 0 = x'. \end{aligned}$$

Thus, the element depends solely upon a, and we denote it by $-a$. The function "difference" is then defined by $a - b = a + (-b)$. Likewise, if $a \neq 0$, then the solution of $a \cdot x = 1$ is unique and may be denoted by a^{-1} or $1/a$. We then define "quotient" by $a/b = a \cdot (1/b)$. On the basis of these postulates on R, all the familiar algebraic rules follow. To cite a few, one may prove that: $(-a) \cdot (-b) = a \cdot b$; $a \cdot 0 = 0$; $(a/b) \cdot (c/d) = (a \cdot c)/(b \cdot d)$; $(a/b) + (c/d) = (a \cdot d + b \cdot c)/(b \cdot d)$; $a \cdot b = 0$ only if $a = 0$ or $b = 0$.

The notion of an ordering relation may be introduced most easily by means of a set of **positive elements.**

Definition. *A field R with a simple order is one in which there is a subset P (called the set of positive elements) such that:*

(O_1) *If a and b are in P, then so are $a + b$ and $a \cdot b$.*

(O_2) *The zero element, 0, is not in P.*

(O_3) *If x is any element not in P, then $x = 0$, or $-x \in P$.*

To convert these postulates into more familiar properties, one defines a relation $>$ on R by: $a > b$ *if and only if* $a - b \in P$. The conditions (O_1), (O_2), (O_3) imply the usual properties of $>$. For example, $a > 0$ is equivalent to saying that a belongs to P. Requirement (O_1) then implies that if $a > b$ and $b > c$, then $a > c$, and if $d > 0$, then $a \cdot d > b \cdot d$. The equivalent form of (O_3) is the statement that if a and b are any elements of R, then either $a = b$, $a > b$, or $b > a$. An ordering relation $>$ which has this last property is said to be **simple** or linear; many important ordering relations are partial orderings in which this law fails, and two elements a and b may be incomparable. We note one important consequence of the existence of a simple order in R, namely, that the sum $x_1^2 + x_2^2 + \cdots + x_n^2$ is always positive (> 0) unless $x_1 = x_2 = \cdots = x_n = 0$.

Finally, we come to the notion of **completeness** of an order relation. As we shall see, this has many equivalent formulations. One of these may be described in terms of what are called **Dedekind cuts.** A cut in R is a pair A, B, where A and B are nonempty subsets of R whose union is R and such that $a \leq b$ whenever $a \in A$ and $b \in B$. Any element c of R can be used to generate a cut by taking A as the set of all $x \in R$ with $x \leq c$, and B as the set of all $x \in R$ with $x \geq c$.

Definition. *A simple ordering on a field R is complete if every cut in R is generated by an element of R.*

Some additional comments are in order. The real field is not the only example of a field. One familiar example is the **complex field** C.

Definition. *The complex field C is the class of all ordered pairs (a, b) with a and b real numbers, and with sum and product defined by*

$$(a, b) + (x, y) = (a + x, b + y)$$
$$(a, b) \cdot (x, y) = (ax - by, ay + bx)$$

One may verify that C satisfies the field axioms $F_1, \ldots, F_6$. For example, $0 = (0, 0)$, $1 = (1, 0)$, $-(x, y) = (-x, -y)$, and

$$(x, y)^{-1} = \left(\frac{x}{(x^2 + y^2)}, \frac{-y}{(x^2 + y^2)}\right).$$

If we write $(0, 1) = i$ and $(a, 0) = a$, then $(x, y) = x + iy$, where $i^2 = -1$. The usual algebraic operations may now be used. The complex field cannot be given a simple order; as we have seen, in any simply ordered field, it is necessary that $x^2 + y^2 \neq 0$ except when $x = y = 0$. This fails in C since $1^2 + i^2 = 0$.

Other examples of fields may be obtained from R. A subset S of R is called a **subfield** if S is a field under the operations of R; one need only verify that if a and b are any two elements of S, then $a + b$, $a \cdot b$, $-a$, and if $b \neq 0$, $1/b$ are all members of S. The smallest subfield of the real field is called the **rational field** R_0. The elements of the rational field are the rational numbers; each may be represented in the form a/b, where a and b belong to the special subsystem called the ring of **integers** J. Every element in J is expressible as m or $-m$ or 0, where m is in J^+, the system of positive integers (whole numbers). As a subfield of R, the rational field R_0 is simply ordered. The class of positive elements of R_0 can be taken as $P_0 = P \cap R_0$. However, unlike the real field, R_0 is not a completely ordered field. The Dedekind cut (A, B) in R_0 defined by

$$A = \{\text{all } x \in R_0 \text{ with } x^3 < 2\}$$
$$B = \{\text{all } x \in R_0 \text{ with } x^3 > 2\}$$

is one which cannot be generated from an element in R_0. In R, the corresponding cut is generated by $\sqrt[3]{2}$, but this number is not present in R_0.

With this preparation, we state without proof, the fundamental result dealing with the real field: *any two fields which are completely ordered are isomorphic.* This gives one the right to speak of *the* real field, and guarantees that the description we have chosen is adequate. To explain by illustration the meaning of "isomorphic," we give another construction of the complex field. Let C^* be the collection of all 2-by-2 matrices with real entries and having the form

$$\begin{bmatrix} a & b \\ -b & a \end{bmatrix}.$$

For multiplication, use the customary product operations for matrices, and add matrices by adding corresponding entries. Then, one may again verify that C^* is a field. The correspondence

$$\begin{bmatrix} a & b \\ -b & a \end{bmatrix} \leftrightarrow a + bi = (a, b)$$

is an isomorphism between C^* and C. (This class of matrices also appears in another connection in Theorem 8, Sec. 6.2. Nor is this entirely a coincidence; conformal transformations are locally expressible as power series with complex coefficients.)

Having obtained a categorical description of the real numbers, is it sufficient to proceed by fiat; "let R be a completely ordered field," and then continue from there? This would leave open the possibility that there might not exist such a field, due perhaps to some undiscovered inconsistency in the postulates. To avoid this, we may attempt to construct an example of such a field, building up from a simpler system whose existence we are willing to accept. This process has been set forth in great detail in Landau, "Grundlagen der Analysis," Leipzig, 1930. We sketch such a construction in a sequence of steps.

Step 1. *Construction of R from R_0.* Two methods have been used here. The first method is conceptually simpler. R_0 is an ordered field which is not complete. Some of its Dedekind cuts can be generated by elements of R_0 and some cannot. Define R to be the collection of all cuts. Those that can be generated from elements of R_0 are identified with the corresponding element of R_0 and are rational numbers; those that cannot be so generated are the irrational real numbers. One then defines sum and product of cuts, and verifies all the postulates for R.

The second method is easier to carry out. Working only with rational numbers, we define convergence of sequences of rational numbers, and Cauchy sequences of rational numbers. It is no longer true in R_0 that every Cauchy sequence converges. Consider the collection $\mathcal{S}$ of all Cauchy sequences of rational numbers, and introduce a notion of equivalence by saying that $\{a_n\} \approx \{b_n\}$ if and only if $\lim_{n\to\infty} a_n - b_n = 0$. This splits $\mathcal{S}$ into equivalence classes. Each of these is now called a real number. The product and sum functions are now defined, and the postulates verified.

Step 2. *Construction of R_0 from J.* Consider the collection $\mathcal{P}$ of all ordered pairs of integers (m, n) with $m \neq 0$. Thinking of (m, n) as representing the rational number n/m, a notion of equivalence is defined in $\mathcal{P}$ by $(m, n) \approx (m', n')$ *if and only if* $mn' = m'n$. This again divides $\mathcal{P}$ into equivalence classes. Each of these classes is called a rational number; with appropriate definitions for sum, $>$, and product, R_0 is seen to be an ordered field.

Step 3. *Construction of J from J^+, the positive whole numbers.* Again, one considers a collection of ordered pairs (m, n) where m and n are in J^+. With (m, n) being thought of as corresponding to the integer $m - n$, one says that $(m, n) \approx (m', n')$ if and only if $m + n' = n + m'$. The resulting equivalence classes are called the integers. The rest goes as before.

Step 4. *Construction of J^+ from axiomatic set theory.* Within an adequate system of logic, one may define the notion of cardinal number for finite sets. From this, one may then obtain J^+.

We conclude this discussion of the real-number system by giving some of the equivalent ways in which the completeness property, which is so

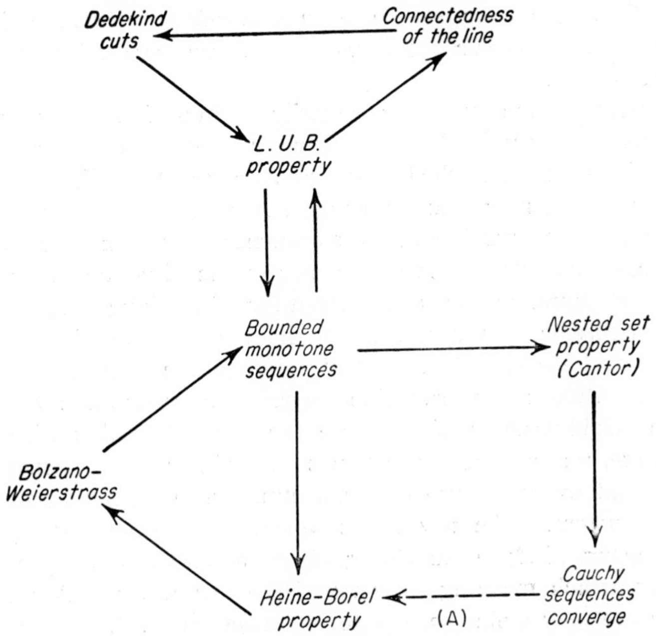

characteristic of R, can be obtained. Most of these involve results which we have assumed, or which have been proved from others which we have assumed. In the accompanying chart, we have indicated by arrows certain mutual implications which hold among these; below is a brief reminder of the definition of each. If the chart is examined, it will be seen that all the following are equivalent to the assertion that the ordering on the field R is complete.

1. **Dedekind:** *Every cut is generated by an element.*
2. **Connectedness:** *The real line is a connected set.*
3. **L.U.B.:** *Every nonempty set which is bounded above has a least upper bound.*

4. **Monotone sequences:** *Any bounded monotone sequence is convergent.*

5. **Bolzano-Weierstrass:** *Every bounded sequence has a convergent subsequence.*

6. **Heine-Borel:** *If a collection of open intervals covers a closed bounded interval E, then some finite subcollection will also.*

In addition all imply two other conditions:

7. **Nested interval:** *A decreasing sequence of closed bounded nonempty intervals has a nonempty intersection.*

8. **Cauchy criterion:** *Any Cauchy sequence is convergent.*

Finally, these two in turn imply all the rest if one additional assumption is allowed. This is a property of the order relation on R.

Definition. *An order relation $>$ on R is said to be* **Archimedian** *if the following holds: whenever $a > 0$ and $b > 0$, then there exists an integer n such that $na > b$.*

The order relation on R is necessarily Archimedian if any one of the conditions (1) through (6) hold; however, there exist ordered fields in which (8) holds, but which are non-Archimedian. To see the role played in analysis by this property, one need only observe that it is equivalent to the assertion that the sequence $\{1/n\}$ converges to 0.

We have not proved these statements; the direction of the arrows in the chart shows one possible pattern for establishing them.†

This discussion should not end without a mention of ∞ and $-\infty$. These are to be regarded as "ideal" points adjoined to the real field R. The neighborhoods of ∞ are defined to be the intervals {all x with $x > b$}, and the neighborhoods of $-\infty$ are the intervals {all x with $x < b$}. Using these, we see that the sequence $\{x_n\}$ with $x_n = n$ is convergent to ∞, and that every sequence of real numbers has a limit point in the extended system. The new points ∞ and $-\infty$ do not participate fully in the algebra of R; in particular, the new system is no longer a field. One may attach meaning to some of the operations, but not all; for example, we may define $\infty + c$ to be ∞ for all $c \in R$, but no meaning within the new system is attached to $\infty + (-\infty)$.

The adjunction of ∞ and $-\infty$ to R is done with the aim of achieving compactness. This may also be done in other ways. If ϕ is a transformation which is one-to-one, bicontinuous, and which maps R onto a set A in a compact set S, then the closure of A in S is a compactification of R. The boundary points for A which do not lie in R form the ideal points which are to be adjoined to R. As a simple illustration of this, let S be the circle of radius 1, center $C = (0, 1)$, and let ϕ be the transformation mapping the point $(x, 0)$ on the horizontal axis ($= R$) into the point p on S which lies on the line through $(x, 0)$ and $Q = (0, 2)$.

† For a detailed treatment, see M. H. Stone, "The Theory of Real Functions," Harvard University Mathematics Department, Cambridge, Mass., 1940.

It is easily seen that the image of R is the set A consisting of all points on S except Q. The closure of A is S itself, and Q is the only boundary point of A which does not lie in A. Thus, R may be compactified by adjoining a single point "at infinity" whose neighborhoods are the sets $\{\text{all } x \text{ with } |x| > c\}$. With the same choice of S, we may take ϕ as the transformation mapping $(x, 0)$ into the point of S lying on the line through $(x, 0)$ and C; the closure of the image set A is a semicircle whose end points correspond to the ideal points ∞ and $-\infty$. Other choices of S and ϕ may yield an infinite number of ideal points "at infinity."

SUGGESTED READING

G. Birkhoff and S. MacLane, "Survey of Modern Algebra," The Macmillan Company, New York, 1953.

R. Courant and H. Robbins, "What Is Mathematics?" Oxford University Press, New York, 1941.

L. M. Graves, "Theory of Functions of Real Variables," McGraw-Hill Book Company, Inc., New York, 1946.

P. R. Halmos, "Measure Theory," D. Van Nostrand Company, Inc., New York, 1950.

J. L. Kelley, "General Topology," D. Van Nostrand Company, Inc., New York, 1955.

E. Landau, "Foundations of Analysis," Chelsea Publishing Co., New York, 1951.

S. Lefschetz, "Introduction to Topology," Princeton University Press, Princeton, N.J., 1949.

C. C. MacDuffee, "Vectors and Matrices," *Carus Mathematical Monograph* 7, 1943.

M. E. Munroe, "Introduction to Measure and Integration," Addison-Wesley Publishing Company, Cambridge, Mass., 1953.

Alfred Tarski, "Introduction to Logic," Oxford University Press, New York, 1950.

ANSWERS AND HINTS

Sec. 1.1

1. $(1, 3, -1)$, $(3, -3, -5)$, -8, $\sqrt{13}$, $\sqrt{43}$, $(8, -6, -13)$.
4. *Hint:* $|p + q|^2 = (p + q) \cdot (p + q)$.
5. Apply Exercise 4.
6. No. Rather, the reverse holds, as may be seen by writing

$$|p| = |p - q + q| \leq |p - q| + |q|.$$

8. The points $\lambda p + (1 - \lambda)q$, for $-\infty < \lambda < \infty$, comprise the line through p and q, if $p \neq q$; when $0 \leq \lambda \leq 1$, one obtains just the line segment joining p and q.
10. (*a*) The half plane whose edge is the perpendicular bisector of the segment from A to the origin; (*b*) an ellipse with foci at $(0, 0)$ and A; (*c*) the empty set.

Sec. 1.2

1. (*a*) Closed, bounded, connected, boundary is itself. (*b*) Closed, unbounded, connected, boundary is parabola $x^2 + y = 0$. (*c*) Closed, unbounded, connected, boundary is itself. (*d*) Open, unbounded, connected, boundary is line. (*e*) Open, unbounded, disconnected, boundary is pair of lines. (*f*) Same as (*c*).
2. (*a*) Open, connected, unbounded, boundary is sphere. (*b*) Closed, connected, unbounded, boundary is cylinder. (*c*) Open, unbounded, connected, boundary is surface whose equation is $xy = z$. (*d*) Closed, connected, unbounded, boundary is itself.
4. The boundary of S is the whole plane.
8. *Hint:* Choose any point $p \in S$, and let S_1 be the collection of all points $q \in S$ which can be joined to p by a polygonal line lying wholly in S. Prove $S_1 = S$ by using the definition of connectedness, i.e., show that S_1 and $S - S_1$ are both open.
10. Show that the general point (x, y) can be connected to the point $(\sqrt{2}, 0)$ by a polygon with vertical and horizontal segments.

Sec. 1.3

1. Cluster points $= \{$all $(0, 1/n)$, all $(1/n, 0)$, and $(0, 0)$, for $n = 1, 2, 3, \ldots\}$. Boundary of S is the union of S and its cluster points.
2. If p is a boundary point for S which is not a cluster point, then $p \in S$ and p is the center of a neighborhood which contains no other point of S.
3. No.
4. For the first, take $I_n = \{\text{all } x \geq n\}$; for the second, take $I_n = \{\text{all } x, 0 < x < 1/n\}$.
7. Let $[0, 1] \subset A \cup B$, where A and B are disjoint open sets on the line. Assume $0 \in A$. Let p be the greatest lower bound of the points of B in $[0, 1]$. Show that $p = 1$, so that A by itself covers $[0, 1]$.

Sec. 1.4

3. When the sequence is ultimately constant.
4. If $D_1 \supset D_2 \supset \cdots$ is a nested sequence of open neighborhoods, closing down on $\bar{p}$, one may select points $p_j \in D_j$ so that $\{p_j\} \to \bar{p}$.

[This assumes that one may make such selections; this involves the use of the so-called axiom of choice. See J. L. Kelley, "General Topology," D. Van Nostrand Company, Inc., New York, 1955.]

5. (*b*) Consider $\lim_{n\to\infty} (p_{2n} - p_n)$.
7. The sequence obtained from an enumeration of the rationals has the whole line for its set of limit points.
8. Two cases. (*a*) The set of distinct terms in the sequence is finite. (*b*) There are infinitely many distinct terms. In the first, one of the terms is a limit point. In the second, the Bolzano-Weierstrass theorem applies.
9. If $\{p_n\}$ fails to converge to its unique limit point p^*, then an infinite number of terms would have to fall outside a neighborhood N of p^*. These would then have a limit point distinct from p^*.

Sec. 1.5

1. (*a*) Prove $\{a_n\}$ monotone decreasing; (*b*) show $a_{n+1}/a_n < 1$ so that again $\{a_n\} \downarrow$.
2. The sequence is not monotone, although $\{a_{2n}\}$ and $\{a_{2n+1}\}$ are monotone. Next, one shows that $\{a_n\}$ converges. [The explicit formula given in the footnote could be used to prove that $\lim a_n = 7/3$; however, this is not the point of the exercise.]
3. Write $a_n = \dfrac{(\sqrt{n^2+n} - n)(\sqrt{n^2+n} + n)}{\sqrt{n^2+n} + n}$
4. Consider $AB - a_n b_n = AB - Ab_n + Ab_n - a_n b_n$.
5. If $A > 0$, show first that $a_n \geq \delta > 0$ for all n. Then, $|(1/A) - (1/a_n)| \leq |A - a_n|/A\delta$.
7. (*a*) $\limsup a_n = 1$, $\liminf a_n = -1$; (*b*) $\limsup a_n = 2$, $\liminf a_n = -2$; (*c*) $\limsup a_n = 3$, $\liminf a_n = -1$; (*d*) $\pm \sqrt{3}/2$.
8. Try $a_n = (-1)^n$, $b_n = (-1)^{n+1}$.
10. Choose any $\epsilon > 0$ and N so that $|a_n| < \epsilon$ whenever $n > N$. If $n \geq N$, then

$$|\sigma_n| \leq \frac{a_1 + \cdots + a_n}{n} + \frac{(n-N)\epsilon}{n}.$$

Let n increase, obtaining $\limsup_{n\to\infty} |\sigma_n| \leq \epsilon$. Then let $\epsilon \downarrow 0$.

Sec. 2.1

2. The graph of f will be another curve lying above C in space.
3. (*a*) 6; (*b*) 13; (*c*) 6; (*d*) $(x^2 + x)(y + 1)$; (*e*) $x(x + 1)^2$; (*f*) $x^2(y + 1)^2 + x(y + 1)$; (*g*) $x^4 + 2x^3 + 2x^2 + x$.
4. (*a*) No; (*b*) yes.
5. The level curves of f are hyperbolas with the lines $y = \pm x$ for asymptotes.
6. (*a*) Coaxial parabolas. (*b*) Concentric circles. (*c*) Unbounded line segments, except when $k = 1$; this brings in the whole open disk $|p| < 1$.
7. Hyperboloids of revolution.
8. It is a plane passing through the origin.

Sec. 2.2

2. (*a*) $\lim_{x\to 0} (1 - x^2) = 1$. (*b*) $\lim_{x\uparrow\infty} \dfrac{x}{1+x} = 1$. (*c*) $\lim_{x\downarrow 0} \sqrt{x} = 0$.
(*d*) $\lim_{x\uparrow 1} (1 - x)^{-1/2} = \infty$.

3. (*a*) -1; (*b*) 1. (Note that if one writes

$$\frac{x-1}{\sqrt{1+x^2}} = \frac{x-1}{x\sqrt{1+1/x^2}} = \frac{1-1/x}{\sqrt{1+1/x^2}},$$

one obtains only the answer 1. The error lies in assuming that $\sqrt{x^2} = x$.)

4. The analogue for Theorem 2 is: $\lim_{x \uparrow \infty} f(x)$ exists if corresponding to any $\epsilon > 0$, a number N can be found such that $|f(x_1) - f(x_2)| < \epsilon$ whenever x_1 and x_2 obey $x_1 > N$, $x_2 > N$.
6. Consult Exercises 4 and 5, Sec. 1.5, and the corresponding theorems for sequences.
7. For each n, choose δ_n so that if x' and x'' obey $0 < |x' - b| < \delta_n$, $0 < |x'' - b| < \delta_n$, then $|f(x') - f(x'')| < \epsilon$. Let x_n be a point with $0 < |x_n - b| < \delta_n$, and let $I_n = \{\text{all } p \text{ with } |p - x_n| \le 1/n\}$. These are closed intervals, and I_1, $I_1 \cap I_2$, . . . form a nested sequence. If L is the point in all of them, then $\lim f(x_n) = L$, from which it may be proved that $\lim_{x \to b} f(x) = L$.
8. Take $L = \text{lub}\,\{f(x), \text{ where } a < x < b\}$.
9. Given ϵ, choose $x_1 > x_0$ so that $|g(x)| < \epsilon/M$ whenever $x \ge x_1$. Then, $|f(x)g(x)| < \epsilon$. Theorem 1 is not usable, since it is not known that $\lim_{x \uparrow \infty} f(x)$ exists.

Sec. 2.3

1. (*a*) Does not exist; (*b*) 0; (*c*) does not exist; (try $x = y = r$, $z = 0$); (*d*) does not exist.
5. Use the triangle law to show that $|f(p)| \le |A - B|$, and $|f(p) - f(p_0)| \le 2|p - p_0|$; $\lim_{|p| \to \infty} f(p)$ does not exist.
7. If it is not the case that $\lim_{p \to p_0} f(p) = L$, then there is $\epsilon_0 > 0$ such that for any integer n, there exists a point p with $0 < |p - p_0| < 1/n$, while $|f(p) - L| \ge \epsilon_0$. Produce a sequence $\{p_n\}$ converging to p_0 for which $\lim_{n \to \infty} f(p_n)$ is not L.

Sec. 2.4

1. (*a*) Continuous everywhere; (*b*) Essential discontinuity at the origin; (*c*) Essential discontinuity at the origin; (*d*) Discontinuous at all points of the line $y = x$, except at the origin
2. The function is continuous nowhere.
3. The function is continuous at each irrational point.
5. Write down the complete formal definition for "f is uniformly continuous on E." Then, write down its formal negation, being careful about the order of quantifiers.
6. Show that if f were not uniformly continuous on E, the Bolzano-Weierstrass theorem would yield a sequence $\{p_n\}$ converging to a point p^* in E, while $\lim f(p_n)$ does not exist.
7. Use Theorem 2.

Sec. 2.5

1. In S, $|x| \le 2$ and $|y| \le 2$. Thus $|f(x, y)| \le 10$. For fixed x, $f(x, y)$ is largest when y is largest. Thus, the maximum occurs on the boundary of S. The maximum value is $7/2$.
3. Take C as given by equations $x = \phi(t)$, $y = \psi(t)$, $0 \le t \le 1$, with $(\phi(0), \psi(0)) = P$ and $(\phi(1), \psi(1)) = Q$. Put $F(t) = f(\phi(t), \psi(t))$. Show that F is continuous and that there exists t_0 with $F(t_0) = c$.

Sec. 2.6

1. If $r < 1\frac{3}{4}$, he should row directly to the pier. Otherwise, he should land at a point $12 - 15(r^2 - 9)^{-\frac{1}{2}}$ miles from the pier, and walk the rest of the way.
2. This is an end point maximum; the largest area occurs when the inscribed cone flattens out to become the base.
4. Use the mean value theorem.
5. (*a*) By the mean value theorem, $F(x) = F(0) + F'(\tau)x \leq F(0) + Cx$. Hence $F(x) - x \leq F(0) - (1 - C)x$, and $F(x) - x$ is negative for sufficiently large x. When $x = 0$, $F(x) - x = F(0) > 0$. Thus, for some x_0, $F(x_0) = x_0$.

   If $F(x_1) = x_1$, then applying the mean value theorem to $F(x_1) - F(x_0)$, one finds that $x_1 = x_0$.

   (*b*) We have $x_{n+1} - x_0 = F(x_n) - F(x_0) = (x_n - x_0)F'(\tau)$. Thus, $|x_{n+1} - x_0| \leq C|x_n - x_0|$. Since $C < 1$, this implies that $\lim x_n = x_0$.
6. Write the equation in the form: $x = 1 + \frac{1}{2} \sin x$. Applying the method of Exercise 5, one finds $x = 1.498$.
7. $3b/(2H + B) = 3 \sin \theta/(2 + \cos \theta) = f(\theta)$. One has $f(\theta) - f(0) = \theta f'(\theta^*)$, where $0 \leq \theta^* \leq \pi/4$. An easy estimate shows that $1 \geq f'(\theta^*) \geq 1/1.011$. Hence, $f(\theta) \leq \theta \leq (1.011)f(\theta)$. (Error $\leq .0086 \sim \frac{1}{2}°$.)
9. One must show that for $a < x < b$

$$f(x) \geq \frac{(b - x)f(a) + (x - a)f(b)}{b - a}.$$

   By the mean value theorem

$$f(x) = f(a) + (x - a)f'(\alpha)$$
$$f(x) = f(b) + (x - b)f'(\beta)$$

   where $a < \alpha < x < \beta < b$. Hence

$$(b - a)f(x) = (b - x + x - a)f(x) = (b - x)f(a) + (x - a)f(b) + (b - x)(x - a)[f'(\alpha) - f'(\beta)].$$

   Finally, $f'(\beta) - f'(\alpha) = (\beta - \alpha)f''(\tau) \leq 0$.
10. (*a*) $\frac{1}{2}$; (*b*) 1; (*c*) -1.

   (*d*) Write this as $\dfrac{\int_0^x t^2 e^{t^2}\, dt}{x e^{x^2}}$

   Applying L'Hospital's rule, the limit is seen to be $\frac{1}{2}$.
11. In obtaining the final form, a factor $\cos x$ was "canceled." This rendered the argument invalid since $\lim f'(x)/g'(x)$ itself did *not* exist, being undefined on the sequence for which $\cos x = 0$.

Sec. 3.1

3. Yes; zero.
5. The upper and lower integrals yield the outer and inner areas of D.
6. $M - f(p)$ is positive so that

$$\iint_D (M - f) = MA(D) - \iint_D f \geq 0.$$

8. As in Exercise 6, show first that $\iint_D fg$ lies between $M \iint_D g$ and $m \iint_D g$. Then

use the intermediate value theorem to find the point $\bar{p}$ with

$$f(\bar{p}) = \left\{ \iint_D fg \right\} \left\{ \iint_D g \right\}^{-1}.$$

9. If $f(p_0) \neq 0$, then there is a neighborhood N about p_0 with $f(p) \geq \delta > 0$ for all $p \in N$. In consequence,

$$\iint_D f \geq \iint_N f > \delta A(N) > 0.$$

10. Use the uniform continuity of f to obtain a covering of the graph with arbitrarily small area.
11. Subdivide [0, 1] and obtain a covering of the trace of the curve by rectangles, whose total area can be made arbitrarily small, using the uniform continuity of f.
13. $\iint_R f = \sum \iint_{D_j} f$ so that

$$\iint_R f - S(\mathcal{S}, f, \{p_j\}) = \sum \iint_{D_j} [f(x, y) - f(p_j)]\, dxdy.$$

Estimate this.

Sec. 3.2

2. Dividing the rectangle in half, one finds the estimate .17558, good to .015. A little more precision gives .17447. The "exact" answer is

$$13 \log 13 + 10 \log 10 - 12 \log 12 - 11 \log 11$$

This is unsatisfactory for computation, due to error accumulation. Writing this instead as $2 \log (13/12) + \log (13/11) - 10 \log [1 + (2/130)]$, and using power series, one gets .174465, good to the last digit.

4. (a) $F(x) = \begin{cases} x^2 - x + 1 & x \geq 1 \\ x & x < 1. \end{cases}$ (b) $F(x) = (e^x - 1) \exp (e^x)$.
5. Use the substitution $v = 1/u$.
6. Let $F' = f$ and evaluate each side.
8. $\int_0^1 dy \int_1^2 f(x, y)\, dx + \int_1^2 dy \int_y^2 f(x, y)\, dx.$
9. $\int_0^2 dx \int_x^2 dz \int_1^{2-\frac{1}{2}x} f(x, y, z)\, dy$

$\int_1^2 dy \int_0^{4-2y} dx \int_x^2 f(x, y, z)\, dz$

$\int_0^2 dz \int_0^z dx \int_1^{2-\frac{1}{2}x} f(x, y, z)\, dy$

$\int_1^2 dy \int_0^{4-2y} dz \int_0^z f(x, y, z)\, dx + \int_1^2 dy \int_{4-2y}^2 dz \int_0^{4-2y} f(x, y, z)\, dx$

$\int_0^2 dz \int_1^{2-\frac{1}{2}z} dy \int_0^z f(x, y, z)\, dx + \int_0^2 dz \int_{2-\frac{1}{2}z}^2 dy \int_0^{4-2y} f(x, y, z)\, dx.$

10. $44/15$.
11. (a) $(e - 1)/2$; (b) $\frac{1}{2}e^4 - e^2$.
12. The reversed order is $\int_{-\sqrt[3]{6}}^0 dy \int_{-6}^{y^3} xy\, dx + \int_0^2 dy \int_{7y-6}^{y^3} xy\, dx.$
13. Use the uniform continuity of f.

14. Consider $\int_a^b (f + \lambda g)^2$, which cannot be negative, and apply the same process used in the proof of the Schwarz inequality in Chap. 1.

15. $\left(\int_0^1 \sqrt{x}\, e^{-x}\, dx\right)^2 \leq \int_0^1 x\, dx \int_0^1 e^{-2x}\, dx < (.47)^2.$

16. (*a*) The integral is less than $\sqrt{5}/2$; (*b*) the integral is less than $\sqrt{2\pi}$.

17. Write $\left(\iint\limits_D \sqrt{4x^2 - y^2}\, dxdy\right)^2 \leq \iint\limits_D (2x - y)\, dxdy \iint\limits_D (2x + y)\, dxdy.$

18. Prove the identity for $P(x) = 1, x, x^2$, and x^3 in turn.

Sec. 3.3

2. The error does not exceed $1/6! = 1/720 < .0014$.
3. By Taylor's theorem, we obtain $|\text{error}| < 1/5$. The actual error is no more than .07.
5. 6, 11.
6. (*a*) .747; (*b*) .944; (*c*) .735.
7. We have $\dfrac{1}{x} < \dfrac{1}{2}\left\{\dfrac{1}{x^{1+\delta}} + \dfrac{1}{x^{1-\delta}}\right\}$ for any δ, $0 < \delta < 1$. Integrate, and obtain $\log x < 1/2\delta\,(x^\delta - x^{-\delta})$. Then take $\delta = 1/2$.
8. Yes. $e^x \geq \dfrac{e^2}{4} x^2$ and this is best possible.
9. $|R_n(x)| \leq \dfrac{B^n(x - a)^n}{n!} \to 0.$
10. Write $f(x) = f(a) + f'(a)(x - a) + \dfrac{f''(\tau)(x - a)^2}{2}$ and set $x = 0$, $x = 1$, and subtract. One then obtains $|f'(a)| \leq \left(\dfrac{A}{2}\right)[a^2 + (1 - a)^2]$. [See also D .V. Widder, "Laplace Transform," pp. 177–179 Princeton University Press, Princeton, N.J., 1946.]
11. Write $R_n(x) = \dfrac{1}{n!}\int_0^x (x - t)^n f^{(n+1)}(t)\, dt$. Putting $t = xs$, this becomes

$$R_n(x) = \frac{x^{n+1}}{n!}\int_0^1 (1 - s)^n f^{(n+1)}(xs) ds.$$

Using the fact that $f^{(n+2)}(x) \geq 0$, we have $0 \leq R_n(x) \leq x^{n+1}R_n(1)$. But, since $f(1) = f(0) + \cdots + R_n(1)$, $R_n(1) \leq f(1)$ for all n, and thus $|R_n(x)| \leq x^{n+1}f(1)$ and $\lim_{n\to\infty} R_n(x) = 0$. [See Widder, "Laplace Transform," pp. 146–147.]

Sec. 3.4

1. Area $= \int_0^\infty e^{-x}\, dx = 1$.
2. (*a*) Diverge; (*b*) Diverge; (*c*) Diverge; (*d*) Converge; (*e*) Converge; (*f*) Converge; (*g*) Converge; (*h*) Diverge.
3. (*a*) Diverge; (*b*) Converge; (*c*) Converge (not improper); (*d*) Converge; (*e*) Converge; (*f*) Converges; (*g*) Diverge; (*h*) Converge.
4. Either $\alpha < 1$ and $\beta > 1$, or $\alpha > 1$ and $\beta < 1$.
5. All (α, β) with $\alpha > -1$, $\beta > -1$ and $\alpha + \beta < -1$.
6. Yes. Evaluate the first half of $\int_r^R dx \int_0^x x^{-3/2} e^{y-x}\, dy$, and examine the resulting integral as $r \downarrow 0$, $R \uparrow \infty$.

Sec. 3.5

1. (*a*) No; (*b*) no; (*c*) yes; (*d*) no.

3. F may not be differentiable. This happens, for example, if $f(x, y) = \dfrac{xy}{x^2 + y^2}$.

Sec. 4.1

1. (*a*) Diverges; (*b*) Diverges; (*c*) Converges; (*d*) Converges; (*e*) Converges; (*f*) Diverges. In the last we observe that the series may be bracketed to obtain the series

$$\sum_1^\infty \left\{\frac{1}{\sqrt{4n-3}} + \frac{1}{\sqrt{4n-1}} - \frac{1}{\sqrt{2n}}\right\}.$$

However, an easy estimate shows that the terms of this exceed those of the series

$$\frac{1}{4}\sum_1^\infty \frac{1}{\sqrt{n}}.$$

2. (*b*) Take $b_n = 1/(n-1)$ for $n \geq 2$.
   (*c*) Take $b_n = 1/(n - A - 1)$ for $n \geq A + 2$.
3. (*a*) $-1 \leq r < 1$ (*b*) $x = 0$ (*c*) $-3 \leq x \leq -1$
   (*d*) $|x| \leq 1/4$ (*e*) $|x - 1| \leq \sqrt{3}$
   (*f*) $s > 0$ (*g*) $-e^{-1} \leq \beta < e^{-1}$
   (*h*) $\gamma > \alpha + \beta$ (*i*) $-1 < x \leq 1$ (*j*) $-\infty < x < \infty$
   (*k*) $x > -1$ or $x \leq -2$ (*l*) $x \leq 0$ or $x > 2$
   (*m*) All x
4. Bracket the series in blocks of successive length 1, 2, 4, 8, etc.
5. The nth term of the product is, except for sign,

$$\frac{1}{\sqrt{n}}\frac{1}{\sqrt{1}} + \frac{1}{\sqrt{n-1}}\frac{1}{\sqrt{2}} + \cdots + \frac{1}{\sqrt{1}}\frac{1}{\sqrt{n}}.$$

The smallest of these products is in the center so that the whole nth term exceeds 2.

6. Put $s_n = \log \left|\dfrac{a_{n+1}}{a_n}\right|$, and observe that

$$\sigma_n = \frac{(s_1 + s_2 + \cdots + s_{n-1})}{n} = \log |a_n|^{1/n} - \log |a_1|^{1/n}.$$

Then use Exercise 10, Sec. 1.5.

7. (*a*) True. (*b*) False. (*c*) True. (*d*) False; $a_n = \dfrac{(-1)^{n+1}}{\sqrt{n}}$, $c_n = a_n$. (*e*) False;

$b_n = \dfrac{(-1)^n}{\sqrt{n}}$, $a_n = b_n + \dfrac{1}{n}$. (*f*) True; use Schwarz's inequality.

(*g*) True; use (*f*). (*h*) True; $\sum_{n+1}^{2n} a_k \geq na_{2n}$, so that $\lim_{n\to\infty} 2nA_{2n} = 0$; likewise

$$\lim_{n\to\infty} (2n+1)a_{2n+1} = 0.$$

8. Put $a_n = f(n)$, $b_n = \int_n^{n+1} f$. Then

$$b_n - a_n = \int_n^{n+1} dx \int_n^x f'(u)\,du = \int_n^{n+1} f'(u)[n+1-u]\,du$$

so that $|b_n - a_n| \le \int_n^{n+1} |f'(u)|\,du$ and $\Sigma(b_n - a_n)$ converges.

9. Approximately 10^{9559} terms.

10. (a) $\frac{1}{2}(\log n)^2 +$ bounded term; (b) $(n + \frac{1}{2})(\log n)^2 - 2n \log n + 2n +$ bounded term.

11. Allow for a radius of rotation of approximately

$$1.95L = \frac{L}{2}\left(1 + \tfrac{1}{2} + \tfrac{1}{3} + \cdots + \tfrac{1}{50}\right).$$

Sec. 4.2

1. Yes; no; yes.

2. Observe that $\|f_n\| = f_n\left(\frac{n}{n+1}\right) \to e^{-1} \ne 0$.

3. $\lim_{x\downarrow 0} F(x) = 0$, $\lim_{x\downarrow 0} \frac{F(x)}{x} = 0$,

$$\lim_{x\downarrow 0} \frac{F(x)}{x^2} = \sum_1^\infty \frac{1}{n^2} = \frac{\pi^2}{6}, \quad \lim_{x\uparrow\infty} F(x) = \infty,$$

$$\lim_{x\to\infty} \frac{F(x)}{x} = \frac{\pi}{2}, \quad \lim_{x\uparrow\infty} \frac{F(x)}{x^2} = 0.$$

4. $\lim \int_0^2 f(nx)\,dx = 2L$, using the Osgood-Lebesgue theorem.

5. Given ϵ, choose c so that $|g(x)| < \epsilon$ for $c \le x \le 1$, and N so that $|x^n g(x)| < \epsilon$ for $n \ge N$ and $0 \le x \le c$.

6. Split the interval of integration into three pieces $[-1, -c]$, $[-c, c]$, $[c, 1]$. Dispose of the first and last using the uniform convergence of $\{\phi_n\}$, and write

$$\left| g(0) - \int_{-c}^{c} g\phi \right| \le \max_{|x|\le c} |g(0) - g(x)| \int_{-c}^{c} \phi_n$$

Then, since g is continuous, and $\int_{-1}^{1} \phi_n \to 1$, the result follows.

7. If q is a point common to all the sets C_n, then $f_n(q) \to F(q)$, so that for large n, $f_n(q) > F(q) - \epsilon$. This cannot happen since f_n and F are continuous. Thus for some N, C_n is empty, and thus $\|f_n - F\|_E < \epsilon$ whenever $n \ge N$.

8. (b) Write $\left| \int_a^b f_n - \int_a^b F \right|^2 = \left| \int_a^b (f_n - F) \right|^2$ and apply the Schwarz inequality (Exercise 14, Sec. 3.2). (c) Let $\{f_n\}$ be the sequence of characteristic functions [1 on the set, 0 off] for the intervals $[0, \frac{1}{2}]$, $[\frac{1}{2}, 1]$, $[0, \frac{1}{4}]$, $[\frac{1}{4}, \frac{1}{2}]$, $[\frac{1}{2}, \frac{3}{4}]$, $[\frac{3}{4}, 1]$, $[0, \frac{1}{8}]$, $[\frac{1}{8}, \frac{1}{4}]$ etc.

Sec. 4.3

1. (a) 0; (b) e; (c) ∞ if $c < 1$, 1 if $c = 1$, 0 if $c > 1$.

3. (a)
$$\sin(x^2) = x^2 - \frac{(x^2)^3}{3!} + \frac{(x^2)^5}{5!} - \cdots$$
$$= x^2 - \frac{x^6}{3!} + \frac{x^{10}}{5!} - \cdots.$$

(b) $\frac{1}{x} = \frac{1}{1 + (x - 1)} = 1 - (x - 1) + (x - 1)^2 - (x - 1)^3 + \cdots$.

(c) $\log (1 + x^2) = x^2 - \frac{(x^2)^2}{2} + \frac{(x^2)^3}{3} - \cdots$.

(d) $\cosh x = \frac{e^x + e^{-x}}{2}$

$$= \left(1 + x + \frac{x^2}{2!} + \cdots\right)\frac{1}{2} + \left(1 - x + \frac{x^2}{2!} - \cdots\right)\frac{1}{2}$$

$$= 1 + \frac{x^2}{2!} + \frac{x^4}{4!} + \cdots.$$

4. (a) $x \frac{d}{dx}\left\{x \frac{d}{dx} \frac{1}{1 - x}\right\} = \frac{x + x^2}{(1 - x)^3}$.

(b) $\cosh \sqrt{x}$.

(c) $\frac{1}{2} \log \left(\frac{1 + x}{1 - x}\right) = \frac{1}{2} \log (1 + x) - \frac{1}{2} \log (1 - x)$.

(d) $\frac{x}{1 - x^3}$.

5. (a) No, since f is not differentiable; (b) yes.
7. Apply the corollary to Theorem 25.

Sec. 4.4

1. $\lim_{t \to 0} \frac{x \sin (xt)}{1 + x^2} = 0$ uniformly for all x.
3. 0.
4. ∞.
5. $\frac{\pi}{2} |x|$ (integrate by parts).
6. $\frac{\pi}{2}$ (put $x = 2\theta$).
7. $\left(\frac{\sqrt{\pi}}{2}\right) \exp \left(\frac{-x^2}{4}\right)$ (differentiate, and integrate by parts).
8. $\frac{\sqrt{\pi}}{2}$.

Sec. 4.5

1. In (4-18), put $t = \frac{s}{y}$.
4. (a) $\Gamma(\frac{4}{3})\Gamma(\frac{1}{2})/3\Gamma(1\frac{1}{6})$
   (b) $2\Gamma(\frac{1}{2}) = \sqrt{2\pi}$
   (c) $-\Gamma(\frac{4}{3})\Gamma(\frac{2}{3})$
   (d) $\frac{1}{2}\Gamma(\frac{1}{4})\Gamma(\frac{3}{4}) = \frac{\pi}{\sqrt{2}}$
5. It may be shown that $\int_0^\infty \frac{u^{x-1}}{1 + u} du = \frac{\pi}{\sin (\pi x)}$. [See, for example, L. V. Ahlfors, "Complex Variables," McGraw-Hill Book Company, Inc., New York, 1953.] Accordingly, $\Gamma(x)\Gamma(1 - x) = \pi/\sin (\pi x)$. This may be used to simplify products of gamma functions.
6. $\frac{1}{q} \Gamma\left(\frac{p + 1}{q}\right)$.

7. $\frac{\Gamma(s+1)}{(r+1)^{s+1}}$.

Sec. 5.1

2. The line $u + v = 0$, in the plane $w = 0$.
3. (*a*) A translation sending the origin into $(3, -1)$. (*b*) A reflection about the line $y = x$. (*c*) A rotation by $\pi/4$, followed by a radial expansion which multiplies points by $\sqrt{2}$. (*d*) A transformation which maps the plane onto the first quadrant, and send lines through the origin into lines through the origin.
4. The whole plane is mapped onto the whole plane. The points p and $-p$ always have the same image. The image of $(r \cos \theta, r \sin \theta)$ is $(r^2 \cos 2\theta, r^2 \sin 2\theta)$. If the plane is regarded as the complex field, and we write $(x, y) = x + iy = z$, then $T(z) = z^2$.
5. One such transformation is $u = (y - 3)x$, $v = (y - x^2)x$. Note however that the factor x cannot be deleted.
6. As an illustration, $(a)(b)$ is the transformation which sends (x, y) into $(y + 3, x - 1)$, while $(b)(a)$ sends (x, y) into $(y - 1, x + 3)$.
8. Each of the coordinate functions is continuous on the compact set and hence bounded there.
9. (*a*) T is uniformly continuous on S if corresponding to any $\epsilon > 0$ there is a $\delta > 0$ such that $|T(p) - T(q)| < \epsilon$ whenever p and q lie in S and $|p - q| < \delta$. (*b*) Let S be a compact (closed and bounded) set in the plane, and let T be described by $T(p) = (\phi(p), \psi(p))$ where ϕ and ψ are continuous on S. Use the fact that they are uniformly continuous on S.
11. The product of a translation and a radial expansion is a transformation which sends p into $\lambda p + P$. This is already the general form; nothing new is obtained by further multiplications.

Sec. 5.2

1. 0, 7.
2. $[2, -1, 3]$.
4. $(0, -3)$, $(-5, 6)$, $(2, -3)$, $(-1, 0)$.
5. $(1, 6)$, $(2, -1)$, $(0, 3)$.
6. (*a*) $\begin{bmatrix} 0 & 1 & 2 \\ 1 & 4 & 3 \\ 1 & 0 & 1 \end{bmatrix}$ (*b*) $\begin{bmatrix} 0 & 0 & 1 \\ 0 & 0 & 0 \\ \frac{1}{2} & \frac{1}{2} & -\frac{1}{2} \end{bmatrix}$
7. The ranks are (*a*) 2; (*b*) 2; (*c*) 2; (*d*) 3.
8. (*a*) All of XYZ-space is mapped onto the plane whose equation is $u + v - w = 0$, in a many-to-one fashion. (*b*) All of XYZ space is mapped onto UVW space, one-to-one. The transformation is nonsingular, and has an inverse with matrix $\begin{bmatrix} 1 & 1 & -2 \\ 0 & -1 & 3 \\ -1 & -1 & 3 \end{bmatrix}$.
9. (*a*) $\begin{bmatrix} -5 & -1 \\ 1 & 3 \end{bmatrix}$.
10. $(ST)(x, y) = (2x - 2y, -2x + 6y)$, and
$(TS)(x, y, z) = (4x - y - 2z, 12x - 2y + 4z, -2x + y + 6z)$.

Sec. 5.3

1. (*a*) $f_1(x, y) = 2x \log (x^2 + y^2) + 2x^3/(x^2 + y^2)$
$f_2(x, y) = 2x^2y/(x^2 + y^2)$, $f_{12}(x, y) = 4xy^3/(x^2 + y^2)^2$.

2. $f_2(x, y) = 3x^2y^2 - 2$, $f_2(2, 3) = 106$, $f_2(y, x) = 3x^2y^2 - 2$.
3. (c) $[-1, -1, -10]$. [-1, -1, -4]
4. (b) For no direction, except those of the axes; (c) no.
5. Using the mean value theorem, show that $|f(p) - f(p_0)| \le M|p - p_0|$.
6. If f is of class C' in a bounded open set D, and is zero everywhere on the boundary of D, then there is a point in D at which all of the first-order partial derivatives of f are zero (assuming that f is continuous in the closure of D.)
7. 0.

Sec. 5.4

1. (b) $\dfrac{dw}{dt} = \dfrac{\partial w}{\partial t} + \dfrac{\partial w}{\partial u}\dfrac{\partial u}{\partial t} + \dfrac{\partial w}{\partial u}\dfrac{\partial u}{\partial x}\dfrac{dx}{dt} + \dfrac{\partial w}{\partial x}\dfrac{dx}{dt}$.

   (c) $\dfrac{\partial w}{\partial x} = F_1 + F_2f_1 + F_3g_1$; $\dfrac{\partial w}{\partial y} = F_2f_2$; $\dfrac{\partial w}{\partial z} = F_3g_2$.

3. $$\frac{d^2w}{dx^2} = \frac{\partial^2 w}{\partial x^2} + 2\frac{\partial^2 w}{\partial x\,\partial y}\frac{dy}{dx} + \frac{\partial^2 w}{\partial y^2}\left(\frac{dy}{dx}\right)^2 + \frac{\partial w}{\partial y}\frac{d^2y}{dx^2}$$
4. At $(-1, 2, 1)$, $\partial y/\partial x = 2/3$, $\partial y/\partial z = 4/3$.
5. $$\frac{\partial u}{\partial x} = -\frac{(2x^3u + 2xy^2v + x^2y - 3y^2)}{x^4 + 4y^3}$$
   $$\frac{\partial u}{\partial x} = \frac{(12y^5 - 12x^2y^4 - 9x^4y^2 + x^6y)}{(x^4 + 4y^3)^2}$$
6. $\dfrac{\partial z}{\partial x} = -\dfrac{F_1}{F_3}$, $\dfrac{\partial z}{\partial y} = -\dfrac{F_2}{F_3}$.
7. $$\frac{\partial^2 z}{\partial x^2} = \frac{\{2F_1F_3F_{13} - F_1^2F_{33} - F_3^2F_{11}\}}{F_3^3}$$
   $$\frac{\partial^2 z}{\partial x\partial y} = \frac{\{F_1F_3F_{23} + F_2F_3F_{13} - F_1F_2F_{33} - F_3^2F_{12}\}}{F_3^3}.$$
9. $\dfrac{dx}{dt} = \dfrac{\partial(F, G)}{\partial(y, t)} \Big/ \dfrac{\partial(F, G)}{\partial(x, y)}$, $\dfrac{dy}{dt} = -\dfrac{\partial(F, G)}{\partial(x, t)} \Big/ \dfrac{\partial(F, G)}{\partial(x, y)}$.
12. Differentiate the equation with respect to t, and set $t = 1$.
17. $y\dfrac{\partial u}{\partial x} - x\dfrac{\partial u}{\partial y} = 0$.
22. Apply Taylor's theorem to express $f(p + \Delta p)$ in the form $f(p) + R(\Delta p)$ for any point p in S. Then use the fact that f_{11}, f_{12}, f_{22} are continuous (and therefore bounded) on S to estimate $R(\Delta p)$.
23. Let p and q belong to S, with $p = (\phi(a), \psi(a))$, $q = (\phi(b), \psi(b))$. Subdivide $[a, b]$ by points t_j, with $t_0 = a$, $t_n = b$. Let $P_j = (\phi(t_j), \psi(t_j))$. Then, $|f(p) - f(q)| \le \Sigma|f(P_{j+1}) - f(P_j)| \le M\Sigma|P_{j+1} - P_j|^2$. Show that the latter sum can be made arbitrarily small by proper choice of the t_j. [For a generalization of this, see a paper by Kakutani, *Proc. Am. Math. Soc.* vol. 3, pp. 532–542, 1952.]
24. $\phi(1) = 1$, $\phi'(1) = a(1 + b + b^2) + b^3$.

Sec. 5.5

1. (b) $\begin{bmatrix} -18 & 25 & -12 \\ 12 & 0 & -4 \end{bmatrix}$ (c) $\begin{bmatrix} 1 & 6 \\ 3 & 3 \\ +2 & -6 \end{bmatrix}$.

5. Take $\Delta p = (h, 0)$ and $(0, h)$ in turn, and compute
$$\lim_{h\to 0} \frac{T(p + \Delta p) - T(p)}{h}$$

6. Let $T(p) = q$ and $T(p + \Delta p) = q + \Delta q$. Then,

$$(ST)(p + \Delta p) = S(q + \Delta q) = S(q) + dS\Big|_q(\Delta q) + R_1(\Delta q).$$

Also, $\Delta q = dT\Big|_p(\Delta p) + R_2(\Delta p)$. Thus, we have

$$(ST)(p + \Delta p) = dD\Big|_q \, dT\Big|_p (\Delta p) + R(\Delta p)$$

where $R(\Delta p) = dS\Big|_q (R_2(\Delta p)) + R_1(\Delta q)$.

Using the fact that $|\Delta q| \le B|\Delta p|$ for sufficiently small $|\Delta p|$, together with the fact that $\lim_{\Delta q \to 0} \frac{|R_2(\Delta p)|}{|\Delta p|} = 0$ and $\lim_{\Delta p \to 0} \frac{|R_1(\Delta q)|}{|\Delta q|} = 0$, one may show that $\lim_{\Delta p \to 0} \frac{|R(\Delta q)|}{|\Delta p|} = 0$.

7. The entries of the matrix for $dT\Big|_p$ are continuous functions of p, so that J is a continuous function. However, the rank of dT may fail to be continuous; it is an integral-valued function, and as such cannot be continuous in a connected set without being constant there. For example, the rank may be 2 at a point p, and be 3 in a deleted neighborhood of p.

9. The graph of T is a two-dimensional manifold (surface) in 4-space. The transformation $dT\Big|_p$ is also a surface; since the transformation is linear, it is a two-dimensional plane. These two surfaces are tangent at $(p, T(p))$.

Sec. 5.6

3. There is only one inverse, since F is monotone.
4. f has no continuous inverse on intervals which contain -1 as an interior point.
5. Since f is one-to-one, $f^{-1} = g$ is defined and maps $[\alpha, \beta]$ onto $[a, b]$, one-to-one. To prove it continuous let $x_n \in [\alpha, \beta]$ with $x_n \to x_0$. Set $y_n = g(x_n)$, $y_0 = g(x_0)$. If y' is any limit point of the sequence $\{y_n\}$, then since f is continuous, $f(y')$ will be a limit point of $\{f(y_n)\} = \{x_n\}$. But, $\lim x_n = x_0$, so that $f(y') = x_0$, and $y' = y_0$. Thus, y_0 is the only limit point of $\{y_n\}$ and $\lim y_n = y_0$. This shows that g is continuous. Alternatively, one may prove that f takes closed sets into closed sets, using the fact that any closed subset of $[a, b]$ is compact and Theorems 2 and 3, Sec. 5.1.

Sec. 5.7

1. (*a*) $4xy - 2y^2$; (*b*) 0; (*c*) e^x; (*d*) 2, for $x \neq 0$.
2. (*b*) Never one-to-one, locally, since it maps the (x, y) plane onto the parabola $v^2 = 4u$; (*c*) locally one-to-one, but not one-to-one in the whole plane, even though J is never zero; (*d*) one-to-one in the right half plane, and in the left half plane.
3. (*c*) $x = (\frac{1}{2}) \log (u^2 + v^2)$, $\tan y = v/u$.
4. (*a*) The image is the set of (u, v) such that $v > 0$, $v > 2u - 2$, $v \le (\frac{8}{27})u^3$; it is not open. (*b*) The portion of the parabola $v^2 = 4u$ for $0 < u < 4$. (*c*) The image is the open set which may be described by polar coordinate in the (u, v) plane by $1 < r < e$, $0 < \theta < 1$. (*d*) The unbounded open set consisting of all (u, v) with $0 < u < 1$, $0 < v < u^{-\frac{1}{2}}$.

Sec. 5.8

1. Yes; no. At (0, 0), $\partial F/\partial y = 1$, $\partial F/\partial x = 0$; moreover, for $|xy|$ small, the equation is approximately $x^2 + y = 0$.
2. No; yes.

4. No such representation exists. (Examine the graph of each.)
5. (*a*) Assume f of class C' near 1, and $f'(1) \neq 0$.
6. There is always the solution $y = 1$, identically. In some cases, this is not the only solution; when $f(t) = (t - 1)^2$, $y = (1 - x)/(1 + x)$ is also a solution.

Sec. 5.9

1. (*a*) $v = 1 + e^{2u}$; (*b*) $uv = u + v$; (*c*) independent; (*d*) $v = (1 + u^2)^{-1}$.
2. (*a*) Locally one-to-one, except on the vertical axis. The effect is similar to a folding of the XY plane along this line. (*b*) This maps the whole XY plane onto a curve in the UV plane. (*d*) This maps XYZ space onto the surface described by $w = (u - v)^2$, many-to-one.
4. The transformation will map each connected component of D onto a single point. Thus, the image of D is either finite or countable.
5. Assume that $\phi \in C'$ and that $\phi_1^2 + \phi_2^2 > 0$ throughout the region D^* which is the image D under $u = F(x, y)$, $v = G(x, y)$. Differentiating the identity

$$\phi(F(x, y), G(x, y)) = 0,$$

holding through D, with respect to x and y, one finds that $\partial(F, G)/\partial(x, y) = 0$ in D.
6. When $x + y \geq 0$. $w = \frac{1}{2}(u + \sqrt{u^2 + 4v}) \exp \{\sqrt{u^2 + 4v} - u\}/2$. A similar relation holds when $x + y \leq 0$.

Sec. 6.1

1. The matrix is $\begin{bmatrix} 1 & 1 \\ 2 & 3 \end{bmatrix}$ whose determinant is 1.
3. (*a*) $\int_0^{1/2} du \int_u^{1-u} 2(v^2 - u^2)\, dv = \frac{1}{8}$.

(*b*) $\int_0^1 du \int_{1-2u}^1 (u^2 + uv)\, dv = \frac{2}{3}$.

(*c*) $\int_{-1}^1 du \int_0^{\sqrt{1-u^2}} 8uv(u^4 - v^4)\, dv = 0$.

4. Putting $u = y - \frac{1}{2}x$, $v = y - 3x$, D^* is mapped onto a rectangle, and the integral transforms to

$$\left(\frac{4}{5^3}\right) \int_0^2 du \int_{-4}^0 (u - v)(6u - v)\, dv.$$

5. Setting $u = xy$, $v = x^2 - y^2$, the integral transforms to $(\frac{1}{2}) \int_1^3 du \int_1^4 dv = 3$.
6. The area is given by $\int_0^{2\pi} d\theta \int_0^{\sin(\theta/2)} r\, dr$.
8. The areas of the faces are $\sqrt{6}$, $\sqrt{29}$, $\sqrt{11}$, and the volume is 5.
9. The upper half of the XY plane is mapped onto the portion of the (s, t) plane lying inside the parabola $(s - t)^2 - 8(s + t) + 16 = 0$. Lines in the (s, t) plane correspond to conics in the XY plane. The Jacobian is zero only on the boundary $y = 0$.

Sec. 6.2

1. The double point corresponds to $t = 2$, $t = -2$, and the slopes of the tangents are 2 and -2.
2. $k = 4\pi(1 + \pi^2 + 4\pi^4)^{1/2}(1 + 4\pi^2)^{-3/2}$.
3. $L = \int_0^1 (9t^4 + 2t^2 - 4t + 2)^{1/2}\, dt$.

6. $k = (76)^{1/2}(14)^{-3/2}$.
7. When $|\gamma'(t)| = 1$, $\gamma' \cdot \gamma' = 1$ so that $\gamma' \cdot \gamma'' = 0$.
10. The problem is easily reduced to a study of the linear transformations having matrices of the form

$$\begin{bmatrix} A & B \\ -B & A \end{bmatrix}.$$

This effects a rotation of the plane about the origin, followed by a radial expansion or contraction. Angles are necessarily preserved.
11. The differential has the requisite form, except at the origin. There, angles are tripled.
13. Since the curves are simple, γ_1 and γ_2 are one-to-one mappings from $[0, 1]$ to the set which is their common trace. Set $f(t) = \gamma^{-1}(\gamma_2(t))$, and show that f is continuous and has a continuous inverse.
14. One choice is $x = (t^2 + 1)/(t^2 - 1)$, $y = 2t/(t^2 - 1)$.
15. Parabolas.
17. $L = a \int_0^{2\pi} \sqrt{2 - 2 \cos t}\, dt = 4a \int_0^{\pi} |\cos \theta|\, d\theta = 8a.$

Sec. 6.3

1. The tangent plane may be given by $x = -\frac{1}{4} - v$, $y = \frac{1}{2} + u + v$, $z = 2 + 4v$, or by $4x + z - 1 = 0$.
4. The curve meets the surface in three points, $(0, 0, 0)$, $(1, 1, 2)$ and $(\frac{1}{3}, \frac{1}{9}, \frac{2}{27})$. The angles between the normal to the surface, and the tangent to the curve are $\pi/2$, and $\arccos (10/\sqrt{(33)(41)})$, $\arccos (42/\sqrt{(145)(17)})$.
5. The area of the ellipsoid is

$$\int_0^{\pi} \sin \phi\, d\phi \int_0^{2\pi} \{a^2b^2 \cos^2 \phi + c^2 \sin^2\phi\, [a^2 \sin^2 \theta + b^2 \cos^2 \theta]\}^{1/2}\, d\theta.$$

8. The area of the Möbius strip is the same as that of Σ_1, which is

$$\int_0^{2\pi} du \int_{-1}^{1} \left\{\left(\frac{v}{2}\right)^2 + \left[2 - v \sin\left(\frac{u}{2}\right)\right]^2\right\}^{1/2} dv.$$

10. $(\frac{49}{3})$.
12. 4π.
14. The general answer is no. If the surface can be represented in the form $z = f(x, y)$ for $(x, y) \in D$, then the area may be given by

$$\iint_D [F_1{}^2 + F_2{}^2 + F_3{}^2]^{1/2} \frac{dx\, dy}{F_3}$$

where in evaluating this, z is to be replaced by $f(x, y)$. But, this solution is not admissible, since it also introduces f.

Sec. 6.4

1 The critical point is $(\frac{1}{2}, 0)$ and is a saddle point. The maximum and minimum occur on the boundary, and are 4 and $-\frac{16}{5}$.
2. Maximum $= 4$; minimum $= -\frac{1}{2}$.
3. (*a*) Saddle; (*b*) Saddle; (*c*) $(0, 0)$ is a maximum, $(\pm\frac{1}{2}, \pm\frac{1}{2})$ are minima, and $(0, \pm 1)$ and $(\pm\frac{1}{2}, 0)$ are saddle points; (*d*) all the points on the line $y = (\frac{2}{3})x$ are minima; (*e*) $(0, 0)$ is a minimum; (*f*) $(0, 0)$ is a saddle point.

5. On $y = mx$, $f(x, y)$ behaves like m^2x^2 for x near 0, so that f has a minimum at the origin, on any line with nonzero slope. On the horizontal axis, $f(x, 0) = 2x^4$, which again has a minimum at the origin. However, f takes on both positive and negative values in any neighborhood of the origin.
6. The centroid $(P_1 + P_2 + \cdots + P_n)/n$.
7. The closest points on the given lines are $(\frac{1}{2}, \frac{1}{2}, 0)$ and $(\frac{1}{3}, \frac{1}{3}, \frac{1}{3})$.
8. The maximum is $106\frac{1}{4}$ occurring at $(\frac{3}{2}, 4)$ and $(-\frac{3}{2}, -4)$. The minimum is -50, attained at $(2, -3)$ and $(-2, 3)$.
9. 9.
10. Minimum 1; maximum 3.
11. $8abc/3\sqrt{3}$.
13. $P = (0, 0, f(0, 0))$. A nonanalytic treatment is possible. The volume of the region bounded by the tangent plane, the cylinder, and the XY plane is πh, where h is the height of the point on the tangent plane which lies directly above $(0, 0, 0)$. Thus, one need only minimize h.
14. Let $k = [A]$, the largest integer obeying $k \le A$. Then, the maximum occurs for the choice $x_1 = x_2 = \cdots = x_k = 1$, $x_{k+1} = \beta$, $x_{k+2} = \cdots = x_n = 0$, where $k + \beta = A$. This type of problem arises in many linear programming situations.
15. Let the line L have the equation $y = mx + b$. One seeks m and b to minimize $F(m, b) = \sum_1^n \frac{(mx_j - y_j + b)^2}{m^2 + 1}$. Solving $F_2(m, b) = 0$, one finds that L must pass through the centroid P of the given points. Writing $E(x) = \sum_1^n \frac{x_j}{n}$, $E(x^2) = \sum_1^n \frac{x_j^2}{n}$, etc., we have $b = E(y) - mE(x)$. Making this substitution, we now seek to minimize $f(m) = \alpha m^2 - 2\gamma m + \beta)/(m^2 + 1)$, where $\alpha = E(x^2) - E(x)^2$, $\beta = E(y^2) - E(y)^2$, $\gamma = E(xy) - E(x)E(y)$. It is an easy matter to see that if $\gamma \neq 0$, this minimum is achieved for the slope m given by the equation $2\gamma m = \beta - \alpha + \sqrt{(\beta - \alpha)^2 + 4\gamma^2}$. When $\gamma = 0$, the optimal line L is the horizontal line through P if $\alpha > \beta$ and the vertical line through P if $\alpha < \beta$.
16. $F = f - g$ is harmonic in D, and bounded above by 0 on the boundary of D. Thus, $F \le 0$ in D, so that $f \le g$. Interchanging f and g, we also have $g \le f$, so that $f = g$.

Sec. 7.1

1. $\bar{x} = 0$, $\bar{y} = (\frac{1}{4})(e + e^{-1}) + (e - e^{-1})^{-1}$.
3. $I = \frac{k}{4}\left[\left(\frac{5}{3}\right)\sqrt{5} + \left(\frac{1}{15}\right)\right]$.
6. $F = \frac{2\rho k}{l}$.
8. $I = 2\iint_D \frac{(x^2 + y^2)R\,dx\,dy}{\sqrt{R^2 - x^2 - y^2}} = \frac{8\pi\rho R^4}{3}$ where D is the disk of radius R.
9. $I = \frac{\pi k}{16}\left(\frac{121}{5} - \frac{26}{3} + 1\right)$.
10. $F = 2\pi k\rho\left(1 - \frac{l}{\sqrt{l^2 + R^2}}\right)$, which approaches $2\pi k\rho$ as $R \uparrow$. The attraction of an infinite plate is independent of the distance from it.
11. Describe the shell by $x = \sin\phi\cos\theta$, $y = \sin\phi\sin\theta$, $z = \cos\phi$, $0 \le \phi \le \pi$, $0 \le \phi \le 2\pi$, and let $P = (0, 0, a)$ with $0 \le a < 1$. With ρ = density (mass per

unit area), the component of the force at P in the vertical direction is

$$F = \int_0^{2\pi} d\theta \int_0^{\pi} \frac{(\cos \phi - a)(\rho \sin \phi)\, d\phi}{(1 + a^2 - 2a \cos \phi)^{3/2}}$$

This may be integrated easily; for example, put $u^2 = 1 + a^2 - 2a \cos \phi$. One finds that $F = 0$.

Sec. 7.2

1. (a) $5/6$; (b) $9/10$; (d) $1/2 - 1/3 + 1/2 = 2/3$.
3. 0, 8, 8, 8.
4. (b) $27/20$; (c) 2π; (d) $0 + 2 - 7/2 + 0 = -3/2$.
5. 2, 2, 0, 0.
11. (a) $2xyz\, dx + x^2z\, dy + x^2y\, dz$; (b) $(x^2 + y^2)^{-1}(2x\, dx + 2y\, dy)$.
13. (a) $x^2\, dydx - z\, dydz$; (c) 0; (e) $(2xy - x)\, dxdydz$; (g) 0.
16. (a) $4 \int_0^1 du \int_0^1 (uv^2 + v^3)\, dv = 5/3$; (b) π; (c) $1 - 1/2 = 1/2$.
18. $\int_0^1 ds \int_0^1 dr\, (r^4 + 2r^3s - 4r^2s^2 + 2rs^3 - s^4) = 1/88$.

Sec. 7.3

1. $(\mathbf{a} \times \mathbf{b}) \cdot \mathbf{c} = 2$, $\mathbf{a} \times (\mathbf{b} \times \mathbf{c}) = 8\mathbf{j} + 24\mathbf{k}$, $(\mathbf{a} \times \mathbf{b}) \times \mathbf{c} = 2\mathbf{i} + \mathbf{j} + 21\mathbf{k}$,
$$(\mathbf{a} \cdot \mathbf{b})\mathbf{c} - (\mathbf{a} \cdot \mathbf{c})\mathbf{b} = -8\mathbf{j} - 24\mathbf{k}.$$
3. With $\mathbf{c} = \mathbf{a} \times \mathbf{b}$, show that
$$\begin{vmatrix} a_1 & a_2 & a_3 \\ b_1 & b_2 & b_3 \\ c_1 & c_2 & c_3 \end{vmatrix} = c_1^2 + c_2^2 + c_3^2.$$
4. If $\mathbf{a} \times \mathbf{v} = \mathbf{b}$, then $\mathbf{a} \times \mathbf{b} = (\mathbf{a} \cdot \mathbf{v})\mathbf{a} - (\mathbf{a} \cdot \mathbf{a})\mathbf{v} = k\mathbf{a} - |a|^2\mathbf{v}$. Thus, if such a vector exists, it must be $k\mathbf{a} - (\mathbf{a} \times \mathbf{b})/|\mathbf{a}|^2$ (provided $|\mathbf{a}| \neq 0$). However, a solution does not always exist; a necessary condition is that $\mathbf{a} \cdot \mathbf{b} = 0$. This may be seen to be sufficient.
5. The vectors p_n lie (for $n \geq 3$) in a plane normal to $\mathbf{a}$, and rotate about it, each being orthogonal to its predecessor. If $|\mathbf{a}| < 1$, $\lim p_n = 0$.
6. Since $\mathbf{f}(t) \cdot \mathbf{f}(t) = 1$, $\mathbf{f}'(t) \cdot \mathbf{f}(t) = 0$. The curve described by $p = \mathbf{f}(t)$ lies on the sphere $|p| = 1$; this therefore states that the tangent vector at p is orthogonal to the vector from 0 to p.
10. (a) $2x\, \mathbf{i} + 2y\, \mathbf{j}$.
12. Direct proof: Let $B = [b_{ij}]$, $B^{-1} = [c_{ij}]$, and $A^* = [a^*_{ij}]$. Then, $a^*_{ij} = \sum_{k,s} c_{ik}a_{ks}b_{sj}$.

Since $B^{-1}B = BB^{-1} = I$, $\sum_k b_{ik}c_{kj} = \delta_{ij}$, defined to be 0 if $i \neq j$, and 1 if $i = j$. Computing the traces of A^*, one readily finds that

$$\text{tr } (A^*) = \sum_i a^*_{ii} = \sum_k a_{kk} = \text{tr } (A).$$

A less direct proof proceeds thus. Observe that

$$\det (\lambda I - A^*) = \lambda^n - \text{tr } (A^*)\, \lambda^{n-1} + \cdots .$$

However, $\lambda I - A^* = B^{-1}(\lambda I - A)B$. Let $\det (B) = \Delta$. Then $\det (\lambda I - A^*) = (1/\Delta) \det (\lambda I - A)\, \Delta = \det (\lambda I - A) = \lambda^n - \text{tr } (A)\, \lambda^{n-1} + \cdots$, showing among other things, that $\text{tr } (A^*) = \text{tr } (A)$.

13. For the second, let $\mathbf{b} = b_1\mathbf{i} + b_2\mathbf{j} + b_3\mathbf{k}$, $\mathbf{c} = c_1\mathbf{i} + c_2\mathbf{j} + c_3\mathbf{k}$ and take $\mathbf{a} = \mathbf{i}$. By direct computation, it is seen that $\mathbf{i} \times (\mathbf{b} \times \mathbf{c}) = c_1(b_2\mathbf{j} + b_3\mathbf{k}) - b_1(c_2\mathbf{j} + c_3\mathbf{k}) = c_1\mathbf{b} - b_1\mathbf{c} = (\mathbf{i}\cdot\mathbf{c})\mathbf{b} - (\mathbf{i}\cdot\mathbf{b})\mathbf{c}$. Similarly, one shows that $\mathbf{j} \times (\mathbf{b} \times \mathbf{c}) = (\mathbf{j}\cdot\mathbf{c})\mathbf{b} - (\mathbf{j}\cdot\mathbf{b})\mathbf{c}$ and

$$\mathbf{k} \times (\mathbf{b} \times \mathbf{c}) = (\mathbf{k}\cdot\mathbf{c})\mathbf{b} - (\mathbf{k}\cdot\mathbf{b})\mathbf{c}.$$

Putting these together, with coefficients a_1, a_2, a_3, one arrives at the general formula.

14. Assuming that f and $\mathbf{V}$ are of class C'', these follow by direct calculation. Formally, they may also be obtained from the relation $\nabla \times \nabla = 0$; thus,

$$\text{curl }(\text{grad } f) = \nabla \times \nabla f = (\nabla \times \nabla) f = 0,$$

and div (curl $\mathbf{V}$) $= \nabla \cdot (\nabla \times \mathbf{V}) = (\nabla \times \nabla) \cdot \mathbf{V} = 0$. This can be made acceptable by discussing vector systems whose components are elements from an arbitrary noncommutative ring.

15. For the second, observe that $\partial^2(fg)/\partial x^2 = g\partial^2 f/\partial x^2 + 2(\partial f/\partial x)(\partial g/\partial x) + f\partial^2 g/\partial x^2$.

16. As an alternative to direct computation, one may use the relation

$$\mathbf{a} \times (\mathbf{b} \times \mathbf{c}) = \mathbf{b}(\mathbf{a}\cdot\mathbf{c}) - (\mathbf{a}\cdot\mathbf{b})\mathbf{c}$$

with $\mathbf{a} = \mathbf{b} = \nabla$, and $\mathbf{c} = \mathbf{V}$, obtaining $\nabla \times (\nabla \times \mathbf{V}) = \nabla(\nabla\cdot\mathbf{V}) - (\nabla\cdot\nabla)\mathbf{V}$. This requires the additional consideration indicated in Exercise 14.

17. An alternative to direct computation is the following. The analogue of the rule for differentiation of a product is $\nabla \cdot (\mathbf{F} \times \mathbf{G}) = \nabla \cdot (\dot{\mathbf{F}} \times \mathbf{G}) + \nabla \cdot (\mathbf{F} \times \dot{\mathbf{G}})$ where the dot indicates the function to which the differentiation is applied. Using the relation $\mathbf{a} \cdot (\mathbf{b} \times \mathbf{c}) = \mathbf{c} \cdot (\mathbf{a} \times \mathbf{b})$, we have

$$\begin{aligned}\nabla \cdot (\mathbf{F} \times \mathbf{G}) &= \mathbf{G} \cdot (\nabla \times \mathbf{F}) - \nabla \cdot (\dot{\mathbf{G}} \times \mathbf{F}) \\ &= \mathbf{G} \cdot (\nabla \times \mathbf{F}) - \mathbf{F} \cdot (\nabla \times \mathbf{G}).\end{aligned}$$

18. If $\omega = f(x, y, z)$, then $d\omega = f_1\,dx + f_2\,dy + f_3\,dz$ and
$dd\omega = (f_{12}\,dy + f_{13}\,dz)\,dx + (f_{21}\,dx + f_{23}\,dz)\,dy + (f_{31}\,dx + f_{32}\,dy)\,dz.$
Assuming that $f \in C''$, $dd\omega = 0$. Likewise, if $\omega = A(x, y, z, w)\,dxdy$, then $d\omega = A_3\,dzdxdy + A_4\,dwdxdy$ and $dd\omega = A_{34}\,dwdzdxdy + A_{43}\,dzdwdxdy$, which is again 0, if $A \in C''$.

19. Use Exercises 14 and 17.

Sec. 7.4

2. $d\omega = 3(x^2 + y^2)\,dxdy$ so that

$$\int_\gamma \omega = 3 \iint_D (x^2 + y^2)\,dxdy = 3 \int_0^{2\pi} d\theta \int_0^1 r^2 r\,dr = (3/2)\pi.$$

5. If V is the solid ball, $x^2 + y^2 + z^2 \leq 1$, and Σ is the sphere which is its boundary, we indicate the proof of the relation $\iint_\Sigma A\,dxdy = \iiint_V A_3$. Let D be the disk $x^2 + y^2 \leq 1$. Then,

$$\iiint_V A_3 = \iint_D \{A(x, y, \sqrt{1 - x^2 - y^2}) - A(x, y, -\sqrt{1 - x^2 - y^2})\}\,dxdy.$$

Using the parametrization $z = \sqrt{1 - x^2 - y^2}$ on the top half of Σ, and its negative on the bottom (with reversed orientation), we obtain for the surface integral

$$\iint_\Sigma A\,dxdy = \iint_D A(x,\, y,\, \sqrt{1 - x^2 - y^2})\,dxdy$$
$$+ \iint_D A(x,\, y,\, -\sqrt{1 - x^2 - y^2})\,dydx$$
$$= \iint_D \{A(x,\, y,\, \sqrt{1 - x^2 - y^2}) - A(x,\, y,\, -\sqrt{1 - x^2 - y^2})\}\,dxdy$$

verifying the relation.

7. Area $= 9a^2 \int_0^\infty \frac{t^2\,dt}{(1 + t^3)^2} = 3a^2.$

9. With $\omega = xy^2\,dy - x^2y\,dx$, $d\omega = (x^2 + y^2)\,dxdy$. Let D_0 be the portion of D in the first quadrant, bounded by the closed curve γ formed of the lines $x + y = 4$, $x = 0$, $y = 0$, and part of the circle $x^2 + y^2 = 1$. Then, $\iint_{D_0} d\omega = \int_\gamma \omega = \frac{128}{3} - \frac{\pi}{8}$. By symmetry, this is the same as the integral of $d\omega$ over the other three pieces of D, so that the result is $512/3 - \pi/2$.

10. $d(x\,dydz + y\,dzdx + z\,dxdy) = 3\,dxdydz.$

11. (b) Using $z = [R^2 - x^2 - y^2]^{1/2}$, we have $dz = -(x/z)\,dx - (y/z)\,dy$ so that

$$I = 2 \iint_D (x^2 + y^2)^2(R^2 - x^2 - y^2)^{-1/2}\,dxdy$$
$$= 2 \int_0^{2\pi} d\theta \int_0^R r^5(R^2 - r^2)^{-1/2}\,dr = (32/15)\pi R^5.$$

12. With $\omega = x\,dydz$, $d\omega = dxdydz$, and $(d\omega)^* = -(4vw + 4uw + 2u)\,dudvdw$. Also,

$$\omega^* = (2u^2 + 2uv - 2uw)\,dudv + (4u^2w + 4uvw - 4uw^2)\,dudw$$
$$- (4uvw + 4v^2w - 4vw^2)\,dvdw,$$

and it is seen that $d(\omega^*) = (d\omega)^*$.

14. This is nothing more than the familiar rule

$$d(fg) = (df)g + f(dg).$$

16. The formula to be proved is $d(\alpha\beta) = (d\alpha)\beta + (-1)^k\alpha(d\beta)$, where α is a form of degree k. One first checks this as above when $k = 0$, and when $k = 1$. Assume that it has been proved for any form α of degree less than k. If α is of degree k, write $\alpha = \gamma\,dx$, where γ is a form of degree $k - 1$ (and where dx stands for any one of the basic differentials which are present in α). By assumption, we may write

$$d\alpha = d(\gamma\,dx) = (d\gamma)(dx) + (-1)^{k-1}\gamma\,d(dx)$$
$$= (d\gamma)(dx).$$

For any β, we have $d((dx)\beta) = d(dx)\beta + (-1)^1(dx)(d\beta) = -dx\,d\beta$. Now, $\alpha\beta = (\gamma\,dx)\beta = \gamma((dx)\beta)$ so that

$$d(\alpha\beta) = (d\gamma)((dx)\beta) + (-1)^{k-1}\gamma\,d((dx)\beta)$$
$$= (d\gamma)(dx)\beta + (-1)^{k-1}(-1)\gamma(dx)(d\beta)$$
$$= (d\alpha)\beta + (-1)^k\alpha(d\beta).$$

18. For the first, apply the divergence theorem to the cylindrical region R obtained by erecting lines of height 1 on the set D. One then sees that

$$\iint_{\partial R} \mathbf{F} \cdot \mathbf{n} = \int_{\partial D} \mathbf{F} \cdot \mathbf{n}$$

and that

$$\iiint_{R} \nabla \cdot \mathbf{F} = \iint_{D} \nabla \cdot \mathbf{F}.$$

Sec. 7.5

1. (*a*) $f(x, y) = x^3y + x^2y + y^2 + C$; (*c*) $f(x, y, z) = x^2yz^3 + xz$; (*d*) since $d\omega \neq 0$, no function f exists.

2. (*b*) $$f_1(x, y, z) = \int_0^1 A + \int_0^1 t(xA_1 + yB_1 + zC_1)$$ $$= \int_0^1 A + \int_0^1 t(xA_1 + yA_2 + zA_3) = A(x, y, z)$$

using part (*a*) and the relations $B_1 = A_2$, $C_1 = A_3$ which come from $d\omega = 0$. (*c*) Along the straight line from (0, 0, 0) to (x, y, z).

4. Yes. $f(x, y) = (\frac{1}{2}) \log (x^2 + y^2)$.
5. Use Exercise 2. The homogeneity of A, B, and C enables one to factor out t^k, and carry out the integration.
6. (*a*) One possible factor is x^{-3}. (*b*) Since $\omega\, d\omega = 0$, integrating factors exist. One is x^2. (*c*) No integrating factor exists.
8. (*c*) If $\sigma = A\, dydz + B\, dzdx + C\, dxdy$ and $\sigma = d\omega$ where $\omega = a\, dx + b\, dy + c\, dz$, then $C = \partial b/\partial x - \partial a/\partial y$. To verify that the given functions have this property, we differentiate $a(x, y, z)$ and $b(x, y, z)$, obtaining

$$\frac{\partial b}{\partial x} = \int_0^1 tC + \int_0^1 t^2(xC_1 - zA_1)$$
$$\frac{\partial a}{\partial y} = -\int_0^1 tC + \int_0^1 t^2(zB_2 - yC_2).$$

By assumption, $d\sigma = 0$ so that $A_1 + B_2 + C_3 = 0$. Using this, replace $z(A_1 + B_2)$ by $-zC_3$, obtaining

$$\frac{\partial b}{\partial x} - \frac{\partial a}{\partial y} = 2\int_0^1 tC + \int_0^1 t^2(xC_1 + yC_2 + zC_3) = C(x, y, z),$$

by part (*a*).

10. (*a*) Using Exercise 9, one obtains

$$\omega = (\tfrac{1}{5})(2x^2yz - z^3y)\, dx + (\tfrac{1}{5})(4xz^3 - 3y^2z^2 - x^3z)\, dy + (\tfrac{1}{5})(3y^3z - 3xyz^2 - x^3y)\, dz.$$

To this, any exact 1-form df may be added. With a judicious choice, one obtains the simpler solution $\omega = x^2yz\, dx + xz^3\, dy + y^3z\, dz$. (*b*) Exercise 8 yields the solution

$$\omega = [(\tfrac{1}{2})xz^2 + (\tfrac{1}{3})(z^2 - y^2)]\, dx + (\tfrac{1}{3})\, xy\, dy - [(\tfrac{1}{2})x^2z + (\tfrac{1}{3})xz]\, dz.$$

However, by inspection, we see that $\sigma = [(2xz + z)\, dz - y\, dy]\, dx = \beta\, dx$. Moreover, β itself is an exact 1-form. Thus, we obtain the simpler solution

$$\omega = (xz^2 + \tfrac{1}{2}z^2 - \tfrac{1}{2}y^2)\, dx.$$

13. If ϕ is an integrating factor for the 2-form, then

$$A\phi_1 + B\phi_2 + C\phi_3 = -(A_1 + B_2 + C_3)\phi.$$

When $\sigma = x\, dydz + y\, dzdx + z\, dxdy$, this differential equation is

$$x\phi_1 + y\phi_2 + z\phi_3 = -3\phi,$$

which is satisfied by any function ϕ which is homogeneous of degree -3. For example, we may take $\phi(x, y, z) = x^{-3}$ and have $\phi\sigma$ an exact 2-form, which is $d\omega$ for $\omega = (\frac{1}{2})(yx^{-2}\, dz - zx^{-2}\, dy)$. It is interesting to notice that in this example, the form $\phi\sigma$ has homogeneous coefficients, but that the methods of Exercise 9 (and also of Exercise 8) fail.

14. If ω is exact, then $\omega = d\beta$. Hence $\omega^* = (d\beta)^* = d(\beta^*)$, and ω^* is also exact.

Sec. 7.6

1. (*a*) In (7-55), take $f = g$. (*b*) Since $\frac{\partial}{\partial \mathbf{n}}(g^* - g) = 0$ on $\partial\Omega$, $\nabla(g^* - g) = 0$ throughout Ω. If Ω is a connected set, we may conclude that $g^* - g$ is constant

3. (*a*) Apply the divergence theorem to $\mathbf{F} \times \nabla \times \mathbf{G}$, and use the relation

$$\nabla \cdot (\mathbf{F} \times \nabla \times \mathbf{G}) = (\nabla \times \mathbf{G}) \cdot (\nabla \times \mathbf{F}) - \mathbf{F} \cdot (\nabla \times \nabla \times \mathbf{G}).$$

(*b*) In (*a*), interchange $\mathbf{F}$ and $\mathbf{G}$, and subtract the two formulas. These relations may be used to solve the vector analogue of Poisson's equation, $\nabla \times \nabla \times \mathbf{V} = \mathbf{F}$.

LIST OF SYMBOLS

INDEX